A History of Engineering and Science in the Bell System

A History of Engineering and Science in the Bell System

Switching Technology (1925–1975)

Prepared by A. E. Joel, Jr. and
Other Members of the Technical Staff,
Bell Telephone Laboratories
G. E. Schindler, Jr., Editor.

Bell Telephone Laboratories, Incorporated

Credits for figures taken from
other than Bell Laboratories sources
appear on page 601.

First Printing, 1982
International Standard Book Number: 0-932764-02-9
Library of Congress Catalog Card Number: 82-072517
Printed in the United States of America

Contents

10. The Complete Electronic Switching Family 307

11. The Service and Feature Era 335

---

*Registered service mark of AT&T Co.

Foreword

Very soon after Alexander Graham Bell invented the telephone, it became obvious that it would be impractical to extend wires from every telephone to all other telephones. To conserve copper and dollars, wires had to converge on central points where individual telephone-to-telephone connections would be made. That is, calls had to be switched. Moreover, another basic concept of telephony also quickly emerged—namely, the trade-off between switching and transmission. The transmission costs of wire, cable, and associated plant could be optimized by having switching offices distributed to serve centers of population. The number of switching offices could be adjusted with changes in transmission costs. A classic and continuing problem of switching, therefore, is to design switching systems with capabilities that enable them to be sited at demographically advantageous points, so that total network costs are kept as low as possible. Also, for public telephony the need for compatibility in the presence of technological growth was established very early. Every item of equipment must function accurately and reliably with every other item of equipment in a network, no matter how spread out nationally or internationally. In addition, the network must absorb a continuous stream of innovations so as to bring the benefits of technology to its users as rapidly as possible.

In this book we see how these principles were applied during a significant period of technological change in Bell System history. The account begins in 1925, when various engineering and research groups of the Bell System were reorganized as Bell Telephone Laboratories. The nominal end point is 1975, which rounded out the first century of telephony.

As it turns out, however, 1975 is a reasonably good year to mark the end of one era of telephone switching and the beginning of another: the rapidly emerging new era of a digital, stored-program-controlled network. So, although we here concentrate primarily on the years 1925-1975, we have not hesitated to cover certain post-1975 developments started prior to 1976, when we knew them to be significant to current trends.

ix

    An earlier volume of this series (*A History of Engineering and Science in the Bell System: The Early Years, 1875–1925*), describes how techniques born of necessity changed the telephone from a novelty to a useful instrument of personal communication and of commerce. Switching technology during this period was characterized by the introduction and improvements in manual switchboards. In the years covered by this volume, we see switching technology change from the final refinements in manual switching to work leading toward the introduction and complete take-over of automatic switching. In the process, the technology went through four successive phases: (1) *indirect control*, with switches requiring large mechanical motions, (2) *common control*, with switches requiring only very small motions, (3) *stored-program control* electronic switching, and, now (4) *time division digital switching*. At Bell Labs, each of these technologies moved from concepts to innovations, and the innovations were introduced to provide improved and expanded resources for the administration and operation of switching offices. The result has been high-quality and constantly improving telephone service and features, not only in the United States where the innovations were first employed, but throughout the world as these concepts were widely emulated.

    The first practical automatic switching system was the step-by-step system, so-called because the switches move in step with, and under the direct control of, the telephone dial. With step-by-step, switch motions are limited by how fast (or slow) the customer dials, by how long it takes for the pulses representing each digit to be received and detected in the central office and, of course, by mechanical inertia. Switching innovation progressed to the first or indirect control phase, the panel system, separating the control of switch mechanisms from the dialing process. With panel, non-decimal power-driven switches of large capacity were introduced, and the independence of dial and switches permitted translation between the information dialed by the customer and the control needs of the system.

    In the second phase, crossbar systems were designed and common control was first introduced. With common control the call-handling control was separated from the interconnection network and great improvements in flexibility were provided. Translations allowed complete flexibility in the assignment of lines and trunks, numbering plan and routing flexibility was provided, and the trunk network became more efficient and service again improved. In addition, the crossbar switches themselves introduced precious metal (platinum alloy) contacts into telephony which improved transmission performance. These relay-like contacts operated with very small motions and therefore with increased speed; this blended nicely with the common control equipment that controlled their operation.

After World War II, the transistor and bulk electronic memory created tremendous new potentials for switching, and many exploratory developments were undertaken at Bell Labs to convert them into realities. The result was the third and entirely new approach to switching systems design—stored-program control— and switching took its place at the frontiers of the new electronic technology in terms of sophisticated hardware and software, systems architectures, complexity and size. The relationship to computers is obvious, but the switching system designs were unique. In real time, electronic switching systems process telephone calls with an objective of two hours downtime in 40 years, or about one-thousandth of one percent, compared to the one percent performance of a typical commercial computer. Now more than 50 percent of Bell System calls are switched using stored-program techniques.

The fourth era of switching technology, and the one currently in progress, is a period of further extending digital techniques into switching to encompass the interface with transmission as well and, indeed, to require the engineering of switching systems and transmission terminals carrying digital signals as single, integrated entities. The Bell System was the first to combine stored-program control and time division digital switching. Furthermore, a new high-speed digital signaling technique, known as common channel interoffice signaling (CCIS), was introduced in 1976 and soon will be serving 50 percent of all toll calls.

Thus the foundation for future high-efficiency, low-cost telecommunications has been established. The new era of integrated digital switching and transmission will continue to extend service beyond the telephone to include more complex terminals and all forms of information—voice, data, and video. The advantages are greatly expanded services, new services, new and more powerful operational and management techniques, and sophisticated measurement and maintenance arrangements. And the network will continue to grow, both domestically with the cooperation of the independent telephone manufacturing and operating companies and internationally with the cooperation of foreign administrations.

In all probability, the next fifty years will see changes take place even more rapidly than those of the first fifty years of Bell Laboratories and the first 100 years of the telephone. While telecommunication switching technology and its application will continue to play important roles, the technical and managerial expertise of Bell System people will be the most important ingredient in insuring this progress.

The contributions of many Bell System people are acknowledged in this book, but it is important to recognize that, as the technology has become more sophisticated, it has taken ever larger teams of designers and managers to convert inventions into developed and engineerable systems and, therefore, individual contributions are not as easily identified. This book is dedicated to the generations of engineers who made these accomplishments possible.

On a personal note, it has been my pleasure to share with many colleagues in this, one of the great technological adventures of the twentieth century. By whatever measure—complexity, numbers of people, development costs, investment, or telephone traffic processed—this adventure is a huge one. The greatest satisfactions, however, come not from designing something big but from seeing the human achievements involved when individuals tackle and solve some of engineering's most challenging problems.

W. O. Fleckenstein
Vice President, Switching Systems
April 1982

Acknowledgments

Although I was the principal author of Chapters 1 through 12, a major Chapter (13) devoted to the development of PBXs and other customer-premises switching systems was prepared by Charles Breen who, prior to his retirement from Bell Laboratories, was associated for many years with the engineering of these systems. Other contributors to the customer-premises switching chapter were George M. Anderson, PBXs from 1970 to 1975, and Frank M. Fenton, key systems from 1970 to 1975. Frank F. Taylor prepared sections IV, V, and VI of Chapter 9, and was most helpful in editing the entire manuscript. Walter S. Hayward reviewed and contributed to section III of Chapter 5, and sections III and IV of Chapter 11. I would also like to acknowledge the considerable help of Janet Edwards, who keyboarded the manuscript and its numerous revisions into the Bell Labs UNIX* system word processor, Ruth L. Stumm, who searched diligently for illustrations and helped with proofreading, Terry Getz, who prepared the illustrations for publication, and Arlene M. Dagostino who took the words and illustrations and made them into a book.

One could not prepare a book of this type without continuously monitoring and collecting data over a period of time. My wife, Rhoda, provided much encouragement, and my secretary, Frances Anderson has been most patient, participating in this process as well as typing all of the original manuscript drafts. All contributors thank George E. Schindler, Jr., our editor and mentor, whose encouragement and continuous help were important to the creation of this history.

In this book, readers should note that numbers of installations and entities refer only to the period covered by this history. Such numbers will in many cases be different when updated through recent years.

---

*UNIX is a trademark of Bell Laboratories.

Over many years, during which colleagues have provided insight into the developments with which they were engaged, I was privileged to observe their progress, reflect on these activities, and now to record in this volume the events as I recall them. The subjects covered have been chosen from a larger set. There are always questions of history that one cannot anticipate even in a most comprehensive volume. I hope readers will find the material included here interesting to peruse and useful for reference. A thorough reading should provide an understanding of how the research and development activities of Bell Laboratories during its first 50 years have made available the switching techniques and technology for serving the nationwide network during a critical period of its growth.

Amos E. Joel, Jr.

Switching Technology
(1925−1975)

The Mulberry office switchboards (originating in the background and terminating in the foreground) used with the first panel switching equipment in Newark, New Jersey in 1915. Although manual and semiautomatic switching were to remain in use for many years, it became apparent that full automatic switching and high-capacity transmission systems were the path to more and better telephone services. To reach that goal, manual systems had to be adapted to work compatibly with the new automatic systems. Moreover, telephone devices, logic circuits, numbering and routing plans, and administration and maintenance techniques all grew in complexity and ability to handle large amounts of local and toll traffic.

Chapter 1

Setting and Scope

By 1925, Bell System engineers had built a large body of knowledge concerning complex logic circuits and had begun to apply this knowledge to the design of automatic switching machines, and, subsequently, to the design of computers. Fifty years later, in 1975, a huge nationwide automated network was in place and working. The soundness of common-control principles and of stored-program control had been repeatedly demonstrated, and customers could look forward to a network of ever-greater machine intelligence and utility.

I. THE SETTING

If one were to attempt a list of the major technological achievements in telephony to date, three of them would surely be analog and digital multiplex transmission, common-control switching, and stored-program control (SPC) switching. Multiplex transmission greatly improves transmission efficiency by sending more than one signal (sometimes thousands or even tens of thousands) over a single transmission medium. Common-control switching and SPC, though less well known outside of engineering communities, are at least of equal importance in terms of economics and technical sophistication.

Common-control switching and SPC are analogous to multiplex transmission in the sense that they greatly improve efficiency. Older systems tied up expensive equipment during the time of a telephone call, but common-control systems segregate equipment into a switching network and the control units. The switching network consists of paths for voice signals that of necessity have to be assigned for continuous use during calls because they carry instantaneous two-way telephone conversations. But the common-control units quickly "jump in and out of" the various stages of setting up and taking down a telephone connection, and so work quickly and with great efficiency. And SPC has added new dimensions of flexibility and speed. From these concepts and their application in many intricate ways throughout the Bell System, there have flowed enor-

1

mous benefits to customers in terms of good service and new services at attractive costs.

II. SCOPE

A previous volume of this series, titled *A History of Engineering and
Science in the Bell System: The Early Years (1875-1925)*, covers important Bell System innovations in manual switching and also covers
the beginnings of attempts to assist operators or to substitute for
operators through the use of switching machines.

From the earliest experiments with automatic switching, and
extending for almost a quarter century, the precise directions the
new switching arts should take were not entirely clear. Basic problems of the configuration and design of central office systems had to
be solved. With time it was appreciated that large cities required
switching capabilities different from those of less densely populated
areas. Large local networks were put in service with manual techniques. Tandem offices (switching offices that serve other switching
offices) afforded opportunities in these networks to try some of the
new technologies of automated switching later to be applied more
generally throughout the Bell System. The new techniques helped
put to rest beliefs that semiautomatic techniques might be superior
to fully automatic switching. On the other hand, the new techniques also showed the need to develop arrangements to handle
calls between manual and automatic offices during the transition
period.

By 1925 the designers of switching systems had become most
adept in devising complex logic circuits using general-purpose electromagnetic relays of telephone quality. Some of these circuits were
the forerunners of those used by designers of computers, who
began their work about 25 years later. Indeed, telephone engineers
at Bell Laboratories applied their art to the early relay computers
(see *A History of Engineering and Science in the Bell System: National
Service in War and Peace: 1925-1975*, pages 133 through 174).

During the second 50 years of telephone switching, covered by
this volume, manual switching was extended by using and improving upon many of the successful techniques invented and applied by
the pre-1925 pioneers. Long distance calling became possible
without the delay caused by the awkward procedure of having the
customer reach a second (toll) operator, hang up, and wait to be
called back.

The bulk of this volume, however, will of necessity be devoted to
a comprehensive account of Bell System developments in automatic
central office switching and in the types of switching used in private
branch exchanges (PBXs) and key telephones—the latter two
categories often characterized as customer-premises switching.

The period covered, 1925 to 1975, is an especially important one since these 50 years saw the integration, automation, and great expansion of a nationwide telecommunications network. As mentioned above, this period is also characterized by the two pioneering achievements of first introducing common-control electronic switching and, later, stored-program control electronic switching. In the area of customer-premises switching, automated PBXs and key telephone systems were gradually and ubiquitously introduced.

Complex logic circuits, and particularly the skill with which they were applied to insure reliable service, were keystones to the development and expansion of the concepts of common-control switching. Prior to the adoption of these principles, system intelligence was in the logic circuits associated with the individual switching mechanisms that progressively established a connection. These circuits could not be reused until the switches became available for use on another call.

Innovative techniques, however, were applied with increasing capability and skill by Bell Laboratories engineers, which meant that the logic circuits could gather facts and make the decisions needed to complete connections, and could do so "in common" for many calls in sequence without awaiting the completion of any one call. Furthermore, the decisions made by these control circuits could be based upon the prior knowledge of the status of connections already established. In a word, the systems were acquiring a form of machine intelligence.

These fundamentals of indirect and common control brought early, worldwide recognition to switching innovations of Bell Laboratories people. Although others had proposed aspects of such logic, Bell Labs engineers had devised the necessary and sufficient conditions for their application in large systems. Most of the systems were perceived as being required to fill the expected growth of the Bell System. These included switching systems not only for small, large, and medium-size local serving areas, but for tandem and toll service as well.

The success of development techniques and the deployment of common control provided momentum towards allowing customers to dial more and more of their own telephone calls. New developments in signaling and the recording of charges provided the tools. Network plans first permitted operators to dial long distance calls, then led to a transition period during which direct distance dialing of long distance calls by customers became a reality. Important to this work were devices, common-control circuit configurations, and numbering and routing plans that today are integral to the nationwide network. At the end of this era, Bell engineers were able to look back on the automated network of switching systems as the largest distributed computer in the world.

The application of common-control techniques approached a peak in the 1950s with the maturing of developments for the No. 4A and No. 5 crossbar systems. At the same time, and drawing on the large base of electromechanical switching expertise, a new generation of switching systems techniques emerged, using the new disciplines of high-speed electronics as conceived and evolved in the research efforts at Bell Laboratories. (These innovations are to be covered in another volume of this series, dealing with research.) An exploratory development effort was started with the objective of applying electronics for the logic and memory and in the network portions of central office and PBX switching systems. The result was the subsequent development of the Morris (1960) space-division central office electronic system, named for Morris, Illinois, the site of the first field trial. This was followed in 1965 by No. 1 ESS (electronic switching system), also a space-division central office electronic system, and the No. 101 ESS (1963) time-division customer-premises switching system.

The most important result of this exploratory effort was the emergence of the concept of storing the logic of the system actions in machine memory, a concept now widely recognized and used worldwide as stored-program control (SPC). The Morris development effort proved the effectiveness of the concept at its initial implementation, and SPC subsequently ushered in a new era in switching. Progress in SPC technology has now made it economical to include SPC in the smaller switching and key telephone systems, such as for community dial offices and customer premises.

The invention of SPC at Bell Laboratories was in part stimulated by the growing capability required by common-control systems, such as No. 5 crossbar, as described in Chapter 11 of this volume. These many requirements for extending service beyond "plain old telephone service" (POTS) made the switching systems of the growing network the locations for introducing many sophisticated features that offered new services. Associated with this growth was the realization of the need for many ancillary systems for traffic and service measurement and evaluation, number services, network management, and service maintenance. These adjuncts started small, but as their need was proved by their development and deployment, sometimes as small systems, they became a major class of systems known as operation support systems (OSS).

This volume describes developments from the time when most calls were handled manually, when the rudimentary long distance network had just a few circuits, and when these circuits were available only after waiting in a queue. As the transmission art developed and the network grew, larger groups of circuits were provided at lower cost. The switching challenge was to bring the calls to the network and to learn to serve them on demand, with essentially no delay.

Recent developments in switching, described in Chapter 12, have brought transmission and switching closer together technologically, since each serves digital signals that represent the speech message signals. Digital signals are switched using time-division techniques—that is, the distinguishing feature of a signal is its occurrence in a particular time slot, as distinct from space division, in which a signal can be identified by its physical location in an array of equipment. When the technology history of the next 50 years is written, the digitization of the network will be a major theme.

Panel dial system Laboratory, New York City 1930. The direction of switching systems development was influenced by the need for automatic equipment in the large central offices served by the Bell System, and the panel system represented a major effort of the years immediately preceding and following the establishment of Bell Laboratories in 1925. Panel successfully divorced switch control from the dial—a necessary prelude to modern switching efficiency and flexibility. The last panel office in the Bell System was removed from service in 1982.

Chapter 2

State of the Art in 1925

By 1925, the Bell System had taken a number of basic steps leading toward full automatic switching. Engineers had developed interfaces with manual systems, without which dial systems could not grow. The principle of indirect control of switches, initially with register-senders, was an established design concept. And experimenters probed the idea of a coordinate switch to decrease mechanical switch motions and thus speed servicing of telephone calls.

The first half century of the telephone[1] was dominated by manual switching systems and equipment. Practical methods of operation were devised, and apparatus was developed for high reliability so as to keep maintenance costs low.

The methods for operating manual switching equipment for both local and toll switching were constantly improved so that the least amount of labor and shortest call-completion times could be realized. Prior to 1925, manual toll switching was also improved to the extent possible with the limited amount of toll transmission facilities then available. This meant devising methods for dealing with large numbers of calls whose completion had to be delayed while awaiting the availability of transmission facilities. Long distance signaling methods were complex but, by today's standards, primitive.

In automatic switching, Bell System developments were quite significant, although they started slowly. While the step-by-step system was being sold throughout the world, Western Electric Company engineers were devising switching mechanisms of greater size so as to provide better service for the larger central offices found in the Bell System. Initially, the approach was to use electromechanical switching as an aid to the operators in establishing connections rather than as a means to allow customers to dial their own calls. This semiautomatic method of operating was first thought to be a better mix between the labor costs and maintenance and operation

---

[1]References are grouped at the end of each chapter.

than full automatic operation. Several field trials of panel and rotary equipment devised by Western Electric engineers were tried in this country and abroad. (See discussions of these systems on pages 580 to 600 in ref. 1, *A History of Engineering and Science in the Bell System: The Early Years, 1875–1925.)*

The application of these "machine" switches brought forth many new design concepts. Primary among these was the indirect control of switches from register-senders. As a result, it was possible to divorce the operation of the switches from the method used for placing information into the system and for making switch selections required to reach the desired destination.

Another basic concept that accelerated the decision to accept full automatic operation was the addition of letters as well as numerals to the telephone dial (PENnsylvania 5000, etc.). As a result, there was greater acceptance of the possibility that customers could accurately dial six or seven digits, since the central office code, as well as the numerical digits, could be dialed from memory. (As discussed in Chapter 11, section 2.3, later human-factors studies showed that there was no need for letters in the dialing sequence.)

To test the new switching systems in actual service meant that the Western Electric designers had to solve the basic problems of interconnection between manual and automatic switching systems. As a result, the call indicator—a method of displaying numbers on calls from automatic systems to operators' positions—was successfully tried, improved, and made ready for introduction. Also developed were switchboards allowing operators to originate calls to be completed by automatic systems.[2] These innovations were known as "semimechanical" systems. Many of them were tried in a "metropolitan tandem" system introduced into New York in 1920.[3]

By 1919, the Bell System had taken the major steps to go to full automatic switching. Both the panel and step-by-step systems were standardized, and Western Electric engineers set out to develop both systems for large-scale manufacture and installation. Thus, by 1925 the number of dial telephones in the Bell System exceeded the number in the U.S. independent telephone industry, which had started automation much earlier.

Almost unnoticed during this period were the seeds planted for the next generation of automatic switching equipment (see Chapter 4, section I). In 1913, patents were secured by Western Electric on coordinate switching mechanisms—methods for closing electrical contacts at points in an x-y coordinate array, rather than by moving a contact over an appreciable distance to make (establish) a desired connection. Over the next ten years, many improvements in coordinate designs were proposed, the purpose being to replace the rotary and Keith[4] line switches used in the panel and step-by-step systems and the large vertical-motion switches of the panel system (see next Chapter, section I). As more laboratory experience with these coordinate line switches was obtained, the designers proposed complete coordinate systems as improvements over the panel system designs. This work went forward until 1923, when a complete coordinate system was designed and set up in the Western Electric laboratories at 463 West Street in New York City (see Chapter 4, section 1.1). In 1926, it was decided not to proceed with the further development of this system since it could not compete economically with the panel system, which was still being improved and reduced in cost.

REFERENCES, CHAPTER 2

1. Fagen, M. D., ed. *A History of Engineering and Science in the Bell System: The Early Years (1875–1925).* Murray Hill, New Jersey: Bell Telephone Laboratories, Incorporated, 1975, Chapter 6, pp. 467–714.
2. Ibid., p. 582.
3. Ibid., p. 584.
4. Smith, A. B., and Campbell, W. L. *Automatic Telephony.* New York: McGraw-Hill, 1914, p. 38.

Incoming selector frames, panel office, Cortlandt Street, New York City, 1931. Installed primarily in larger cities, the panel system was the most sophisticated automatic switching system of its day. Innovations incorporated by Bell Laboratories included a decoder using large multicontact relays, trouble indicators with lamp or teletypewriter output, and line finders that removed the need for having an individual switch for every telephone line. One version of panel included a "call announcer"—a system of announcing station-code numbers by converting dialed digits into voice messages using strips of sound-on-film. By 1958, panel served over 3.8 million telephone lines in the Bell System.

Chapter 3

The Evolution of Electromechanical and Manual Switching Technology 1925–1935

One of the first large switching jobs of the newly incorporated Bell Laboratories in 1925 was to make major improvements in the panel system—an effort that by 1927 resulted in a 60 percent cost reduction. Panel sender tandem was also developed and introduced into service in 1931. Another major effort was a thorough redesign of step-by-step to incorporate many innovations, especially changes to improve short-haul toll performance and to enhance access to regional networks by toll operators. So successful were these and later innovations that by 1973 step-by-step served over 24 million telephone lines. Concurrently, many new switchboard designs and signaling developments were undertaken to interface with the growing automation of local service, and these led to systems, beginning in 1936, whereby operators could dial up long distance connections.

I. PANEL SYSTEM IMPROVEMENTS

As with all switching developments, one finds many vintages of equipment and varieties of features required to meet current and foreseen service needs. During the initial development of the panel system, some of these needs were obvious. For example, in those days the number of digits dialed on a call was limited to the requirements of the community in which the central office was located. Thus, the first Bell System panel system, placed in service in Omaha, Nebraska in 1921, was designed to interpret only two-digit office codes. This process, known as "translation," was provided by using a separate power-driven rotary switch (see Fig. 3-1) in

Fig. 3-1. Power-driven rotary switch used for translation in initial Bell System panel switching system.

each sender with access to 44 terminals as code points. When the panel system was extended to work with three-digit office codes (first cut over in the PENnsylvania New York City office in 1922), two panel selectors per sender were used[1] for this function (see Fig. 3-2). This gave a capacity of 400 code points. At the time, it was felt that the resultant 400 office codes would be sufficient for the largest cities. With the 400 code points, however, the up-and-down movement of panel selectors for translation was found to be undesirably time-consuming.

From the development work on the coordinate system (see Chapter 4, section 1.1), a new translation technology using multicontact relays (see Fig. 3-3) was explored. As a result, the panel decoder was developed, the first major new improvement in the panel system after Bell Laboratories was incorporated as a separate company of the Bell System in 1925[2] (see Fig. 3-4). The decoder development was the first to use large multicontact relays (based on the flat-spring R relay design) and short holding time common controls (less than three tenths of a second). As many as 300 senders were connected to no more than five decoders, greatly concentrating this control function. A large number of leads passed between the senders and decoders and were connected using the multicontact relays that comprised the major elements of the decoder connector. Also, a technique for checking the vast multiple wiring through the decoder connector was developed to insure that dirty contacts and crossed wires would not give false translation information.[3] To make this arrangement practical, the stepping

Fig. 3-2. Panel selector used for translation with later versions of the panel system, beginning with the New York City PENnsylvania office in 1922. (New York Telephone Company, December 1926.)

switches used to register the called number in panel senders were eliminated and replaced by relays.[4] Fig. 3-5 shows an "all-relay" panel subscriber sender frame, and Fig. 3-6 shows a sender unit with the doors open.

The ability to detect and locate troubles opened up a new era in the maintenance of switching systems. Up to this time only routine test sets were used to generate calls to check that the equipment was functioning properly[5] (see Chapter 11, section 3.3). The use of controls that could act on many calls in the busy hour opened the door to new maintenance techniques. The panel senders were designed to test the trunks over which pulsing took place. If trouble was detected, the sender "stuck" or held the facility so that the trouble could be traced to its source. The invention of the central decoder with the self-checking of internal logic of the system brought forth the development of the first centralized maintenance tool designed

Fig. 3-3. Multicontact relay used for panel system translation. This new technology led to the panel decoder, a major post-1925 improvement in the panel system. (New York Telephone Company, December 1926.)

specifically to aid in locating troubles detected in processing calls. This was known as the "trouble indicator,"[6] shown in Fig. 3-4. It was used to record on lamps the identity of the particular combination of system elements involved in a given trouble. After leaving a trouble record, the call was given a "second trial" using, if possible, a different decoder. For the first time, full advantage could be taken of using memory to register and reuse the call information.

Prior to the panel system development, most systems used small rotary switches per line to access the first stage of selection. These were known as "line switches." They were used in the first panel system offices, and a version known as "Keith" or plunger line switches was used in step-by-step offices manufactured by the Automatic Electric Company. The Bell System pioneered in the concept of the "line finder" in the panel system and later in the step-by-step system (see section II below). Associated with each first selector were other panel selectors that could access lines. These selectors were known as "line finders" and avoided the need for an individual selector switch per line.

The first line finder development for the panel system was begun in March 1919. These line finders were designed to serve 300 lines and were required to hunt for a line over as many as 50 terminals.

Fig. 3-4. Panel decoder frame (left) and decoder trouble indicator and test frame (right). (New York Telephone Company, December 1926.)

They were tried in Paterson, New Jersey in May 1922, and the first standard installation was in Seattle, Washington in March 1923. Where these were used, it was found that, for those lines at the top of a multiple, the time to connect a line to a sender was too long. Also, the floor space taken by these frames was greater than that required for the rotary line switches used in the initial installations. Finally, since the panel system could be engineered for offices in residential areas in large cities, it was found that higher concentration ratios were more economical.

Therefore, by 1925, the first improved line finder was placed in service.[7] This had a capacity of 400 lines with a maximum hunt over 40 lines and a multiple reversal such that the average hunt was only ten lines (see Fig. 3-7). This line finder arrangement, first placed in service in Philadelphia, Pennsylvania, became standard thereafter. The line finder required new traffic engineering considerations, and the first published line finder traffic tables were made available in 1924.

Fig. 3-5. An "all relay" subscriber sender frame for the panel system.
(New York Telephone Company, December 1926.)

Fig. 3-6. Two senders of type mounted on frame (see Fig. 3-5) with
doors open.

Fig. 3-7. Improved line finder placed in service in 1925 to allow more economical concentration ratios. (Miller, Kempster B., *Telephone Theory and Practice*, McGraw-Hill, 1930.)

The line finder and the decoder arrangements reduced the need for individual 22-point electromechanical rotary switches, which had proved difficult to maintain in adjustment. Another step toward eliminating these switches from the panel system was taken when they were removed from the sender finders.[8] Initially a two-stage power rotary link had been used to improve the efficiency of the access between district selectors and senders, which previously were limited to 22 senders per district. These links were first placed in service in 1926.[9] In 1927, developments had proceeded to the point where special panel link frames, shown in Fig. 3-8, had been developed to replace the rotary switches.[10]

The major panel system developments—such as decoders, panel links, 400-point line finders, etc.—were accompanied by many detailed arrangements and improvements. For example, better methods were developed for grading the multiple of the district and incoming selector frames and for monitoring stuck senders at dial system "A" (DSA) switchboards.[11] Constant effort was applied to

Fig. 3-8. Special panel link frames, developed in 1927 to replace earlier rotary switches. (Miller, Kempster B., *Telephone Theory and Practice*, McGraw-Hill, 1930.)

the development of the panel system, resulting in cost reductions amounting to over 60 percent in the three years from 1925 to 1927. As a result, a whole new look was taken at the panel system and, as with many large switching projects, a new improved generation of equipment was developed. (See Fig. 3-9 for a block diagram of the revised system.) For convenience, this equipment is broadly identified as panel equipment with "battery cutoff"—meaning battery on the cutoff relay. By this time more than 600,000 lines of panel equipment with "ground on the cutoff relay" had been shipped and installed by Western Electric.

Placing battery on the cutoff relay improved the circuit margins and reduced the possibility of double connections when final selectors were hunting over PBX trunk terminals. The Bell System electromechanical design standards required that apparatus connected directly to central office battery be "self-protecting"; i.e., a direct ground on a terminal opposite battery will not start a fire. By placing battery on the cutoff relay winding rather than on a resistor in the final selector circuit, lower sleeve resistance to battery resulted and a greater busy-idle voltage differential could be obtained.

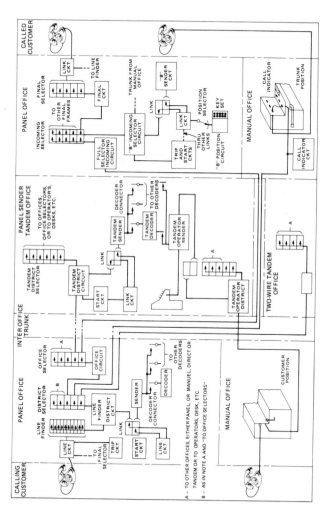

Fig. 3-9. Block diagram of panel system of the "battery cutoff" type, as redesigned during the early years of Bell Laboratories. In the panel system four or five switches, called selectors, are employed in series for each call. Each office has selectors of all types but only the line finder, office selector, and district selector are shown here in the calling office, and only the incoming and final selectors are shown in the called office. There were two types of tandem offices—2-wire office tandem and sender tandem. Calls to manual offices could be completed using call indicator and later call announcer. Calls from manual offices were distributed to operators at cordless positions with keysets at the sender tandem or terminating panel offices.

All panel selector circuits were improved in this redesign.[12] The first installation of this equipment was in Detroit, Michigan in 1929. In particular, improvements were made in the supervisory arrangements of panel incoming selectors, so that they could operate over distances of as much as 25 miles.[13] Later extensions permitted them to operate over more than double this range. In particular, panel selectors were operated in Providence, Rhode Island, under control of senders in panel tandem offices in Boston, a distance of some 60 miles.

The panel system was indeed an illustrious example of the type of innovation of which the Bell System was most capable. Many new concepts were introduced. By judicious effort based upon experience, costs were reduced to the original objectives. Methods used for engineering and installation were constantly improved and complexity overcome. Eventually (by 1958) more than 3,830,000 lines of panel equipment had been produced and placed in service. The last new office was installed in New York City (HYacinth-9) in 1950. Although the panel system was designed to function for 30 years, many systems served well over longer periods. Besides the continuous changes and additions needed to make it a viable component to meet the telephone demand in the post World War II years, the system was modified to accommodate customer nationwide area code dialing,[14,15] changes in call charging methods (see Chapter 4, section 2.2) and routing, and even the provision of TOUCH-TONE® dialing.[16] Many improvements were made in the apparatus such as the sequence switch contacts[17] and selector clutches.[18]

Panel systems were installed primarily in the larger cities, such as Boston, Chicago, New York City, Philadelphia, San Francisco, St. Louis, and Washington, D. C., which formed the backbone of service for the business communities. The planning and implementation of the electronic switching developments of the 1950s and 1960s (see Chapter 9, section IV) evolved at a time when the panel offices were reaching the end of their useful lives. In this way a new generation of switching equipment for use in large cities (beside the No. 1 crossbar system introduced in 1938) was brought into service at a time when business communities could benefit from the many new features that electronic switching was able to provide.

The application of panel switches to local tandem operation had been introduced with the semimechanical metropolitan tandem in New York City in 1920.[19] Initially this served to improve the efficiency of manual tandems in an all-manual environment. A unique feature of the panel system was the development of office selector tandems that enabled more efficient gathering of traffic from a number of originating offices to the same terminating offices.[20] Since these office selectors operated over a trunk pair, they were known as "2-wire" office selectors as contrasted to the 3-wire variety used within an originating office.

With improved panel equipment and growth of panel systems in the larger cities where manual tandems were in operation, it was natural that a full-mechanical panel tandem would be developed. This system used the latest decoders, all-relay senders, and improved selectors. The 2-wire office selector tandems were limited to selections among only 25 groups of trunks and could only work on a revertive pulse basis. The "panel sender tandem,"[21] as the new development was named, could receive the entire called number (7 or 8 digits) by the same form of pulsing used to operate with call indicators, known as "panel call indicator" or PCI pulsing.[22] This is a form of direct current 4-bit binary signaling where two bits of the code are positive or null and two bits a high or low negative current flow. Digits can be transmitted interoffice at a rate of about 3 digits per second.

The panel sender tandem could outpulse with revertive, dial, or PCI pulsing, according to the dictates of the called office. In addition, it could serve "B" switchboards on a straightforward (noncall-indicator) basis with calls from originating operators through the panel sender tandem. The system also included call-distribution operator positions so that manually originated calls, particularly from the growing suburbs, could be routed and completed into terminating panel units (see Fig. 3-10).

Fig. 3-10. Operator positions for the panel sender tandem system. (Miller, Kempster B., *Telephone Theory and Practice*, McGraw-Hill, 1930.)

As the number of dial offices in an area increased, and as the phasing-out of manual offices could be foreseen, the economic viability of adding call indicators to these offices diminished. In response, an invention derived from the work of Bell Laboratories in the sound-motion picture business filled the gap. It was known as the "call announcer,"[23] and was used to convert the station code portion of dialed numbers into a voice announcement produced by sound-on-film strips (see Fig. 3-11). This, then, constituted another form of "outpulsing" made available to senders in these tandem offices, making possible the more economical, simple, and easy extension of dial-originated calling into the manual offices remaining in metropolitan areas.

The decoder trouble indicator proved so successful in the local panel offices that for the panel sender tandem a teletypewriter form of trouble recorder was used.[24] This enabled the recording of more successive troubles while the trouble indicator could store only one indication at a time and had to be reset manually.

The first panel sender tandem, known as "suburban tandem," was placed in service in New York City in January 1931, and included the call announcer feature. Five other panel sender tandems were subsequently placed in service in Boston, Philadelphia, and Chicago. All have now been retired.

Detailed improvements in panel apparatus continued well into the 1940s.[25] Also there was much experimentation to keep the bank and sequence switch terminals clean to reduce noise introduced into the connections by poor contacts.[26] As new circuit and testing techniques became available, particularly after the invention of the transistor, many new maintenance techniques were applied to the panel system, even in the 1960s.[27]

II. STEP-BY-STEP IMPROVEMENTS

Although the Bell System decided in 1919 to adopt the step-by-step dial system for single and small multioffice exchange areas, Western Electric did not begin production of step-by-step equipment until 1926. During this period Western Electric installed equipment manufactured by Automatic Electric.

Once the step-by-step system was standardized by the Bell System, the Western Electric engineering department and its successor, Bell Laboratories, were engaged in an extensive program of improving the design and engineering of step-by-step equipment.[28] The list of improvements contributed by the Bell System is too long to discuss in detail. Fig. 3-12 shows some of the apparatus improvements made between 1926 and 1948. The principal thrust was to improve operation for short-haul toll dialing and to provide adequate inter-

Fig. 3-11. Call announcer system using sound-on-film to produce voice announcements of dialed numbers. Left to right: C. J. Beck, F. K. Low, and C. C. Towne.

faces between the step-by-step dial offices and operator access to the toll network.

Also during this period, long-range development plans were made for improving and extending the application of step-by-step equipment. For the first time, prepaid coin service features and message register arrangements were added to step-by-step systems. By 1925 the Bell System design requirements information for all step-by-step central office equipment had been established. These were also adopted by Automatic Electric Company. Included in the standard specification was the introduction of 11 foot, 6 inch high frames to the step-by-step system as designed by Bell Laboratories.[29] Previously the Automatic Electric Company equipment was arranged for 9 foot double-sided frames. In 1925, the first Western Electric-engineered job using equipment manufactured by Automatic Electric Company was completed (Champaign, Illinois). The first job engineered and manufactured by Western Electric was for Springfield, Massachusetts, and was completed in January 1927 (see Fig. 3-13).

Once Bell Laboratories engineers became thoroughly familiar with the state of the art in step-by-step switching, they proceeded to

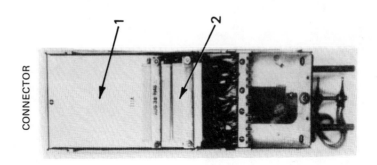

CONNECTOR

SELECTOR

LINE FINDER

LINE FINDER

1. **Normal Post and Spring Assemblies**
   Four changes, 1928-1940: Redesigned post, springs, and operating cam.
   Results: 2,9,11.

2. **Vertical Off-Normal Spring Assemblies**
   Five changes, 1926-1948: Redesigned lever and springs.
   Results: 2,11,17.

3. **Rotary Armature**
   Nine changes, 1926-1946.
   Results: 5,9,11.

4. **Test Jack and Lower Cover Plate**
   Eight changes, 1926-1948: Redesigned test jack; hinged number plate holder.
   Results: 2,9,11.

5. **Wiper**
   Six changes, 1925-1947: Contour of tip; improved assembly; detachable guide; replacement spring; noble metal tip.
   Results: 2,6,11.

6. **Shaft Spring Assembly**
   Two changes, 1931-1946: Changed to helical spring.
   Results: 5,9,11.

7. **Shaft**
   Three changes, 1928-1939: Reduced varieties; improved construction.
   Results: 2,10.

8. **Interrupter Springs (Vertical and Rotary)**
   Two changes, 1929-1942: Bell crank design; improved design of spring.
   Results: 5,910.

9. **Commutator and Wiper**
   Five changes, 1927-1947: Redesigned spring; changed terminal and mounting.
   Results: 5,9,15.

SELECTOR

1. **"B" Position Relay**
   Five changes, 1926-1945: Redesigned bearing; 1:1 ratio armature.
   Results: 9,11,13.

2. **Double Dogs**
   Three changes, 1931-1939: Improved bearing; cover guide added.
   Results: 2,10.

3. **Wiper Cords**
   Three changes, 1925-1929: Termination at test jack; tinsel cords; solderless tips.
   Results: 2,10.

4. **Cam Springs**
   Three changes, 1926-1928: Eyelected studs; redesigned cam and bracket.
   Results: 9,11.

5. **Relays**
   22 changes, 1928-1947: Improved coil construction, bearings, and mounting; redesigned armatures.
   Results: 2,4,8,9.

6. **Vertical Armature**
   Eight changes, 1926-1946.
   Results: 5,9,11.

7. **Magnet Coils**
   Four changes, 1926-1940: Self protecting windings; filled coil construction.
   Results: 3,7.

8. **Banks**
   Seven changes, 1928-1945: Radial-sided contacts; mechanized assembly; solderless terminals.
   Results: 2,6.

9. **Release Mechanism**
   Three changes, 1929-1947: Redesigned armature and spring; redesigned armature and spring; redesigned release link.
   Results: 1,2,9.

CONNECTOR

1. **Mounting Plates and Covers**
   Nine changes, 1925-1948: Redesigned front and rear covers and mounting plates.
   Results: 2,10.

2. **Condensers and Networks**
   Three changes, 1938-1948: Developed smaller units; included in switch assembly.
   Results: 2,12,16.

General Changes

Ten changes, 1928-1948: Improved finishes and spring pileups; lubrication; increased pulsing range.
Results: 2,11.

Results: Legend

1. Easier Adjustment
2. Reduced Cost
3. Avoided Fire Hazard
4. Improved Capability (Capacity)
5. Improved Operation
6. Improved Service
7. Improved Stepping Capabilities
8. Improved Transmission
9. Longer Life
10. Easier Maintenance
11. Reduced Maintenance
12. Easier Rearrangements
13. Improved Release Time Capability
14. Improved Release Time
15. Easier Wiring
16. Simplified Wiring
17. Improved Operating Margin

Fig. 3-12. Improvements in step-by-step switching, 1926-1948.

Fig. 3-13. Springfield, Massachusetts, 1927 installation of step-by-step equipment, the first job engineered and manufactured by Western Electric.

apply their creativity and standards to many parts of the system. From 1925 to 1927, most of the basic selector and connector circuits were redesigned. Not only were connectors and other circuits developed to provide for the superimposed selective ringing as used by the Bell System to some party lines, but provision was also made for automatic revertive calling on these lines. As shown in Fig. 3-14, new types of selectors were developed which for the first time provided for digit absorption.[30] These were used with discriminating selector repeaters in small offices,[31] but later proved most useful when the Bell System went to universal 7-digit dialing in the early 1950s (see Chapter 6, section 3.2).

Arrangements were developed to prevent wrong numbers due to preliminary pulses which might be falsely generated at the start of a call when the receiver is first taken off-hook.[32] This also resulted in the standardization of "11X" service codes as compared with "X11" for the panel system (see Fig. 3-15).

Fig. 3-14. Two-digit, digit-absorbing step-by-step selector.

In 1926 Bell Labs engineers adapted from the panel system the ideas of commutators and multiple reversals and applied them to the basic step-by-step switching mechanism, so that this mechanism could be used as a line finder to replace the individual or plunger line switches that had been standard to that time[33] (see Fig. 3-16). A simple arrangement was developed to allot idle finders with the shortest travel distance to serve calls from each level.

Due to the limited access inherent in each level of the step-by-step switch, much effort was expended to obtain efficient gradings[34] (see Chapter 5, section III). In addition, the concept of providing access greater than 10 was adopted. This was done by introducing an additional stage of 22 terminal switches, known as rotary out-trunk selectors (ROTS) to reduce the number of succeeding switches and trunks.[35]

At the terminating end of the switch train, new level-hunting connectors were developed that enabled the system to serve PBXs with more than ten trunks without the grading of the connector multiple, thereby obtaining better call completion.[36] New dial long line circuits and improved relays increased the subscriber loop range of the system.

The administrative and maintenance aspects of the step-by-step system improved. Test trains and dial and ringer testers that could

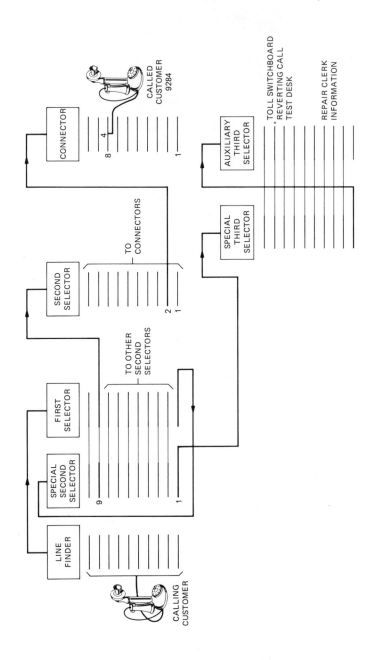

Fig. 3-15. Use of supplementary switches for preliminary pulses. (The boxes with ten underlines represent step-by-step switches.)

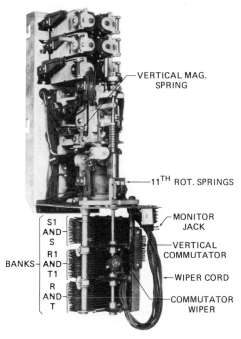

Fig. 3-16. Step-by-step switch adapted for use as a line finder.

be used by installers were added[37] (also for the panel system, as shown in Fig. 3-17).

The Springfield, Massachusetts office cutover in January 1927, was not only the first office completely engineered, manufactured, and installed by Western Electric, but it also contained many of the Bell Laboratories innovations to that date.

Early work on new applications of the step-by-step system to intermediate (tandem) offices was started in 1924 with the rehabilitation of the Los Angeles plant that the Bell System had consolidated in 1918. These changes, while not standardized, were placed in service in 1926 and paved the way for new standard developments for tandem and toll applications.[38] Until these improvements were made, all calls from within Los Angeles to the suburbs were treated as toll calls and were passed to toll switchboards. The new arrangements permitted "A" or dial system assistance (DSA) as well as toll switchboard operators to dial these points directly and complete the calls to distant offices. This method became known as "A-B Toll" and was applied to dial and manual completion.

These arrangements, which included improvements in signaling as well as new selectors and connectors, provided for toll grade transmission, improved pulsing range, and pulse repeating selectors that could be located in intermediate offices (see Fig. 3-18).

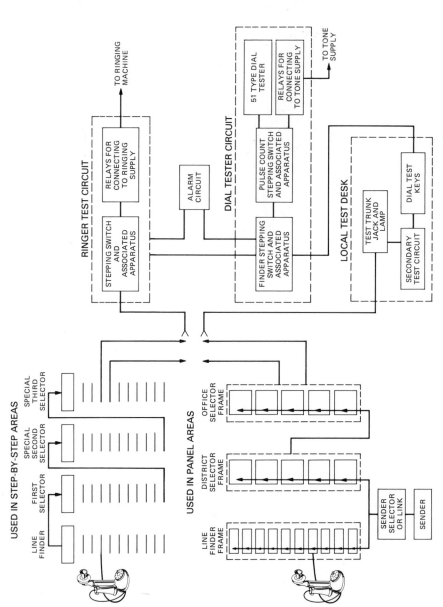

Fig. 3-17. Dial and ringer test circuits, applied to both step-by-step and panel systems.

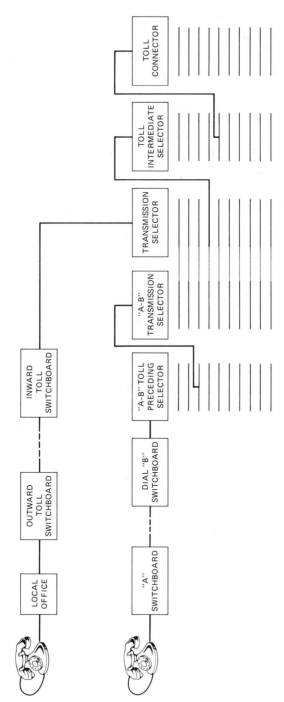

Fig. 3-18. The A-B Toll system used to improve step-by-step dial services over extended distances.

After a successful trial, the Los Angeles development was standard-ized in 1931[39] after being applied in most of the state of Connecticut in 1929,[40] and in Denver, Colorado, Albany, New York, and San Diego, California.

Since the Bell System was using the panel system for automating service in large cities, and since the 1919 decision assigned step-by-step the task of automating service in smaller communities, Bell Laboratories devoted some of its efforts to developing very small step-by-step offices. Here the operator functions were located remote from the switching office. The maintenance needs were so infrequent that resident craftspeople were not necessary. Fig. 3-19 shows a general schematic of such an office, which became known as unattended community dial offices (CDOs). The first one, later

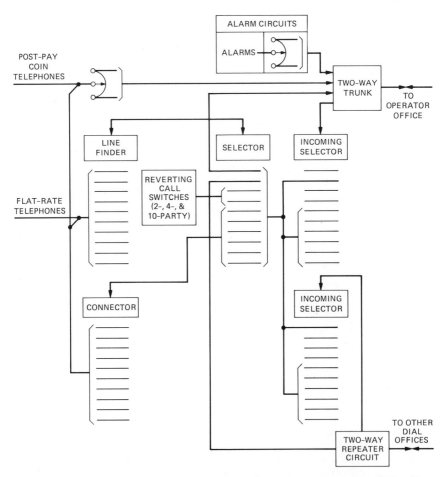

Fig. 3-19. Schematic of a typical step-by-step community dial office (CDO) with two-way dial and operator trunk group.

coded the 350A, was placed in service in San Clemente, California in July 1927.[41]

A trial of this system was held in Sinking Springs, Pennsylvania in 1926. The 350A, which has a maximum capacity of 1500 lines, was soon followed by the 360A with a capacity of only 500 lines[42] and the 370A and B (1932) with very small capacity (fewer than 100 lines), with selector connectors, and operating over two-way trunks[43] (see Fig. 3-20). A network of 14 of these offices was placed in Southern California by the end of 1929.[44]

Since the contract with Automatic Electric Company guaranteed a minimum production level, Western Electric suspended production of step-by-step equipment during the depression from 1932 to 1936. Community dial offices by Automatic Electric Company were introduced, most notably the system identified as 35E97. (Others were 375A/B, 385, 386, 32A32, 32A44, and 36A1.)

The Bell System acquired through purchase of independent telephone companies about 100,000 lines of step-by-step equipment of Automatic Electric Company manufacture prior to the 1919 agreement. Under this agreement, another 2.3 million lines of Automatic Electric Company manufactured equipment meeting Bell Laboratories specifications were placed in service in the Bell System. After

Fig. 3-20. Small-capacity 370B step-by-step office in Manakin, Virginia.

World War II when the Automatic Electric Company could not meet both the Bell System and independent telephone company needs, Bell Labs designed and Western Electric manufactured step-by-step equipment (initially manufactured by the Automatic Electric Company) for use as additions in Bell System offices.

The success of and demand for small offices after the depression stimulated a new equipment design with uniform-size frames and switch types that were packaged for easy engineering and installation. This system, developed by Bell Laboratories, was known as the "355A"[45] (see Fig. 3-21). Among the features was a new combined line and cutoff relay as well as a separate optional "line lockout" relay for use of lines with a high incidence of line faults.

The first installation was cut over in Batavia, Ohio in 1939. A total of about 3500 offices serving about 4 million lines demonstrate the success of this development. There is more of this code of switching system manufactured and placed in service in the Bell System than any other code at any time. After World War II an improved package known as the "356A" was developed but found limited success. As late as 1957, new equipment designs were being made for the still popular 355A CDO.[46]

Many individual innovations continued to be made in the step-by-step system. For example, an arrangement was added to provide for early detection and operator interception of permanent signals in 1963,[47] and also the timed disconnect of connectors when only the called party goes on-hook so that he or she may originate a new call.

Other improvements to maintain the step-by-step system as a viable member of the Bell System network are described elsewhere in this chapter. The step-by-step system provided automatic service for more Bell System lines than any other switching system when it reached its peak of 24,440,000 lines in 1973. (Later the same year the No. 5 crossbar system exceeded this number.)

III. APPARATUS AND EQUIPMENT

From its beginning, switching has depended upon the availability of specific and unique apparatus designs that could perform with high reliability. Moreover, until the introduction of digital time-division electronic switching (see Chapter 12, section I), switching required apparatus or devices that went hand-in-hand with switching developments and generally preceded the design of new systems. The relays and switches, as well as the improvements referred to in the previous section, are examples of this close partnership. Not only was new apparatus developed to accompany system improvements, but existing apparatus in large-scale production was modified to reduce cost[48] and to improve performance.[49]

Fig. 3-21. Line finder equipment of a small step-by-step office, 355A design. This community dial office was produced in large numbers, beginning in 1939.

Other partners in the development of systems were the equipment designers. They had the knack of "putting it all together," so that the bits and pieces of a system were made into a whole when placed in the hands of the operating telephone companies. They also were responsible for documentation that described the generalities of the system before one plunged into its specific details. During the pre-World War II period at Bell Laboratories, many new system concepts as well as improvements reached the point where field testing or field trials were necessary. The Bell Labs equipment engineering organization headed by H. H. Lowry had separate departments for organizing, constructing, and implementing field trials. It was through this organization that many young engineers passed before becoming full-fledged equipment designers.

In the switching systems organization there was a similar department devoted to the construction and testing of laboratory models of systems. These system laboratories were established in separate buildings at the West Street location of Bell Labs in New York City, where many young engineers learned about switching on the job. This included learning firsthand about the construction of switching equipment frames and the adjusting and testing of the apparatus.

The relays and switches used in the prewar systems all required adjustments. Fig. 3-22 shows the array of tools required to adjust step-by-step switches. A separate organization in the systems testing department provided engineering information for the apparatus codes for specific circuit applications of apparatus designed in the switching apparatus organization. It was here, also, that many young engineers learned the intricacies of switching circuit design.

A book covering switching technology during the electromechanical era would not be complete without recognizing the contributions made by Bell Laboratories apparatus engineers in understanding and applying the principles of electromagnetics in relay technology. Many designs were placed into production and continually improved. These designs were necessary to meet the changing and greater capabilities required by each succeeding generation of switching systems. Much of this progress has been recorded in ref. 50.

IV. SWITCHBOARD AND TESTBOARD IMPROVEMENTS

The development of manual switchboards peaked before 1925, but many significant innovations were introduced after this date. "Straightforward operation" of manual switchboards eliminated call wire and provided "automatic listening" at the "B" board, and was introduced after 1925.[51] Automatic listening required that only one call at a time be connected to "B" operator positions. This was the first among development requirements for a non-marginal relay lockout or contention circuit.[52] These circuits were among the most complex ever introduced into manual switchboards. They paved the way for understanding similar problems in circuits competing for service within the crossbar systems when those systems were designed a decade later.

Several new switchboards were developed and introduced during the early years of Bell Labs. The most innovative was the No. 3 toll switchboard shown in Fig. 3-23, introduced in 1927. Although it was never used as a local central office switchboard, it was the most successful manual switchboard ever introduced, accounting for more than 50,000 positions over more than 35 years of production. Previous switchboards such as Nos. 1 and 11 used different cord circuits for the particular type of traffic being served. The No. 3 switchboard represented a major change in design philosophy with very simple cord circuits and the complexity of signaling and supervision being provided, as shown in Fig. 3-24, in the trunk circuits mounted on separate relay racks away from the switchboard.[53]

Fig. 3-22. Tools needed to adjust step-by-step switches.

Fig. 3-23. No. 3 toll switchboard, high keyshelf type. Over 50,000 positions of the No. 3 were produced.

Fig. 3-24. Relay racks designed to handle complexities of signaling and supervision, thus simplifying the manual positions of the No. 3 switchboard. No. 3 equipment represented a major change in design philosophy.

Features included transmission pad switching and provision for 20-, 135- or 1000-hertz ringing, depending upon the origin and destination of the call and the technical requirements of the trunk.

As trunk groups became larger, toll switchboard operation was improved by providing magnetic drops in the multiple to indicate the next idle trunk in the group.[54] Since at least one of these was operated at each position for each trunk group, the use of lamps to replace the drops created power distribution problems. A Bell Labs innovation was the use of ac to power them.[55]

In 1940, a new version of the No. 3 switchboard including both 30-inch and 40-inch keyshelf heights, the No. 3C, was introduced to serve as a combined toll and DSA switchboard.[56] A packaged version, the No. 3CF, was also introduced. A new design eliminating platforms and high-type chairs with a low keyshelf (30 inches) was developed after World War II and became generally available in 1950. It was known as the 3CL switchboard, shown in Fig. 3-25, and was used to replace the then standard 15-type DSA board as well as to provide a new standard toll switchboard.

As the number of toll lines to large cities increased, it was no longer possible to reach all of them from each toll switchboard position. (The No. 3 switchboard provided for a maximum of 600 toll trunks.) To provide for the outward switching of calls from local and outlying combined line and recording (CLR) toll positions (see further discussion of the CLR method later in this section),[57] the toll tandem switchboard, using the No. 3 switchboard principles, was developed in 1930.[58] These positions, with single-ended cords (Figs. 3-26 and 3-27), could reach 3600 trunks. A 3B switchboard was developed in 1937,[59] further improving on the concept of the toll tandem. For inward calls, automatic distribution using the first application of crossbar switches was developed in 1935.

In 1931, the No. 12 manual switchboard[60] was developed (see Fig. 3-28). It was a small-capacity system (640 to 2000 lines) without line relays. Its primary function, in small communities, was to replace switchboards used with magneto lines as they were converted to common battery. It was one of the first applications of solid state technology to switching since it used a varistor to reduce lamp failures due to line voltage surges.[61]

The physical and equipment aspects of switchboards were greatly improved: keyshelf clocks,[62] keys, ticket handling and dispatching, and operator chairs[63] (see Fig. 3-29). Throughout this early Bell Labs period, many new ancillary switchboards and desks were developed so that administrative personnel could conveniently assist customers. Many new information (now "directory assistance") desks were developed to accommodate the growth of telephone service and the accompanying increase in directories and

Fig. 3-25. No. 3CL switchboard with low keyshelf.

Fig. 3-26. The toll tandem switchboard, developed in 1930.

their size. The No. 1 and No. 2 information desks[64] were arranged for operator call selection, while the No. 3 information desk was the first to provide automatic call distribution using selector switches[65] (see Fig. 3-30) and including call storage and call waiting indicators. New repair service desks for responding to trouble reports were developed, including the popular 14-type local test desk (see Fig. 3-31) introduced in 1931.

To centralize the local test desk operation, particularly during off-hours, an arrangement was developed in the early 1960s so that lines could be tested remotely. Local test trunks included test devices that could be accessed and controlled from distant locations.[66] By 1970 a new cordless local desk, shown in Fig. 3-32, was developed that also could be used in centralized repair service centers.[67]

Toll testboards were introduced with the expansion of toll service. Jacks on "primary" testboards permitted toll lines to be disconnected

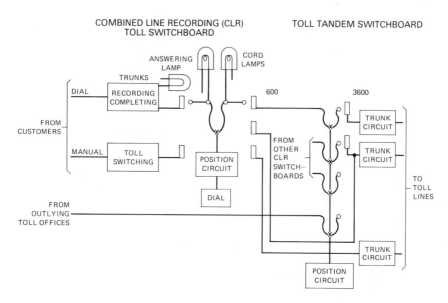

Fig. 3-27. Typical arrangement of trunks as used with a toll tandem board, a design based on No. 3 switchboard principles.

Fig. 3-28. The No. 12 manual switchboard, developed in 1931 to serve 640 to 2000 lines without line relays.

Fig. 3-29. Large switchboard installation of the 1930s. Note operators on roller skates.

from the toll switchboards, signaling, and other terminal equipment.[68] Measurements then can be made on toll lines to isolate and locate troubles.[69] The Nos. 5, 16, and 16A are examples of early toll testboard developments[70] (see Fig. 3-33). The No. 8 test and control board was an attempt to extend the toll test function to include an overview of service operations from both plant and traffic points of view. As shown in Fig. 3-34, circuits could be plugged "out-of-service" with lamps at control centers indicating this condition.[71]

This testboard also included "patch jacks," later called "secondary jacks," between the switching equipment and the terminal equipment (see Fig. 3-35). These were to permit patching around terminal equipment in trouble using spare or other facilities, or to permit the use of toll facilities for rerouting.[72]

A number of toll testboards and smaller toll test units later were developed and became standard. Most notable are the 3A, 4A, 5A, 17B, and 17C types for secondary testing and the 1A, 2A, and 19B types for primary testing. Also developed were many testboards for special services such as private lines and government projects.

The first manual mass announcement and distribution system was introduced in 1930, initially for time-of-day announcements[73] (see Fig. 3-36). In 1939, after public use at the New York World Fair, Bell Laboratories developed the first commercial use of magnetic tape recording, applying it to weather announcing.[74] For the more difficult time announcements that change continuously, a completely automatic system was introduced in 1953.[75] Each of these service offerings required trunk circuits designed for each switching system so as to synchronize charging with the announcement and to prevent excessive holding time. More specific recorded announcements to inform customers about service situations were introduced in 1958.

As electromechanical switching took hold, greater emphasis was placed on efficient interconnection between automatic and manual switching offices. New cordless call distributing "B" switchboards, known as dial system "B" or DSB switchboards, were developed.[76,77] They were of importance particularly for the step-by-step system where pulsing to the manual office required considerable time, making it advantageous to use registers that were independent of the positions.[78] Included were centralized call distributing

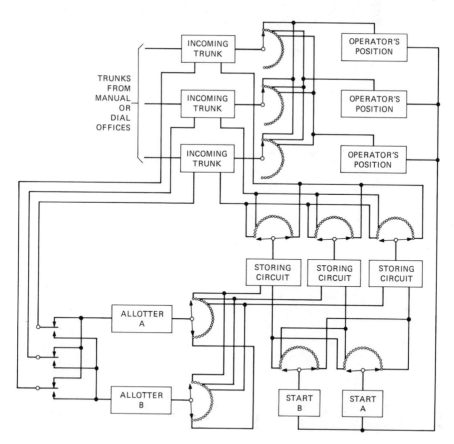

Fig. 3-30. Main switching steps (simplified) showing call distribution system for the No. 3 information desk.

Fig. 3-31. The popular No. 14 local test desk, introduced in 1931.

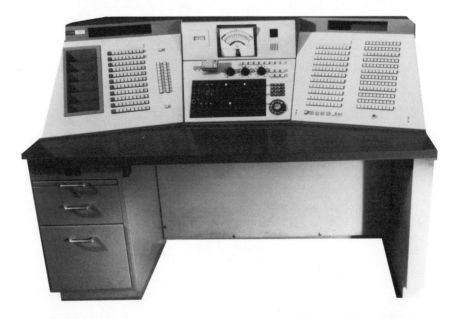

Fig. 3-32. The No. 16 cordless local test desk, introduced in 1970.

arrangements that could serve terminating dial equipment in several buildings.[79] This need arose as more and more switching was fully automated. Among other DSB functions, centralization required special provision for holding and reringing on calls from a distant office. As the incidence of manual into automatic calling decreased, centralization enabled more efficient operator grouping.

Where the panel sender tandem system was used to complete calls to manual offices, the innovation of automatic call announcing made it possible for the first time to automate calls to operators at cord switchboards without adding call indicators at "B" positions (see Section I above). Nevertheless, for areas where panel sender tandem could not be economically applied, a small call indicator was developed which took the place of several cord circuits.[80] Call indicators originally arranged to display when a key was depressed (KDCI)[81] were redesigned and modified for automatic display (ADCI).[82] Many types of local switchboard designs were involved.

Early in the deployment of dial systems, it became Bell System policy that customers served by dial offices could reach operators for assistance. This required the development of dial system "A" or DSA switchboards.[83] These switchboards were also convenient for monitoring dial system alarms, "stuck sender" conditions, overtime and stuck coin conditions on coin telephone calls, and for line-busy verification. As the public became more accustomed to dial opera-

Fig. 3-33. No. 5 toll testboard, an example of early toll testboard developments.

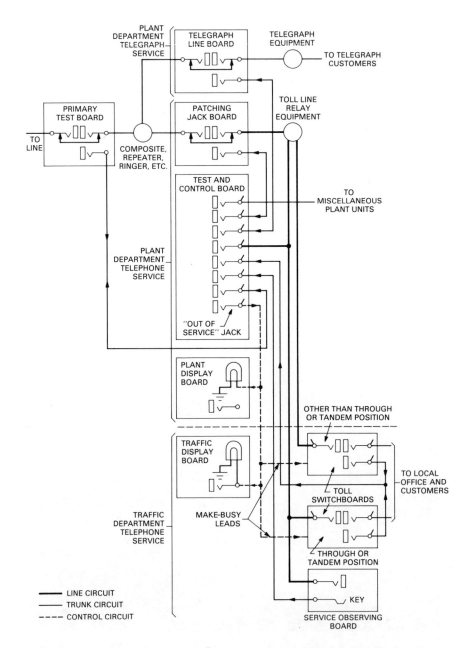

Fig. 3-34. Schematic of No. 8 test and control board and its association with other toll office units reporting on troubles and their clearance.

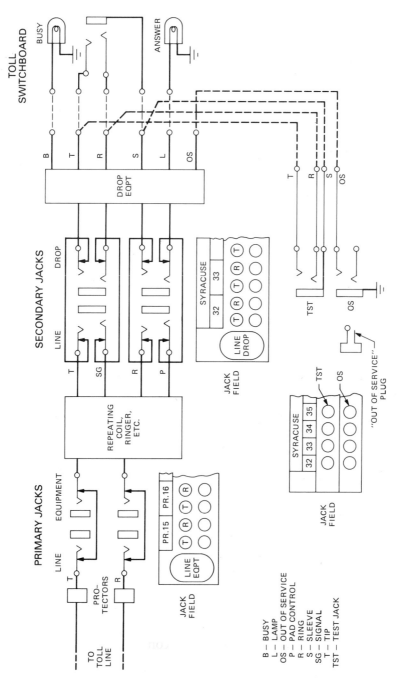

Fig. 3-35. Arrangements for both primary and secondary jacks as used with the No. 8 test and control board.

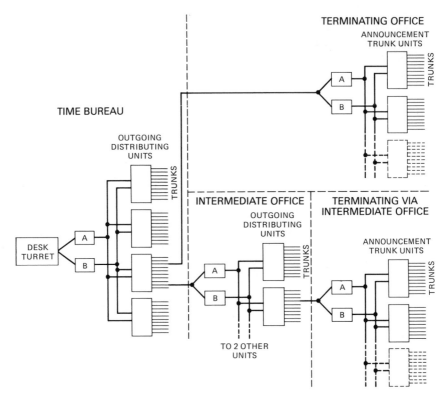

Fig. 3-36. Schematic of 1930 system of distributing time-of-day announcements.

tion, the traffic handled by these operators decreased, and these switchboards were centralized[84] in large cities or combined with the toll switching boards in smaller cities. Many types of DSA boards were developed for application with different dial systems.[85] The DSB function diminished along with manual service and, as described above, was either centralized for a number of offices[86] or added to DSA boards.

Also, as local switching for more of the metropolitan areas became automated, it was necessary to introduce into them new features accessible from switchboards that would give the operators and craft personnel the same capabilities that had been available to them with manual operation. One of these was the provision of no-test access to lines from test desks and from dial system "A" switchboards. With no-test trunks, it was possible to verify that lines found repeatedly busy or engaged in conversation could be interrupted for emergencies.

The combined line and recording (CLR) method of toll operation became widespread to provide toll service without requiring the calling customer to hang up and be called back. It then became necessary to verify or check the number of the calling customer as it was given to the recording operator. Number-checking directly from CLR switchboards or through the services of the DSA switchboard was developed for the panel and step-by-step systems. In large city offices the DSA switchboards were equipped with a special compact single-conductor multiple field of line jacks,[87] as shown in Fig. 3-37. By touching the tip of a number-checking cord to the line identified by the customer, the operator could hear a tone if the correct number was as given. Although toll calling was initially less frequent in step-by-step areas, a number-checking switchtrain was developed for this system but abandoned for lack of economic justification.

To reduce operator work time in handling calls, arrangements were developed for manual switchboards so that in place of dials the more efficient keysets could be provided.[88] These keysets sent dc

Fig. 3-37. Special compact field of line jacks, developed for verifying the calling line number. (New York Telephone Company, December 1926.)

signals similar to those used in the panel system between senders and call indicators. The signals were sent, over the tip and ring of the cord (2-wire method) with which the keyset was associated, to special senders that were attached to the trunk circuit to which the cord had been connected by the operator (see Fig. 3-38). The sender generated the type of pulsing required by the trunk: dial pulses in step-by-step areas and revertive pulses in panel areas. In dial offices, a 3-wire method of signaling was used between the keysets of DSB operators with special senders that controlled the terminating switches.[89] Fig. 3-39 shows a switchboard position with a keyset in place of a dial.

This type of switchboard sender was installed first in Detroit, Michigan in 1930 and greatly increased the efficiency of operators completing calls into local as well as more distant dial systems, since the time required to key a number was much less than that required to dial a number.

V. SIGNALING

Initially, the only type of signaling used over toll lines was ringing. This started as high-power 16–2/3 hertz (later 20), then 135 hertz, and finally 1000 hertz (modulated at 20 hertz) so that it could be transmitted through repeaters over the same long distances as

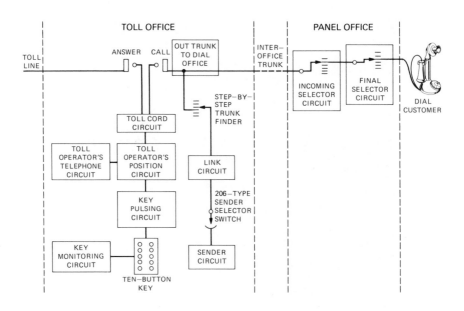

Fig. 3-38. Keypulse sender arrangement.

Fig. 3-39. Switchboard position with keyset.

voice.[90] "Ring down" became the standard manual toll method for call origination and disconnect. With non-hang up manual service, automatic supervision and, eventually, with the coming of the dial system, dial pulsing over longer distances became a necessity. Initially opening and closing the direct current (dc) loop was reserved for these functions. It was not until the late 1920s that improved circuits for extending the range of dc signaling were developed. These were first applied commercially in the Seattle, Washington area in 1925 over distances up to 160 miles over open wire. The principal technique employed was to use one or both sides of the line as a simplex (SX) or composite (CX) circuit for signaling purposes using initially positive and negative 120 volts.[91] These signaling methods used the metallic path as only one side of the signaling circuit, the other side being ground return. Methods were developed for compensating for ground potential difference between the two ends of the circuit for CX signaling by using one of the signaling legs together with a balancing network. In this way two pairs could provide three ground-compensated signaling circuits. To prevent signaling noise from entering the talking circuits, composite "sets" or high-pass, low-pass filters were used. Also, means were developed for extending composite signaling around voice frequency repeaters, since the range of this form of signaling could be as much as 300 miles.

Composite and simplex signaling were not only used for supervising circuits between manual switchboards but were also developed so that dialing could be introduced over the circuits. This opened the way for short haul toll dialing networks. Standard interfaces were developed between composite signaling sets and the relay equipment associated with switchboard and dial system trunk circuits. These interfaces used the letters of the alphabet to designate the standard functional leads between circuits. Two of these designations, "E" and "M," have become well known and are used to this day as the interface between signaling and switching equipment. They represent, on a local circuit dc basis, the outgoing and incoming signals from the signaling circuit, respectively. Many different mnemonic names such as "Ear" and "Mouth" have been added to these letters, but the choice of letters seems to have been fortuitous.

A post-World War II development was duplex signaling (DX) for short trunks providing ground compensation on one side and the signal path on the other side of one composite circuit.[92] DX signaling has the advantage that it is provided on a "per trunk" basis.[93] Eventually, improved circuits were developed to operate on standard negative 48 volts.

VI. START OF OPERATOR DISTANCE DIALING

With the availability of signaling systems that could satisfactorily repeat dial pulses and supervision over distances greater than those experienced with loop signaling, the dialing of short-haul toll calls became feasible. During and immediately after World War I, experiments and ad hoc arrangements were developed by Bell System companies to dial from toll switchboards into independent step-by-step local offices.

Formal development of composite signaling started after the early trial installations in the Seattle area (see section V above). New step-by-step selectors were developed at Bell Laboratories and, together with composite signaling, these formed the backbone of a step-by-step tandem network established in Los Angeles in May 1926. Although the distances here were relatively short, no greater than 25 miles, still the volume of traffic handled over this short haul network was rather large. Improvements in signaling and step-by-step tandem operation, and the use of switchboard senders, made it possible over the succeeding 15 years to establish short-distance AB toll and tandem networks that covered states or portions of states, the most notable being in Connecticut, Ohio, and Pennsylvania.

The idea of having recording-completing operators dial longer distance toll calls was pursued from 1921, first in connection with panel system developments for Seattle, Washington, and then with the step-by-step system. The panel equipment was tried in 1925 and

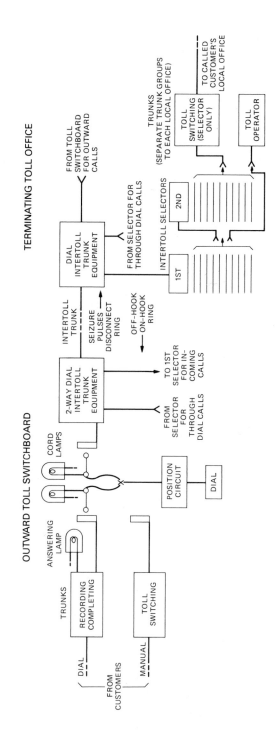

Fig. 3-40. Essential elements of an intertoll dialing system, about 1936.

1926 but was removed primarily due to signaling problems on the rather poor open wire circuits that existed in the territory. Much exploratory work was done to improve dial signaling over composite and simplex phantom legs of open wire and cable circuits.

Starting in 1935, general requirements were formulated for a system whereby operators at toll switchboards could access toll trunks and complete calls to distant toll centers, manual offices, and local dial offices using step-by-step switching developed for tandem short-haul applications.[94] Development of the step-by-step intertoll (long distance) dial system started in 1936, based on studies in Ohio. The system provided for accessing one- and two-way intertoll trunks with toll-grade transmission including automatically switched transmission loss pads, access to inward operators with ring down, manual and automatic start of ringing, and reringing from either end (see Fig. 3-40) using the selectors described in section II above. This permitted the handling, among other things, of person-to-person calls. The improved composite and simplex signaling was used, and this accounted for much of the success of the extended application of step-by-step switching. At its peak, as many as 800 of these step-by-step intertoll switching systems were in operation. Initially they served only toll operator-originated traffic, but when customer direct distance dialing (DDD) was introduced, they were modified so that they could also service this traffic (see Chapter 6, section 5.1).

Further operator distance dialing had to await the development of crossbar switching and multifrequency pulsing.

REFERENCES, CHAPTER 3

1. Goldsmith, E. H. "Panel Type Machine Switching." New York Telephone Company, December 1926, First edition, p. 33.
2. Raymond, R. "The Decoder." *Bell Laboratories Record* **6**, May 1928, p. 273.
3. McAlpine, R. K. "Automatic Prevention of Trouble by Decoders." *Bell Laboratories Record* **8**, July 1930, p. 518.
4. Raymond, R. "All-Relay Register Circuit." *Bell Laboratories Record* **7**, June 1929, p. 400.
5. Allen, L. M. "Routine Tests in a Panel Office." *Bell Laboratories Record* **7**, May 1929, p. 365.
6. Marino, R. "Trouble Indicator." *Bell Laboratories Record* **7**, May 1929, p. 371.
7. Busch, A. J. "Subscriber's Line Finder and District Selector." *Bell Laboratories Record* **8**, May 1930, p. 412.
8. Goldsmith, E. H. "The Panel Type Dial Telephone System." New York Telephone Company, October 1930, Third edition, p. 21.
9. Erwin, E. L. "Hunting Features in the Panel System." *Bell Laboratories Record* **7**, September 1928, p. 5.
10. Miller, K. B. *Telephone Theory and Practice Automatic Switching and Auxiliary Equipment.* New York and London: McGraw-Hill Book Company, Incorporated, First edition 1933, pp. 206–211.

11. See ref. 1 above, p. 49.
12. Boman, C. E. "Notes on Panel Development." *Bell Laboratories Record* **8**, January 1930, p. 226.
13. Collis, R. E.; U.S. Patent 1,804,150; filed January 4, 1929; issued May 5, 1931.
14. Kirchoff, J. W. and Parks, C. O. "Direct Distance Dialing from Panel and No. 1 Crossbar Offices." *Bell Laboratories Record* **35**, June 1957, p. 212.
15. Poole, J. F. "The New Numbering Plan in Panel Switching Offices." *Bell Laboratories Record* **41**, September 1963, p. 323.
16. Lazo, N. and Martins, A. S. "Central Office Modifications for TOUCH-TONE Calling." *Bell Laboratories Record* **39**, December 1961, p. 436.
17. Barber, C. C. "The Sequence Switch." *Bell Laboratories Record* **10**, December 1931, p. 119.
18. Buch, P. E. "Clutches for the Panel System." *Bell Laboratories Record* **8**, April 1930, p. 367.
19. Fagen, M. D., ed. *A History of Engineering and Science in the Bell System: The Early Years (1875–1925).* Bell Telephone Laboratories, Incorporated, 1975, p. 584.
20. See ref. 10 above, p. 244.
21. Bronson, F. M. "Tandem Operation in the Bell System." *Bell System Technical Journal* **15**, July 1936, p. 380.
22. Breen, C. and Dahlbom, C. A. "Signaling Systems for Control of Telephone Switching." *Bell System Technical Journal* **39**, November 1960, p. 1381.
23. Matthies, W. H. "The Call Announcer." *Bell Laboratories Record* **8**, January 1930, p. 210.
24. Irvine, F. S. and Roberts, T. H.; U.S. Patent 1,848,174; filed February 28, 1931; issued March 8, 1932.
25. McWilliams, C. W. "Panel Apparatus Improvements." *Bell Laboratories Record* **21**, February 1943, p. 141.
26. Mann, B. B. and Hermance, H. W. "A New Method for Cleaning Sequence Switches." *Bell Laboratories Record* **36**, February 1958, p. 65.
27. Bertels, J. L. and Nolan, R. I. "Improving Maintenance in Panel Offices." *Bell Laboratories Record* **41**, November 1963, p. 401.
28. Proposed Report Telephone Investigation, FCC, U.S. Government Printing Office, Washington, 1938, p. 326.
29. Smith, E. H. "New Step-By-Step Equipment." *Bell Laboratories Record* **5**, September 1927, p. 7.
30. Atkinson, J. *Telephony,* Vol. II. London, Sir Issac Pitman and Sons, Ltd., 1950, p. 339.
31. See ref. 30 above, p. 340.
32. Dimond, T. L. "Counteracting Dialing Errors in the Step-by-Step System." *Bell Laboratories Record* **7**, January 1929, p. 198.
33. Dodge, W. L. "Development of Step-by-Step Line Finders." *Bell Laboratories Record* **7**, February 1929, p. 236.
34. Dustin, G. E. "Improved Graded Multiple for Step-by-Step Offices." *Bell Laboratories Record* **22**, September 1944, p. 514.
35. Quass, R. L. "Trunk Hunting Switches." *Bell Laboratories Record* **7**, December 1928, p. 157.
36. Korn, F. A. "Level-Hunting Connectors." *Bell Laboratories Record* **7**, March 1929, p. 291.
37. Bertels, A. S. "Testing Ringers and Dials at Subscribers' Stations." *Bell Laboratories Record* **8**, February 1930, p. 263.
38. Wheelock, F. O. and Jacobsen, E. "Tandem System of Handling Short-Haul Toll Calls In and About Los Angeles." *Trans. of AIEE* **47**, January 1928, p. 9.
39. See ref. 21 above.

40. Robb, W. F., Millard, A. M., and McPhee, G. M. "Dial Switching of Connecticut Toll Calls." *Electrical Engineering* **55**, July 1936, p. 773.
41. Meyer, F. T. "Dial Offices for Small Communities." *Bell Laboratories Record* **9**, August 1931, p. 562.
42. See ref. 41 above.
43. Collins, C. A. "Dial Service for Small Communities." *Bell Laboratories Record* **10**, August 1932, p. 424.
44. Wheelock, F. O. "Dial Telephone System Serving Small Communities of Southern California." *Trans. of AIEE* **49**, January 1930, p. 117.
45. Motter, J. T. "The 355A Community Dial Office." *Bell Laboratories Record* **19**, June 1941, p. 316.
46. King, A. S. "Modernized Line-Finder Units for Step-by-Step." *Bell Laboratories Record* **35**, March 1957, p. 105.
47. Hackett, J. A. "New 'Permanent Signal' Equipment." *Bell Laboratories Record* **45**, January 1967, p. 16.
48. Kirchoff, J. W. and Parks, C. O. "Direct Distance Dialing from Panel and No. 1 Crossbar Offices." *Bell Laboratories Record* **35**, June 1957, p. 212.
49. Sailliard, J. H. "Panel System Maintenance." *Bell Laboratories Record* **32**, July 1954, p. 277.
50. Peek, R. L., Jr. and Wagar, H. N. *Switching Relay Design*. Princeton, New Jersey: D. Van Nostrand Co., Inc. 1955.
51. Oakes, W. C. "Straightforward Trunking." *Bell Laboratories Record* **7**, April 1929, p. 323.
52. See ref. 10 above, pp. 360-370.
53. Davidson, J. "Toll Switchboard No. 3." *Bell System Technical Journal* **6**, January 1927, p. 18.
54. Prince, W. B. "Idle Trunk and Position Indicating." *Bell Laboratories Record* **8**, February 1930, p. 267.
55. Koontz, R. G. "A-C Busy Lamps for Toll Boards." *Bell Laboratories Record* **9**, June 1931, p. 467.
56. Johnston, D. F. "Handling DSA Traffic at Toll Boards." *Bell Laboratories Record* **19**, March 1941, p. 206.
57. See ref. 19 above, p. 622.
58. Hokanson, C. E. "Toll Tandem Switchboard." *Bell Laboratories Record* **8**, June 1930, p. 473.
59. Shoffstall, H. F. "Circuit Features of the 3B Toll Board." *Bell Laboratories Record* **18**, February 1940, p. 167.
60. Ulrich, H. W. "A New Common-Battery Board for Small Offices." *Bell Laboratories Record* **11**, December 1932, p. 94.
61. Darrow, W. E. "Protecting Switchboard Lamps With Varistors." *Bell Laboratories Record* **19**, November 1940, p. 85.
62. News item, "Motor Driven Switchboard Clock." *Bell Laboratories Record* **18**, April 1940, p. 235.
63. Ottman, R. E. "Distributing Toll Tickets by Pneumatic Tubes." *Bell Laboratories Record* **12**, January 1934, p. 145; Bouman, B. M. "A New Chair for Operators." *Bell Laboratories Record* **15**, January 1937, p. 170.
64. See ref. 19 above, p. 510.
65. Dahl, J. F. "Improved Equipment for Information Service." *Bell Laboratories Record* **8**, March 1930, p. 328.
66. Stone, K. E. "Extending the Range of Telephone Testing." *Bell Laboratories Record* **44**, December 1966, p. 371.
67. Olson, C. E. and Simone, K. D. "Faster Diagnosis for Ailing Telephone Service." *Bell Laboratories Record* **51**, March 1973, p. 66.

68. Pascarella, A. J. "Locating Faults on Toll Lines." *Bell Laboratories Record* 7, December 1928, p. 161.

69. Zammataro, S. J. "A Universal Laboratory Transmission-Measuring Set." *Bell Laboratories Record* 2, May 1926, p. 98. See also Lutomirski, K. "Toll Transmission Measuring System for the No. 8 Test and Control Board." *Bell Laboratories Record* 12, August 1934, p. 367.

70. Krazinski, L. C. "Primary Toll Test Boards." *Bell Laboratories Record* 13, April 1935, p. 245.

71. Bailey, G. E. "No. 8 Test and Control Board." *Bell Laboratories Record* 12, July 1934, p. 337.

72. Pascarella, A. J. "The Philosophy of Toll-Test Boards." *Bell Laboratories Record* 21, May 1943, p. 278.

73. Lewis, H. A. "Correct Time by Telephone." *Bell Laboratories Record* 9, March 1931, p. 335.

74. Bennett, W., "Weather by Telephone." *Bell Laboratories Record* 18, November 1939, p. 66.

75. Bennett, W. "Telephone-System Applications of Recorded Machine Announcements." *Trans. of AIEE* 72, September 1953, p. 478.

76. See ref. 19 above, p. 603.

77. Hersey, R. E. "A New 'B' Board for Panel Offices." *Bell Laboratories Record* 9, December 1930, p. 162.

78. Lacerte, W. J. "Step-by-Step Cordless 'B' Board." *Bell Laboratories Record* 6, March 1928, p. 210.

79. Strickler, W. B. "Crossbar Central B Board." *Bell Laboratories Record* 20, October 1941, p. 53.

80. Curran, S. T. "A Small Call Indicator." *Bell Laboratories Record* 9, March 1931, p. 325.

81. Curran, S. T. "Key-Display Type Call Indicators." *Bell Laboratories Record* 8, July 1930, p. 515.

82. Brown, W. W. "Automatic Display Call Indicator System." *Bell Laboratories Record* 9, November 1930, p. 115.

83. Davis, R. C. "—And the Operator Will Answer." *Bell Laboratories Record* 9, August 1931, p. 576.

84. Flint, E. W. "Central DSA Switchboard." *Bell Laboratories Record* 21, November 1942, p. 77.

85. Brymer, S. J. "Developments in the DSA Board." *Bell Laboratories Record* 20, April 1942, p. 195.

86. See ref. 79 above.

87. See ref. 8 above, p. 50.

88. Newsom, J. B. "Key Pulsing for No. 3 Toll Boards." *Bell Laboratories Record* 9, November 1930, p. 131.

89. Caverly, H. C. "Pulsing Between Dial and Manual Offices." *Bell Laboratories Record* 22, November 1943, p. 110.

90. See ref. 19 above, p. 631.

91. Sheppard, H. A. "A Signaling System for Intertoll Dialing." *Bell Laboratories Record* 18, July 1940, p. 337.

92. Newell, N. A. "DX Signaling—A Modern Aid to Telephone Switching." *Bell Laboratories Record* 38, June 1960, p. 216.

93. Swain, R. R. "Intertoll Dialing with Step-by-Step Selectors." *Bell Laboratories Record* 18, May 1940, p. 266.

94. See ref. 93 above.

Local crossbar system laboratory, West Street Bell Labs location, New York City, 1939. The crossbar switch ushered in a new era of switching development. Because it could operate at high speed, with many electrical contacts per crosspoint in a coordinate array, the crossbar switch allowed a small amount of complex equipment, called markers, to control the networks over which the telephone connections are established. Termed "common control" because the markers are used in common for all connections, this principle greatly increased the efficiency of switching systems. It also permitted a second-trial feature if a first attempt to establish a connection failed, and made possible new and better forms of detecting and locating troubles.

Chapter 4

Introduction of Crossbar

From an early date switching engineers foresaw the potential of a switch needing only a small number of magnets to operate a large number of relay contacts at crosspoints in a coordinate array, and in which the contacts operated with only a small mechanical motion. A patent for such a device was issued to J. N. Reynolds of Western Electric in 1915. Subsequent developments, including advances in Sweden, resulted in the highly efficient crossbar switch, which formed the basis of the No. 1 crossbar local and crossbar tandem systems, developed during the financial depression of the 1930s. Since the crossbar switch could accommodate a comparatively large number of electrical contacts per crosspoint, even more sophisticated systems became possible. The result was toll crossbar, which first allowed operators and, later, customers to dial long distance calls.

I. GENESIS OF CROSSBAR IN THE BELL SYSTEM

The basic idea of a crossbar switch—to provide a matrix of n by m sets of contacts with only $n + m$ actuators to select one of the $n \times m$ sets of contacts—was proposed early in the automation of switching.[1]

In 1913 a patent application was filed by Western Electric for J. N. Reynolds for a crossbar switch, and the basic patent[2] was issued in May 1915. The device was based on contact elements multipled in one direction, as in a panel bank (see Fig. 4-1). An early suggested use for this switch was in connection with an automatic private branch exchange. Active development of the switch started in 1916, directed toward its use as an "instantaneous" line finder for the step-by-step system, to replace the line switches then used in that system. The crossbar switch that resulted from this work was designed for 120 lines, 20 trunks. It was found, on analysis, to be too costly to compete with existing equipment. Subsequently a new design evolved providing for 100 lines and 12 trunks. The plan was to complete the commercial development of this switch and to put it into production, but activities were halted in late 1921 or early 1922, due to the decision that a larger coordinate switch (see section 1.2 below) offered more attractive possibilities.

59

J. N. REYNOLDS.
SELECTOR SWITCH.
APPLICATION FILED MAY 10, 1913. RENEWED MAR. 25, 1915.

1,139,722.   Patented May 18, 1915.

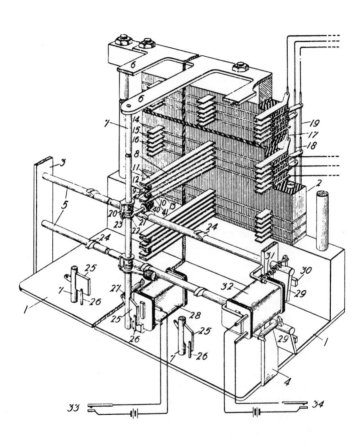

Witnesses:

Inventor:
John N. Reynolds.
by *Howard R. Emery* Att'y

Fig. 4-1.   Illustration from basic 1915 patent for the crossbar switch.

From 1921 to 1926, only a small amount of effort was expended on the crossbar switch, and this was discontinued in the latter year. Studies showed that the apparatus would have been too expensive when considered for use either as a customer line switch or as an out trunk switch, especially since the overall costs would have included the costs of complex associated circuits.

1.1 The Coordinate Switching System

Development work on a wire contact coordinate switch, invented at Western Electric by C. L. Goodrum and J. N. Reynolds,[3] began in the fall of 1921. The emphasis from the start was upon its use as a selector in a new fully automatic system which could handle all classes of traffic and work in conjunction with other systems in the same exchange area. A partially equipped model was completed early in 1922, and, by the spring of 1923, three fully equipped models had been completed. The switch was 8 feet 4 inches by 4 feet 5 inches by 7½ inches deep and consisted of 60 vertical rods and from 45 to 70 horizontal rods, depending upon the number of conductors per circuit (see Fig. 4-2). The horizontal grid wires were made of copper with a silver-tin alloy, whereas the vertical comb wires were made of phosphor-bronze. To establish a connection, two vertical magnets and one horizontal magnet operated, with the vertical magnets releasing after the selection process. Active development of the switch continued during the next two years, and the equipment designs underwent many changes to keep pace with apparatus and changes in the system plan. These, together with an increase in the size of the frames dictated by traffic requirements, made the final system considerably more expensive than originally estimated. By the latter part of 1925, the work had reached a stage where the system was about ready for commercial manufacture. However, the cost studies completed in the following year showed that the system did not produce sufficient savings over the panel or step-by-step systems to warrant its commercial introduction, and work upon the coordinate development was discontinued permanently. However, the system was an important step in the development of common control and associated multicontact relays as employed in the later standardized crossbar systems.

Principal among the ideas emerging from this work was the use of complex relay circuits that acted for a short period during the establishment of each connection, thereby reducing the amount of control equipment required to be held for the duration of each connection. These system proposals became known as common-control systems, with the switch control being common to either two stages or several stages of coordinate switches. The controls were called markers since, in establishing the connections, they placed electrical

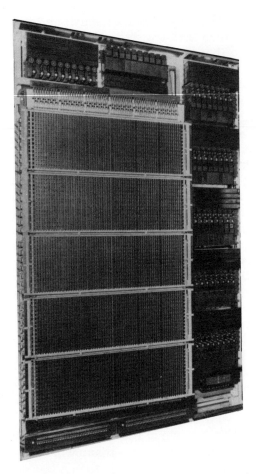

Fig. 4-2. The coordinate switch, an important early (1921–1925) forerunner of subsequent common-control crossbar systems.

signals or "marked" the terminals to be interconnected. (This was not the first use of the word "marker," it having been used earlier by Betulander.[4]) When the marker acted across several stages of switching, a new characteristic was introduced into the system. It was then possible to "look ahead" to find a terminal to which it was ultimately desired to establish a connection and then to provide connections or "links" in successive intermediate stages between the marked terminals. Instead of individual links, an entire "channel" (sequence of links) was selected.

The call information is first received, as in the panel system, by a "sender." The sender then connects to an idle one of a plurality of markers, any one of which can establish the desired connection. An important aspect of this type of common control is that if for any reason the marker should fail to establish the desired connection, a second trial may be initiated by the sender, preferably using a different marker. Should the second trial fail, all of the information as to the data used, and the progress made by the marker in establishing the connection, is available to provide maintenance personnel with a record of the call. In early systems this information was recorded on trouble indicator lamp panels (see Chapter 3, section I). Later, punched card recorders or teletypewriters were used, and more recently computers have been employed to record and analyze this information (see Chapter 11, section 3.3). (The coordinate system was the first to use a teletypewriter, later standardized for panel sender tandem.)

Other concepts arising from the work done on the coordinate system have been described in connection with the improvements made in the panel system by replacing code translators with all-relay senders and decoders. Here, for the first time, switching engineers learned the art of designing complex relay circuits and the parallel transfer of digital information between functional system blocks.

This work also provided a challenge to apparatus designers. First, they had to develop relays that could carry many more pairs of contacts. Secondly, as a result of the high degree of concentration of calls through these common circuits, it was necessary to improve the reliability of relays, due to the large number of anticipated operations.

1.2 Resumption of Work on the Crossbar Switch

The cost reduction and improvement phase of the panel system improvement program was almost completed by 1929. In July, 1930, W. H. Matthies, director of local switching development, returned from a visit to the Telecommunications Administration of Sweden, where he saw the crossbar switch and system which they were using in their very small rural offices.[5] The outstanding feature of this switch in comparison with the coordinate switch was that it was built as a unit and with relay-type precious metal contacts.[6] This switch contained only 100 crosspoints in a 10×10 array, and five selecting bars were rotated by separate magnets in two directions to access 10 sets of crosspoints. This was in marked contrast to the coordinate switch, which was 70×50 (120 bars and magnets) and used phosphorus-bronze springs as crosspoints.

By December 1930, it was agreed that apparatus development work would commence to produce a switch of this type. A study of the Swedish crossbar switch indicated the need of modifications for reasons of operation and manufacture. Briefly, these included (1) a change in the frame structure, to make possible the removal of a single hold magnet unit of the switch without removing the entire switch, (2) a change in the off-normal contact springs to place them in a vertical plane (to reduce the possibility of dust accumulation), (3) a change in magnet design to decrease power drain, and (4) the use of double or bifurcated precious metal contacts. A switch design considered satisfactory was obtained in the second half of 1932. Fig. 4-3 shows a laboratories installation and the early model crossbar switches with round select bars (see Fig. 4-4).

Meanwhile, in October 1930, a study was started to develop a sender link for the panel system, assuming the availability of a "selective relay," as the Bell Laboratories engineers then called the crossbar switch. This application was selected, since in the panel system it required six wires to be brought from the line finder/district selector links to the senders. This had been difficult to implement with panel selectors. Work was also started on the application of the switch to panel and step-by-step line finders, for a toll trunk concentrator, and for PBXs.

Other applications of the switch were also being suggested, many of which looked quite attractive economically. By 1934, exploratory

Fig. 4-3. Bell Labs experimental crossbar switching equipment, early in the 1930s.

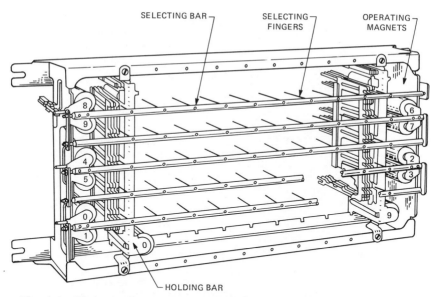

Fig. 4-4. Early model crossbar switch. Actuating a vertical and a horizontal magnet operates a crosspoint in the 10 × 10 array.

development, engineering studies, and apparatus development had proceeded to a point where plans for the development and manufacture of crossbar switches for various applications showed much promise, and development work was started on several items. The plans for the use of the switch in the panel and step-by-step systems were abandoned, and attention focused upon the production of an entirely separate local system (see section II below). Paralleling its use in a local dial system, the switch was employed in the toll plant as a concentrating switch for trunks to and from combined line and recording (CLR) and tandem switchboards.

1.3 Switchboard Tandem Trunk Concentrator

The first commercial application of the initial crossbar switch design was in November 1935 as a concentrator and call distributor for incoming toll trunks from distant toll points for distributing calls to inward and tandem manual toll switchboards[7] (Fig. 4-5). Four 50-cord positions were served by the system. (The control for this system was called a "discriminator," a term also used in the 3B switchboard.)[8] In this development, detached-contact schematics (see Chapter 5, section VII) were used for the first time in the Bell System. The system was placed in service at 32 Avenue of the Americas in New York City and, on the basis of this field experience, the switch design was modified, particularly to employ a U-shaped channelized select bar so that the selecting fingers could be adjusted individually.

Fig. 4-5. Frames of crossbar equipment, 1935, used with toll switch-boards as a concentrator and call distributor.

1.4 Other Apparatus Developments

In 1936, new relays to accompany crossbar switching were under development, but for systems laboratory models, R-type relays were used. To provide extra reliability, all contact spring sets were duplicated and wired in multiple. Later, the new relays[9,10] called the U and Y types emerged as the standard relay for use with crossbar systems, since they could accommodate many more pairs of flat contact springs, each of which contain bifurcated springs with separate, and for all practical purposes, independent contacts. The operating characteristics were also much improved. Also needed were new multicontact relays. For these relays as well as for crossbar switches, provision was made for bare-wire strapping or multipling of one side of each contact to the corresponding contact of other relays or verticals[11] (see Fig. 4-6).

II. LOCAL CROSSBAR

In 1933, exploratory work on the application of crossbar switching to PBX, local, tandem, and toll switching systems was started, but this work was low-keyed in view of the retrenching that had taken place as a result of the economic depression. However, by the third quarter of 1933 a rather complete description of a system for local office application was available. Much of this work was resurrected from the coordinate system designs.

Although the panel system had been providing excellent service and meeting the needs of heavy traffic in large metropolitan offices, a number of advantages that the marker-type crossbar system could include were felt to be important to the future of providing service economy and flexibility in large cities. (This was the start of the services evolution made possible with common-control switching.) By selecting trunks in the marker, it was not necessary to assign trunks in fixed group patterns. They could be identified nonconsecutively and spread over several switches or terminal groups. This feature was particularly attractive for large trunk groups serving PBXs where terminations not identified by directory numbers could be reached by "jump hunting" to other terminal groups. It meant that traffic could be distributed evenly over the switches. For the first time alternate routing (see Chapter 5, section 3.1) was possible so that tightly engineered direct trunk groups could be supple-

Fig. 4-6. For multipling switches, design changes permitted bare-wire strapping of crossbar switches (shown here) and relays.

mented by a common group of trunks to a tandem switching point. The use of precious metal contacts would reduce or eliminate the electrical noise in circuits caused by vibration created in the contact brushes or wipers of panel and step-by-step selectors. By using common control with crossbar switches in the network, one was no longer tied to the characteristics of the switch in determining the form of signaling to be employed; therefore, it was envisioned that higher-speed signaling between new system offices and shorter call completion times could be realized. An objective in designing the network was to minimize the relay equipment required to be associated with a call throughout its duration and preferably to concentrate these relays in a so-called junctor relay circuit in a link or trunk circuit. These capabilities were achieved from the very beginning in the No. 1 crossbar system.

2.1 No. 1 Crossbar System

Funding to develop the No. 1 crossbar system was arranged in late 1934. Work proceeded on this development throughout the economic depression. Fig. 4-7 shows a block diagram of the system with a brief description of the system's operation included in the caption. Bell Laboratories issued a reprint booklet on the series of articles that appeared in the *Bell Laboratories Record* on this system.* These are listed under refs. 12–22.

The first No. 1 crossbar office was placed in service in Troy Avenue, Brooklyn in February 1938. It initially served 1400 telephones. Prior to the cutover, more than 350,000 test calls were placed through the system starting in September 1937. This installation was unique since it was the only No. 1 crossbar system to be installed without a line choice connector between the terminating markers and the line link switches.

The basic network building blocks were "link frames" consisting of twenty crossbar switches arranged in two stages, called primary and secondary, with "links" between them to obtain access to a larger number of outputs than is available on a single switch, hence providing greater selectivity (see Fig. 4-8). The initial plans for the No. 1 crossbar system followed the organization of the panel system, with completely separate terminating and originating switchtrains. However, one of the important innovations of the No. 1 crossbar system was that for the first time the line switches serving both originating and terminating traffic were combined. This was done by providing access from the incoming link frames

---

*Similar brochures were later issued for the No. 4 and No. 5 crossbar and AMA systems. Later special issues of the *Bell System Technical Journal* (BSTJ) were produced for the electronic switching developments.

directly to the line link secondary switches. In this way the line links could be accessed by terminating traffic and also be used for originating calls.

Experience with the first No. 1 crossbar system at Troy Avenue showed that the traffic capacity of the terminating markers could be improved by making a busy test and finding the desired idle termi-

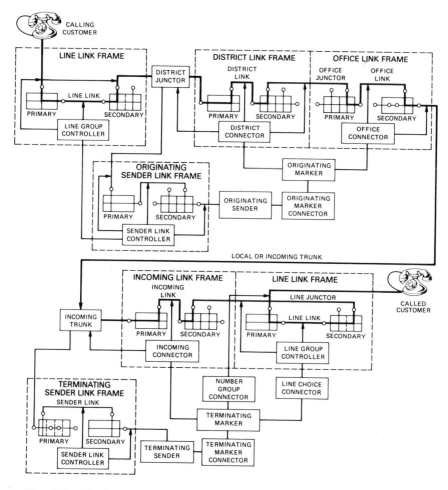

Fig. 4-7. Block diagram of the No. 1 crossbar system. The voice connection traces from the calling telephone on the upper left through various link frames to the called telephone on the middle right. Below this voice path the originating marker, terminating marker, and associated subsystems are the common control, which functions efficiently because it serves all calls at high speed and is not held for the duration of any call. The markers select the path through the links and trunks. The originating marker also interprets (decodes) the central office code.

nation before seizing a "line choice connector" that accessed a maximum of four line link frames. The result was the invention of the "number group" (see article by J. W. Dehn listed in ref. 19), as shown in Figs. 4-9 and 4-10. The number group not only accessed the line sleeve leads to permit a line busy test and to operate the line crosspoint (hold magnet), but also gave other information, such as

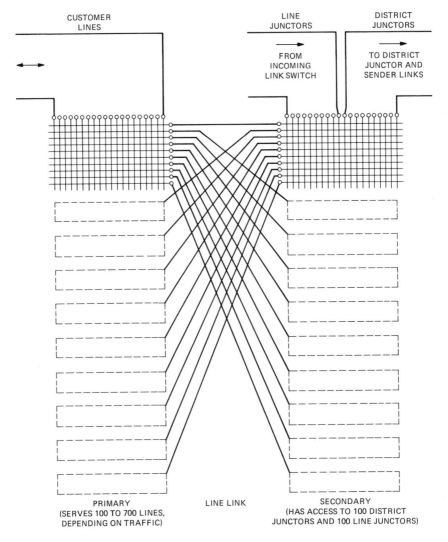

Fig. 4-8. Arrangement of link frames. Any call incoming on a vertical of a crossbar switch, as at upper left, can be switched to any of the 10 switches in the secondary. There, the connection can be extended to any of 100 district junctors or 100 line junctors. Such designs greatly increase the number of choices from which a connection may be selected.

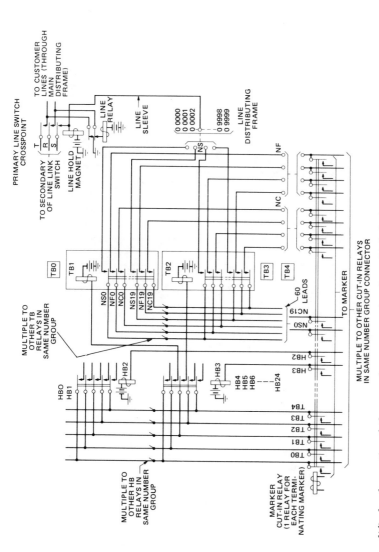

Fig. 4-9. Simplified schematic of the number-group circuit, which helped No. 1 crossbar serve more calls by testing whether the called line is busy before setting up other parts of the total connection. The marker operates the cut-in relay (lower left) to reach 1000 terminating directory numbers. The number group connects the sleeve lead and two other leads of 20 lines back to the marker. Cross-connections NF and NC (lower right) provide ringing, frame, and other information about 20 numbers to the marker, which makes the final selection and establishes the connection to a particular terminal.

Fig. 4-10. Bays of number-group circuits, which improved the traffic-handling capacity and flexibility of the No. 1 crossbar system.

line class, type of ringing, and line choice identification so that the marker could connect to the indicated line choice. All succeeding No. 1 crossbar installations included this feature.

The second No. 1 crossbar office, and the first large installation, was placed in service in July 1938, serving 16,000 telephones from the East 30th Street telephone building in New York City. Here for the first time the elaborate PBX features were introduced into the system, for example those that permitted jump hunting and busy testing of nonconsecutively numbered PBX trunks as part of the same group. All of these features, plus reduced maintenance costs together with the advantages enumerated earlier, proved to be quite successful and demonstrated not only the increased flexibility of crossbar switching over the panel machine-switching system, but also its economic viability for use in large metropolitan offices. Many features were later added to the No. 1 crossbar system, including automatic message accounting (AMA), automatic number identification (ANI), auxiliary senders, and even a new wire spring version of the originating senders. An innovation first introduced into the No. 1 crossbar system incoming link frame was the concept of the split crossbar switch vertical.[23] Here a 6-wire 100-point crossbar switch can be wired and controlled to act like a 3-wire 160 point switch (see Fig. 4-11).

Later, when the No. 1 electronic switching system was developed (see Chapter 9), a primary application was to replace No. 1 crossbar offices. Replacement of the panel offices by No. 1/1A electronic switching systems was almost completed by 1976. About that time, replacement of the No. 1 crossbar offices that served the larger cities was begun. At the peak in April 1970, there were 325 terminating entities serving 7.25 million lines. The last new terminating marker group was installed in Philadelphia in 1969, and the last originating marker group in Chicago in 1970.

2.2 Crossbar Tandem

With the growing confidence in crossbar switching, many new areas were examined for possible application of these principles. One of the features of the panel system that had proved so successful was the 2-wire office selector tandem. However, this tandem had several limitations, among them that it could serve only 50 groups of 10 to 90 trunk terminals per group (each 10 trunks reduced by one the

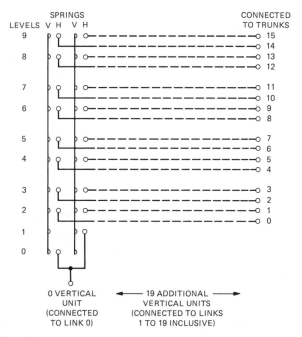

Fig. 4-11. Simplified schematic of a split crossbar switch. Rearrangement of the two lower horizontal levels of crosspoints (0 and 1) allowed choice of 160 crosspoints in what would otherwise be a 100-point switch.

number of groups that could be served). It was proposed in 1934, therefore, that a crossbar tandem arrangement be developed which combined some of the better features of both the 2-wire office tandems and sender tandems of the panel system. With crossbar switching it was possible to provide a crossbar switch link between the incoming trunks and senders (registers) so that different senders could be selected from different groups, depending upon the class of service of the incoming trunk. This meant that the trunks could serve panel, crossbar, and step-by-step offices each with their own type of pulsing (revertive, multifrequency, and dial pulse).[24] The remainder of the crossbar tandem system was almost a copy of the originating switchtrain of the No. 1 crossbar system, except that the incoming trunks took the place of the district junctors, and of course there were no line link frames (see Fig. 4-12). For this reason it was considered a part of the No. 1 crossbar development and not given a separate code identity. The first crossbar tandem systems were placed in service in late 1941, in Detroit, Manhattan, and San Francisco.

For the first time it was possible to provide alternate routing in an automatic tandem switching system. This was possible with the crossbar tandem system since the sender was designed so that it could send forward the entire called number, including the central office code. If the marker found all direct trunks to a called office busy, it could alternately select a route to another tandem, and the sender would provide the proper digits. It was also planned in

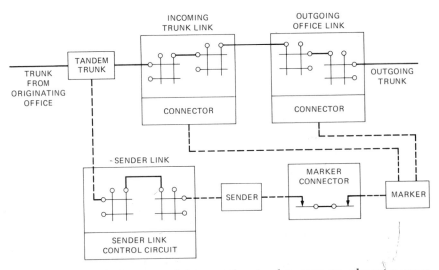

Fig. 4-12. Block diagram of the crossbar tandem system, almost a copy of the No. 1 crossbar except that there are no district junctors or line link frames. (*AIEE Transactions*, Vol. 69, 1950.)

several large metropolitan areas to have double tandem operation. This was most useful, providing large trunk groups between different sections of metropolitan areas. For example, it provided such trunk groups between San Francisco and Oakland and between Manhattan and Brooklyn. The flexibility of crossbar tandem from a signaling and traffic standpoint is illustrated in Fig. 4-13.

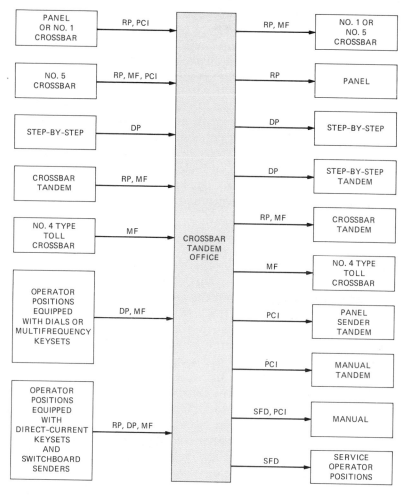

Fig. 4-13. Types of signaling from various types of offices that are possible with crossbar tandem. (*AIEE Transactions,* Vol. 75, 1956.)

In some metropolitan areas, particularly New York City, individual message registers per line were provided for charging purposes. Generally the register was scored once for each call. As the dialing distances increased, complex district selector and junctor circuits were developed for the panel and No. 1 crossbar systems that permitted the multiple scoring of registers on the answering of the call, as well as additional scorings at the beginning of each overtime period. These circuits were complex, using rotary switches, and in No. 1 crossbar used special timers. With the expansion of tandem operation with crossbar tandem, this part of the charging function was moved to the tandem location, through which most of these calls would pass. Therefore, instead of providing costly district selectors or junctors in each local office, it was possible to provide the feature in incoming trunk circuits at the tandem office that would handle mostly this type of call.[25] This remote control (zone registration or multiple) charging arrangement required only the addition of a gas tube in each panel district selector or crossbar junctor, and this tube was fired from the crossbar tandem on a simplex basis over the tip and ring conductors to ground. The first (1941) crossbar tandem in New York City, known as "interzone," included this feature. This was the beginning of centralized message charging (see Chapter 6, section 5.3).

2.3 No. 2 Crossbar System

As a result of the successful introduction of crossbar switching to these large city applications, three less successful developments were started, applying some of the techniques to smaller offices. In 1938, development was started on a modified version of No. 1 crossbar, known as the No. 2 crossbar system (see Fig. 4-14). This system was developed to serve offices with a high percentage of intraoffice calling, such as would occur in a single-office city, or in a city with but a few offices. In those days the high community of interest and rate structure in suburban offices also tended toward high intraoffice calling. Development of this system, using many frames developed for No. 1 crossbar, proceeded to the point where a laboratory model was constructed by 1940. The system was designed so that on intraoffice calls, only one sender and one marker—the originating marker—was used. The call was routed directly from a district link frame to a line link frame on which the called line was located. One group of markers served all types of calls. Price studies made as the design proceeded indicated that, while the system was lower in first cost than No. 1 crossbar for this type of traffic, it did not compete with a senderized version of the step-by-step then being considered (see Chapter 5, section 2.2); therefore, the No. 2 crossbar system was abandoned.

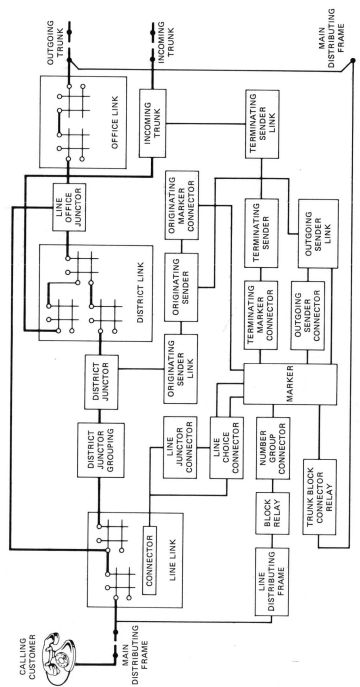

Fig. 4-14. Block diagram of No. 2 crossbar, developed as a small crossbar office but never put in production.

2.4 Early Crossbar CDOs and PBXs

In 1935, development was also started on a crossbar community dial office (CDO). It was known as the No. 380 crossbar community dial office and had a capacity of 400 lines (see Fig. 4-15). One installation of 80 lines was placed in service in Jonesville, New York in 1940. The system was not standardized since its design did not include sufficient safeguards against double connections that might occur due to crossed-wire troubles. This office gave a good account of itself but was removed from service in 1946 when an addition was necessary. A similarly designed PBX with only a single marker, known as the 745A, was placed in service in the Sun Oil Company, Philadelphia, and as a result of the poor performance it too was removed from service and never standardized (see Chapter 13, section 2.1). Another plan for CDOs was known as the "43" system (see Fig. 4-16). This identification came from a dash number associated with a planning case. The system was frequently used as a basis for comparison in price studies because it made very efficient use of crosspoints. It never competed favorably with step-by-step CDO equipment, so development was not undertaken.

III. TOLL CROSSBAR

As discussed in Chapter 3, section VI, shortly after the beginning of the development of operator toll dialing with step-by-step, designers and planners were anxious to apply straightforward call supervisory techniques to toll switchboard operation, as was then being used in local manual switching. This avoided the necessity of ringdown operation. It would also be a step in reducing call completion time once toll circuits became more plentiful. These concepts were advocated as early as 1928, and their consideration led to a recommendation for a cordless switchboard with 4-wire switching. The cordless switchboard made possible the divorcing of the operator functions from the switching means employed. Panel selector banks and brushes plated with noble metal contacts were considered to overcome the noise inherent in their base metal contacts. However, this arrangement did not prove feasible, since it was later discovered that the silver migrated to short circuit the contacts. Also, the indirectly controlled panel selectors were too slow, adding from three to five seconds of valuable toll trunk call completion time.

One of the principal advantages of crossbar switching was that the number of wires that could be interconnected at a crosspoint was much more flexible than in the panel and step-by-step switches, where multiple wipers and brushes had to be employed. The number of selectors that could be driven to the same selection point was severely limited, so that to obtain 6-wire switching in panel

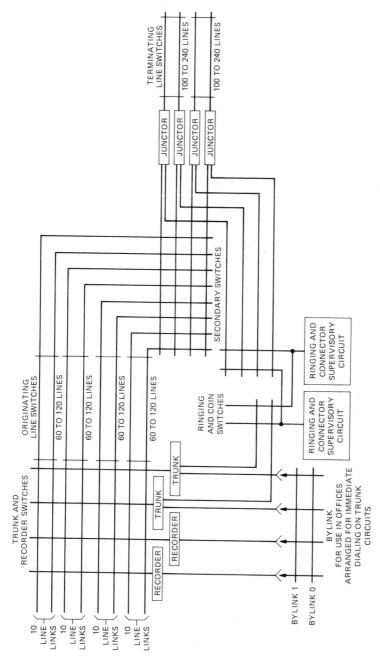

Fig. 4-15. Schematic of No. 380 crossbar community dial office. Only one system was placed in service.

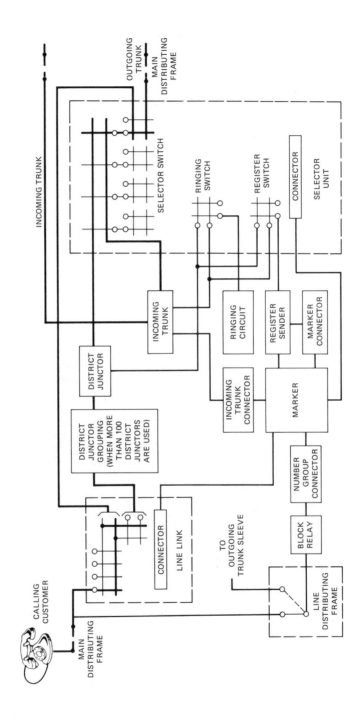

Fig. 4-16. Block diagram of the "43" crossbar community dial office plan, which was not economically feasible.

sender links, for example, only one out of 100 selections could be made. Similarly, on a step-by-step selector, three 2-wire wipers were generally the limit, so that a maximum of six wires could make the one out of 100 selection.

With crossbar switches this limit was removed, so that for the first time it was possible for the designers to conceive of very sophisticated switching systems, particularly for toll application where there was an advantage to separating the two directions of transmission. Toll required two sets of tip and ring wires and had the advantage that it was not necessary when interconnecting two repeatered or carrier channels to insert hybrids at both sides of the switching system. With the freedom to introduce 4-wire switching, a serious engineering study was started in 1936, looking toward a crossbar toll switching system supporting a cordless switchboard. As described in Chapter 3, section V, automation of calls of any appreciable distance was restricted by the signaling range; therefore, the initial studies of the application of crossbar switching of toll facilities were oriented to assist operator toll calling. This required considerable operational, signaling, and transmission planning—which required extensive, time-consuming development.

Although 4-wire crossbar switching for toll was first proposed in 1935, development of a cordless switchboard toll crossbar system started in 1936 on a 2-wire basis. By 1938, the added cost of 4-wire had been justified as a result of studies of the transmission benefits. At that time the development direction was changed to 4-wire.

The system as well as the cordless switchboard became known as the "No. 4 crossbar system" (the No. 3 was skipped to avoid confusion with the No. 3 toll switchboard, since this system also included a switchboard).[26]

The No. 4 crossbar system was arranged to complete both inward and outward toll calls (see Fig. 4-17). Outward calls came from regular cord DSA or toll switchboards. For inward calls from distant toll switchboards, a cordless position was connected to the trunk (see Fig. 4-18). These trunks operated on either a ringdown or straightforward supervisory signaling basis. The operator at the cordless position would be connected through a link frame, answer the call, and keypulse the desired called number into the crossbar equipment through a sender. The call could be completed within the area served by the toll center, or could access an outgoing dial or ringdown toll line to some distant toll point.

In planning the system the developers saw that distant operators with dials or key sets would be able to place calls into senders equipped for the proper type of signaling without requiring an operator at a No. 4 crossbar cordless position to be added to the connection.

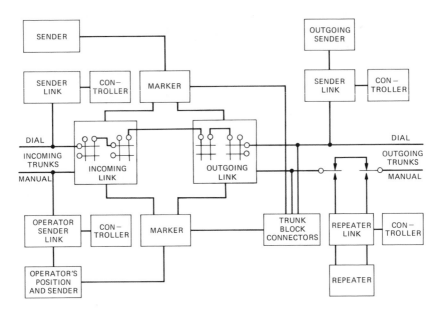

Fig. 4-17. Arrangement of the No. 4 toll crossbar system.

Fig. 4-18. No. 4 cordless switchboard, which separated operator functions from switching equipment.

The first No. 4 crossbar toll system was placed in service in October 1943, in Philadelphia, Pennsylvania.[27] Immediately after World War II an additional five of these systems were placed in service in Boston, New York City, Cleveland, Chicago, and Oakland, California. These offices, together with the step-by-step toll switching systems (see Chapter 3, section VI), formed the backbone of the nationwide operator toll dialing network that was placed into service in the late 1940s.

In addition to the usual crossbar switching advantages, the No. 4 crossbar system could switch repeaters and transmission loss pads into connections as well as provide traffic control tools for dealing with unusual peaks in traffic destined for particular trunk groups that could not always be served on a demand. For delayed calls, a special 4-wire cord switchboard with twin plugs and jacks was developed. This was known as the No. 5 toll switchboard[28] (see Fig. 4-19). Versions of this switchboard with smaller plugs and jacks (known as the 5C and 5D switchboards) were developed by Bell Laboratories for the military in 1957.[29]

The No. 4 crossbar was the first system to make extensive use of multifrequency pulsing (see Chapter 5, section I). Not only was it possible to use multifrequency pulsing between offices, but mul-

Fig. 4-19. No. 5 toll switchboard—a special 4-wire cord switchboard for delayed calls.

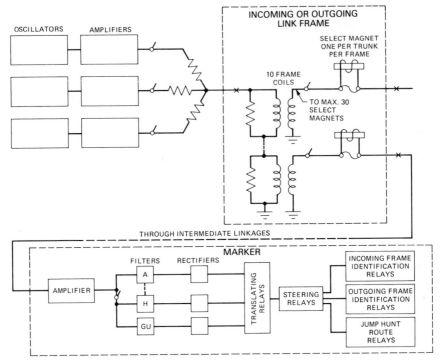

Fig. 4-20. Arrangement showing how No. 4 crossbar used multifrequency pulsing within offices to identify incoming and outgoing trunk
frames.

tifrequency signals were used within the office to identify to the
marker incoming and outgoing trunk frames to which it must connect to establish a requested connection. This so-called frame identification arrangement used three out of eight frequencies to identify
40 frames, or to indicate the need for jump hunting[30] (see Fig. 4-20).
Many sophisticated features of the No. 4 crossbar system, particularly reliability features, gave it the excellent performance reputation upon which future automatic toll switching for the nationwide
network would be based.

The advantages of crossbar switching in this application extended
beyond the introduction of operator nationwide dialing, since the
system formed the basis for the No. 4A crossbar system developed
for customer Direct Distance Dialing (see Chapter 8, section I) and
these offices form the backbone of the nationwide switched network
services.

REFERENCES, CHAPTER 4

1. Connolly, T. A.; U.S. Patent 295,356; filed April 10, 1883; issued March 18, 1884.
2. Reynolds, J. N.; U.S. Patent 1,131,734; filed May 10, 1913; issued March 16, 1915.

3. Goodrum, C. L. and Reynolds, J. N.; U.S. Patent 1,515,735; filed July 21, 1921; issued November 18, 1924.
4. Dipple, H. W. "The Relay System of Automatic Switching." *Institute of Post Office Electrical Engineers,* Paper **84**, 1921.
5. Bjurel, B. "Rural Automation in the Swedish Telephone System." *Trans. of AIEE* **73**, November 1954, p. 552.
6. Bjurel, B., "Milestones on the Road to Complete Automatization of the Swedish Telephone Network." *Tele* **2**, 1972, p. 2.
7. Meszar, J. "Toll Crossbar Call-Distributing System." *Bell Laboratories Record* **19**, September 1940, p. 26.
8. Shoffstall, H. F., "Circuit Features of the 3B Toll Board." *Bell Laboratories Record* **18**, February 1940, p. 167.
9. Wagar, H. N. "The U-Type Relay." *Bell Laboratories Record* **16**, May 1938, p. 300.
10. Zupa, F. A. "The Y-Type Relay." *Bell Laboratories Record* **16**, May 1938, p. 310.
11. Freile, B. "The Multi-Contact Relay." *Bell Laboratories Record* **17**, May 1939, p. 301.
12. Davis, R. C. "The Crossbar System." *Bell Laboratories Record* **17**, February 1939, p. 173.
13. Kittredge, L. E. "Crossbar Trunking." *Bell Laboratories Record* **17**, March 1939, p. 217.
14. Newsom, J. B. "Crossbar Senders." *Bell Laboratories Record* **17**, April 1939, p. 234.
15. Busch, A. J. "The Crossbar Line-Link Frame." *Bell Laboratories Record* **17**, May 1939, p. 266.
16. See Ref. 11 above.
17. Busch, A. J. "Sender-Link and Controller Circuits." *Bell Laboratories Record* **17**, June 1939, p. 321.
18. Myers, O. "Originating Markers." *Bell Laboratories Record* **17**, June 1939, p. 327.
19. Dehn, J. W. "Number Decoding by Terminating Markers." *Bell Laboratories Record* **17**, July 1939, p. 356.
20. Dehn, J. W. "Terminating Markers: Busy Testing and Line-Choice Selection." *Bell Laboratories Record* **17**, August 1939, p. 373.
21. Korn, F. A. "Lockout Circuits." *Bell Laboratories Record* **18**, September 1939, p. 21.
22. Reynolds, J. N. "The Crossbar Switch in the 755 PBX." *Bell Laboratories Record* **16**, June 1938, p. 332.
23. Theuner, A. E. K. "160-Trunk Incoming Frames." *Bell Laboratories Record* **20**, January 1942, p. 114.
24. Collis, R. E. "Crossbar Tandem System." *Trans. of AIEE* **69**, 1950, p. 997.
25. See ref. 24 above.
26. Shipley, F. F. "Crossbar Toll Switching System." *Bell Laboratories Record* **22**, April 1944, p. 355.
27. Bellows, B. C. "Philadelphia Adopts Automatic Toll Switching." *Bell Laboratories Record* **22**, November 1943, p. 101.
28. Shipley, F. F. "Handling Delayed Calls in Crossbar Toll." *Bell Laboratories Record* **22**, December 1944, p. 614.
29. Gilmore, A. C., Gray, P. R., and Irvine, W. S. "New Developments in Military Switching." *Bell System Technical Journal* **37**, March 1958, p. 375.
30. Myers, O. "Multi-Frequency Frame Identification in Crossbar Toll." *Bell Laboratories Record* **22**, September 1944, p. 528.

"Throwdown" machine for simulating No. 5 crossbar traffic, 1949. The random element of telephone calls being received at a central office can be simulated by throwing dice or by using a machine to generate numbers. The "throwdown" machine was an extensive simulation in which all parts of a No. 5 crossbar office of significance to traffic flow were represented. Today, such simulations are programmed on modern general-purpose electronic computers. Simulations and other traffic studies are critical to the design of switching systems, since departures from optimum traffic-handling capacities can result in excessive costs or degraded service.

Chapter 5

A Better Understanding of Switching

As service demands grew ever larger, the Bell System was challenged to cope with new levels of switching systems size and complexity. From 1930 to 1950 Bell Labs engineers met this challenge—despite the interruption caused by World War II—and made a number of advances, both theoretical and practical that allowed the emergence in the 1950s of the huge, automated and rapidly growing Bell System network. Shannon's information theory and applications of Boolean algebra, plus the progress of the sophisticated mathematics of traffic theory and its application, laid much of the groundwork. On the equipment side, the development of logic circuits, multifrequency signaling, contact protection, solderless wrapped connections, sealed relays, detached-contact schematics, and many other innovations provided the components and circuits for new generations of electromechanical switching systems.

I. EARLY RESEARCH CONTRIBUTIONS

By the late 1930s, Bell Laboratories engineers had developed or made important contributions to three basically different types of switching systems. The step-by-step system was directly controlled from the customer's dial; the panel system introduced indirect control enabling the selectors to be independent of the customer's dial; and the crossbar system enabled common control by high-speed markers of the switches used to establish talking paths. For the first time, engineers knowledgeable in these many system arrangements were philosophizing about these system "principles." As a result, new types of study activities and, for the first time, the more fundamental research and exploratory development activities began to appear in the switching efforts at Bell Laboratories.

In research, F. A. Hubbard wrote a series of memoranda generalizing on systems and the application of traffic principles. The advantages of introducing speed as a factor into the control and signaling between switching systems was indicated as a way to the future. Speed could be obtained by considering the application of electronics. As a result, many ideas applying multielement gas tubes to the control of crossbar switches were proposed. In particular, W. H. T. Holden received over 100 patents, many on such arrangements. Many more were suggested by others working in the field. Vacuum tube experts, led by A. M. Skellett, proposed the electronic equivalent of selector switches using beam tubes[1] (see Fig. 5-1). The success of the common control idea led to the concept of "common medium" switching, where the techniques of frequency multiplexing were combined with electromechanical selecting[2] (see Fig. 5-2). For the first time, switching in another domain was proposed, as compared with what is now called "space division," in which established paths are separated in space.

Perhaps the most important contribution emerging from research related to switching at this point was the development of alternating current (ac) methods of signaling. With tones it was possible to send supervisory and pulsing signals over the same distances as voice signals. Initially, single tones were used to represent the open periods of dial pulses, and to "ringdown" on toll lines.[3] As this research proceeded, tests were made in the field, and it was found that these signals were subject to distortion, so that the speed of pulsing was slowed. Gradually, a new concept was introduced, that of sending multiple tones that in combinations represent a digit. Although these signals could not be used directly to control selectors, the idea of using registers and senders was becoming accepted, since they were used in both the originating and terminating portions of local crossbar systems.

After many field tests, a coded combination of two out of five frequencies was found to be most satisfactory. To avoid false operation of the receiver with voice, another combination of tones applied for a longer period and known as the "KP signal" preceded the digits to sensitize the receiver, and an ST or "start signal" indicated the end of pulsing[4] (see Fig. 5-3). This is the form of digit pulsing known as "multifrequency."

This research effort was taken into the development stage in the late 1930s with a trial in Baltimore in 1940. In this trial, operator keysets were connected to a set of multifrequency oscillators common to all switchboard positions. Terminating multifrequency senders were provided in a local No. 1 crossbar office. Incoming toll calls to this office were established using multifrequency pulsing for the first time. With this arrangement, senders were not required to be associated with the switchboard trunk circuits, resulting in considerable savings over the previous dc key pulsing arrangement

March 31, 1942.   A. M. SKELLETT   2,277,858

ELECTRONIC DISCHARGE DEVICE

Filed May 17, 1941

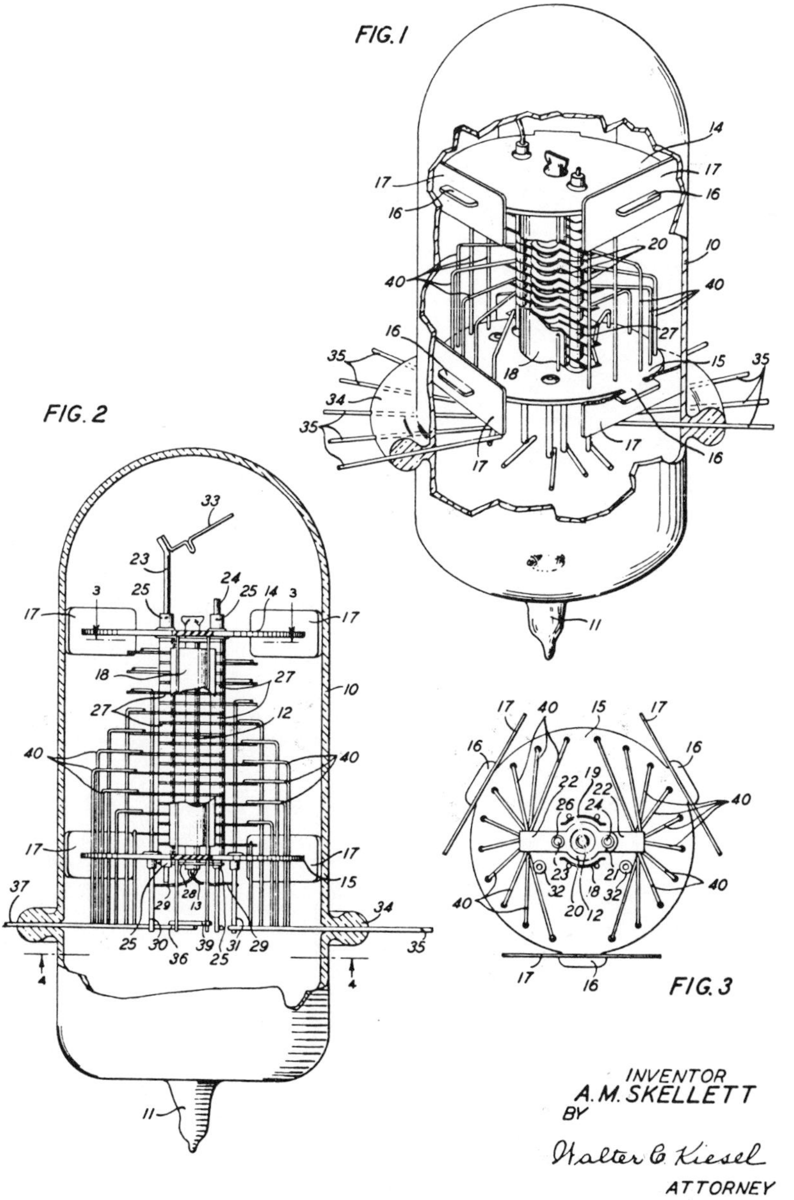

FIG. 1

FIG. 2

FIG. 3

INVENTOR
A.M. SKELLETT
BY

Walter C Kiesel

ATTORNEY

Fig. 5-1. Beam switching tube, from U.S. Patent 2,277,858, filed May 17, 1941, an example of early attempts to increase switching speeds through electronics.

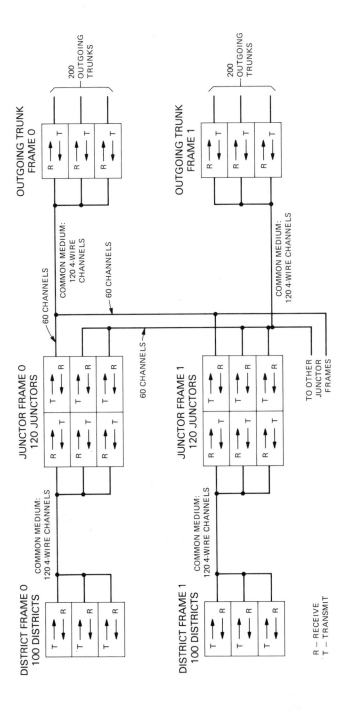

Fig. 5-2. Common Media Switching System from U.S. Patent 2,345,048, filed November 13, 1941, an example of an attempt to apply frequency multiplex transmission techniques to switching.

FREQUENCY & DESIGNATION	0	1	2	3	4	5	6	7	8	9	KP	ST
1700 HERTZ 10											X	X
1500 7	X							X	X	X		X
1300 4	X				X	X	X					
1100 2			X	X			X			X	X	
900 1		X		X		X			X			
900 0		X	X		X			X				

Fig. 5-3. Frequency allocations specifying dialing digits for multifrequency signaling. Also shown are the combinations for the start (KP) and end (ST) signals.

(see Chapter 3, section IV and Fig. 5-4). The keysets on the switchboards were arranged to send either multifrequency or dc key pulsing. The trunk to which the operator position was connected on each call determined the type of pulsing to be generated.

The Baltimore trial was a precursor of the more general application of multifrequency pulsing to switchboards operating into the No. 4 toll crossbar system in Philadelphia, Pennsylvania in 1943.

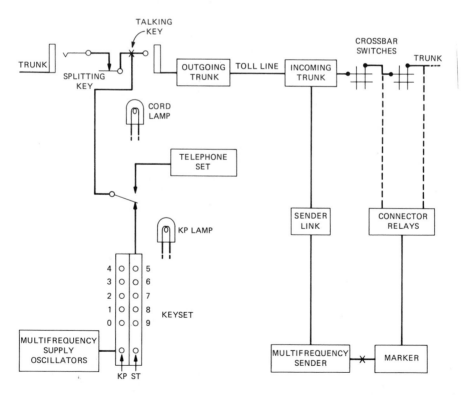

Fig. 5-4. Arrangement, 1940, for allowing a manual operator to use a multifrequency keyset (left) to place a call using a No. 1 crossbar office (right).

For a review of post World War II switching research, see Chapter 9, sections I to III, of this volume.

II. NEW SYSTEM IDEAS AND TRADES

2.1 Automatic Ticketing

In 1934, the Development and Research department of AT&T was merged into Bell Laboratories and the closer association stimulated new ideas in switching. This merged group of systems engineers not only laid the foundation for networks of crossbar tandem and toll offices but also promoted the further application of step-by-step equipment. In particular, developments were started on the senderizing of the step-by-step system and the automating of the recording of call information for billing purposes. While various methods were studied at Bell Laboratories as early as 1928, and a number of important patents granted in the 1930s, such as that cited in ref. 5, it was not until the late 1930s that a definite need appeared to develop a system for recording charge information on individual customer-dialed toll calls.

The heavy operator traffic in the metropolitan Los Angeles dialing network indicated the desirability of customer dialing to reduce the growth of the large operator force in this area—growth that was occurring despite the fact that most of the local offices employed automatic switching equipment. Needed was a suitable scheme to charge customers for the longer calls in this network. Multiple or zone registration arrangements were studied, but this meant equipping all lines with message registers. These would be used only for longer-haul calls, since the shorter calls were on a flat rate basis.

A very simple message ticketer was proposed (see Chapter 6, section 5.1 for more details). Its simplicity and low cost made it possible to associate one ticketer with each outgoing long distance trunk. On this ticket was recorded the equivalent of the information required on a manually prepared ticket, including the calling line number. An arrangement was developed for obtaining the calling line number by searching for a 2700-hertz tone on the sleeve leads, through a network of capacitors and transformers. The results were registered in the senders and used to control the calling line number portion of the ticket record (for more details see Chapter 6, section 5.4).

After a field trial of this identification arrangement, commercial development of this form of automatic ticketing for the step-by-step system was initiated in 1939. The initial office was to be Culver City, California. The automatic ticketing equipment was ready for shipment in 1942, but due to wartime restrictions it was not until January 1944 that the equipment was placed in service.

2.2 Step-by-Step Senderization

The results of systems engineering studies favored the senderization of suburban step-by-step offices, as had been done in the large cities of the United Kingdom.[6] Development of this equipment was also started in 1939. As the development proceeded, it was found to be more expensive than could be justified at that time. Also, crossbar systems were showing markedly lower maintenance costs. As a result, after a laboratory model was built, development was terminated.

2.3 Higher Speed Step-by-Step

The close cooperation mentioned in Chapter 3, section III between system and apparatus designers also led to a number of exploratory developments which were terminated as a result of the commencement of World War II. These included toggle- and escapement-type step-by-step switch designs. These were modifications of the basic step-by-step switch that enabled it to operate more rapidly. The senders of the panel and crossbar systems could accept dial pulses at the rate of 20 per second from faster dials that were placed on PBX attendant and operator positions, but the step-by-step system from its very beginning could keep up with pulses at only a 10 pulse-per-second rate. A new switch design would have enabled the step-by-step system to compete with the other systems with respect to this attribute, but studies showed considerable adjustment and wear problems as well as cost problems in successfully introducing these switches throughout step-by-step offices.

2.4 Motorelay System

Another interesting and important exploratory development was known as the "motorelay" or "tape drive" switch and system. The advantages of the combination of individually driven switches and built-in multiple of panel-type bank had long been recognized. Even in 1918 attempts were made by Western Electric engineers to use it with a step-by-step type of mechanism, and PBXs of this type were field tested (see Fig. 5-5). (One PBX using these switches was in service in a Washington, D.C. post office until 1934.)

The common-control concepts of the crossbar system and the progress made in inexpensive small motors such as those employed in electric clocks were combined in this development. Each switch consisted of individual up and down drive motors that imparted motion to a metallic tape carrying brushes that were actually relay devices[7] (see Fig. 5-6). These switch units were mounted on a 100-point panel bank and could be driven very rapidly up and down. One terminal of the brush assembly was a wiper that was always in contact with the bank. As the brush assembly was driven over the banks at high speed, the circuit through the wiper could detect an electrically marked terminal, which caused the switch to stop and the brush magnet to be operated, closing the tip and ring conductors. Since the brushes were in contact with the bank only when they stopped at the marked terminals, precious metal contacts could be used for these conductors, eliminating the electronically noisy contacts that were one of the major drawbacks of panel and step-by-step systems. (Precious metal contacts could not be used in these systems due to excessive wear.) The marking control idea, as well as the simple brush relay per switch stage, made this an attractive proposal for a common-control system. In fact the system diagram was much like that of the No. 1 crossbar system, including two-stage link frames. Economic studies did not show this switch to be of any great advantage over crossbar, and thus exploratory development was dropped shortly after the beginning of World War II.

Even one last attempt was made to develop a large multiple-less switch, as in some simple switchboards, using modern high-speed cord handling mechanisms.[8]

2.5 The "Browser" Group

Many of the ideas mentioned above as well as automatic message accounting (AMA) (see Chapter 6, section 5.2) and some of the traffic work described in the next section came from the precursor of a formal exploratory development group in switching. It was infor-

Fig. 5-5. Early step-by-step switches using a panel bank.

Fig. 5-6. A motorelay switch which took advantage of the built-in multiple of a panel bank, but for economic reasons the system was never developed.

mally called the "browser" group and consisted of about a dozen well-known switching experts and inventors who compared and devised different switching proposals. This group was active from 1938 to 1945 when it was absorbed into the more formal switching engineering effort.

III. TRAFFIC THEORY AND ENGINEERING

Before automatic switching, the major traffic problems were those of providing sufficient but not excessive numbers of trunks to carry calls between central offices and sufficient numbers of operator positions and operators to set up and take down connections. Automatic switching systems introduced new, more complicated traffic problems both within the switching systems and within the complex trunk networks that they made possible. Here we will cover, in order, traffic on the interoffice network, traffic in switching systems, traffic measurement, and general traffic problems.

3.1 Interoffice Networks

As telephone systems grow in size and as telephone traffic increases, the number of trunks serving this traffic must also increase but does not need to increase in direct proportion. The reason is that, with large numbers of trunks carrying large amounts of traffic, some of the trunks can be kept busy almost continuously. Thus, the overall efficiency of a large trunk group can be higher than that of a small group of trunks serving a smaller amount of traffic.[9]

Such economies of scale depend, however, on telephone calls having adequate access to the trunks. For example, if a particular call can be connected to, say, any of 10 trunks out of a larger trunk group, it may find all ten busy, even though there are idle trunks in the group. In this circumstance, the call is blocked and service suffers. If this occurs too often, additional trunks must be installed, which is expensive. However, if a call can have access to all the trunks or to large groups, substantial efficiencies are possible.

The basic 10-trunk access of the step-by-step system limited that system's ability to provide efficient trunking. Even the panel system, which used a bigger switch for larger access, could not use the full potential capacity of the large trunk groups in major cities.

A partial solution to the limited access switch was the introduction of grading, invented in 1907 by E. A. Gray of AT&T.[10] The concept of how a grade increases efficiency is illustrated in Fig. 5-7. Here, to show the principle involved in grading, 8.0 erlangs of telephone traffic are assumed to be offered, 4.0 erlangs each, to 2 groups of 10 trunks each, as indicated in part (a) of the figure. Part (b) shows that sharing one trunk reduces the number of trunks

---

Fig. 5-7 (right). Improving trunking efficiency through "grading." In (a), four erlangs of telephone traffic (erlangs equal number of calls per unit time divided by holding time) are offered to each of two groups of ten trunks each. Calls are first offered to trunk 1; if that is busy to trunk 2, etc. Trunk 1 in each group handles 0.800 erlang of this traffic, trunk 2 handles 0.739 erlang, etc. The trunk groups handle all but the overflow of 0.021 erlang each. If the service objective were set at a maximum of 0.08 erlang overflow, this arrangement would require the use of 18 of these 20 trunks (0.032 plus 0.021 equals 0.053, which is within the objective, whereas with only eight trunks in each group, 0.066 plus 0.032 plus 0.021 would equal 1.19, over the objective). In (b), 19 trunks are used, two

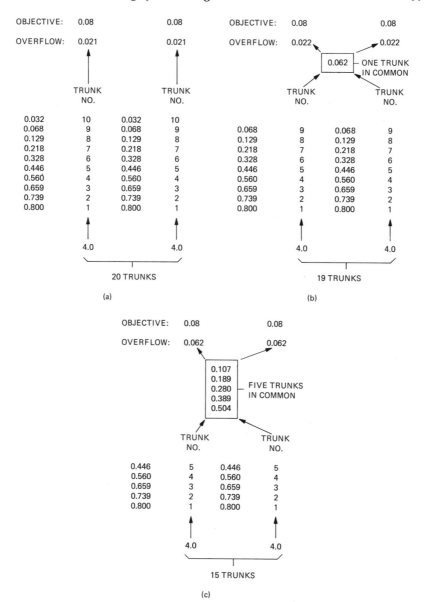

(a)

(b)

(c)

groups of nine each plus one in common. Now the overflow has increased to 0.022 erlang per group but is still less than the objective of 0.08. Next, the number of trunks in common is increased until, in (c), five trunks are in common and the overflow at 0.062 is still less than (service is better than) the 0.08 objective. If six trunks were placed in common, overflow would be 0.096 erlang, exceeding the objective. Thus five trunks in common is the optimum, and the service objective is met with 15 trunks (two groups of 5 plus 5 in common) instead of 18.

to 19, with only a slight effect on overflow. As shown in part (c), the sharing of 5 trunks, for a total of 15 trunks, will still meet the service objective.

The theoretical determination of the capacity of this single grading is far from easy. Even with a large computer, the exact solution of the thousands of simultaneous linear equations for a typical graded multiple calls for some ingenuity. In the 1920s, approximations were necessary, and the most notable Bell System approximation, called the "no-holes-in-the-multiple solution," was derived by E. C. Molina.[11] Experimental data showed that Molina's formula was applicable to many practical gradings if only half of the predicted gain in efficiency was achieved. Not until the 1950s was a new approximation derived which gives a much closer solution.

When traffic is so light that a direct trunk group between two offices operates at low efficiency, tandem switching offers the ability to collect traffic destined for several distant offices and to route it over a single trunk group to a tandem point, where it is switched to the final destination (see Fig. 5-8). The tandem groups contain traffic destined for or coming from many offices, so that the sum of the traffic loads requires a large, and therefore efficient, trunk

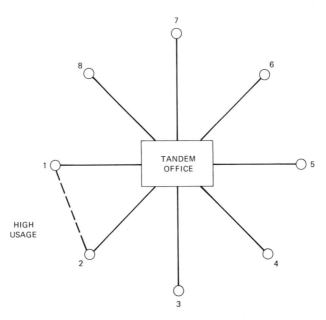

Fig. 5-8. In tandem switching, high-usage trunks carry traffic directly from office 1 to office 2. Overflow traffic is alternate-routed through the tandem office.

group. It was recognized that when tandemed traffic between a pair of offices reaches a high enough value, a lower-cost network can be achieved by offering traffic first to a small group of trunks directly connecting two offices (called a "high-usage group") while allowing traffic encountering all direct trunks busy to complete through a tandem. The latter traffic is said to be alternate routed. It is seen that this plan is very similar to the simple grading discussed earlier, where the first-choice trunks correspond to the high-usage trunks and the final trunks correspond to the trunks through the tandem office.

At first it might be assumed that the traffic carried by trunks to a tandem office—since they receive both direct routed traffic and overflow traffic to many different destinations—could be considered as random traffic, like that offered to direct trunk groups. However, as in the graded multiple, the final-choice trunks cannot be operated at as high an efficiency as is achieved in a direct group of the same size. The reason for this is that traffic overflowing from trunk groups tends to come in bursts which arise from random peaks in the underlying offered traffic (see Fig. 5-9). The "peaked" nature of overflow traffic results in higher losses. R. I. Wilkinson in 1955 proposed a traffic model which defined the degree of peakedness of traffic as the ratio of the variance (average squared deviation from the mean) to the mean.[12] He then hypothesized that all traffic with a given mean value and a given peakedness value would receive about the same grade of service from a given sized trunk group. If one has an ordered hunt of trunks on a single trunk group and splits it at some arbitrary point, one can, through theory well known by 1950, determine the average traffic offered to the upper group (and the blocking of the upper group) as a function of the traffic offered to the whole group and the number of trunks in the two subgroups. E. C. Molina, H. Nyquist, and J. Riordan solved the more complex problem of determining the peakedness of the overflow traffic.[13] Results were used to tabulate "equivalent" split single groups and loads for any desired mean and peakedness. This procedure, applied to trunk engineering, became known as the "Wilkinson Equivalent Random Method."

Even this was not completely satisfactory in its application. Some trunk groups were observed to have higher loss (more calls blocked) than predicted by the Wilkinson method while others showed good agreement. The problem was found to lie in the variation of average loads from day to day, which were in excess of those assumed in the traffic model. For a solution, Wilkinson collected data on many different sizes and kinds of trunk groups. From these he obtained three levels of variability in day-to-day traffic which cover the more

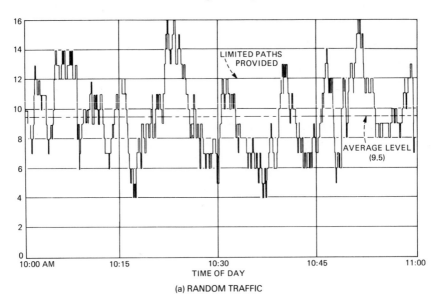

(a) RANDOM TRAFFIC

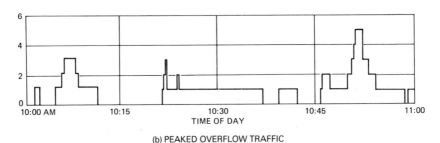

(b) PEAKED OVERFLOW TRAFFIC

Fig. 5-9. Traffic offered to groups of direct trunks arrives randomly (top). Overflow from direct trunks (bottom) tends to come in bursts.

frequently encountered field situations. He then combined the variable models with the peakedness model to produce trunk engineering tables which, with further refinements, are still in use.

3.2 Switching Center Networks

The economic design of the network which establishes connections within a central office is quite different from that of an interoffice network. In the latter, trunk costs predominate, while in the former, switch and control costs predominate. Even so, the use of grading made possible increased efficiencies in the step-by-step, panel, and No. 1 crossbar systems. Once the concept of end-to-end channel selection was adopted in central office design, however, a new theory of network traffic analysis was required.

In the older switching systems, the path was selected one link at a time. At any point in the connection, if no idle link could be found, the call was blocked. However, crossbar switches and their successors, the reed switches, and solid state space- and time-division switches, all lend themselves to end-to-end channel selection. All possible paths between two network terminals to be connected can be examined, and any usable one can be set up. The traffic problem of matching idle links was even more difficult for precise calculation than the graded multiple. Approximations were necessary, as were traffic simulations to test their validity.

No. 1 crossbar incoming trunk-to-line network blocking probability is an example of how elementary probability theory was applied by making simplifying assumptions. An incoming trunk in No. 1 crossbar terminates on a switch that can connect to any of 10 links, and these 10 links are usable in the first stage of reaching a particular line. Each of these in turn may connect to any of 10 links, but only one is usable for this connection. Again the selected link similarly may connect to a single link which can be switched to the desired line (see Fig. 5-10). There are, then, 10 possible paths

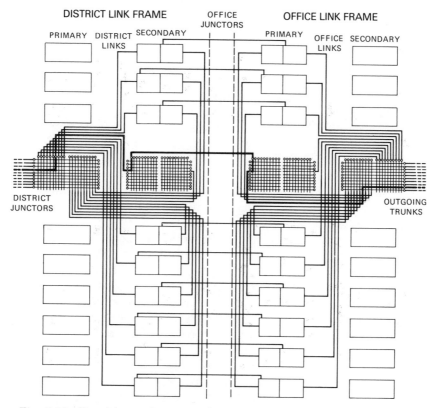

Fig. 5-10. Trunking scheme within a No. 1 crossbar office. Traffic engineering and theory with crossbar and later systems were more difficult than those encountered in earlier systems with only graded multiples.

through the network, each made up of 3 links in series. (These links can be used for other calls with different destinations, so they may be unusable at the time of the desired connection.)

For an approximate solution to the problem of finding the probability of blocking an incoming call, assume (1) that the busy-idle state of a link at the time this call is being placed is independent of that of any other link and (2) that all links have the same probability of being busy. Using simple probability theory and letting q be the probability of a link being idle, the probability that a "channel" of three links in series has all three links idle is q^3. Then the probability that a channel cannot be used because one or more links are busy is $(1 - q^3)$. Still assuming link independence, the probability that all ten channels are unavailable is $(1 - q^3)^{10}$ the probability of blocking. Links are not independent, however, so this formula is useful only as a first approximation.

E. C. Molina made several analyses of crossbar networks using less restrictive assumptions. These were tested by L. E. Kittredge by simulation and the most usable became known as the Kittredge-Molina formula. C. Y. Lee in 1955 formalized the Molina approach using linear graph theory,[14] while R. F. Grantges and N. R. Sinowitz in their computer program, NEASIM (NEtwork Analytical SIMulator), devised a computer simulation approach to the analysis of complicated networks.[15] The latter was used in No. 1 ESS and subsequent electronic switching designs.

In 1953, C. Clos discovered nonblocking network arrangements that would connect n inlets to n outlets in a multistage network with less than the total of n^2 crosspoints required in a single-stage network[16] (see Fig. 5-11). This disclosure spurred much new work on network topologies. Later, M. C. Paull showed how blocking could be eliminated in some networks if it was possible to rearrange calls already in progress.[17] Paull later showed the nonreciprocal duality between space- and time-division networks.

The mathematical analysis of congestion in switching networks took on new meaning with developments associated with electronic switching. With crossbar switches, the size of the coordinate matrix was fixed by mechanical design at 10×10 or 10×20. Crosspoints being considered for electronic switching systems added a new variable that could be applied in making trades in the choice of switching networks. The sizes of these arrays could be varied depending upon the application.

More recent advances have been those by J. G. Kappel and A. Feiner to extend the principles of network analysis to network synthesis.[18] Both control and switch costs are considered by them in a procedure that aids the designer of central office networks in meeting desired traffic-carrying properties at near minimum system cost.

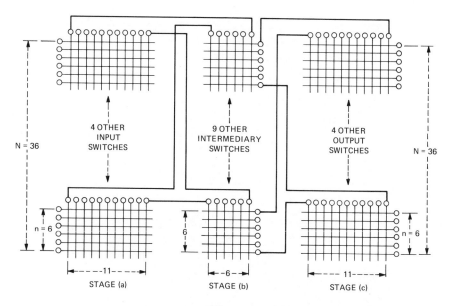

NUMBER OF CROSSPOINTS = $6N^{3/2}-3N$ (1188 CROSSPOINTS WHEN N = 36)

Fig. 5-11. A three-stage, nonblocking switching array requiring fewer crosspoints than a single-stage array.

3.3 Traffic Measurement (see also Chapter 11, section 3.4)

Critical to the administration of both switching offices and telephone networks is the collection of data on the traffic load being carried and the service being given. The importance of traffic volume in the design and administration of switching systems was realized quite early in telephony.

The first traffic measurements were counts of calls using cribbage-like boards adapted for use at manual switchboard positions, hence the term "peg-counts."[19] Later these counts were made by electrical counters that periodically were read visually. Use of the data led to the development of methods for determining estimates of the required number of operators and interoffice trunks by applying early traffic theories, as described in ref. 20. These theories indicated the need to know not only the number of calls carried, but also the number of calls handled or "overflow" calls, and the average length of a conversation, or its holding time.

For many years, calls in progress, or "usage," in automatic systems were measured in panel and step-by-step offices by making periodic visual counts during busy hours of the number of switches of a given type that were in use[21] (see Fig. 5-12). (This technique was also used at some manual toll switchboards by counting plugs

Fig. 5-12. The "switch-count" procedure for measuring usage during busy hours—visually counting the number of switches in use.

in use.) This provided not only usage information but also data from which holding time could be computed.

With the development of the panel system, peg counts could be obtained automatically, not only for the major subsystems but also for individual trunk groups. With the development of more complex control logic of the crossbar system, it became possible to count more precisely defined call events—for example, call counts that omit false attempts. With so many traffic counters or "registers," cabinets to house them were developed and generally placed in the switchboard room where clerks could be located to record the data (see Fig. 5-13). Later, automatic cameras were designed that periodically photographed 150 traffic register readings[22] (see Fig. 5-14).

Prior to 1940, in addition to automatic call and overflow (or last trunk busy) counters, answering time recorders (for 25 switchboard terminated trunks)[23] and holding time measurements circuits were developed. In the latter, ten circuits were checked for busy every 10 seconds. The total seconds of use divided by the peg count of calls gave holding times. R. I. Wilkinson pioneered the first analysis of holding time measurement accuracy in 1941.[24]

The next decade (1940–1950) saw the development of a circuit to measure the percent of sample call attempts within selected line

Fig. 5-13. Cabinets of traffic registers, from which data could be collected manually.

Fig. 5-14. Traffic usage recorder cameras, used to photograph the readings from banks of registers.

groups that take over three seconds to receive dial tone. This was known as a "dial tone speed" measuring set. It was particularly needed during World War II when line load control was instituted in overloaded switching offices. Also during this period the first of a series of usage measuring equipment was developed. It was known as trunk group usage equipment (TGUE) and was the first to use crossbar switches rather than stepping switches to scan the circuit points being measured. However, it looked only at trunk group busy leads.

The ammeter was also a most useful traffic measurement tool. In electromechanical switching the total energy load could be correlated to the traffic load (see Fig. 5-15), while in No. 4 crossbar a special contact on the crossbar switch vertical was used to send current through an ammeter.[25]

With the need for careful engineering of costly trunk groups for nationwide dialing of toll calls (see Chapter 6, section III) and with the large capacity of new switching systems, such as the No. 4 crossbar system designed as the backbone of the nationwide network, further automation of traffic data collection became necessary. After theoretical studies by W. S. Hayward, Jr.[26] showed that

Fig. 5-15. Recording ammeters could be used for traffic-measurement, since total energy load was a measure of the number of calls in progress.

switch count traffic measures were sufficiently accurate, it was decided early in the 1950s to develop traffic usage recorders (TUR).

Like the visual switch counters, these recorders periodically examine or scan circuit points, such as sleeve leads, that indicate a circuit is busy. Such busy conditions are summarized to give a measure of circuit usage. Thus, if a circuit is scanned every 100 seconds and is found busy on 18 scans, its occupancy during an hour (3600 seconds) can be estimated at 1800 seconds or 50 percent.

3.4 Other Traffic Activities

In addition to these three mainstream traffic activities there have been many studies and engineering recommendations made on different traffic aspects of communication.

3.4.1 Network Management

In Chapter 3, section IV the development of the No. 8 test board and associated emergency traffic control provisions were described as they were used during the growth of manual toll switching. Later AT&T Long Lines and Bell Operating Companies established traffic control bureaus (see Fig. 5-16)[27] as operator toll dialing reached its peak. With the advent of direct distance dialing, the

Fig. 5-16. Traffic control bureau in New York City, about 1951. Network management techniques were used to prevent the spread of traffic congestion. (*Bell Telephone Magazine*, Vol. 30, 1951.)

routing of a toll call involved several switching systems and several transmission systems. As a result, a higher exposure to possible failure was encountered. Without an operator associated with a call, it is difficult to detect or to measure the extent or the nature of such failures when they occur. Added to this, when some part of the network becomes overloaded, it is apparent that service can be affected not only at the overloaded point but over a large part of the network.

A simulation study by P. J. Burke in 1963 demonstrated the interdependence of trunk groups and switching systems and their sensitivity to overloads caused by high calling rates or system failures.[28] Methods of monitoring critical elements and of exercising control to prevent the spread of congestion were derived. Application of these methods was named "network management," an activity which has become essential in both local and toll networks. The first step to manage traffic in the DDD network was the introduction of the capability wired into the common-control switching systems to change routing under remote control. Dynamic overload controls (DOC) are used to cancel alternate routed traffic when reaching congested offices.[29] Traffic overload reroute control (TORC) is used to route traffic from one region to another to avoid congestion in the normally used interregional final group[30] (see Fig. 5-17). Regional, and in some cases sectional, network management centers were established to invoke traffic controls when congestion develops in the network.[31] Fig. 5-18 shows a network management center. The display board shows the status of switching systems and trunk groups in a region or section of the country. The first computer-aided network management system went into service in 1975.

3.4.2 Simulation

From the beginning of traffic theory, simulation or "throwdown" was an essential tool in reducing traffic theory to practice. Exact solutions to circuit reactions to traffic loads are usually too complicated for exact computation—even by today's high-speed computers. To test an approximation, a conceptual model is designed in which the circuit elements are represented by numbers which can take on the value 0 for idle or 1 for busy. Traffic is modeled by a set of rules controlling the manner in which these elements become idle or busy. The chance element of traffic is then introduced by the use of dice or machine-generated "random numbers."

While several earlier simulations were conducted on crossbar link networks,[32] the last and most extensive Bell Laboratories special-purpose simulator was nicknamed the "KRF" machine after W. Keister, A. E. Ritchie, and G. R. Frost, who designed it in 1949.[33] In this machine, all of the significant traffic elements of a No. 5 crossbar office were simulated. Lines and trunks were represented

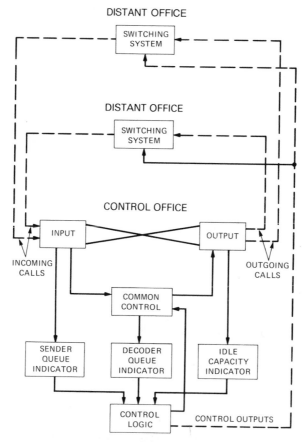

Fig. 5-17. Automatic Traffic Overload Control reroutes calls to distant toll offices to avoid congestion.

Fig. 5-18. Long Lines network management center, about 1962. *(Bell Telephone Magazine*, Vol. 41, 1962.)

by pegs, busy links within the switching system by plastic strips, and markers by switches, tickets, lamps, and human operators (see Fig. 5-19). The rules for the sequence of traffic flow were a combination of wired logic contained in relay and rotary switches and written instructions for the four people required to operate the machine. Data obtained from the KRF machine were used both to determine traffic capacities and to change some of No. 5 crossbar design to facilitate traffic flow.

By 1955 simulations were being run on electronic computers. In particular, the network from No. 1 ESS was simulated by W. S. Hayward, Jr. and J. A. Bader. The results of these detailed simulations were used to verify the NEASIM program mentioned in section 3.2 above, which could cover many different switching network configurations at a fraction of the cost of a detailed simulation.

Simulations of networks of offices were also made by J. H. Weber for a better understanding of alternate routing in hierarchical networks.[34] NEASIM was also used for these studies.[35] Fig. 5-20 shows the general difference in network blocking with and without alternate routing obtained from these studies.

IV. OTHER THEORETICAL STUDIES

Among other theoretical studies, special mention should be made of the information theory conceived by C. E. Shannon.[36] This theory stimulated him and other Bell Laboratories staff members to look at

Fig. 5-19. The "KRF" machine, designed in 1949 to simulate traffic in a No. 5 crossbar office.

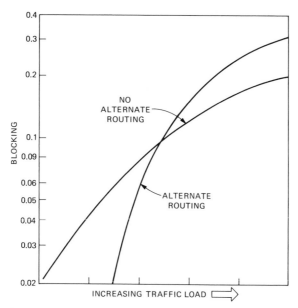

Fig. 5-20. Graph comparing two networks with an equal number of trunks; with alternate routing blocking rises faster with increasing overload.

switching problems from a more theoretical point of view. Shannon himself attempted to place bounds on the amount of memory required in a telephone system,[37] and to formalize the design of circuits with relays that may fail.[38] V. E. Beneš wrote extensively on traffic and network theory, including traffic measurement (summarized in ref. 39).

While traffic theory and engineering have grown throughout the world, the contributions by Bell Laboratories personnel have kept pace and have enjoyed a good reputation in the field.

V. FROM BOOLEAN ALGEBRA TO SWITCHING ALGEBRA AND SYNTHESIS

For many years the circuit logic of automatic switching had been growing in complexity, and the designers at Bell Laboratories were the first to encounter and successfully realize relay and switch circuits of this complexity. At M.I.T. C. E. Shannon, for his master's thesis, applied the algebra attributable to the mathematician G. A. Boole to the logic encountered in these complex circuits.[40] At Bell Laboratories, W. Keister further applied this logic to some of the examples found in switching systems and gained further insight into the difficulties encountered in the more formalistic design of complex relay circuits.[41] Another approach, taken by A. E. Joel, Jr., was a handbook of frequently used relay configurations that had been used by designers in the past, and a synthesis of designs that might be useful in the future.[42] As a result of this work, the basic functional logic circuits were first classified as combinatorial, sequential, and lockout.[43-47] During the mid-1950s Bell Laboratories scientists made significant contributions to move logic circuit design from an art to a science. The works of C. Y. Lee, E. F. Moore, E. J. McClusky, Jr., G. H. Mealy, M. C. Paull, and S. H. Unger frequently are referenced in the many texts on this subject published after the book by W. Keister, A. E. Ritchie, and S.H. Washburn appeared.[48]

VI. THE TEACHING OF SWITCHING

The insight gained in the examination of the tools of switching circuit design, viz., switching algebra, led to a broader examination of switching systems and their composition along the lines explored by F. A. Hubbard and referred to in section I above. A proposal to organize the knowledge of switching into a formal text and course was prepared by A. E. Joel, Jr. By the end of World War II, many new engineers were being employed at Bell Laboratories to contribute to the development of the growing numbers of new switching systems. Vice President A. B. Clark recognized the need for a school that would train young engineers in switching, a field that had not previously been formalized.[49] In this respect switching differed from transmission, various aspects of which were being taught in the schools and colleges as a result of the more formal mathematical approach pioneered by G. A. Campbell, J. P. Maxwell, and their successors.

The school was organized under the leadership of J. Meszar and became the forerunner of a successful era at Bell Laboratories in the teaching of telecommunication technology. The switching school, organized in 1946, became integrated into the Bell Labs Communication Development Training Program when it was started in 1949.[50] As a result of the training new engineers received in switching system organization, philosophy, and application of switching algebra to logic circuit design, communication among switching engineers was vastly improved, and no doubt contributed to the accelerated pace of technology progress in this discipline.

Some of the class notes developed in the switching school were edited into a book by the instructors W. Keister, A. E. Ritchie, and S. H. Washburn in 1951 (see ref. 48 above). In 1949, Mr. Ritchie used a version of the text to present at M.I.T. the first formal college level course. Many other texts on the design of logic circuits were stimulated by this publication.

VII. DOCUMENTATION

From the beginning of the Bell Laboratories involvement in the development of the panel system, a wealth of documentation, rules, and procedures were issued giving standards as a means for depicting the design of switching systems. Moreover, as new apparatus and feature requirements and improvements were made, circuit drawings became increasingly complex with many options. It therefore became difficult for craftspeople in the telephone companies to use these drawings as applied to their particular installations. In particular, the circuits of the No. 5 crossbar and automatic message accounting systems (see Chapter 6 section 5.2) were among the most complex ever to be developed. Consequently, an effort was undertaken in 1946 to explore better methods for depicting the details of switching system developments. As a result, detached-contact schematic drawings were developed and standardized.[51,52] In this type of drawing, contacts and other electrical connections to devices are not shown together, and the result is shorter lines and greater clarity.

To aid the telephone companies in getting started with the new complex switching systems being developed at Bell Laboratories, such as the No. 4A, and No. 5 crossbar systems (and later the No. 1 electronic switching system), a school for telephone company instructors was established at Bell Laboratories and functioned concurrently with systems development. As a result, further improvements were made in documentation, so that the circuit functions were appropriately delineated when drawn in detached-contact form. The success of this school led to a broader program known as the Operating Engineers Training Program, established in 1953.[53] Through this school the new postwar technology, spurred by the development of the transistor, was more quickly imparted to those in the Bell System who were to be making engineering decisions.

VIII. IMPROVEMENTS IN SYSTEM RELIABILITY

The experiences with early No. 1 crossbar offices showed that the longer they were in service, the greater the difficulties encountered in the pitting and welding of contacts. For a better understanding of the phenomenon of relay contacts, an important joint research, systems engineering, and development study was organized. Data were collected from operating offices to indicate the location and frequency of contact trouble in the system. High-speed oscillograph photographs of contact phenomena were obtained, and controlled environment and life study equipment was constructed and operated in the laboratories.[54,55] Many experiments were conducted with relays sealed in containers to control their ambient conditions[56] (see Fig. 5-21). Open-contact phenomena were also studied.[57]

Fig. 5-21. R. H. Gumley adjusting relays sealed in containers as part of studies of contact reliability in controlled environments.

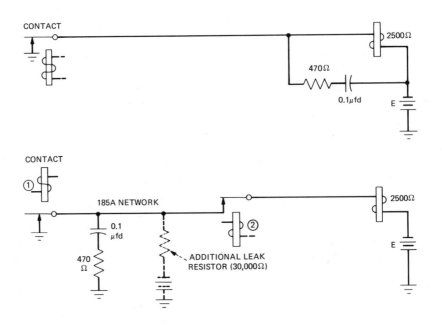

Fig. 5-22. Circuits using contact protection as a result of studies about 1945–1955. Top is a typical protection circuit; bottom shows use of additional resistance.

As a result of these investigations, conducted between the mid-1940s and the early 1950s, it was possible to recommend the type of contact metal to be used on relays and the need to introduce a greater degree of contact protection in circuits[58] (see Fig. 5-22). Apparatus and rules for the implementation of contact protection in relay and switch circuits were developed, and, as a result, the reliability of electromechanical switching systems was greatly improved.

Another problem that caused troubles in switching systems was the presence of solder splashes and clippings, which would create short circuits. The designers of crossbar systems realized that these conditions existed and designed common-control circuits to look for false crosses and grounds, as well as to make second trials that in all probability would use different combinations of circuit paths. As a result, the service these systems gave was quite adequate, but the maintenance effort in tracking down these sources of trouble was costly.

Important work in the late 1940s and early 1950s by H. A. Miloche and R. F. Mallina, carried out in conjunction with the redesign of apparatus terminals, all but eliminated these problems. This solution was known as "solderless wrapped connections."[59] Instead of connecting wire ends to eyelet terminals on relays and other apparatus and soldering them, a special gun was developed to wrap the wire around square-cornered terminals for which the apparatus had been modified (see Fig. 5-23).

Fig. 5-23. Wire-wrapping gun used to achieve solderless electrical connections to apparatus terminals.

When the making and breaking of high currents could not be adequately controlled by contact protection, mercury contact relays were made available as another tool in the design of relay circuits. Where unusual dirt and environmental conditions would create open circuits even on the bifurcated relay and switching contacts, the sealed contact relay was now available.

So, with contact protection, sealed relays, and solderless wrapped connections, the reliability and maintainability of electromechanical switching systems were much improved by the early 1950s. This opened the way to the large-scale introduction of automated switching into the entire Bell System network.[60]

REFERENCES, CHAPTER 5

1. Espenschied, L.; U.S. Patent 2,379,221; filed October 9, 1942; issued June 26, 1945.

2. Myers, O. "Some Neglected Switching Techniques." *Switching Techniques for Telecommunication Networks,* IEE Conference Publication **52**, London, April 1969, p. 10.

3. Fagen, M. D., ed. *A History of Engineering and Science in the Bell System: The Early Years (1875–1925).* Bell Telephone Laboratories, Incorporated, 1975, p. 467.

4. Moody, D. L. "Multi-Frequency Pulsing." *Bell Laboratories Record* **23**, December 1945, p. 466.

5. Carpenter, W. W. et al; U.S. Patent 2,112,951; filed April 28, 1934; issued April 5, 1938.

6. Hudson, W. E. *The Director System of Automatic Telephony,* London: I. Pitman and Sons, 1927.

7. Carpenter, W. W.; U.S. Patent 2,123,229; filed March 31, 1937; issued July 12, 1938.

8. Carpenter, W. W.; U.S. Patent 2,633,502; filed April 26, 1949; issued March 31, 1953.

9. See ref. 3, p. 538. See also Fry, T. C. *Probability and Its Engineering Uses.* New York: D. Van Nostrand Company, Incorporated, 1928.

10. Gray, E. A.; U.S. Patent 1,002,388; filed July 30, 1907; issued September 5, 1911. See also ref. 3, p. 569.

11. Wilkinson, R. I. "The Interconnection of Telephone Systems-Graded Multiples." *Bell System Technical Journal* **10**, October 1931, p. 531.

12. Wilkinson, R. I. "Theories for Toll Traffic Engineering in the U.S.A." *Bell System Technical Journal* **35**, March 1956, p. 421.

13. See ref. 12 above, p. 507.

14. Lee C. Y. "Analysis of Switching Networks." *Bell System Technical Journal* **34**, November 1955, p. 1287.

15. Turner, W. O. "Traffic Simulation." *Bell Laboratories Record* **41**, October 1963, p. 346.

16. Clos, C. "A Study of Non-Blocking Switching Networks." *Bell System Technical Journal* **32**, March 1953, p. 406.

17. Paull, M. C. "Reswitching of Connection Networks." *Bell System Technical Journal* **41**, May 1962, p. 833.

18. Feiner, A., and Kappel, J. G. "A Method of Deriving Efficient Switching Network Configurations." *Proceedings of the National Electronics Conference*, December 7, 8, and 9, 1970, p. 818.

19. Hibbard, A. *Hello Goodbye, My Story of Telephone Pioneering.* A. C. McClurg & Company, Chicago, 1941, p. 152.

20. See ref. 3 above, p. 535.

21. Morse, M. F. "Traffic-Usage Measuring: The Key to Dial Office Engineering." *Bell Laboratories Record* **35**, October 1957, p. 413.

22. Barnes, D. H. and Rutter, W. J. "Automatic Recording of Traffic Data." *Bell Laboratories Record* **34**, July 1956, p. 262.

23. Brown, H. G. W. "An Answering-Time Recorder." *Bell Laboratories Record* **19**, March 1941, p. 227.

24. Wilkinson, R. I. "The Reliability of Holding Time Measurements." *Bell System Technical Journal* **20**, October 1941, p. 365.

25. Meyer, W. J. "Traffic Registration in 4A Toll Crossbar." *Bell Laboratories Record* **33**, April 1955, p. 149.

26. Hayward, W. S., Jr. "The Reliability of Telephone Traffic Load Measurements by Switch Counts." *Bell System Technical Journal* **31**, March 1952, p. 357.

27. Hadlock, C. W. "Reweaving the Long Lines Circuit Fabric." *Bell Telephone Magazine* **30**, Summer 1951, p. 126.

28. Burke, P. J. "Automatic Overload Controls in a Circuit Switched Communications Network." *Proceedings of the National Electronics Conference* **24**, 1968, p. 667.

29. News item. "Dynamic Overload Controls Perform Well In Tests." *Bell Laboratories Record* **43**, February 1965, p. 56.

30. Lewis, E. E. and Schwenzfeger, E. E. "Automatically Controlling Heavy Telephone Traffic." *Bell Laboratories Record* **44**, April 1966, p. 135.

31. Ogren, W. E. "Network Management." *Bell Telephone Magazine* **41**, Winter 1962–1963, p. 62.

32. Lovell, C. A. "Crossbar Trunking Studies." *Bell Laboratories Record* **18**, October 1939, p. 38.

33. Frost, G. R., Keister, W., and Ritchie, A. E. "A Throwdown Machine for Telephone Traffic Studies." *Bell System Technical Journal* **32**, March 1953, p. 292.

34. Weber, J. H. "Some Traffic Characteristics of Communications Networks with Automatic Alternate Routing." *Bell System Technical Journal* **41**, March 1962, p. 769.

35. Turner, W. O. "Traffic Simulation." *Bell Laboratories Record* **41**, October 1963, p. 346.

36. Shannon, C. E. "A Mathematical Theory of Communication." *Bell System Technical Journal* **27**, July 1948, p. 379 and p. 623.

37. Shannon, C. E. "Memory Requirements in a Telephone Exchange." *Bell System Technical Journal* **29**, July 1950, p. 343.

38. Shannon, C. E. and Moore, E. F. "Reliable Circuits Using Less Reliable Relays." *Journal of the Franklin Institute* **262**, September 1956, p. 191.

39. Beneš, V. E. *Mathematical Theory of Connecting Networks and Telephone Traffic.* New York: Academic Press, 1965.

40. Shannon, C. E. "A Symbolic Analysis of Relay and Switching Circuits." *Trans. of AIEE* **57**, 1938, p. 713.

41. Keister, W. "The Logic of Relay Circuits." *Trans. of AIEE* **68**, 1949, p. 571.

42. Joel, A. E. "The Development of Relay and Switch Circuits," Masters thesis, M.I.T., 1942.

43. Ritchie, A. E. "Sequential Aspects of Relay Circuits." *Trans. of AIEE* **68**, 1949, p. 577.

44. Frost, G. R. "Counting with Relays," *Trans. of AIEE* **68**, 1949, p. 587.

45. Washburn, S. H. "Relay 'Trees' and Symmetric Circuits." *Trans. of AIEE* **68**, 1949, p. 582.

46. Meyers, O. "Codes and Translations." *Trans. of AIEE* **68**, 1949, p. 592.

47. Joel, A. E., Jr. "Relay Preference Lockout Circuits in Telephone Switching." *Trans. of AIEE* **67**, 1948, p. 1720.

48. Keister, W., Ritchie, A. E., and Washburn, S. H. *The Design of Switching Circuits*. Princeton, New Jersey: D. Van Nostrand Company, Inc., 1951.

49. Clark, A. B. "Telephone Switching." *Bell Laboratories Record* **24**, June 1946, p. 233.

50. Ingram, S. B. "Communications Development Training Program." *Bell Laboratories Record* **30**, October 1952, p. 404.

51. Gorgas, J. W. "Sequence Charts for Switching Circuits." *Bell Laboratories Record* **31**, December 1953, p. 492.

52. Meyer, F. T. "An Improved Detached-Contact Type of Schematic Circuit Drawing." *Trans. of AIEE* **74**, September 1955, p. 505.

53. Shive, J. N. "The New School for Operating Company Engineers." *Bell Laboratories Record* **35**, November 1957, p. 446.

54. Curtis, A. M. "Contact Phenomena in Telephone Switching Circuits." *Bell System Technical Journal* **19**, June 1940, p. 40.

55. Swenson, P. W. "Contacts." *Bell Laboratories Record* **27**, February 1949, p. 50.

56. Gumley, R. H. "Contact Phenomena in Sealed Containers." *Bell Laboratories Record* **32**, June 1954, p. 226.

57. Atalla, M. M. and Cox, R. E. "Theory of Open-Contact Performance of Twin Contacts." *Bell System Technical Journal* **33**, November 1954, p. 1373.

58. Gumley, R. H. "Relay Contact Protection." *Bell Laboratories Record* **34**, September 1956, p. 350.

59. Fagen, M. D., ed. *Impact* (1st edition). "Solderless Wrapped Connections." Bell Telephone Laboratories, Incorporated, 1971, p. 101.

60. Hamilton, C. "The Study of Performance in Switching Systems." *Bell Laboratories Record* **36**, April 1958, p. 133.

Accounting center in Philadelphia, 1948, equipped to process automatic message accounting (AMA) tapes. AMA centers, installed in the Bell System from 1948 to 1963, were an important first step toward the eventual complete automation of telephone billing. A wide AMA paper tape recorded the calling and called numbers, trunk number, type of billing, and times of beginning and end of each call. Such data were entered as perforations in the paper, rather than as die-cut punched holes as in teletypewriter tape. At accounting centers the tapes were read by machines that produced monthly bills for customers.

Chapter 6

Preparing for
Full Automation

During World War II the Bell System was able to foresee profound changes in postwar telephony—changes that demanded increased automation and increased attention to the problems of suburban as well as big-city telephone systems. Two keys to these changes were better signaling methods and methods for automatically recording the information needed to render customers' telephone bills. By consolidating a number of prewar developments, it was possible for the Bell System to institute long distance dialing of telephone calls by operators. Later, with the completion of a nationwide numbering plan and extensive modifications of equipment throughout the country, direct distance dialing by customers was initiated. Innovations that made this service possible included multifrequency and single-frequency signaling systems. Automatic ticketing was introduced in 1944 in the Los Angeles area, but full-scale automation had to await the system of automatic message accounting (AMA), introduced in Philadelphia in 1948, and the development of automatic systems for identifying calling telephone numbers.

I. THE SWITCHING PRODUCT LINE OF 1945

Although Bell Laboratories during World War II was devoted almost exclusively to war work, a few people had the opportunity to consider the general status of switching. What they saw was a mixture of base metal contact technology—such as manual, step-by-step, and panel switching—and prewar noble metal contact crossbar systems, which had just begun to see service. The problem, of course, was to use these technologies to maximum advantage at the conclusion of hostilities and to project the needs of the Bell System over the longer term.

No one had a better perspective on these needs than A. B. Clark, then Vice President of Systems Development. It was largely through his efforts that the steps toward a better understanding of switching, covered in the previous chapter, were initiated. With the results of these investigations as background, and with a general expectation of the population expansion from cities to the suburbs, plans were made for switching developments that the Bell System could initiate.

II. NEEDS FOR DIAL SERVICE IN THE SMALLER AND SUBURBAN COMMUNITIES

Up to this time the No. 1 crossbar and panel systems were available for use in large multioffice cities, where there were heavy concentrations of lines and telephones. For all of the remaining manually served locations, the step-by-step systems—both No. 1 and the various branch or community dial offices of the 300 type, more recently the 355A—were available. Although step-by-step switching proved satisfactory in these many applications, the small prewar experience with crossbar proved its superiority and added impetus to the desire for a more modern switching system for the smaller and suburban communities.

In the immediate postwar era, the Bell System, from a switching point of view, was tied together through manual toll offices. There was no nationwide automatic switching and associated numbering plan. The number of digits or "dial pulls" corresponded to the needs of the particular community, so that 3, 4, 5, 6, and 7 digit numbering could be found in different cities. It was foreseen that there would be a movement of households to the suburbs, and that suburban users would wish not only to communicate among themselves but also to call central cities easily. People in general were becoming more mobile and were finding different numbering plans in different parts of the country more difficult to use.

Since mobility tends to increase long distance calling, it was apparent that automation of this traffic was an important part of postwar planning. This in turn led to the recognition that two key ingredients were needed to implement such plans: longer distance signaling and better ways of automatically recording the information needed to charge for long distance calls.

Finally, for automating the service in the growing suburbs, a need was seen for a smaller but more flexible and growable crossbar system. Crossbar was preferred because of the excellent performance of the larger crossbar systems then in service. The No. 5 crossbar system was to fulfill this objective (see Chapter 7).

III. NATIONWIDE CALLING

Most long distance calling at this time was serviced through No. 1 and No. 3 manual toll switchboards. In the larger switching centers, toll tandem switchboards were needed to give the originating recording operator the ability to reach the growing numbers of toll trunks leaving these centers (see Chapter 3, section 4). For long distance traffic the customer dialed "211" ("112" or "110" in step-by-step areas) to reach an operator at a combined line and recording toll switchboard position.

The No. 4 crossbar system installed in Philadelphia had shown that automatic switching could be introduced to operate with the toll trunk equipment then in use with manual switching, particularly with respect to ringdown signaling and the insertion of attenuation pads and repeaters to meet the transmission requirements. With this system, the advantages of A-B (A board to B board) short haul toll dialing could be brought to long distance toll operation.

3.1 Operator Distance Dialing

These considerations led to a revision of a general plan to allow dialing of an increasingly large percentage of long distance calls.[1] It became known as the "operator distance dialing" plan, and its principal object was to complete most toll calls with only one operator, viz., the originating operator who wrote the charge ticket for the call.

As part of this implementation, the routing of calls had to be simplified. Manual toll switching frequently required switching service at intermediate points. However, the new carrier systems, including coaxial and later microwave facilities, meant that operators had available larger numbers of toll lines to a given destination. As a result, more calls could be served without delays in completing them—that is, without the calling party hanging up once the toll call was initiated. No one technological improvement was responsible for operator distance dialing, but it represented a consolidation of prewar developments that could bring about an important service improvement during the postwar period of great expansion (see Fig. 6-1). Also, some elements of the nationwide numbering plan were introduced at this time.

3.2 Nationwide Numbering Plan

The success of operator distance dialing obviously meant that it was just a matter of time before the charge recording step could be automated and customers could dial toll calls directly. It was also obvious, however, that allowing customers to dial calls nationwide required a universal numbering plan. There were many proposals, some very novel. For example, one plan proposed that the number of digits dialed should increase with the distance called, so that people in the smaller communities then dialing three or four digits for local calls could continue without change dialing longer numbers

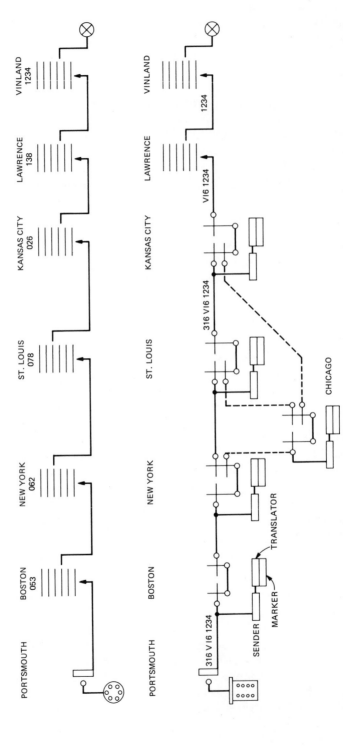

Fig. 6-1. Example of early (1945) planning for operator dialing of long distance calls. A nationwide number, here imagined to be 316 VI6–1234 (bottom), allows an operator in Portsmouth, New Hampshire, to dial a telephone in Vinland, Kansas. Top diagram shows less workable arrangement if systems without senders and common control were to be used.

only when their calls extended beyond their communities. But the plan as adopted recognized the need for a nationwide numbering plan, one that applied universally, so that callers would not have to be familiar with the plans in the communities that they might be visiting. The result was that, in 1945, the toll switching engineering group under the leadership of F. F. Shipley proposed, and AT&T adopted, the foundation for our current system of universal seven-digit numbers within an area and three-digit area codes.[2] No numbering plan area was to extend beyond the boundaries of a state, but a state might include more than one numbering plan area. The three-digit area codes all included the digit 0 or 1 as the middle digit to distinguish them from office codes that did not have this characteristic. Initially, states with only one area code used area codes with "0" and others used "1," but with the growth of the service, this method of assignment was abandoned. Fig. 6-2 shows the very first proposed map with 86 area codes assigned, including 8 in Canada. A 1976 map (Fig. 6-3) shows the growth of number-ing plan areas to the total of 132 that included Mexico and the Caribbean.

Numbering plan improvements have been the key to many steps in the extension of automatic switching, e.g., adopting letters on the dial to overcome the learning and memory problems initially associ-ated with dialing in the larger cities with numerous central offices.[3] As the number of offices grew and it became more difficult to assign names with meaningful letter combinations, identification of central office codes was changed from 3 letters to 2 letters and 1 number,[4] which together with the 4-digit station codes gave 2 letters and 5 numerals, or "2-5" numbering. This became the universal form of telephone number identification and was important to the introduc-tion of direct distance dialing. As familiarity with the dialing pro-cess grew, it was possible to shift from letters to the international standard, which is limited to decimal digits for addresses. The Bell System carried out this conversion over a period of twenty years, completing it in 1979. Implementation required much planning as well as modification of existing switching systems, particularly to accept the additional digits to be dialed by the customer to provide for uniform local dialing and for receipt and interpretation of the area codes.

Even the step-by-step system was modified. The existing switch trains in step-by-step offices provided adequate discrimination among office codes. However, with uniform dialing, extra digits would be dialed. To accept these digits would normally have required, at great expense, the building-out of the switch train for each 3-digit office code and in some cases for the thousands digit as well.

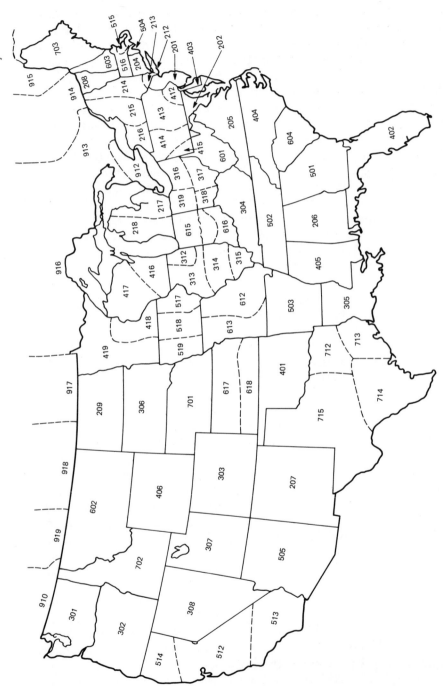

Fig. 6-2. Initial nationwide numbering plan with 86 area codes, including those in Canada.

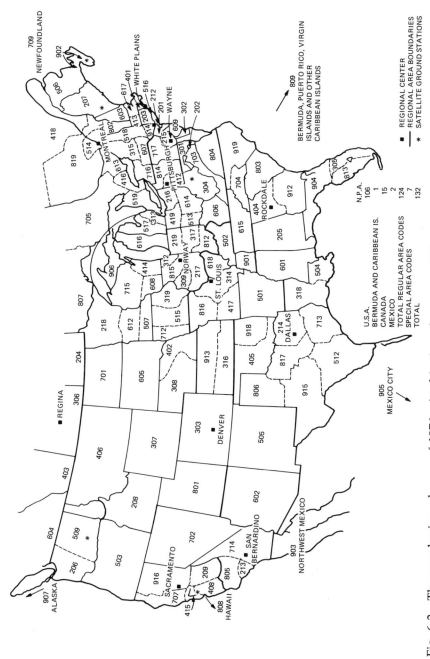

Fig. 6-3. The numbering plan as of 1976. At this time there were 132 area codes assigned in the U.S., Canada, and Mexico, plus one for Bermuda and the Caribbean Islands.

A Bell Laboratories invention, the digit-absorbing selector (see Chapter 3, section II), usually placed as the first selector in a train, was designed to ignore dialed digits by returning to normal when the newly added office code digits were introduced.[5] These selectors could be arranged to absorb one or two digits of a particular value. This feature was obtained by contacts operated on the rise of the selector to particular levels, which were designated for each application by the bending of tangs (see Fig. 3-14).

With the introduction of direct customer access to toll trunks, new methods of engineering had to be introduced, and a great many more trunks had to be planned for, so that service could be provided on a demand rather than on a delay basis, as was usually the case for operator-handled calls.

IV. LONGER DISTANCE SIGNALING

Multifrequency pulsing for address signaling was proved satisfactory with the introduction of the No. 4 crossbar system (Chapter 4, section III). As more of these systems were introduced into the network, multifrequency pulsing became the standard method of long distance address signaling (see Fig. 6-4).[6] Improved versions of receivers[7] (see Fig. 6-5) and common tone generators were developed. Later, transistorized versions were developed for many different applications in newer switching systems.[8] The first transistorized multifrequency (MF) receiver was used in the No. 1 ESS in 1965. By 1970 it was used in electromechanical switching systems. Eventually, transistorized tone generators as part of the senders (see Chapter 7, section III) replaced the common supplies in many switching systems.

Fig. 6-4. Multifrequency receiver, 1945. Multifrequency pulsing became standard for long distance signaling.

Fig. 6-5. G. Plaag adjusting one of a group of an improved version of multifrequency receivers, 1954.

For supervisory signaling and where multifrequency pulsing could not be used, such as for calls to step-by-step offices, both inband and out-of-band single-frequency (SF) signaling methods were developed for dial pulsing as well as for supervision.[9] Although ideal in a number of respects, out-of-band signaling was restricted by the wartime emergency banks (EBs) introduced into the transmission systems during World War II to provide greater carrier channel capacity by limiting the frequency band of a voice channel.[10] Nevertheless, out-of-band signaling was initially developed for application with early analog carrier systems.[11] The frequencies were generally in the 3200-hertz range. Out-of-band signaling had the advantage that the signals could not be simulated by human voice sounds ("talk off") and, therefore, were immune to false disconnects. The only successful out-of-band system (3700 hertz) was developed for use with the N1, O1, and ON carrier systems.[12] For more general application, inband signaling equipment was developed for use on repeater and carrier circuits. The first of these used frequencies of 1600 hertz and 2000 hertz in the reverse direction, approximately half of those frequencies experimented with for out-of-band signaling.[13] About 20,000 of these units were placed in service starting in 1948. To reduce "talk-off," higher frequencies were used. These systems used 2600 hertz (2400 hertz in the reverse direction), and thereby enabled distant switching systems to be controlled over any path customers could use for conversation[14] (see Fig. 6-6). Some 170,000 of these vacuum tube units were placed in service beginning in 1952.

After transistors were developed, new single-frequency signaling units, compatible with the vacuum tube type, were designed and produced. These were known as the "E type" signaling units and were first placed in service in 1958[15] (see Fig. 6-7). More than 3,300,000 units were produced, not only for interoffice signaling including revertive pulsing, but also for foreign exchange and PBX lines. An improved, more compact SF system, the F type, was developed in 1969[16] (see Fig. 6-8). Fig. 6-9 shows the basic function of these signaling units. By 1976 over one million of these units were produced.

V. CHARGE RECORDING METHODS

The other important ingredient required for the start of full automation of the nationwide telephone network was machine methods for recording information about calls that could be used for billing. Two methods were studied, one known as automatic ticketing and the other as automatic message accounting (AMA).

5.1 Automatic Ticketing

Automatic ticketing was first introduced in Belgium in 1938.[17] Bell Laboratories engineers, working with Teletype Corporation engineers about that time, devised a simpler numerical printer or "message ticketer" (see Figs. 6-10 and 6-11). This printer was low enough in cost that one could be provided on each outgoing trunk circuit from an originating office that required detailed charge infor-

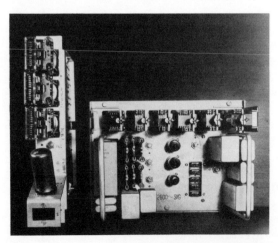

Fig. 6-6. In-band signaling units: transistorized unit, left, and earlier vacuum tube model, right.

Fig. 6-7. E-type single-frequency signaling unit; over 3,300,000 of these units were produced, beginning in 1958.

Fig. 6-8. Patrick McLaughlin with the F-type design of 1969, an improved, more compact single-frequency unit.

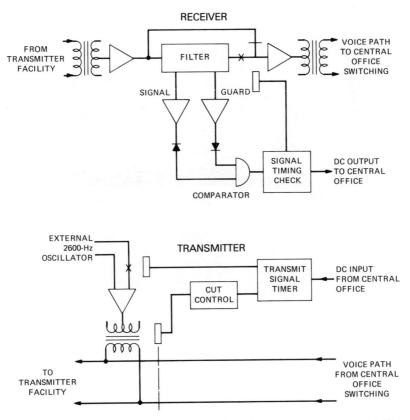

Fig. 6-9. Diagram of an F-type unit showing tone generator and detector connections to transmitting and receiving lines.

mation about the calls it served.[18] Fig. 6-12 shows a sample automatic ticket compared with a manually written ticket.

A critical ingredient in this as well as most charge recording systems was to provide the identity of the calling line number. The arrangement, developed initially for the automatic ticketing system, used a 2700-hertz tone applied to the sleeve lead from the trunk back through the originating switch train to a matrix of capacitors, resistors, and transformers[19] (see Fig. 6-13). A set of ten vacuum tube detectors successively connected with different parts of this matrix to determine the office thousands, hundreds, tens, and units digits of the calling line. Provision was made in the process to identify the number of either of the parties on a two-party line, based upon the party test made in the trunk circuit.[20]

As mentioned earlier, Los Angeles was one of the first areas to use operator and customer distance dialing. It was also an area with

Fig. 6-10. The ticketing unit of the automatic ticketing system: front view above, rear view below.

only step-by-step equipment since it had an early history of the introduction of this type of equipment by many independent telephone companies prior to unification by the Bell System, and prior to the introduction of the panel system into large cities. It was quite natural that as Los Angeles grew, it became necessary to charge on an individual or detailed bill basis for customer-dialed calls across this expanding metropolis. Los Angeles thus became a logical area in which to introduce some form of automatic charge recording.

In 1944, the automatic ticketing system described above was first placed in service in Culver City, in the Los Angeles area.[21] In addition to the trunk ticketers and automatic line number identifiers, this system provided register-senders that were accessed by outgoing trunk circuits (see Fig. 6-14). These senders stored the called and calling number to control the simple trunk ticketers and also translated the central office code digits (reconstructed by the identifiers from the digits dialed by the customer to reach the outgoing trunk). Further, they transmitted decimal pulses of the central office code or arbitrary digits so that the call could be directed through step-by-step tandem offices to reach the called office.[22]

This system was placed in service in some 50 offices in the Los Angeles metropolitan area, as well as a few others in the Sacramento, California area. Over the years, as the amount of

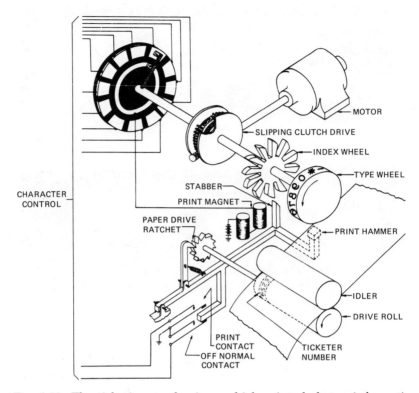

Fig. 6-11. The ticketing mechanism, which printed charge information needed for billing customers.

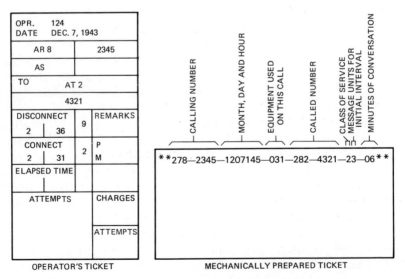

Fig. 6-12. Manual ticket, left, and automatic ticket, right.

traffic served by these systems increased, several important modifications were made to them. The subsequent development and success of AMA (see next section) led to the removal of the trunk ticketers, so that the system was later modified to record the same information on AMA paper tape.[23] This arrangement became known as "step-by-step AMA" or SAMA.

The identification process became more generally known as "automatic number identification" (ANI). The particular form used in this system was labeled as "ANI-A." It initially was inherently slow since a separate identification was required for each digit of the calling line number and office code reconstruction. As traffic increased, greater speed was necessary. Several tone frequencies were introduced so that each identifier responded to its own frequency; therefore several tones could be present in the identification matrices simultaneously. In more recent years with the introduction of the traffic service position system (TSPS), the system was modified so that an identification could be made and the ANI information could be multifrequency pulsed forward to the TSPS on first selector "0" level trunks not arranged for SAMA. This feature was called "automatic number forwarding" (ANF). In 1974 the system was further modified for operation with 1 + 10 digit dialing for which increased digit capacity was required.[24]

5.2 Automatic Message Accounting

The automatic ticketing systems were an obvious method for automating call charge records. However, providing equipment even as simple as the message ticketers on a per-trunk basis was costly, particularly as one looked forward to the growth of this type of traffic. In 1934, W. W. Carpenter and W. H. Matthies explored this problem and received patents on several centralized methods for recording charge information.[25] These generally used punched paper tape, such as employed in teletypewriter operation. The teletypewriter punches required rather expensive dies and were limited in speed, so that a large number of them would be required to record the large volume of data resulting from the many telephone calls originating in a single central office.

In the early 1940s, Carpenter conceived a die-less form of punched paper tape. The paper was broken by the point of a nail driven against a countersunk hole. This break in the paper formed an embossing. The width over which the tape could be punched was controlled only by the size and spacing of the countersunk holes. When pressed against the holes, the 3-inch wide paper tape would move without a drive sprocket. To provide a simple mechanism for advancing the paper in this manner, Carpenter used the

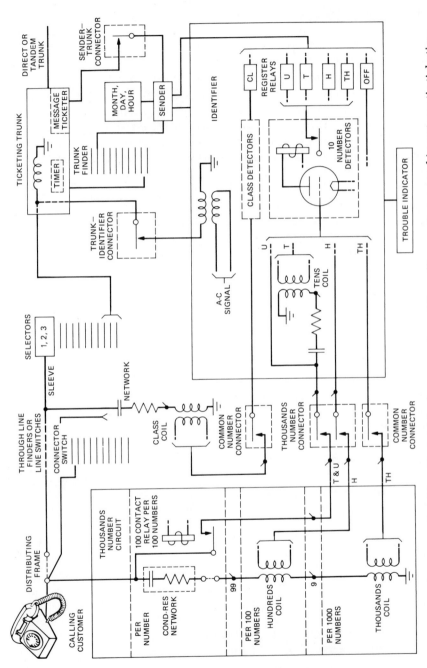

Fig. 6-13. Circuit used to identify the telephone number of the calling party, as used in automatic ticketing.

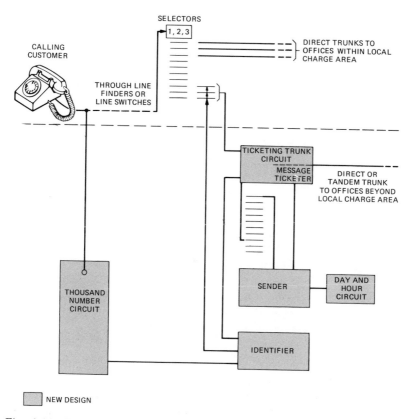

NEW DESIGN

Fig. 6-14. Diagram of the automatic ticketing system, first used in Culver City, California in 1944.

drive mechanism of a 206-type selector, which had 44 evenly spaced steps. With the diameter chosen, there were six perforations per inch. During World War II, Carpenter made a number of these simple tape perforating mechanisms in the basement of his home, using an automatically controlled drill press. Fig. 6-15 shows a perspective view of the perforator mechanism. The tape is 28 hole positions wide.[26] Fig. 6-16 shows the way the perforations were used to record digital information.

To read this tape it was necessary to have pins that applied a small amount of pressure and so would pass through the holes where they existed, but that would not perforate the paper when there were no holes. The pins were in turn attached to sets of contacts, so that the information coded on the tape could be read. Fig. 6-17 shows a tape perforator and reader in cabinets as used at the accounting center where the tapes were processed.[27]

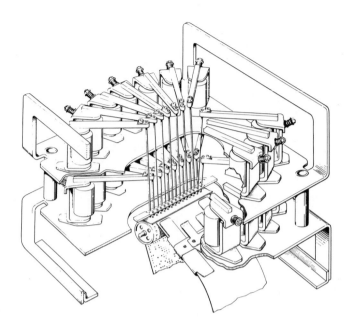

Fig. 6-15. Perspective view of the perforator. "Nails" emboss paper perforations into countersunk holes in the cylinder.

Another feature of this recording system was that one tape recorder served 100 district junctors or trunks through a "call identity indexer"[28] (see Fig. 6-18). The information about all the calls served by these trunks was placed on the tape in chronological order. This system was developed for use only in offices of the common-control type so that the called number was available from a sender. In crossbar offices the identity of the calling line number was available when establishing the connection to an originating sender or register. This information was translated from the equipment location to a directory number with a Dimond-ring translator (see Chapter 7, section 1.1), taking into account the identity of the party on two-party lines.[29] The common-control equipment placed an initial entry on the tape, generally providing the calling and called numbers, the time of day, information concerning the type of billing for the call, and the number of the trunk serving the call. Later, when and if the call was answered, the trunk number and time would be recorded on the tape, and an identical timing entry would be placed on the tape at the conclusion of the call. Interspersed among the three entries of a particular call were similar entries for calls served by the other 99 trunk circuits as well as hourly and daily timing entries.

Periodically, usually once a day, these tapes would be collected and delivered to an accounting center where the tape readers and other tape perforators were located. A complete accounting system for calls handled by AMA was developed at Bell Laboratories from 1946 to 1948. The "AMA accounting centers," as they were called, produced printed records, one for each customer per month, listing each call, the elapsed time, and in some cases the charges. Similar processing was used for calls billed on a message unit rather than detail basis. The accounting process consists of successively reading and reperforating AMA tape as shown in Fig. 6-19. Fig. 6-20

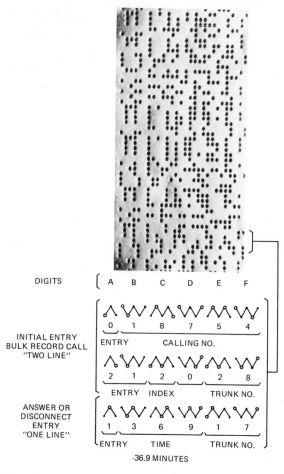

Fig. 6-16. Top: method of recording information on AMA tape; patterns of perforations specify digits describing details of call. Bottom: code patterns for recording calling and called numbers, time information, and other details used for preparing bills.

Fig. 6-17. A tape reader, left, and two perforators, right, as used in an automatic message accounting center.

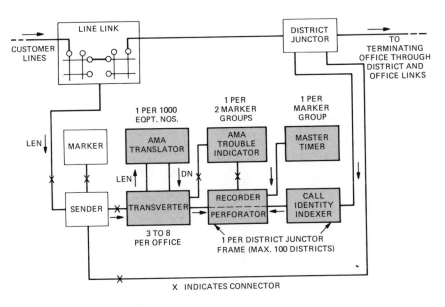

DN — DIRECTORY NUMBER
LEN — LINE EQUIPMENT NUMBER

Fig. 6-18. Arrangement of equipment to provide AMA in a common-control office showing, in the lower right, the call identity indexer as applied to No. 1 crossbar. The call indexer provided the number of the trunk or district junctor to be recorded on the AMA tape.

shows the original printed output for detail and bulk-billed calls. Reference 30 is a list of papers giving additional details on the AMA central office paper tape recording system.

In 1948, the first AMA accounting center was placed in operation in Philadelphia, Pennsylvania, coincident with the cutover of the first No. 5 crossbar system, which included the AMA feature. Previously a trial of AMA central office equipment in a No. 1 crossbar office was conducted in Washington, D.C. Both the No. 1 and No. 5 crossbar systems were arranged for AMA recording, which in time became known as "Local AMA" or "LAMA."

About this time (late 1940s) a number of new methods of recording data were being developed as pioneering work for digital computers. One development proposed but rejected after considerable study was a magnetic wire version of AMA. It was not until the early 1960s that magnetic tape standards and reliability had reached

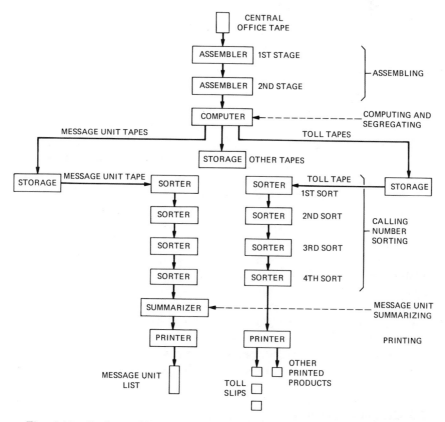

Fig. 6-19. Outline of the process of reading, reperforating, assembling, and sorting AMA tapes. End product was the information for an individual customer's bill.

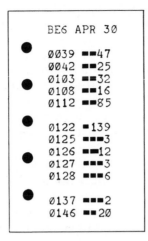
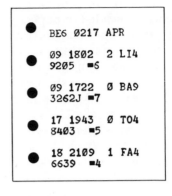

Fig. 6-20. Left: AMA summary list of telephone numbers showing number of message units charged to each. Right: toll slip showing details of toll calls made from telephone number BE6-0217.

a point where it was considered satisfactory for recording call charge information. At that time, LAMA was introduced into the No. 1 electronic switching system using a magnetic tape (see Chapter 9, section 5.2).

AMA accounting centers were established in the Bell System for a period of 15 years. Improvements made in the accounting center process included a machine that automatically assembled the call records and computed the elapsed time for the assembled calls. This machine, known as the "assembler-computer," replaced many intermediate sorting stages and used new apparatus, principally sealed contact digit register relays and the UB relays.[31] The inventor of the assembler-computer was A. E. Joel, Jr., and the patent resulting from this invention was the largest one issued in the United States up to that time, comprising almost 250 claims and drawing figures[32] (see Fig. 6-21). Over 100 of these machines were built.

The AMA accounting center was one of the first steps in computerized centralization of plant operations. With the advent of electronic data processing the AMA centers were replaced by machines that converted punched paper tape to magnetic tape to enter into the other portions of the automated billing process.

5.3 Centralization of AMA

Although the AMA recording system was quite successful, it was used primarily for detail-billed toll calls, since only a few areas had message unit billing for local calls. At that time the amount of toll

Fig. 6-21. A. E. Joel, Jr., with his assembler-computer patent—the largest patent issued up to that time (1960).

calling from many offices could not justify the expense of LAMA equipment. Also, the application of AMA in the step-by-step and panel systems could not be justified economically. As a result, the concept of centralized AMA (CAMA) was developed. With centralized AMA, toll calls were routed to a tandem or toll office where trunks and registers were arranged to operate with the AMA recording equipment. In addition, the registers were connected to cordless operator positions after the called number was received by the sender. An idle position was connected momentarily for the operator to request the calling line number, which the operator keyed into the sender for billing purposes. The calls using these CAMA operator positions (see Fig. 6-22) provided what became known as "operator number identification" or "ONI."[33] For light traffic periods, arrangements were made for cord-board (DSA) operators to respond to these calls.

Fig. 6-22. Washington, D.C. installation of centralized automatic message accounting (CAMA) operator positions.

The CAMA principle was applied to all systems used for tandem and toll service except for the panel system. The concept was first developed starting in 1950 for the crossbar tandem system[34] (see Chapter 8, section 3.1 and Fig. 6-23) with the first installation cutting over in Washington, D.C. in 1953. Ultimately 189 or approximately 65 percent of the tandem systems were equipped for CAMA operation.

A basic problem when connecting step-by-step offices to common-control offices is that dial pulse (DP) transmission from a customer's dial can reach the trunk prior to connecting a sender to receive them. Dialing a "1" reaches these trunks. Two methods of insuring the receipt of succeeding digits may be employed. The digits may be stored in the trunk, or a bypass or "bylink" may be used to bring the digits that may be dialed into the sender while the full link connection is being established (see Fig. 6-24).

To serve calls reaching the offices directly from local step-by-step offices over CAMA trunks, a separate register-sender arrangement was designed for the crossbar tandem system.[35] Here a high-speed single stage "bylink" connects the trunk to a 3-digit register while the sender link connects the trunk to a regular dial pulse sender (see Fig. 6-25) to receive the remaining digits. Later the register deposits the earlier digits into the sender. Similar bylink arrangements are provided in other CAMA applications.

Tandem features were made available to the No. 5 crossbar system (see Chapter 7) in early 1952,[36] and CAMA features were added in 1958. The first cutover was in Newhall, California in 1959.[37]

Much of the toll calling from around the country is recorded in toll offices of the 4A crossbar type (see Chapter 8). CAMA features were developed for this system starting in 1954 with the first cut-over in Albuquerque, New Mexico in 1960.[38] Special features included remote operator number identification (ONI) positions,[39] bylinks,[40] and new dial pulse registers.[41] The registers store all digits and send them as multifrequency pulses to a CAMA sender when it is attached to the trunk in the usual manner (see Fig. 6-26). A common group of senders then serves all offered dial pulse and multifrequency traffic. Approximately 80 of the 182 4A crossbar offices were placed in service with these features.

Finally, similar arrangements were developed for the step-by-step intertoll system, many of them very small[42] (see Fig. 6-27). The first of about 90 systems was placed in service in Steubenville, Ohio in September 1961.

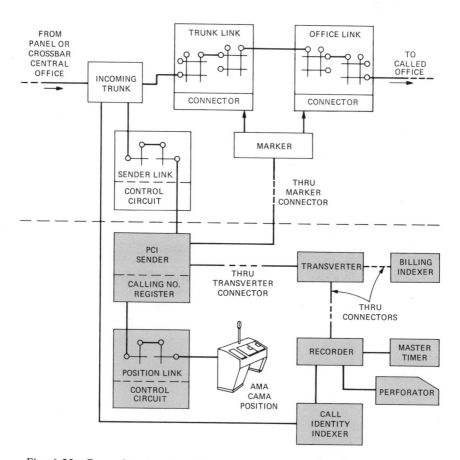

Fig. 6-23. Centralized automatic message accounting feature (bottom) as applied to crossbar tandem switching (top), first placed in service in 1953.

In some areas the ONI method proved unsatisfactory due to the frequency of recording of incorrect calling numbers and the subsequent billing errors. Also, as the volume of toll calling increased, the number of operator positions increased. Therefore, it became necessary to develop automatic number identification equipment for most local switching systems so that ONI could be eliminated as a routine operation on most calls, to be reserved only for calls where the ANI equipment fails, for identifying the calling line number for multiparty lines, and for recording special billing numbers.

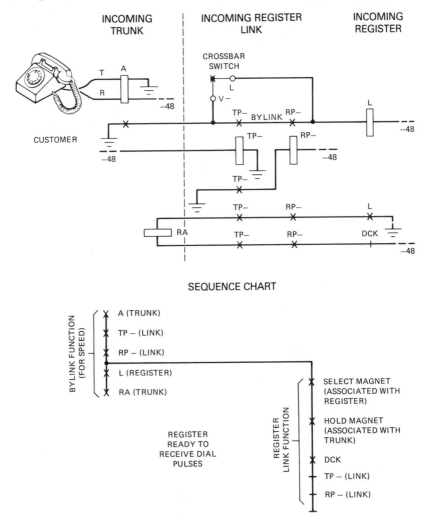

Fig. 6-24. The bylink circuit and sequence chart showing how step-by-step offices can connect to common-control systems.

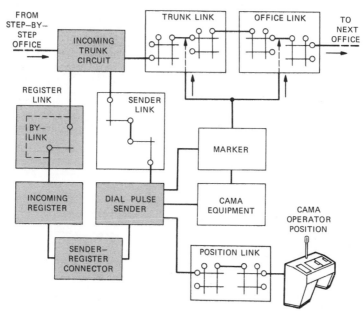

Fig. 6-25. Bylink arrangements for crossbar tandem switching.

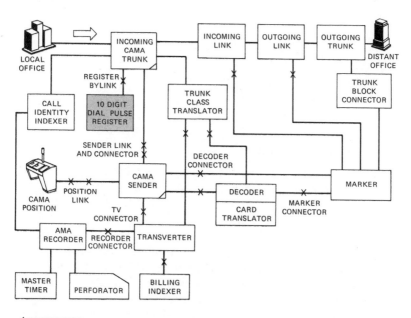

△ MODIFICATION

Fig. 6-26. Arrangement for 4A crossbar CAMA. New dial pulse register (shaded box) was one of several special features, first placed in service in 1960. Another new feature was remote ONI positions.

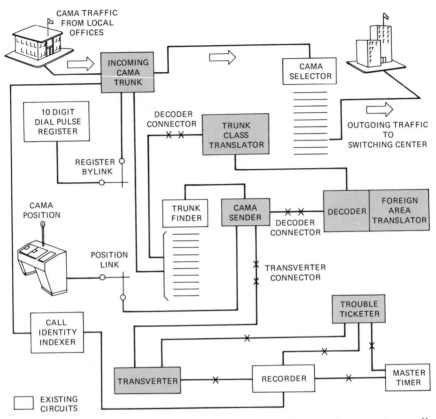

Fig. 6-27. Shaded boxes show CAMA units in step-by-step intertoll office, first placed in service in 1961.

5.4 Automatic Number Identification

Many methods for identifying calling lines and translating between equipment and directory number were studied.[43] The initial general-purpose ANI method devised for use in panel, step-by-step, and No. 1 crossbar offices became known as "ANI-B." This system functioned in a manner similar to the ANI-A in automatic ticketing, except that the matrix was more economically divided to provide for the simultaneous identification of one among 10,000 numbers by digits, then into 100 groups of 100 (see Fig. 6-28).[44] A 5800-hertz tone was placed on the local sleeve lead to the outgoing trunk to the CAMA office[45] (see Fig. 6-29). After the called number has been received by the CAMA sender, this sender signals back to the outgoing trunk in the originating office and the calling line number is pulsed forward by multifrequency pulsing from an ANI sender.

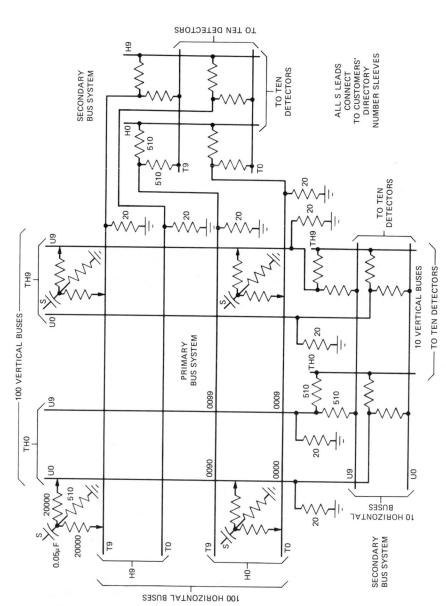

Fig. 6-28. ANI-B arrangement as used in No. 1 crossbar panel and step-by-step offices.

Fig. 6-29. H. A. Miloche standing in front of an ANI-B number network frame that serves 1000 lines. He holds a primary network unit for ten telephone lines.

ANI-B was designed to be most economical in larger offices where large amounts of detail-billed calling was expected. As a result, the per-line and trunk equipment was kept simple and low in cost while the common equipment had a high getting-started cost. The key equipment item was the 1000-line number network frame. The system was not transistorized because at the time the development started, reliable transistors with the required but unusual detector and amplification characteristics were not yet available. Nonetheless, ANI-B has given a good account of itself in the field with over 30.4 million lines installed. The first standard installation in a No. 1 crossbar office was in Seattle, Washington in February 1961. The first panel office installation (Newark, New Jersey) and No. 1 step-by-step office (Stamford, Connecticut) followed closely in the same year. It was also during the development of wiring for the line networks that H. A. Miloche, R. F. Mallina, and F. Reck invented a solderless wrapped connection technique to eliminate solder crosses and clippings in this wiring maze[46] (see Chapter 5, section VIII).

It was found that for small step-by-step offices, generally those serving fewer than 5000 lines, providing ANI-B was too expensive.

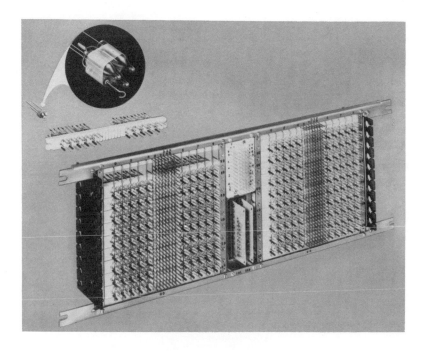

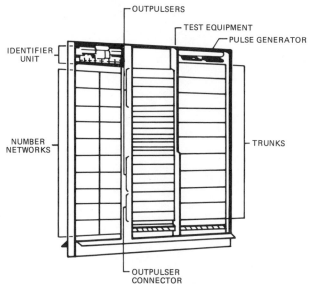

Fig. 6-30. ANI-C and ANI-D use 100-number network assemblies. Two of these are shown in the upper part of the figure, with two plug-in diode cards and a common terminal array between the two 100-number networks. The inset shows a number network: three neon glow lamps and a resistor held by a plastic band and placed between terminal posts. Bottom: a three-bay frame that provides the trunk, sender, and network circuits for up to 2000 numbers.

This meant that as direct distance dialing (DDD) was applied to more of the Bell System, the smaller offices could participate only by utilizing operator number identification. With increasing labor cost and percentage of DDD calls it was necessary to devise a more economical version for customers in smaller offices.

A more economical system, ANI-C, was developed for this application.[47] The first office was South Sioux City, Nebraska in January 1965. This system had more expensive active devices, gas tubes, for each line appearance and lower getting-started costs in the common equipment (see Fig. 6-30). Instead of a tone, this system used a

Fig. 6-31. Composite space-saving ANI-D frame containing line-identification networks, trunks, and sender.

heavy positive pulse on the sleeve lead that ionized the gas tubes associated with the calling line. This design was to extend ANI to offices in the 1000- to 5000-line range. The number frame accommodated 2600-line networks.

For slow-growing offices the equipment arrangements were not economical, since too much spare space was provided. A repackaged version, ANI-D, introduced with first service in Van Dyne, Wisconsin in March 1973, provided a system that economically filled the need in smaller offices[48] (see Fig. 6-31). A single frame could provide ANI capability for as many as 3600 lines. ANI-C with more than 4.3 million lines installed and ANI-D with more than 2.6 million lines installed provided community dial offices with the same high-quality toll calling, without the intervention of an operator, as provided in the larger metropolitan offices.

REFERENCES, CHAPTER 6

1. Shipley, F. F. "Nation-Wide Dialing." *Bell Laboratories Record* **23**, October 1945, p. 368.
2. Nunn, W. H. "Nationwide Numbering Plan." *Bell System Technical Journal* **31**, September 1952, p. 851.
3. Fagen, M. D., ed. *A History of Engineering and Science in the Bell System: The Early Years (1875–1925).* Bell Telephone Laboratories, Incorporated, 1975, p. 584.
4. Ericson, S. G. "What's Your Telephone Number?" *Bell Telephone Magazine* **33**, Winter 1954/55, p. 232.
5. Atkinson, J. *Telephony,* Vol. II. London: Sir Issac Pitman and Sons, Ltd., 1950, p. 339.
6. See ref. 2 above.
7. Moody, D. L. "Multifrequency Pulsing." *Bell Laboratories Record* **23**, December 1945, p. 466.
8. Yokelson, B. J. "A New Multifrequency Receiver." *Bell Laboratories Record* **32**, June 1954, p. 221.
9. Sheppard, H. A. "A Signaling System for Intertoll Dialing." *Bell Laboratories Record* **18**, July 1940, p. 337.
10. Bellows, B. C. "Stretching Toll Facilities for the Emergency." *Bell Laboratories Record* **21**, January 1943, p. 110.
11. Breen, C. and Dahlbom, C. A. "Signaling Systems for Control of Telephone Switching." *Bell System Technical Journal* **39**, November 1960, p. 1381.
12. Van Tassel, E. K. "Type-N Carrier Telephone System." *Bell Laboratories Record* **30**, July 1952, p. 277.
13. Newell, N. A. and Weaver, A. "Single-Frequency Signaling System for Supervision and Dialing Over Long-Distance Telephone Trunks," *Trans. of Am. Inst. of Electrical Engineers,* **70**, Pt. 1, 1951, p. 489.
14. Newell, N. A. "In-Band Single-Frequency Signaling." *Bell System Technical Journal* **33**, November 1954, p. 1309.
15. Dahlbom, C. A. "A Transistorized Signaling System: Engineering Aspects." *Bell Laboratories Record* **37**, July 1959, p. 254.
16. Battista, R. N., Roscoe, L. C. J., and Guguere, W. J. "A New Single-Frequency Signaling System." *Bell Laboratories Record* **48**, March 1970, p. 85.

17. Hatton, William. "Automatic Ticketing of Long-Distance Telephone Connections," *Electrical Communication* **18**, January 1940, p. 195.
18. Friend, O. A. "Automatic Ticketing." *Bell Laboratories Record* **22**, July 1944, p. 445.
19. Gooderham, J. W. "The Identifier—A New Member of the Switching Family." *Bell Laboratories Record* **22**, December 1944, p. 633.
20. Sheatsley, P. W. "Coordinate Cross-Connectors for Automatic Toll Ticketing." *Bell Laboratories Record* **23**, January 1945, p. 29.
21. Friend, O. A. "Automatic Ticketing of Telephone Calls," *Trans. of Am. Inst. of Electrical Engineers*, **63**, March 1944, p. 81.
22. Hersey, R. E. "Senders for Automatic Ticketing in Step-by-Step Offices." *Bell Laboratories Record* **22**, October 1944, p. 550.
23. Martins, A. S. "Conversion of Automatic Ticketing to AMA." *Bell Laboratories Record* **35**, March 1957, p. 89.
24. Junkus, J. J. "Keeping Step in Place," *Western Electric Engineer* **18**, July 1974, p. 12.
25. Carpenter, W. W. et al.; U.S. Patent 2,112,951; filed April 28, 1934; issued April 5, 1938.
26. Drake, P. B. "The AMA Tape Perforator." *Bell Laboratories Record* **29**, November 1951, p. 504.
27. Kuch, F. C. "The AMA Reader." *Bell Laboratories Record* **30**, June 1952, p. 237.
28. Pennoyer, D. H. "Basic AMA Central Office Features." *Bell Laboratories Record* **29**, October 1951, p. 454.
29. Dimond, T. L. "No. 5 Crossbar AMA Translator." *Bell Laboratories Record* **29**, February 1951, p. 62.
30. Articles dealing with AMA system:
Seibel, C. F. "Automatic Message Accounting." *Bell Laboratories Record* **29**, September 1951, p. 401.
Cahill, H. D. "Recording on AMA Tape in Central Offices." *Bell Laboratories Record* **29**, December 1951, p. 565.
Meszar, John. "Basic Features of the AMA Center." *Bell Laboratories Record* **30**, February 1952, p. 70.
Jordan, W. C. "The AMA Timer." *Bell Laboratories Record* **30**, March 1952, p. 122.
Sheatsley, P. W. "Central Office Equipment for AMA." *Bell Laboratories Record* **30**, April 1952, p. 173.
Drew, G. G. "The AMA Assembler." *Bell Laboratories Record* **30**, May 1952, p. 227.
Hague, A. E. "The AMA Computer." *Bell Laboratories Record* **30**, July 1952, p. 289.
Pilliod, M. E. "The AMA Computer: Chargeable Time and Message Unit Computations." *Bell Laboratories Record* **31**, February 1953, p. 53.
Joel, A. E., Jr. "Tracing Time Backward in AMA." *Bell Laboratories Record* **30**, November 1952, p. 422.
Meszar, J. "Basic Features of the AMA Center." *Bell Laboratories Record* **30**, February 1952, p. 70.
Rolf, F. N. "The Sorter for Automatic Message Accounting." *Bell Laboratories Record* **30**, July 1952, p. 299.
Riggs, G. "The AMA Summarizer." *Bell Laboratories Record* **30**, August 1952, p. 321.
Marshall, T. A. "The AMA Printer." *Bell Laboratories Record* **30**, September 1952, p. 368.
Branson, D. E. "The AMA Called-Office Name Translator." *Bell Laboratories Record* **31**, July 1953, p. 269.

Groth, W. B. "A Tape-To-Card Converter for Automatic Message Accounting." *Bell Laboratories Record* **31**, September 1953, p. 333.

Kille, L. A. "Test Tapes for Automatic Accounting Centers." *Bell Laboratories Record* **30**, September 1952, p. 349.

Bonorden, A. R. "A Test Unit for AMA Perforators and Readers." *Bell Laboratories Record* **30**, October 1952, p. 398.

Douglass, H. T. "Performance Studies of AMA Readers and Perforators." *Bell Laboratories Record* **31**, March 1953, p. 81.

King, G. V. "Accuracy Provisions in AMA." *Bell Laboratories Record* **30**, December 1952, p. 471.

31. Rehm, T. C. "The AMA Assembler-Computer." *Bell Laboratories Record* **35**, October 1957, p. 423.

32. Joel, A. E., Jr.; U.S. Patent 2,925,957; filed April 4, 1955; issued February 23, 1960.

33. Martin, F. H. "Centralized AMA Switchboard." *Bell Laboratories Record* **32**, October 1954, p. 371.

34. Maloney, M. E. "Centralized Automatic Message Accounting." *Bell Laboratories Record* **32**, July 1954, p. 241.

35. Goldstein, E. "CAMA for Step-By-Step Areas." *Bell Laboratories Record* **35**, August 1957, p. 312.

36. Brubaker, J. W. "No. 5 Crossbar Tandem Revertive-Pulse Incoming Register." *Bell Laboratories Record* **32**, July 1954, p. 268.

37. Hurst, G. A. "Extending CAMA with No. 5 Crossbar." *Bell Laboratories Record* **36**, October 1958, p. 372.

38. Jaeger, R. J. and Maloney, M. E. "4A and 4M Toll Crossbar With CAMA Equipment." *Bell Laboratories Record* **37**, September 1959, p. 345.

39. Rolf, F. N. "Remote Positions for CAMA." *Bell Laboratories Record* **35**, September 1957, p. 353.

40. Middleton, A. S. "No. 4 CAMA and the 'Bylink' Circuit." *Bell Laboratories Record* **37**, October 1959, p. 387.

41. Dusenberry, R. F. "New Dial-Pulse Register for No. 4-Type CAMA." *Bell Laboratories Record* **37**, November 1959, p. 422.

42. Martins, A. S. and Ruwell, R. G. "CAMA for Step-by-Step Intertoll." *Bell Laboratories Record* **40**, February 1962, p. 55.

43. Schneckloth, H. H. "Some Basic Concepts of Translators and Identifiers Used in Telephone Switching Systems." *Bell System Technical Journal* **30**, July 1951, p. 588.

44. Pennoyer, D. H. "Automatic Number Identification and Its Application to No. 1 Crossbar, Panel and Step-by-Step Offices." *Bell System Technical Journal* **37**, September 1958, p. 1295.

45. Dagnall, C. H., Jr. "Automatic Number Identification: Outpulsers and Identifiers." *Bell Laboratories Record* **39**, March 1961, p. 97.

46. Miloche, H. A. "Automatic Number Identification." *Bell Laboratories Record* **38**, June 1960, p. 211.

47. Ghiloni, P. A. and Moore, H. R. "ANI For Small Step-by-Step Offices." *Bell Laboratories Record* **44**, June 1966, p. 201.

48. News Item. "Automatic Number Identification for Small Step-by-Step Offices." *Bell Laboratories Record* **51**, October 1973, p. 287.

Frames of No. 5 crossbar equipment in a commercial office, about 1950. No. 5 was a local system with great flexibility in signaling and trunking. Its many innovations included incorporation of automatic message accounting, a single set of switch frames for originating and terminating traffic, a unique multi-digit Dimond ring translator, and the ability to receive digit-identifying tones from the customer's telephone.

Chapter 7

No. 5 Crossbar

Even though the technological trend after World War II was toward crossbar switching, step-by-step remained a formidable economic competitor in suburban areas. The answer was No. 5 crossbar, for which development began in 1945 and which first saw commercial service in Media, Pennsylvania in 1948. The No. 5 system incorporated a marker containing more than 1500 relays—one of the most complex relay logic circuits ever designed. Gradually the system proved its worth because of the flexibility provided by its complexity. Since the initial No. 5 concept called for accepting additional digits dialed by customers, this system was used for the introduction of direct distance dialing in 1951.

I. THE INNOVATION

As indicated earlier, Bell Laboratories engineers for many years had been trying to find an economic application of common-control principles to smaller offices. Crossbar systems such as the No. 380 and No. 2 crossbar were designed and built, and systems like the "43" system (see Chapter 4, section 2.4) were studied intensively. As World War II drew to a close, there were even stronger motivations for developing a new crossbar system. In particular there was a need for a system with the advantages of crossbar for growth in large cities served by the step-by-step system, such as Los Angeles. Also, the suburbs of metropolitan areas served by panel, crossbar, or step-by-step systems were expected to grow, requiring a system that would provide for calling to fringe areas, including community dial offices and around the large cities, as well as into the cities. It might, like the step-by-step system, be expected to act as a local, tandem, or toll office with unique features for each.

Exploration was started for a system to meet these objectives. Such a system needed a form of charge recording to care for many short haul calls between suburbs, cities, and rural areas, and needed to operate with the many different forms of interoffice pulsing, such as dial, revertive, panel call indicator, and possibly multifrequency, that might be encountered in different applications.

One proposal on which development was started was the No. 1S crossbar system.[1] The "S" indicated interworking with step-by-step. This system had an arrangement for registering some of the dial pulse digits received in the incoming trunks and for forwarding them to a special group of terminating senders. Similarly, outgoing dial pulsing capability was to be added to the originating senders. Since automatic message accounting (AMA) was to be added to No. 1 crossbar, this would have provided the basic capability needed to meet the objective. However, the arrangement proved too costly, particularly since all originating senders had to provide for all types of pulsing, regardless of how often they were needed. For this projected office application, AMA was required for only a small portion of the calls. The No. 1 crossbar system required all district junctors to be equipped for AMA. This also proved costly.

In March 1945, vice president A. B. Clark set down objectives for new local switching systems with the expectation of a crossbar system to compete favorably with step-by-step on a first-cost basis. After re-examining the "43" plan, A. J. Busch in April 1945 proposed a new system particularly adaptable to serve calls with many possible variations, especially in signaling and trunk feature requirements. The advantages of this system were recognized quickly, and studies showed it would be economically competitive with the planned systems, such as the No. 2 crossbar and the No. 43 plan, or with modification of existing systems such as No. 1S crossbar. It was decided to proceed with its development, and the system was identified as the No. 5 crossbar system.

No. 5 crossbar,[2] besides signaling and trunking flexibility, has only a single set of switch frames, the line and trunk link frames, and, as shown in Fig. 7-1, only one group of markers to set up originating and terminating calls. A unique characteristic of this system is that the same network is used for both call completions and originating register access. This means that, on every originating call, the marker is used on two separate occasions, once to establish the connection and a second time for the "call back" when the register connection is released and a trunk connection is established. A similar proposal was made earlier by C. E. Brooks.

Because of the call-back operation, all digits must be registered from the calling line before the marker may act on the second connection. To know when sufficient digits have been received, the originating register connects to a "pretranslator" after three digits have been received. The pretranslator indicates the number of digits to be expected.[3]

The first connection is known as the "dial tone" connection since the calling line is connected through the regular switch frames to the

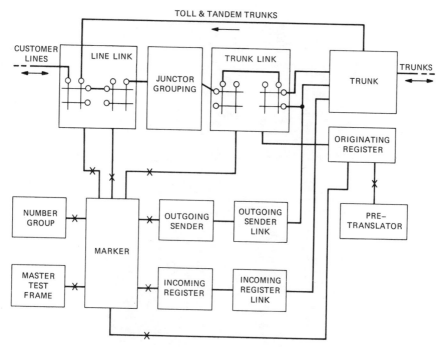

Fig. 7-1. Block diagram of the No. 5 crossbar system, showing use of single group of markers and single set of line and trunk link frames.

originating register to receive dial tone. On the basis of the results of the KRF machine throwdowns (see Chapter 5, section 3.4.2), a priority was established in cases of simultaneous requests for markers to establish dial tone or "completing" calls.

The marker for this system[4] contains more than 1500 relays and is one of the most complex relay logic circuits ever designed (see Fig. 7-2). It performs the combined functions of the line link controllers and originating and terminating markers of the No. 1 crossbar system. To aid in understanding the marker operation and in manufacturing it, it is divided into functional units,[5] an arrangement that had been previously used only for complex test frames. It makes extensive use of self-checking two-out-of-five circuits and serves as the transfer point or, in modern terminology, the "bus" for moving the called numbers from the registers to the senders and for moving the calling line equipment numbers from the registers to the transverters.[6]

It was realized early that economies could be obtained in larger offices by separating the dial tone from the completing functions of the marker. As a result, a separate dial tone marker was developed in 1950, primarily as a cost-reduction item. This circuit contained

Fig. 7-2. A No. 5 crossbar marker, containing more than 1500 relays.

fewer relays to perform the simple function of connecting lines requesting service to idle originating registers.

As in the No. 1 crossbar system, the lines could be placed on the line link frames without regard to directory number. In this way, the traffic load on the line link groups could be equalized throughout the office, thereby providing uniform and balanced service for all customers. The directory-to-equipment number translation was provided by a number group circuit, as in the No. 1 crossbar system, except that for most lines the sleeve leads need not be cabled to the number group frames, thereby simplifying the installation of the system.[7] The No. 5 crossbar number group includes two cross-connections, each of which provides two pieces of information.[8] This was made possible by a marginal circuit using new mercury contact relays developed during World War II.[9] This arrangement reduced the number of marker connector contacts.

Since the system included AMA, it required both directory-to-equipment number translation (the number group function) and equipment-to-directory number translation (the AMA translation function). New proposals for two-way translation were made, but none were successfully introduced.[10]

1.1 The Ring Translator

A new invention for the AMA translator proved to be a great
advance in memory functions, particularly considering the date
1945. The inventor was T. L. Dimond, and it used solenoid windings, called "rings," through which were threaded wires representing the translations[11] (see Fig. 7-3). It rapidly became known as the
Dimond ring translator. Pulses were sent through the wires
selected by a relay tree. The pulses were induced into the threaded
rings and detected by gas tubes. The initial translator accommodated only 1000 translations. Later (1958) a more compact version
for 2000 translations was developed.[12] The Dimond ring translator
was also used later in the crossbar tandem system. This basic translator principle has been used by many others, not only in crossbar
systems but also in adapted form as the translation and program

Fig. 7-3. A Dimond ring translator: gas tubes at left, "rings" at right.

memories in some electronic switching systems.[13] The separation of the register and sender functions and the development of No. 5 crossbar stimulated many to estimate total memory requirements for switching, among them C. E. Shannon.[14]

1.2 Other Inventions

Other new apparatus developed for the No. 5 crossbar system included a punched card trouble recorder in place of a trouble indicator[15] (see Figs. 7-4a and 7-4b). A recorder was considered necessary since it was planned that the system would provide service in smaller offices and would be unattended at nights and on weekends. This necessitated the automatic recording of successive trouble indications.

Another unique feature was a simple one-stage crossbar link to connect trunks to the required type of ringing supply for the called telephone and/or tone for the calling line or trunk.[16]

Fig. 7-4a. No. 5 crossbar trouble recorder in the left-hand bay of the maintenance center, Media, Pennsylvania.

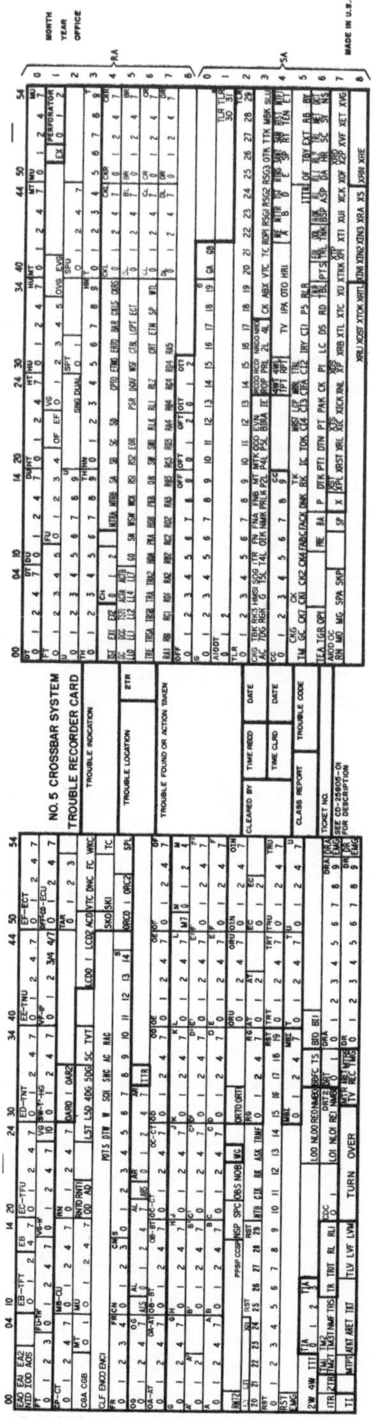

Fig. 7-4b. Trouble Record Card.

In the panel and crossbar dial systems, many timed periods are required to permit certain circuit operations to be carried out, and to give an alarm if these operations are not completed by the end of the period. In the past, these time intervals were provided by power-driven, cam-actuated interrupters. With the introduction of the No. 5 crossbar system, however, the power-driven interrupters were replaced by circuits employing cold-cathode tubes. Time delays are obtained by using the time required to charge a capacitor in series with a high resistance. The potential on the capacitor is applied to the control anode of the tube, and when this potential builds up to a value sufficient to cause the tube to ionize, the relay in the tube circuit operates.

Many other maintenance features were provided and concentrated at a central location in the central office. This location included the "master test frame" and test circuits for the marker, registers, lines, and trunks. Several unique test circuits were introduced for the first time. One was the line insulation test frame that, in the early morning hours when the maximum dew was on the outside distribution plant, tested the insulation of each line for leakage.[17] Another circuit connected in parallel with the originating registers one at a time while they served regular calls and checked that the registration agreed with that reported to the marker. This was known as an "Automatic Monitor."[18] Since it only sampled calls, it was later dropped from the office requirements.

The No. 5 crossbar system also included many innovative developments in equipment practices.[19] In particular, for the first time the frames were formed from sheet metal (see Fig. 7-5) and established the pattern for all future central office equipment.[20] Hinged plexiglass covers were also used.

II. MEDIA, PA. – THE FIRST NO. 5 CROSSBAR

Development of the No. 5 crossbar system began in October 1945. The initial installation was in Media, Pennsylvania. It was cut over on July 11, 1948, only three years after development was started and at a cost of about $7 million ($5 million systems development). The Media installation was not only the first No. 5 crossbar system, it was the first commercial system to include the AMA feature. To process the AMA tapes, the first AMA center was established by the Bell Telephone Company of Pennsylvania in their downtown Philadelphia headquarters on Arch Street. This installation was tested and placed in regular service coincident with the Media cutover (see Frontispiece to Chapter 6).

Another feature made economically feasible by separating the originating registers from the senders in the No. 5 crossbar system was the ability to receive other than dial pulse signals from the calling lines. A trial was held in this first office using early models of

Fig. 7-5. Typical No. 5 equipment arrangements with frames formed from sheet metal.

pushbutton telephones (see Fig. 7-6). A separate set of originating registers was designed to receive multifrequency signals from these sets, which generated the tones from vibrating reeds that were plucked when the buttons were depressed.[21] The frequencies, used two-at-a-time, were the same as those used between offices (see Chapter 6, section IV). As compared with the use of this form of signaling by operators, the receivers here were connected to lines and hence were exposed to spurious speech or background transmissions from the customer while he or she used the pushbuttons. Also, the plucked reeds were found not to be stable and rugged enough to maintain adjustment with constant usage in a station environment.

III. ENGLEWOOD—THE FIRST DDD EQUIPPED LOCAL OFFICE

Included as an option in the initial capability of the originating registers and senders of the No. 5 system was the ability to accept and store additional digits in preparation for nationwide customer

Fig. 7-6. Early (1948) pushbutton telephones used with No. 5 crossbar. Two frequencies from plucked reeds identified each digit.

dialing (see Chapter 6, section 3.2). The system included provision for operator distance dialing so that the key pulsing or dialing from operator "A" (assistance) switchboard positions associated with a collocated No. 5 office could, on operator calls, be "pulse converted" to whatever type of pulsing was required by the distant office.[22]

It was quite natural that a No. 5 crossbar office should be chosen for the trial of customer nationwide dialing or "direct distance dialing" (DDD), as it later was named. (The initial name for the service was "foreign area customer dialing" or FACD to distinguish it from the short distance intrastate "home area customer dialing" or HACD.) The Englewood, New Jersey office was equipped with 10-digit originating registers and in November 1951, DDD service was tested for the first time.[23] This service during the next twenty years was to become the accepted toll service of the Bell System network. Three-digit prefix codes identified the distant cities. Some codes were identical with those that eventually became "area codes" in the nationwide numbering plan.

The multifrequency senders in this No. 5 crossbar were modified to include individual transistorized multifrequency generators. The transistors used in these generators were experimental and were the first to be employed in any commercial operation in the Bell System.[24]

IV. THE MATURING OF NO. 5 CROSSBAR

From a service standpoint the No. 5 crossbar system was a success from the moment of its introduction. Like most new switching systems the initial installed price was higher than expected. Within the first four years a considerable joint effort of Western Electric and Bell

Laboratories greatly reduced the price difference between No. 5 crossbar and the step-by-step system. More importantly, the advantages of the basic system architecture were gradually accepted by the operating telephone companies as a result of the addition of numerous features (see Chapter 11). These features demonstrated that the system architecture was flexible enough to be adapted for operation with a large variety of engineering and field environments.

Training proved somewhat of a stumbling block, since a more complex system was being introduced into areas that to that time had been exposed only to the simplicity of the step-by-step system. As a result, Bell Laboratories, for the first time, organized and provided instructors for a school for telephone company instructors. New documentation was devised to simplify the understanding of the complex circuits. Detached-contact schematics (see Chapter 5, section VII), were adopted for the first time for this system. While they were an improvement over the attached-contact schematics, they did not go far enough. In particular, the circuit paths were not shown adequately across functional circuit boundaries. This deficiency was corrected by the introduction of detached schematics (functional schematics) that crossed the boundaries. A complete and standard set of flow charts and diagrams was produced,[25] a function previously carried out by each individual telephone company school. The success of this school was a precursor to other joint Bell Labs-operating telephone company educational ventures, including the Operating Engineers Training Program (OETP), the No. 1 ESS training school, and more recently the Operating Company Associate Program (OCAP).

Beside the specific efforts to reduce the cost of the No. 5 crossbar system as it was designed initially, the program to design an improved general-purpose relay was moving from exploratory to the final development stage. Several versions of this generation of so-called "wire spring" relays competed for eventual commitment to production.[26] These relays offered many advantages. Principal among them were semiautomated production, ease of obtaining various spring combinations with card actuation of the springs, and pretensioned springs to eliminate manual adjustment of assembled relays in the factory and in the field.

The adoption of the wire spring relay required new equipment designs since the mounting centers were generally different. Also the greater capacity of the relays meant that fewer were required. Wire spring multicontact relays were also designed.[27] New equipment arrangements, more efficient in the use of space, were designed. Moreover, this redesign gave the circuit designers an opportunity to introduce improvements that could not otherwise be justified on their own merits. The result was that, gradually, a new version of the No. 5 crossbar system, the wire spring version, replaced the "flat spring" (U and Y type) relay original version, starting with the trunk circuits in 1953 and the marker and other control circuits in 1954.

To save space in No. 5 crossbar offices and to increase trunk capacity, system development based on a smaller crossbar switch was started in 1966. An initial installation of sample switches in 1968 in the Blue Island, Illinois office started the modification of the No. 5 crossbar system to take advantage of this development. In particular, the new switch increased the maximum number of trunk terminations per frame from 160 to 200 since the switches had 12 instead of 10 levels.[28] The first complete trunk link frame was installed in Port Huron, Michigan in 1970. Other switching system developments to use this switch followed rapidly: No. 5 crossbar call waiting (1971) (not standardized), 5A crossbar (1972), No. 4A crossbar frames (1973), 2B automatic call distributor (1972), subscriber loop multiplexer (1972), 812A PBX (1972) (see Chapter 13, section 2.5), switched maintenance access system No. 3 (1973), the 300 special switching system (1973), and the Traffic Service Position System-Remote Trunk Arrangement (1976) (see Chapter 10, section 1.8).[29]

As indicated earlier, the architecture of No. 5 crossbar was flexible in providing trunking and pulsing features, and also provided AMA charging flexibility. It therefore is understandable that the No. 5 crossbar system was modified for a variety of applications including the addition of a large number of features and more new services than any previous system. Many of the added features and services are described in Chapter 11. The No. 5 crossbar system was in the vanguard of economically providing many of these services and features.

V. PACKAGES AND SMALLER VERSIONS

The increasing number of features gave telephone company engineers many choices in deciding how to provide automatic switching when replacing manual offices and for growth. While No. 5 was most popular for these applications, it could not compete in price with step-by-step for the very simple, small offices.

In 1961, after being recommended by a joint Bell Labs-Western Electric Committee, a limited set of features and a fixed number of traffic-engineered circuits were incorporated into packages of 990, 1690, and 2190 lines with fixed prices.[30] Since the offices were generally unattended, maintenance facilities were modified and minimized by replacing the master test frame with an office test frame. The price was also attractive since it eliminated complex and costly engineering and installation variables. To gain experience with the "packaged" installation, the first office was placed in service in

Portland, Connecticut in the later part of 1960. Subsequently, the committee developed standard package features. While more than 400 of these offices were manufactured and installed by Western Electric, they did not satisfy their objectives since most orders were supplemented with changes and additions, thereby practically defeating the original intentions.

The demand for these systems was gradually reduced. Later systems developed in Canada and Japan and attractively priced were purchased by some companies. About 80 foreign systems were purchased after Bell Labs made technical evaluation of the systems for AT&T on behalf of the operating companies.

In 1971 a joint development project with Western Electric was started on a reduced-cost version of the system, to be known as the No. 5A crossbar system.[31] This system was mounted in precabled and shop-tested modules.[32] The system could be assembled and tested in the factory and transported to the central office site ready for service. One module served 980 lines; an additional module could be ordered to serve 1960 lines, all with a traffic capacity of over 300 call-seconds per line. The equipment was redesigned for 7-foot frames while trunks, registers, and senders were plug-ended to facilitate the making of additions. The new, smaller-size crossbar switch helped make possible this size reduction. The first of a total of about 25 installations was cut over in Portville, New York on August 20, 1972—67 days after a flood destroyed the step-by-step office there.

Later in 1973, a version of the No. 5A crossbar system was developed by reducing the size of the network to three stages so that it could be ordered in sizes of 300 to 600 lines. (Later in 1975 this capability was extended to 1200 lines.) This system was known as the "No. 3 crossbar system."[33] The first installation was placed in service in Howells, Nebraska in June 1974, and 23 were eventually placed in service.

While the No. 1 crossbar system with its new switching principles attracted worldwide attention, it was not until the successful introduction of the No. 5 system that other manufacturers in the United States, Canada, Japan, Great Britain, Belgium, France, and elsewhere started to develop comparable systems. This was quite natural since the No. 5 system was intended for smaller offices than No. 1, the kind that at that time were more prevalent in world markets. Even years later, while electronic switching systems are being introduced around the world, new crossbar systems patterned after No. 5 crossbar are still being sold in significant numbers. The last Western Electric manufactured No. 5 crossbar system was for Birmingham, Alabama in early 1976. More than 2700 entities were provided by Western Electric (688 of the flat spring variety). By the end of 1976 close to 27 million lines in the Bell System were served by No. 5 crossbar. Extensions to existing systems were still being installed, and a peak of 28.5 million customer lines was reached in October 1978.

VI. NON-NEW JERSEY LOCATIONS FOR SWITCHING DEVELOPMENT

In the late 1940s Bell Laboratories established branch laboratories for the purpose of facilitating the transfer of technology from developer to manufacturer. The Allentown, Pennsylvania laboratory was established for device development in 1947. In June 1959, the first switching system branch laboratory was established at Columbus, Ohio. Here all local crossbar development and later (1964) all crossbar systems development were collocated with those responsible for Western Electric standards engineering.

The success of the crossbar branch laboratories led in 1966 to the establishment of a new laboratory in Naperville, Illinois. It is known as the Indian Hill laboratory. It was established there, as a center for electronic switching developments, to be close to the Hawthorne Works of Western Electric, which at that time was the product engineering control center (PECC) headquarters for electronic switching. Since then the PECC for electronic switching has been moved to Lisle, Illinois, and it is known as the "Northern Illinois Works."

The branch laboratory concept is also used for customer switching equipment at a laboratory collocated with the Western Electric Company in Denver, Colorado. This laboratory location, established in 1971, also includes AT&T groups responsible for these products.

REFERENCES, CHAPTER 7

1. Joel, A. E., Jr.; U.S. Patent 2,491,377; filed December 31, 1946; issued December 13, 1949.
2. Korn, F. A. and Ferguson, J. G. "The No. 5 Crossbar Dial Telephone Switching System." *Transactions of the American Institute of Electrical Engineers* **69**, Pt. 1, 1950, p. 244.
3. Avery, R. C. "Pretranslation in No. 5 Crossbar." *Bell Laboratories Record* **28**, April 1950, p. 156.
4. Adam, A. O. "No. 5 Crossbar Marker." *Bell Laboratories Record* **28**, November 1950, p. 502.
5. Graupner, W. B. "Equipment Arrangements for No. 5 Crossbar Markers." *Bell Laboratories Record* **28**, September 1950, p. 396.
6. Dehn, J. W. "Code Patterns in Telephone Switching and Accounting Systems." *Bell Laboratories Record* **30**, January 1952, p. 9.
7. Morzenti, O. J. "Number Group Frame for No. 5 Crossbar." *Bell Laboratories Record* **28**, July 1950, p. 298.
8. Schneckloth, H. H. "Some Basic Concepts of Translators and Identifiers Used in Telephone Switching Systems." *Bell System Technical Journal* **30**, July 1951, p. 588.

9. McCormick, C. G. "Glass-Sealed Switches and Relays." *Bell Laboratories Record* **25**, September 1947, p. 342.
10. See ref. 8 above.
11. Dimond, T. L. "No. 5 Crossbar AMA Translator." *Bell Laboratories Record* **29**, February 1951, p. 62.
12. Bishop, G. S. "A New AMA Translator for No. 5 Crossbar." *Bell Laboratories Record* **36**, November 1958, p. 415.
13. Duttie, R. W. "Electronic Automatic Exchange for the Small Central Office (C1-EAX)." *Auto. Elec. Tech. Journal* July 1967, p. 276.
14. Shannon, C. E. "Memory Requirements in a Telephone Exchange." *Bell System Technical Journal* **29**, July 1950, p. 343.
15. Mehring, A. C. "Trouble Recording for the No. 5 Crossbar System." *Bell Laboratories Record* **28**, May 1950, p. 214.
16. Goddard, M. C. "Ringing Selection in No. 5 Crossbar." *Bell Laboratories Record* **28**, April 1950, p. 168.
17. Burns, R. W. and Dehn, J. W. "Automatic Line Insulation Test Equipment for Local Crossbar Systems." *Bell System Technical Journal* **32**, May 1953, p. 627.
18. Brubaker, J. W. "The Automatic Monitor." *Bell Laboratories Record* **28**, August 1950, p. 343.
19. Ferguson, J. G. "Design Patterns for No. 5 Crossbar." *Bell Laboratories Record* **28**, June 1950, p. 245.
20. Ball, E. T. "No. 5 Crossbar Frames." *Bell Laboratories Record* **29**, September 1951, p. 422.
21. Depp, W. A. and Meacham, L. A. "Station Apparatus, Power and Special Systems." *Bell Laboratories Record* **36**, June 1958, p. 216.
22. Michael, H. J. "Pulse Conversion in No. 5 Crossbar." *Bell Laboratories Record* **28**, December 1950, p. 533.
23. Getz, E. L. "The Englewood Story." *Bell Laboratories Record* **32**, January 1954, p. 11.
24. Ritchie, A. E. "The Transistor: Applications in Telephone Switching." *Bell Laboratories Record* **36**, June 1958, p. 212.
25. Meyer, F. T. "Improved Detached-Contact-Type Schematic Drawing." *Trans. of AIEE* **74**, September 1955, p. 505.
26. Keller, A. C. "New General Purpose Relay for Telephone Switching Systems." *Electrical Engineer* **71**, November 1952, p. 1007.
27. Stearns, R. "A Wire-Spring Multicontact Relay." *Bell Laboratories Record* **35**, April 1957, p. 131.
28. Holtfreter, R. P. "A Switch to Smaller Switches." *Bell Laboratories Record* **48**, February 1970, p. 47.
29. Smith, F. H. and Catterall, J. M. "Uses for the New Small Crossbar Switch." *Bell Laboratories Record* **49**, August 1971, p. 217.
30. Greene, J. E. "For No. 5 Crossbar—A Packaged Central Office." *Bell Laboratories Record* **40**, October 1962, p. 337.
31. Heckendorn, H. R. "No. 5A Crossbar Telephone Switching System." *National Telecommunications Conference Record* 1972, p. 37B-1.
32. Nicholl, W. J. "Structural Design for a Transportable Central Office." *Western Electric Engineer* **18**, January 1974, p. 2.
33. Heckendorn, H. R. and Johnston, J. J. "The No. 3 Crossbar Telephone Switching System." *National Telecommunications Conference Record* 1974, p. 330.

Laboratory installation of card translators, about 1952. A key system element in the growth of nationwide dialing by customers, the card translator interpreted the six digits of the area code and office code of a called telephone number. These digits caused one metal card to drop down from a stack of about 1000 cards. According to which holes in the cards were or were not enlarged, light passed through to photo-detectors to specify the information needed to select a route for a long distance call.

Chapter 8

Direct Distance Dialing

Direct distance dialing of calls nationwide by customers required a major investment in development by the Bell System. Automatic alternate routing was incorporated into a multilevel hierarchy of switching centers, and a routing plan was developed to allow efficient choice of routes to a toll office in the region of the called telephone. No. 4 crossbar was adapted in several versions to take on the added functions of accepting more dialed digits from customers and of performing more code conversions or translations. The card translator solved the problem of handling the large amounts of information required to service calls nationwide, and the crossbar tandem system, despite its 2-wire design, was modified extensively for toll service and gave a good account of itself, with 213 toll systems in place by 1968. Crossbar tandem was, in addition, the first host system for centralized automatic message accounting, another important ingredient in making DDD available to all customers, regardless of the type of local office serving them. Selected No. 5 crossbar systems were modified, beginning in 1967, to inaugurate customer-dialing of calls overseas.

I. NATIONWIDE PLANNING

Initially, much of the equipment used by operators to complete toll calls was of the step-by-step variety, since this system was most suitable for the smaller-size trunk groups and was available, having been developed before World War II (see Chapter 3, section VI). Later, when there was a greater concentration of toll facilities, the No. 4 crossbar was available and was indeed adapted for the larger cities with five post-war installations in New York, Chicago, Boston, Cleveland, and Oakland (see Chapter 4, section III and Chapter 6, section 3.1).

For shorter distance dialing, the crossbar tandem system rapidly became a most useful member of the toll switching family, although it required rather costly transmission balancing requirements, since it switched on a 2-wire basis. In short distance service crossbar tandem, like the No. 5 crossbar system, encountered a wide variety of pulsing needs, and perhaps no other system was provided with such a large array of sender capabilities.[1] While it had these capabilities, at that time it lacked a number of other features considered essential for the routing of nationwide customer-dialed calls. (Later many of those toll features were added.[2])

As indicated in Chapter 6, the dialing of long distance calls directly by customers was part of a plan that formed the basis for most post-World War II switching developments. Recording of charge information details—including calling and called numbers, answer and disconnect time, and the type of call—was made possible by the development of AMA for crossbar systems and the accounting centers that processed the perforated paper tape records. Signaling over long distances was made possible by the introduction of multifrequency signaling of address information between most crossbar systems and by single-frequency signaling of supervisory information as well as dial pulsing. A transmission plan had evolved for manually switched long distance service but needed revision for operator distance dialing.[3]

There remained two basic planning steps before nationwide dialing directly by the customer could be introduced. One was the development of the numbering plan (see Chapter 6, section 3.2) and the second was a network and routing plan.

A general toll switching plan of the Bell System was devised in the late 1920s.[4] It incorporated three levels called regional centers, primary outlets, and toll centers. Eight regional centers (San Francisco, Los Angeles, Dallas, Denver, Chicago, St. Louis, Atlanta, and New York) were completely interconnected by direct trunks. Primary outlets generally served states and provided access to the network for toll centers that served communities and had direct trunks to one or more regional centers. (The term "supplementary offices" was also used to denote secondary outlets to provide alternate routes to regional centers and secondary switching points for intra-area toll switching. Also, the term "tributary" was used to denote cities or towns where little or no toll switching was performed.)

When customer dialing of toll calls was studied, the same network configuration was assumed, although at one point more regions were considered. Bell System engineers proposed the disciplined use of multiple automatic alternate routing to maximize the chance of completing calls in a network where toll facilities, at least initially, might be sparse. Alternate routing is a concept that began in the Bell System with manual toll operation as early as 1926. Automatic alternate routing was proposed about the same time by W. W. Carpenter of Bell Laboratories. Later another Bell pioneer, C. E. Brooks, proposed multiple automatic alternate routing.

Early planning included "crank back" so that calls might be alternately routed in earlier offices if all desired paths at a distant office were found busy. The routing plan as it evolved made extensive use of alternate routing (but without crank back) and provided for more intermediate switching centers. This increased the number of possible intertoll links from five to eight. The switching centers with the alternate routing and other capabilities that were later defined (see below) were to be known as "control switching points."

For nationwide toll dialing, complete connectivity is required for universal service. The switching plan for nationwide dialing had to restrict the maximum number of links to a specific number for transmission stability, uniformity, and efficiency. With manual toll switching, the maximum was four toll switching centers in series,[5] but the loss could be as high as 20 decibels. With dial switching a plan, now known as the "hierarchical" plan, was devised that permitted as many as nine toll switching centers in tandem. To make this type of service viable, the demand basis for engineering trunks (no delay) was used. The higher number of possible switching centers in a connection resulted from the desire to make maximum use of every available trunk to reduce the possibility of giving the customer reorder. As shown in Fig. 8-1, two ranks of offices were added: one, the sectional centers between the primary and regional centers, and the other, a national center connecting to all regions.[6] Within a region, calls may progress up a "ladder" from toll, to primary, to sectional, and then to the regional center. They are interconnected by trunk groups engineered for low probability of lost calls and are known as "final trunk groups." Other groups, known as "high-usage," are engineered on the basis of traffic volume and economics and interconnect centers out of the strict hierarchical order. Most intertoll trunks have been and continue to be two-way while those that connect with local (or end) offices are one-way. (This was due originally to the scarcity of facilities, but later efficiencies continue to make them favorable, due in part to the differing traffic peaks in the different time zones in the United States.) The transmission plan that accompanied the switching plan called for adding essentially no loss if both ends of a connection were intertoll (known as "via net loss"), 2-decibels if only one end was intertoll, and 4 decibels if both ends terminated in toll connecting trunks (known as "terminal net loss"). The maximum loss has been held to 13 decibels. The loss plan was implemented by the No. 4A crossbar switching system, which can add 2-decibel pads in the incoming and outgoing trunks and can also select trunks with the correct transmission characteristics, depending on the call being switched.

A national center was originally assumed at St. Louis, Missouri for connecting to all regions, but this was never implemented since adequate trunk facilities at lower levels kept pace with traffic demands. In the plan, all regions are fully interconnected, and final groups between them are provided if no facilities are available at lower orders. As the network and service have grown, the tendency has been for increasing numbers of high-usage groups to be formed between major cities, thereby reducing the amount of traffic flowing at the higher levels of the hierarchy.

The routing plan for use of the network was even more critical. It was based on the ability of the marker to select among multiple alternate routes. With the technology then available, it would have been difficult to indicate the route by which a call reached a given toll switching office. Therefore, to avoid the routing of calls back and forth or "ring around the rosey" (until all trunks are used), the routing plan specified a given order of alternate routes or routing sequence (see Fig. 8-1). First, all high-usage groups to the region of

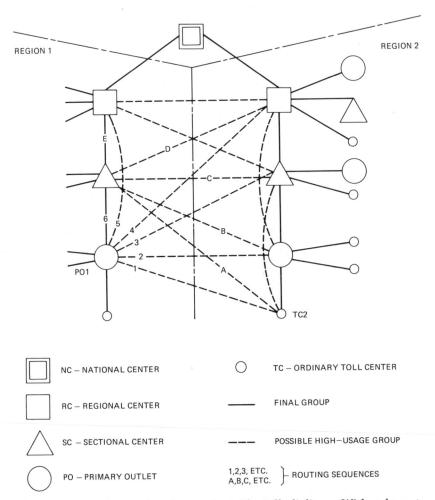

Fig. 8-1. Switching plan for nationwide toll dialing. With adequate numbers of trunks in the lower levels of this hierarchy, the national center did not have to be implemented.

the called office were tried in ascending order and then from the highest order down in the hierarchy (ladder) of the calling office. In this way, the higher-order trunks are used only as the lower-order ones are exhausted. The offices are given class numbers in descending order to represent their function in the hierarchy, with class 5 denoting an end office and class 1 a regional center. Also, in recent years there has developed a "principal city" toll center in each numbering plan area to which calls to that area may be directed as a last resort and for special services such as operator access and INWATS.

These features defined what was known in the routing plan as control switching points (CSPs) and included (1) three- or six-digit translation, (2) variable-digit sending—such as deletion if registered digits are not required for outpulsing (such as the deletion of the area code), (3) digit prefixing (the addition of new digits, particularly for completing calls through step-by-step intertoll offices), (4) code conversion (the combination of digit prefixing and deletion) (see Fig. 8-2), and (5) multialternate routing (most necessary to implement the hierarchical routing plan).[7] Six-digit translation can be provided in local offices. As shown in Fig. 8-3, it is used primarily to reach local offices in adjacent numbering plan areas to avoid the long distances, known as back haul, that might be involved in routing calls via a toll center. This feature is known as foreign area translation and is implemented by providing additional three-digit office code translators for a particular limited number of areas other than the home area at local offices.[8]

The numbering plan evolved as part of the nationwide operator dialing in the mid-1940s (see Chapter 6, section III). It was a simple plan, since the second digit, unlike office codes in the "2–5" plan, is a "0" or "1." The dialing procedure was a little different and is still not universal.

Routing calls from step-by-step offices into the toll network on the basis of the area codes would have required very expensive modifications, either in the form of the addition of register-senders (common control) or the building out of switch trains to detect the dialing of area codes. Furthermore, in the latter situation, some means of identification would have been required to recover the digits dialed to reach a toll connecting trunk. For most step-by-step offices, therefore, major equipment changes were avoided by the simple expedient of dialing an initial "1" on toll calls (see Fig. 8-4). An exception was the elimination of preliminary pulse detection (see Chapter 3, section II), a feature that was abandoned with the obsolescence of the desk stand telephone.

The "1" is known as a toll barrier prefix and is also used in some states to distinguish between extended area and toll calling within a

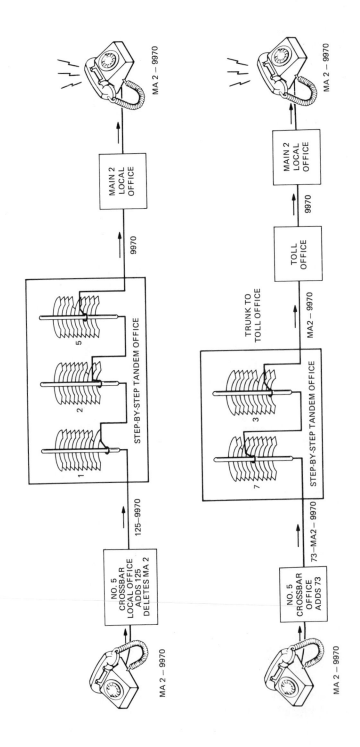

Fig. 8-2. Two examples of code conversion. Top: from a No. 5 office through a step-by-step tandem. Bottom: from a No. 5 office through a step-by-step tandem and a toll office (assumes no direct trunks).

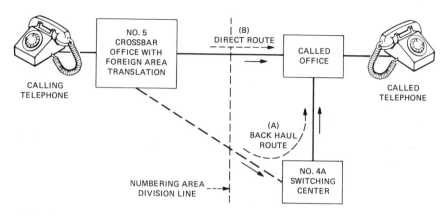

Fig. 8-3. Foreign area translator uses code conversion to pick route B over longer route A.

numbering plan area. Also, with the introduction of DDD it was necessary to provide codes in the numbering plan for operators, but not customers, to reach other operators in distant centers for assistance in reaching points not yet accessible by DDD, or for other forms of routing or special call-handling procedures. These codes, known as "TX," are of a form "0XX" and are blocked by the local switching equipment to which the calling customer had access.

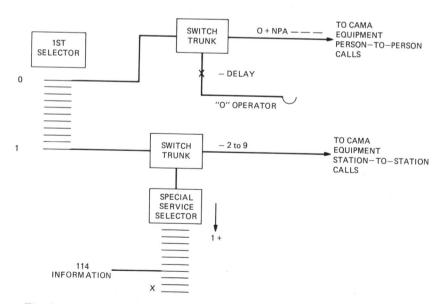

Fig. 8-4. Diagram indicating the adding of a digit "1" (lower path) for step-by-step toll calls.

The interpretation of the dialed digits was the most important element in the design of switching systems for DDD. The changes in the step-by-step offices, just described, were relatively simple. For common-control local offices, register-sender capacity for the additional three area code digits was needed. As mentioned earlier, this was relatively easy in No. 5 crossbar offices since No. 5 was designed initially with this new service in mind. But for panel and No. 1 crossbar offices, the task was more difficult and called for the design of an "auxiliary sender" (see this chapter, section IV).

The crossbar toll offices were to become the backbone of the DDD network. Features for the implementation of DDD service were assigned to these offices.

Since nationwide planning involved the other partners in the message network, the independent telephone companies, an elaborate set of "Notes on Distance Dialing" was first issued in 1955. The notes served as a foundation for educating design, engineering, and administrative personnel in the broad method of operation and interface requirements for nationwide customer-dialing. These notes were periodically revised in 1956, 1961, 1968, and 1975.[9]

II. NO. 4A CROSSBAR

2.1 No. A4A and 4M Crossbar

The process for accepting DDD calls directly from customers and for switching them automatically involved additional toll offices with new features. These were first applied to the 4-wire No. 4 crossbar system. In particular, new senders were required to accept dialing from local offices and directly from local step-by-step office customers as well as operators. Provision was made for changing the digits outpulsed from those dialed (code conversion). More important and complex were modifications of the markers to meet the new translation and routing requirements.[10] Continued deployment of the original No. 4 crossbar system was dictated by the need for operator nationwide dialing. The new version of the system for customer-dialing was coded 4A. While some of the new features could be designed in a short time, the translator developments in particular required more time. Therefore, new systems installed in the interim were partially modified, anticipating the new translators, and were designated as "A4A crossbar"[11] (see Fig. 8-5). The first A4A system was installed in Albany, New York in 1950. Later these systems were raised to full 4A status. The six original No. 4 crossbar systems were also modified to contain 4A features and became known as "4M crossbar." The last 4A system was cut over in Madison, Wisconsin in April 1976. It was the 182nd in the Bell System. In addition, there are 10 in Canada, 2 in Alaska, and 8 provided to independent companies.

2.2 Card Translator

The nationwide numbering, transmission, and routing plans not only required the ability of local and toll offices to receive 10 digits, but also required the common control to interpret the six area and office code digits.[12] In general, this interpretation requires the simultaneous "translation" of these six digits. Needed were ways

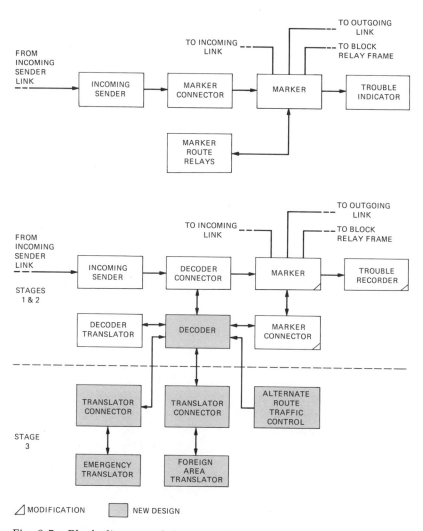

△ MODIFICATION   ▢ NEW DESIGN

Fig. 8-5. Block diagram of the control portion of the 4 or A4A crossbar system (top), introduced to permit customer dialing nationwide. When an office is converted to a 4A system (bottom), the marker connector becomes a decoder connector, the trouble indicator becomes a trouble recorder, and the marker route relays are replaced by a decoder, a decoder translator, and foreign area translators with associated equipment.

not only to select one out of more than 1,000,000 possibilities but also to provide more output information per translation than was economical when employing "route" relays as used in the existing translators. In all previous indirect control systems, translation was performed by combinations of relays and wired cross-connections.[13] This technique, to encompass the entire North American numbering plan, would have required the equivalent of many local office translators in each toll office.

A new invention in the art of translation was required, and Bell Laboratories engineers came through with a most ingenious electromechanical device, the card translator[14] (see Fig. 8-6). Principal contributors were J. W. Gooderham, E. W. Gent, O. Myers, E. D. Kingsbury, C. B. Brown, and F. A. Thiel. Before describing this device, however, we should note that a number of other technologies were considered for solving the problem. In particular, mention should be made of the use of magnetic drums, a technique that

Fig. 8-6. A card translator, a development that filled the need to receive 10 digits and translate 6. The card translator speeded nationwide direct distance dialing.

was then being researched for a number of applications (see Chapter 9, section 4.3.3).

The card translator consisted of at least one perforated metal card per translation (see Fig. 8-7). The digits representing the area and, in many cases, a particular office code were placed into the lower edge of the card by the omission of tangs representing the values of the digits on a two-out-of-five basis. As a minimum, one card was needed to represent an area, but usually cards representing combinations of area and office codes were required. A "box" of cards contained a maximum of about 1,000 cards.

As shown in Fig. 8-8, the cards are punched by enlarging holes to represent coded routing information. A card is selected by notched bars that run under the cards in a box. The bars are moved vertically by electromagnets. A magnetic field is applied to press the metallic cards against the bars. When a card drops, the light passes through only the enlarged holes, thus providing the desired output translation. When the moved bars correspond to the missing tangs on the edge of a card, the card "drops" due to the magnetic pull. Light beams normally pass through all 118 holes in each card (see Fig. 8-9).

To detect the light, a phototransistor was used. The phototransistor outputs passed through transistor amplifiers and triggered gas tubes to operate output relays. This was the first commercial application of transistors in the Bell System.[15] The output information represents all that is needed for one route selection. Additional cards may be selected or "dropped" if all trunks on the preferred route are busy, as indicated by the alternate route pattern of the initially selected card.

The No. 4 crossbar system control was modified to include access to at least one box of translator cards. This box, known as the "home" box, was part of the decoder portion of each marker. In addition, a number of other "foreign area" boxes of cards and a spare "home" box were usually provided to include the remainder of the translations and were accessible by all markers (see Fig. 8-10).

The first card translator was placed in service in Pittsburgh on March 29, 1953. Before they were replaced by stored program electronic translators in 1969, some 1700 card translators were built and used as the basis for routing all calls through the 4A crossbar control switching points (CSPs). The electronic translator was one of the latest in a long list of features developed for 4A crossbar (see Chapter 10, section II).

From the beginning, the No. 4 crossbar included two separate switching networks. Originally, these were for inward and outward traffic. With the 4A development, they were given the names "intertoll' and "toll connecting." The office size capability was increased from 20 to 40 sets of frames for each train.[16]

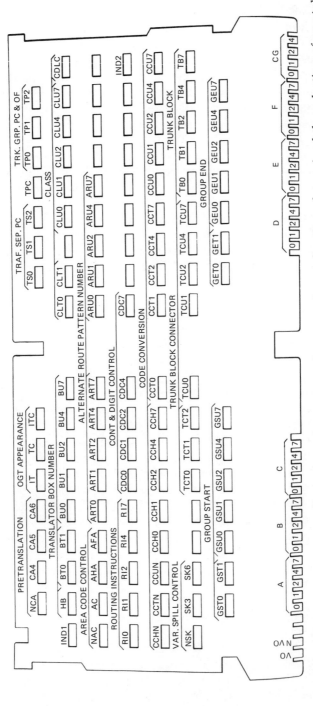

Fig. 8-7.　Outline of a metal card. Light shining through rectangular perforations determined the selection of one toll route out of more than a million possibilities.

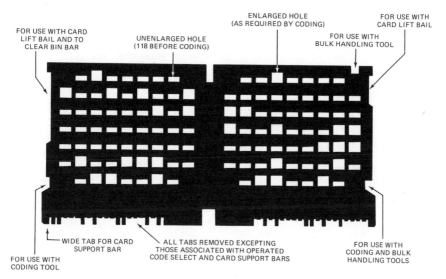

Fig. 8-8. Coded card. When a card drops, light is blocked except where holes are enlarged.

2.3 Cost Reduction and Capacity Improvements

The frames of 4A crossbar were also extended in capacity to provide more terminations.[17] This was needed as the offices served larger areas as the entry points to the toll network. The trunks had lower occupancy since they were in smaller groups and since the traffic from a more dispersed area was less coincidental.

As DDD and intertoll facilities grew, and new technology such as the wire spring relay and electronic components became available, the No. 4A system was modified to take advantage of them. A major cost reduction development effort was started in the 1960s.[18] New features were developed, and call-carrying capacity was increased well into the 1970s. As mentioned above, stored-program control was added (see Chapter 10, section II). As described for the CAMA feature (see Chapter 6, section V), dial pulse reception from customer-dialed traffic is slow, and for the 4A system expensive senders had long holding times. To improve this situation, separate dial pulse registers were developed that retransmitted the called number in multifrequency form after all digits were received. Access to these senders was through a link that provided rapid "bylink" access so that a second dial tone was not required on calls from step-by-step offices. Improved automatic trunk test circuits were introduced. Furthermore, the system has been kept up to date by the use of plug-in trunk circuits,[19] unified facilities terminals and cross-connect bays,[20] the addition of common channel interoffice

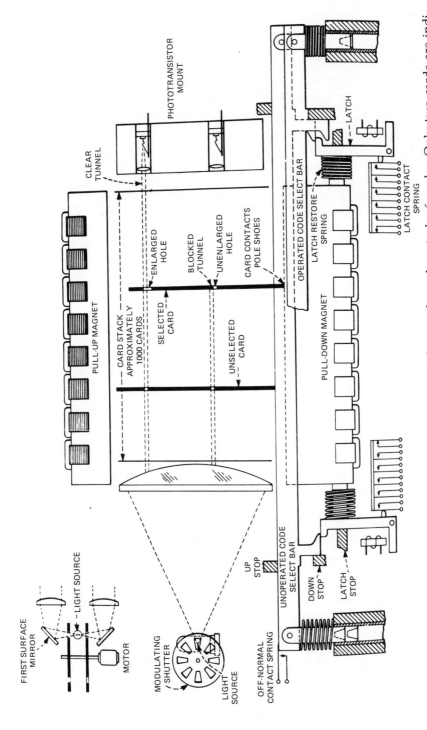

Fig. 8-9. Mechanism of the card translator. Light from left goes through a stack of cards. Only two cards are indicated: first one (on left) is in normal position; light passes through all holes. Second card has dropped, blocking light except where holes are enlarged. Light is detected by phototransistors at right.

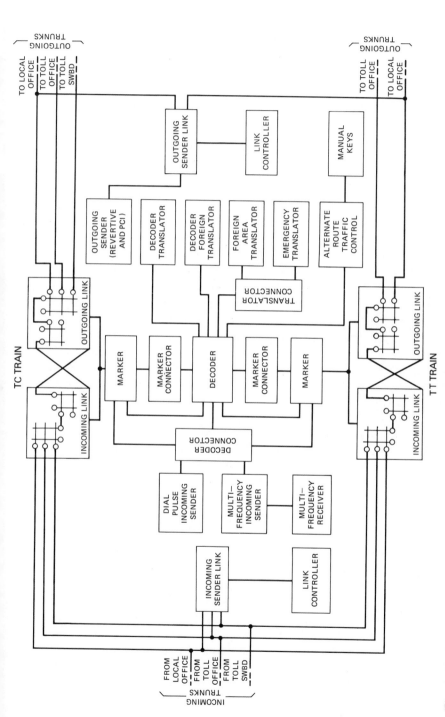

Fig. 8-10. Diagram of the 4A crossbar system. 4A had at least one box of card translator cards, a "home" box as part of the decoder (center of diagram).

signaling (see Chapter 12, section III), and the provision of features for operation as a gateway for international traffic. In particular, for operator-originated traffic to overseas points, a reentrant plan using a regular and a newly developed "overseas" sender was devised and used, starting in 1964.[21]

III. THE FULL STATURE OF CROSSBAR TANDEM

While the 4A crossbar system was designed specifically to implement the control switching point function needed for nationwide toll dialing (see this chapter, section I), the crossbar tandem system was developed initially as a local tandem. However, like the panel sender tandem system (see Chapter 3, section I), it was used to extend calls within a metropolitan area and short haul toll calls to contiguous areas. The quality of service offered by the crossbar tandem system had already made it popular as a switching vehicle in the local tandem operation. In fact, it was not unusual for calls crossing large areas to pass through two crossbar tandems using two successive office selections for revertive pulsing.[22]

The signaling capacity was extended to send dial pulses as well as to receive them.[23] In fact the signaling capabilities of the crossbar tandem system were the most extensive of any switching system (see Chapter 4, Fig. 4-13). It could be used, therefore, as a point of signaling language conversion and, like the No. 5 crossbar system, to interconnect the more sophisticated central city systems with the suburban or rural systems.

Later, when services like Centrex, mobile radio, centralized paging, and wide area telephone service (WATS) were developed, the crossbar tandem system was used to serve these special service lines directly—a function it could perform since it could receive and send dial pulses.

3.1 Centralized Automatic Message Accounting (CAMA)

As mentioned in Chapter 4, section 2.2, the location of tandem offices also made them ideal to provide for the special charging needs of multimessage units for the longer distance calls across an area. And, with the introduction of the No. 5 crossbar system, it was possible to connect the suburbs with the central city. Automatic message accounting (AMA) in these local offices (LAMA) provided a means for recording charge details on these calls. But for calls from the older panel, step-by-step, and No. 1 crossbar offices, it was not always economically feasible to add LAMA for the smaller percentage of short haul calls requiring detailed billing. The concept of using crossbar tandem as a central point for charge recording using AMA was devised and called centralized AMA or CAMA (see Chapter 6, section 5.3).

The calling directory number was required to bill customers, and for this purpose the CAMA concept included access from the register-senders through crossbar switch links to operator positions.[24] After the called number was received from the originating office, an idle operator position was connected to the sender, and the operator at that position verbally requested the calling number from the caller. The position contained a simple, cordless 12-button keyset. Calls were distributed to idle positions automatically. The operator keyed the calling number (four digits since the tandem office generally could determine the identity of the originating office by identifying the trunk group), which was recorded in the sender. This form of operation was known as operator number identification or ONI. For greater efficiency, provision was made for remoting the operator positions[25] as automatic number identification (ANI) was introduced, and the need for these positions decreased. The traffic was then transferred to cord switchboards and later TSPS (see Chapter 10, section 1.4). ONI is still required for recording special billing numbers and the calling number when there are ANI failures or for multiparty (more than two) lines.

Besides performing the regular call-processing functions, the sender now passed the calling and called number information to common AMA equipment, not unlike the equipment used in No. 1 crossbar for LAMA.[26] The greatest differences between the two arrangements are those that relate to forming the correct calling office code from the incoming trunk and office identity digit from ANI, using them to determine the type of call billing and routing treatment.

For serving customer dialing from step-by-step offices, CAMA originally included access to a three-digit register connected to the incoming trunk circuit on a "bylink" basis. These digits were transferred on a dc basis to the selected dial pulse sender once it was connected to the trunk circuit. Later, with TSP operation (see Chapter 10, section 1.3) all ten digits were transferred to a sender in this manner when dialing was completed.

The first CAMA installation of any kind was placed in service in a crossbar tandem in Washington, D.C. in November 1953 and, within a short time, was serving 83 originating central offices in that city and in nearby Maryland and Virginia. Similar installations were rapidly placed in service in Detroit, New York, San Francisco, and Philadelphia.

The concept was also applied to the No. 4A crossbar system (first cut over in Albuquerque, New Mexico in 1960) so that the charge recording for long distance calls could take place without LAMA equipment, thereby greatly expanding the opportunities for DDD.[27] About the same time, the CAMA feature became available in the

No. 5 crossbar[28] and step-by-step intertoll (Steubenville, Ohio, September 1961) systems.[29]

3.2 Toll Features[30]

Crossbar tandem was first used for toll in 1947, when the Gotham tandem was installed in New York City to accept operator-dialed calls to cities in surrounding states. The availability of the more expensive 4-wire switching of the No. 4 crossbar system made the designers sensitive to the care with which transmission performance of 2-wire toll switching must be designed and engineered. Four-wire circuits must pass through hybrids to be switched on a 2-wire basis. Echoes are the bane of 2-wire switching. Echoes can be effectively reduced by providing a high degree of office balance and by using impedance compensators and fixed pads.

The pulsing capabilities of the initially developed system included revertive and dial pulsing. A subclass (end-to-end) of revertive pulsing allowed panel call-indicator pulsing from the originating office to a distant tandem or terminating office through the crossbar tandem sender. In 1951, incoming multifrequency senders were added as well as providing for multifrequency outpulsing from all types of senders.

Examination of Fig. 4-13 in Chapter 4 shows the large number of pulsing combinations and conversions made possible with the crossbar tandem system. The system was able to interpret all of the over-the-channel signaling languages and required digit-handling capabilities, and was able to communicate with all of the switching systems. Only call announcer (see Chapter 3, section I) was omitted, since manual switching was fast disappearing. To act in a limited manner as a toll office, it also included ten-digit sender capability, increased alternate route capability, and six-digit translation for routing calls into five adjacent areas without routing to the principal city in the area. This was the first application of the Dimond ring translator (see Chapter 7, section 1.1) outside of the original No. 5 crossbar system application.

The crossbar tandem system thereby serves as both a local tandem and an economical but flexible toll switching system. At its peak (1968) there were 34 crossbar tandem systems used in local service and 213 used in toll applications. The last installation was in Twin Falls, Idaho in August 1974.

IV. AUXILIARY SENDERS

Implementing DDD required local offices to be arranged to reach points outside of their home numbering plan area. In the nonsenderized step-by-step system, it would have been costly to expand the selector stages to select and to send the dialed area code to a toll center. For this reason, in these systems a toll access code, "112," was initially introduced so that these calls would be directed toward a CAMA office. Later, after step-by-step service codes were changed from 11X to X11, the toll access code was changed to "1." To avoid a second dial tone on these calls, a special group of rapidly accessible senders was developed for use with dial pulse trunks from step-by-step to crossbar tandem and 4A crossbar (see Chapter 6, section 5.3). The No. 5 crossbar system was developed with the anticipation of DDD so that the extra digit and translation capability was included in the original design as an option. Later, foreign area translation capability was added for the same reason as given above for the crossbar tandem system.[31]

The principal development challenge was the panel and No. 1 crossbar local offices. Extensive modifications appeared to be required for the subscriber senders of these systems.

One of the first attractive applications for exploring electronic switching techniques was to provide a common parallel electronic memory for registering and sending the digits dialed into subscriber senders. While this arrangement, known as the "magnetic drum auxiliary sender" (MDAS), looked attractive as a result of exploratory efforts, it was dropped so that increased effort could be devoted to electronic switching system development (see Chapter 9, section 4.3.4).

A competitive conventional switching arrangement known as auxiliary senders provided the extra digit capacity and also multifrequency outpulsing capability for the smaller percentage of calls that used DDD[32] (see Fig. 8-11). When the regular sender detected that an area code was dialed, it connected to one of a small group of auxiliary senders through a single-stage crossbar link. The auxiliary sender received all digits in excess of the eight that the regular sender could register. At the end of dialing the regular sender unloaded its eight digits (in two groups of four each) into the auxiliary sender by panel call indicator pulsing.[33] The auxiliary sender outpulsed the multifrequency digits as fast as these digits were received.

All panel and No. 1 crossbar system senders and offices were modified for this feature, starting in 1957. The links and auxiliary senders were mounted apart from the subscriber senders. After many other features were modified in the No. 1 crossbar system, a new subscriber sender incorporating all DDD and multifrequency features was developed to replace the original and much-modified senders in some offices. The design of these senders included the use of wire spring relays. The first installation was in New York City (30th Street) in March 1967.

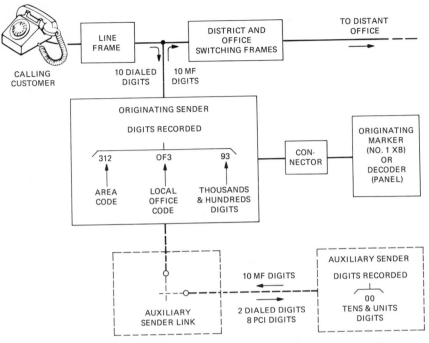

Fig. 8-11. Auxiliary sender as applied to panel or No. 1 crossbar.

V. INTERNATIONAL DDD (IDDD)

As transmission facilities to overseas points grew in the 1960s as a result of submarine cables and, later, satellites, it became feasible to offer customer-dialed international calling, since service could be offered on a no-delay or retrial basis to points outside North America. Operators at gateway switching centers have been dialing into overseas points since 1963.[34]

In 1967, trials were conducted with customer-dialed international calls using a No. 5 crossbar office in New York with special area codes representing Paris and London.[35] A small number of customer registers were modified for this trial, the modifications accounting for the difference between the London and United States telephone dials. This experiment was very successful despite the need for special dialing instructions, the unfamiliar tones and signals encountered, and the longer completion times. Consequently, in March 1970, additional No. 5 crossbar offices were modified to permit dialing into the United Kingdom and later into 13 other countries in Europe and Asia.

Modifying all electromechanical switching offices and toll offices required to reach gateway offices would have resulted in IDDD being too expensive to implement, so a long-range plan was devised. Essentially this plan called for all calls from electromechanical offices to be routed to overseas gateway offices via a Traffic Service Position System (TSPS) (see Chapter 10, section I). Local electronic switching offices functioned in the same manner to advance calls to gateway offices.[36] The first ESS office so modified was in the New York World Trade Center in 1971.

From nonsenderized step-by-step offices the TSPS receives the digits required for international calls. Extra digits are dialed for international access (01 for person-to-person and other special calls, or 011 for station-to-station calls and digits for the country code). The "0" is used for TSPS trunk selection but is absorbed and not sent forward. Senderized offices (panel, crossbar, and step-by-step) would require additional digit capacity. This option was available only for No. 5 crossbar offices. Additional register and sender digit capacity was not added to other offices. Customers in new ESS offices dial "0" and reach TSPS in most cases. Bell Laboratories engineers developed a two-stage outpulsing scheme so that modifications were required only in gateway No. 4A crossbar toll offices.[37] Upon recognizing one of these calls at TSPS and ESS, the two-stage pulsing arrangement acted by first sending digits to advance the call to a particular gateway office. At the gateway office the call is routed to a "loop-around" trunk which in turn is connected to one of a group of special "overseas" senders (see Fig. 8-12). When the sender is attached, it returns a "sender attached" wink signal to start the second stage of outpulsing from ESS or TSPS.

These senders then accept the customer-dialed number that is sent during the second stage of pulsing and used to select a route to the called country. The overseas sender adds language codes on operator-assisted calls and also generates special multifrequency signals to operate with the Time Assignment Speech Interpolation (TASI) transmission system.[38] These senders also receive calls over international facilities transiting through or destined for the United States and provide the proper format for completing through the network. IDDD is a most popular feature, growing at the rate of 20 percent per year (see Table 8-1) and reaching an ever-increasing list of countries (see Table 8-2).

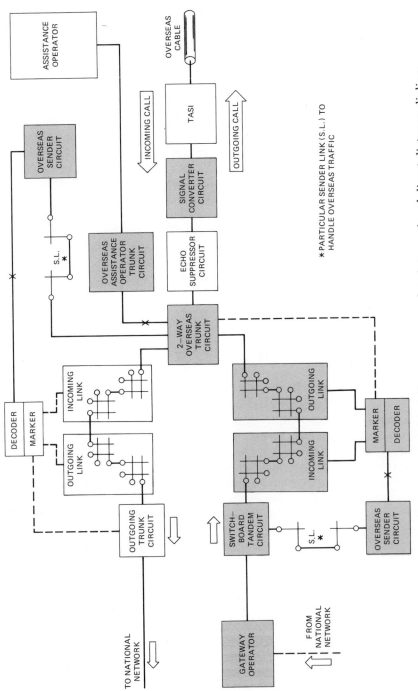

Fig. 8-12. Arrangements in 4A crossbar office to accommodate international direct distance dialing.

Table 8-1. Progress in International Direct Distance Dialing (IDDD).

Year	Number of Dialable Countries	Percent IDDDs of Total Out Messages
1970	9	0.1
1971	14	0.7
1972	20	1.4
1973	20	3.6
1974	20	7.8
1975	32	13.5
1976	36	20.7
1977	36	23.3
1978	47	25.8

Table 8-2. Countries Reached by International Direct Distance Dialing from the U.S. (circa 1977), with Country Code.

27	South Africa	506	Costa Rica
30	Greece	51	Peru
31	Netherlands	55	Brazil
32	Belgium	56	Chile
33	France (includes Andorra, Monaco)	58	Venezuela
		593	Ecuador
34	Spain	61	Australia
351	Portugal	63	Philippines
352	Luxembourg	64	New Zealand
353	Ireland	65	Singapore
357	Cyprus	66	Thailand
358	Finland	671	Guam
39	Italy	675	Papua
41	Switzerland (includes Lichtenstein)	679	Fiji
		81	Japan
43	Austria	82	Korea
44	United Kingdom	86	China (Taipei)
45	Denmark	965	Kuwait
46	Sweden	971	UAE (Five Emirates)
47	Norway		
49	West Germany	972	Israel
502	Guatemala	978	UAE (Dudia)
503	El Salvador	979	UAE (Abu Dhabi)

REFERENCES, CHAPTER 8

1. Collis, R. E. "Crossbar Tandem System." *Transactions of the American Institute of Electrical Engineers* **69**, Part II, June 1950, p. 997.
2. Adam, A. O. "Crossbar Tandem as a Long Distance Switching System." *Bell System Technical Journal* **35**, January 1956, p. 91.
3. Huntley, H. R. "Transmission Design of Intertoll Telephone Trunks." *Bell System Technical Journal* **32**, September 1953, p. 1019.
4. Osborne, H. S. "A General Switching Plan for Telephone Toll Service." *Bell System Technical Journal* **9**, July 1930, p. 429.
5. Pilliod, J. J. "Fundamental Plans for Toll Telephone Plant." *Bell System Technical Journal* **31**, September 1952, p. 832.
6. Shipley, F. F. "Automatic Toll Switching Systems." *Bell System Technical Journal* **31**, September 1952, p. 860.
7. Myers, O. "Problems in Nationwide Dialing." *Bell Laboratories Record* **29**, May 1951, p. 197.
8. Knepper, C. F. "Foreign Area Translation in No. 5 Crossbar." *Bell Laboratories Record* **33**, February 1955, p. 54.
9. *Notes on Distance Dialing 1968.* American Telephone and Telegraph Company, 1968.
10. Jacobitti, E. "Automatic Alternate Routing in the 4A Crossbar System." *Bell Laboratories Record* **33**, May 1955, p. 141.
11. Brymer, S. J. "Converting Toll Crossbar Offices for Nationwide Dialing." *Bell Laboratories Record* **33**, May 1955, p. 188.
12. Newsom, J. B. "Common-Control Features in Nationwide Dialing." *Bell Laboratories Record* **31**, December 1953, p. 481.
13. See ref. 8 above.
14. Hampton, L. N. and Newsom, J. B. "The Card Translator for Nationwide Dialing." *Bell System Technical Journal*, September 1953, p. 1037.
15. Mallery, P. "Transistors and Their Circuits in the 4A Toll Crossbar Switching System." *Transactions of the American Institute of Electrical Engineering* **72**, September 1953, p. 388.
16. Brymer, S. J. "Increased Traffic Capacity for the 4A and 4M Switching Systems." *Bell Laboratories Record* **42**, November 1964, p. 375.
17. Robrock, A. A. "Increasing the Capacity of the No. 4 Crossbar." *National Telecommunications Conference* **2**, 1976, p. 19.1–1.
18. Keevers, R. J. "4A Toll Crossbar—Keeping a System Young." *Bell Laboratories Record* **48**, September 1970, p. 239.
19. Baltz, L. E., Jr. and Falk, R. J. "New 4A Trunk Circuits Save Space and Power." *Bell Laboratories Record* **55**, February 1977, p. 50.
20. Canty, C. R. "New Techniques to Overcome Problems on Trunk Distributing Frames in No. 4 Crossbar Offices." *ICC Conference Record* 1976, p. 13.
21. Scott, L. J. "Overseas Dialing: Yesterday, Today, and Tomorrow." *Bell Laboratories Record* **48**, May 1970, p. 142.
22. Maloney, M. E. "Versatility of Crossbar Tandem." *Bell Laboratories Record* **34**, April 1956, p. 143.
23. Meszar, J. "The Full Stature of the Crossbar Tandem Switching System." *Transactions of the American Institute of Electrical Engineers* **75**, Part I, September 1956, p. 486.
24. Germanton, C. E. "CAMA—Position Link Circuit." *Bell Laboratories Record* **33**, May 1955, p. 193.
25. Rolf, F. N. "Remote Positions for CAMA." *Bell Laboratories Record* **35**, September 1957, p. 353.

26. Pennoyer, D. H. "Basic AMA Central Office Features." *Bell Laboratories Record* **29**, October 1951, p. 454.

27. Jaeger, R. J. and Maloney, M. E. "4A and 4M Toll Crossbar with CAMA Equipment." *Bell Laboratories Record* **37**, September 1959, p. 345.

28. Hurst, G. A. "Extending CAMA with No. 5 Crossbar." *Bell Laboratories Record* **36**, October 1958, p. 372.

29. Martins, A. S. and Ruwell, R. G. "CAMA for Step-by-Step Intertoll." *Bell Laboratories Record* **40**, February 1962, p. 55.

30. See ref. 23 above.

31. See ref. 8 above.

32. Kirchhoff, J. W. and Parks, C. O. "Direct Distance Dialing from Panel and No. 1 Crossbar Offices." *Bell Laboratories Record* **35**, June 1957, p. 212.

33. Breen, C. and Dahlbom, C. A. "Signaling Systems for Control of Telephone Switching." *Bell System Technical Journal* **39**, November 1960, p. 1381.

34. Becker, J. and Deming, R. D. "Switching International Calls via Submarine Cable." *Bell Laboratories Record* **42**, July/August 1964, p. 235.

35. See ref. 21 above.

36. Keevers, R. J. and Vigilante, F. S. "Existing Solutions and Future Plans for Handling International Telecommunication Traffic in the Bell System." *International Switching Symposium,* Munich 1974, p. 126/1.

37. See ref. 21 above.

38. See ref. 34 above.

Newark, New Jersey electronic switching office, 1971. With ESS techniques, electronic scanning of telephone lines replaces the use of relays and switches to detect requests for service and incoming dial pulses, electronic memory substitutes for the earlier electromechanical registers and senders; and electronic logic circuits and electronic memory for storing programs replace the wired-in logic of electromechanical systems. Although system memory and logic suggest analogies to computers, ESS systems are unique in their ability to provide virtually uninterrupted service 24 hours per day every day and to operate with many inputs in real time. Since the first commercial offering in 1963, electronic switching grew until, by the end of 1981, nearly 2700 local ESS systems served more than half of all Bell System lines.

Chapter 9

Beginnings of
Electronic Switching

The advantages of speed realizable from electronics were evident from an early date, and even before World War II Bell Labs experimented with gas tube control of crossbar switches. After the war, the impetus toward electronics was increased by the invention of the transistor at Bell Labs in 1947, and a number of experiments in both the research and development areas made use of the properties of transistors, gas diodes, magnetic drums, and cathode ray tubes. The results of these experiments were encouraging enough to spur the development of an electronic switching system for a field trial at Morris, Illinois; an important milestone was reached in 1955 with the incorporation into the Morris design of stored-program control. Even before the successful conclusion of the Morris trial in 1962, the Bell System recognized that full-scale development of electronic switching was the road to the future. One consequence was the No. 101 electronic switching system, a time-division PBX which first saw commercial service in 1963. Development effort at Bell Laboratories culminated in the No. 1 ESS, first placed in commercial service in 1965, and the 4-wire version incorporated into the government's AUTOVON (AUTOmatic VOice Network) system, beginning in 1966. Since the mid-1960s, the history of ESS and stored-program control has been one of rapid, continuous growth in versatility and range of services.

I. EARLY APPLICATIONS OF ELECTRONICS

The successful application of electronics to transmission led to many attempts to seek its potential for switching, as described in Chapter 5, section I. Some of these started before World War II in the research area, such as the call announcer (see Chapter 3, section I), remote zone registration (Chapter 4, section 2.2), and multifrequency pulsing (Chapter 6, section IV). Circuits using gas tubes were developed and deployed for remote zone registration and for selective ringing of party lines. After the war, the development area found increasing application for such items as vacuum tubes in single-frequency signaling (Chapter 6, section IV), gas tubes in No. 5 crossbar in the ring translator (Chapter 7, section 1.1), timing circuits (Chapter 7, section 1.2), transistors in the card translator (Chapter 8, section 1.2), and the line insulation test circuit (Chapter 7, section 1.2). In Chapter 5, section I, other early research efforts are mentioned.

II. THE START OF SYSTEMS THINKING

One of the prewar research experiments was the gas tube control of crossbar switches, included in the design of a laboratory model No. 1 crossbar line link frame (see Fig. 9-1). After World War II, this effort was revived with a view toward a small crossbar community dial office (CDO) that would be more reliable than the No. 380 system (see Chapter 4, section 2.4). The result was an exploratory development carried out in the research department

Fig. 9-1. Pre-World War II experimental No. 1 crossbar line link frame with crossbar switches controlled by gas tubes.

under the supervision of F. A. Korn from the development organization. The system design was started in 1946 and tentatively identified as the No. 385 crossbar CDO (see Fig. 9-2). The system plan was very similar to the No. 43 system (see Chapter 4, section 2.4). Final development was dropped because this system could not compete economically with step-by-step CDOs.

As early as 1942, some study was made of time-division switching, but systems using this technique were found to be limited in capacity. As a result, most postwar effort started with space-division systems, first using sealed-contact switches, as in the experimental system known as ECASS (for "Electronically Controlled Automatic Switching System").[1] Other efforts involved gas tubes in 1946,[2] or semiconductor crosspoints.[3] In all of this effort the basic idea was to apply control "marks" to an input and output of a multistage network so that one path and only one path through crosspoints connecting idle links would be established without double connections. This was known as "end-marking" with automatic lockout, and the objectives were to reduce network control complexity and to establish connections rapidly, one at a time.

A time-division signaling scheme using a separate signaling channel was investigated[4] and was used in the ECASS model. This gave

Fig. 9-2. Experimental No. 385 crossbar community dial office, a 1946 attempt to incorporate electronics into switching.

rise to the scanning concept used later in another experimental system called DIAD (for "magnetic Drum Information Assembler-Dispatcher"),[5] and in electronic switching systems.[6] By 1949, models of many of these concepts were in existence and stimulated the thinking of many engineers about electronic switching systems in general. A 100-line time-separation system, as time division was then called, was built in 1950, and a frequency-division system was studied. Transistor lockout circuits and, eventually, crosspoints were made and network experiments conducted in 1951. In 1947 and again in 1955, proposals were made to use light-beam switching to establish talking connections.

Magnetic drum storage was applied in the DIAD system in 1954 with the basic idea of writing at the same address immediately after reading the stored information so that the same control logic circuits could act on a time-division basis for calls stored at each successive address. A magnetic drum translator system was explored for use with the 4A crossbar system in place of the card translator (see below, section 4.3.3), but did not go into production. An experimental model of a two-way gas tube translator was also explored for use in local switching systems to meet the automatic message accounting requirement of equipment-to-directory number, and the number group directory-to-equipment translation.[7]

III. RESEARCH SYSTEM EXPERIMENTS

The many basic ideas of scanning, end-marking, electronic (gas tube and semiconductor) crosspoints, and call wire signaling resulted in the research systems ECASS and DIAD and in a third system termed ESSEX (for "Experimental Solid State EXchange"),[8] all of which were built as laboratory experiments in the late 1940s and 1950s. They formed test beds into which the various new switching ideas could be tried and demonstrated. Under the direction of W. D. Lewis, the team of E. B. Ferrell, W. A. Malthaner, C. A. Lovell, M. Karnaugh, W. A. MacNair, H. E. Vaughan, J. D. Johannesen, D. B. James, J. R. Runyon, E. Bruce, N. D. Newby, and many others established new ideas and devices for switching, and stirred interest in electronic switching not only at Bell Laboratories but also worldwide. Once electronic switching developments were undertaken, this research effort was gradually phased out during the 1960s.

In the late 1960s, a new effort under H. S. McDonald was started to determine the applicability of integrated circuits to switching for the future. As a result, digital central offices and adjuncts were proposed. It is expected that digital techniques will have as profound an effect on switching in the future as the early research efforts had on the development of electronic switching.

Switching research is scheduled to be covered in detail in a forthcoming volume of this series.

IV. THE START OF ELECTRONIC SWITCHING DEVELOPMENT

4.1 System Studies

In 1951, C. E. Brooks and his group of systems engineers at the Bell Laboratories West Street location in New York City began defining the requirements for an electronic central office. The older dial central offices such as panel and step-by-step would eventually need more modern replacements, and electronics appeared to offer an opportunity for significant cost and space savings. This was an era that had seen the invention of the transistor and the introduction of the electronic stored-program computer. Moreover, very rapid technological changes were just beginning to make available new high-speed components for use in telephone switching. Experimental skeletonized central offices or functional subsystems were designed, constructed, and tested by Bell Labs engineers in switching research at Murray Hill, New Jersey and switching development at West Street. These efforts were paralleled and supported with innovations by the physical research and electronic apparatus development organizations at Murray Hill. The design of ECASS and DIAD provided a basis for the study, but continuing innovation and changing technologies were already shifting the choices of apparatus and methods of system operation.

Fairly complete studies for a "transistor switching system" were completed by Brooks and members of his group in 1952 to achieve a paper design and to test its cost effectiveness compared to step-by-step and No. 5 crossbar offices. The system was envisioned as having three major elements: the switching network and the control circuits (to comprise the "central office"), and an accounting center at a different location. In addition, portions of the network were to be distributed closer to groups of customers in units known as remote line concentrators.

4.1.1 Transistor Switching System—The Network and Scanner

The switching network was seen as an "end-marked" network. The control circuits had only to apply the proper electrical marking signals at the two terminals to be interconnected; the network would automatically seek and connect a single transmission path to the appropriately marked terminals. The connection would be released by end-marking (with a different signal) at least one of the terminals to be disconnected. An arrangement of the reed-gas tube diode switch, used in the ECASS experiment, was operated in this fashion. The gas tube diodes provided the end-marking feature, the reed relays the 2-wire (electrically balanced transmission) metallic connection for voice transmission, dial pulse signals, and ringing or busy signals. One alternative was a gas tube network that would both respond to dc end-marking signals and, when operated, provide a speech transmission path with gain. The gain would be used to offset other losses incurred in the network so as to have transmission characteristics equivalent to those of electromechanical switching systems. (Fig. 9-3 shows a comparison of the reed diode and the talking-path diode configurations.) The third choice was like the second. A junction transistor took the place of the "talking-path gas diode"; however, the transistor network would exhibit a slight transmission loss rather than a gain.

Neither the talking-path diode nor the transistor network could pass large signals such as the line ringing voltages and currents. Furthermore, to reduce the number of switching elements meant that the networks had to be connected to a single path (unbalanced transmission) from terminal to terminal, requiring a return via a ground common to all paths. Consequently, each balanced line or trunk was transformer-coupled to the network; dial pulse signals from the customer could not be transmitted through the network to digit-receiving circuits.

These signaling limitations were seen as opportunities. There was interest in adding electronics to the customer's telephone to: 1) permit high-speed ac signaling instead of ten-pulse-per-second dial pulsing, 2) provide amplifiers for speech and low-level ringing signals transmitted through the network to the set, and 3) include automatic identification of party line telephones by pulses transmitted from the telephone to the central office. Speech amplification allowed the transistorized telephone to operate with substantially less current and power than the existing telephone required.

The need for ac signaling from the telephone set was obviated with the capacitively coupled rotating scanner invented for DIAD by N. D. Newby.[9] The scanner would sequentially interrogate each of a great many lines at microsecond speeds for origination requests and dial pulses. One device would serve as the equivalent of both the line relay and dial pulse detector. The actual registration of digits could be kept in a common memory associated with the control means. Eliminating the high-speed ac signaling requirement greatly simplified the electronics needed for the telephone set. (In his proposal Brooks included a scanner and common memory for storing digits; these used cathode ray tubes and phototransistors.)

Several important steps in the evolution of electronic central offices are seen here. First, high-speed electronics could be used more advantageously in a common centralized circuit (the scanner), and many individual registers could be replaced with a bulk electronic memory (the cathode ray tube). Second, the scanner was used in performing two functions—detecting originations and col-

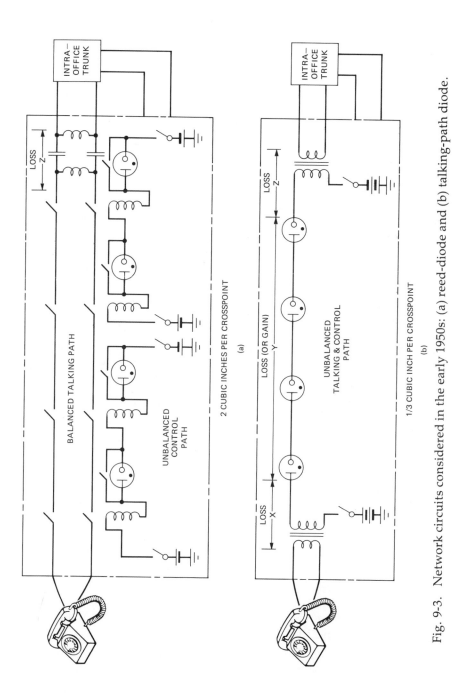

Fig. 9-3. Network circuits considered in the early 1950s: (a) reed-diode and (b) talking-path diode.

lecting dial pulse digits. A controlling means alternatively used the scanner to perform these different tasks at different times, rather than delegating such complexity to the scanner itself.

Initially, the system studies included recommendations for the transistor network. The transistor network required much lower marking and operating voltages than the gas tube alternatives, and transistors required less space and power. Economic estimates favored the transistor, although a device and circuit implementation was not then at hand.

With the transistor network it was further thought that a six-stage end-marked network could be obtained, whereas only a four-stage network would be obtainable with gas tubes. The network was to be modular so that it could grow from fewer than 1000 lines to a maximum size of 10,000 line terminals. A six-stage design would handle this span of network size more economically (fewer crosspoints per line) than would a four-stage configuration. To save crosspoints in smaller offices, the network modules could be assembled into a four-stage configuration, enabling intraoffice calls to be routed more economically. This latter feature would take advantage of the "community of interest" of calling patterns usually associated with small offices.

As the small office grows larger, the efficiency of the intraoffice link scheme falls, and these links would be removed and replaced by two-port intraoffice trunks. Growth would be accomplished by adding network frames and by redistributing the links by rearranging connections on the junctor grouping frames. At first it was thought that the junctor rearrangement would require rewiring, but the idea of using plug-in cards to simplify and speed this task was considered a future possibility. The network switch stages were to be plug-in modules to make repair easier.

Early network plans included the option of removing a portion of the first stage of switching and the associated line scanner and replacing this equipment with remote line concentrators to reduce the copper requirements of the outside plant. Supportive studies were begun in 1951 to look at remote line concentrators for application to the transistor switching system and, more immediately, to No. 5 crossbar. Other studies showed plans for six-stage networks which, with the use of concentrators, could grow to a capacity of 500,000 lines. Field trial systems of remote line concentrators resulted, but commercial application did not appear until later. (See Chapter 11, section 2.10.)

4.1.2 Transistor Switching System—The Control

The control of the transistor switching system relied heavily on cathode ray tube (CRT) technology. A CRT with an associated array of phototransistors at its face would serve to scan lines and trunks for the busy-idle condition, for call originations, and for dial pulses. A second associated CRT would provide an erasable memory for keeping per-line or per-trunk information for scan points associated with each phototransistor. One group of CRTs would serve lines, and the second would serve trunks. A third CRT erasable memory system provides memory for transient information associated with individual calls. Wired logic and flip-flop arrays would access the three CRT systems at microsecond speeds under the synchronization of an electronic "clock" to detect and assemble the intelligence needed to determine the network connections required. The wired logic and flip-flop arrays would also access the network frames and trunk circuits through diode matrices in order to control the establishment of the actual network connections. Fig. 9-4 shows a 1952 vintage block diagram of the system. It closely resembles the configuration used in the Morris and No. 1 ESS systems (see below), although the stored-program control was not yet incorporated and the memory was still somewhat less consolidated than in the later systems.

Lines and trunks would be scanned at high speed by deflecting the CRT beam from one phototransistor to the next. The combination of the beam's presence and the proper voltage signal on the wired lead connected to its phototransistor would generate a signal indicating the idle condition, request for service or busy state, or dial pulse information (see Fig. 9-5). The address of the beam, i.e., the X and Y axis deflection voltages, would correspond to the line equipment number. By repetitively accessing all the scanner cells in rapid succession, the control is able to count dial pulses and detect interdigital intervals.

The digits would be counted and registered in a temporary storage memory. One proposed memory was the barrier grid tube. These CRT devices used the electron beam to deposit static charges on an insulating layer (mica) to represent binary information. Subsequent interrogation of the site by the beam yielded differing amounts of secondary electrons, which could be detected by a collecting anode[10] (see Fig. 9-6). Although the barrier grid tube was not commercially available, experimental models of this device made at Bell Labs in Murray Hill, New Jersey demonstrated sufficient memory capacity.

For economy, the transistor switching system, like DIAD, used a common bulk memory rather than individual registers to accumulate and store dialed digits. Unlike the DIAD drum memory, the barrier grid tube could read or write only one bit of memory per operation. The latter's very high-speed random access to any memory site was considered sufficient to meet the needs of the transistor switching system. The barrier grid tube was more economical than a drum

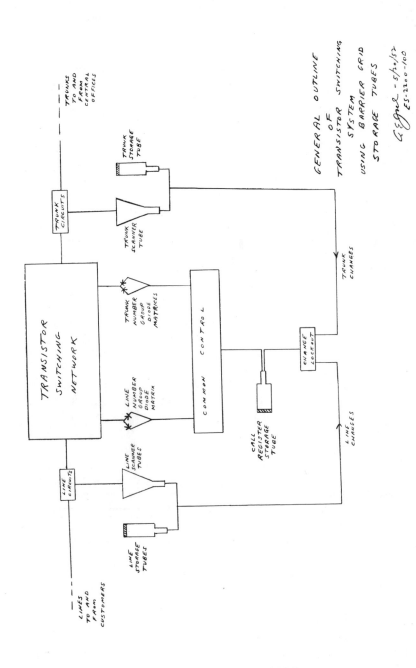

Fig. 9-4.   A 1952 view of electronic control for a transistorized switching network.   Control thinking was then based on cathode ray tube technology.

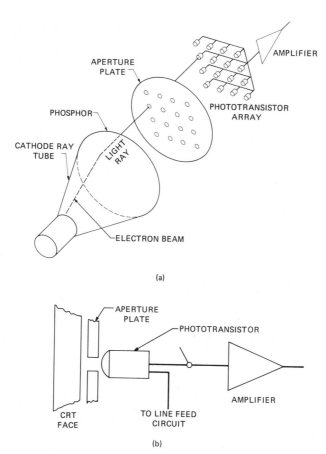

Fig. 9-5. Cathode ray tube scanner for the transistor switching system:
(a) overall geometry and (b) cross section of one cell.

memory, which required many read/write circuits and associated
flip-flop registers—at least one per track for the drum. This trade-off
between speed of operation and economy of memory access circuits
later shifted back to word-organized memories in the first production
designs of electronic switching systems.

Once the digits were registered, the need then was to translate
the directory number into the equipment number so as to be able to
locate the called line in the office or to locate the appropriate group
of trunks if the call was to go to another exchange or to an operator.
A bulk memory could be addressed with the number to be
translated, and the stored data would represent the corresponding
translated values. This memory was to be placed in a centralized
accounting center.

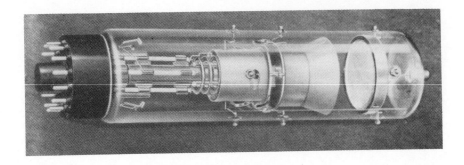

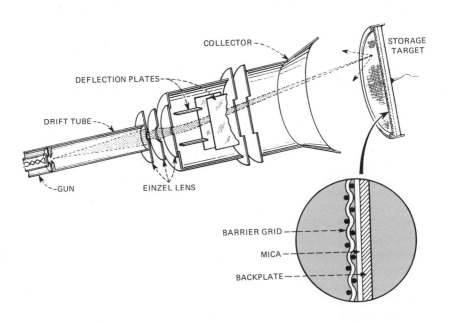

Fig. 9-6. Barrier grid tube and cross section. Electron beam deposits static charges on mica insulating layer.

4.1.3 *Transistor Switching System—The Accounting Center*

The accounting center function associated with the transistor switching system was to include shared information and was to use barrier grid tubes and another CRT system described below. A two-way data link would connect the control of the transistor switching system to the accounting center office, which could be located in another building. (Data linking over telephone lines was a subject of research in the 1950s.[11]) A single data base for the translation between equipment numbers and directory numbers could be conveniently administered for a number of electronic central offices connected to the revenue accounting office, and the sharing of the data base would provide obvious economies in the total system. Although not implemented at the time of the introduction of the No. 1 Electronic Switching System (ESS), the data link transmission of billing information to a centralized recording center was introduced in 1975 and is described in Chapter 11, section 2.8.

A very large fast-access memory was needed to carry out the translation function, and a cathode ray tube system was also suggested for this task. In the example just noted above, the called-line directory number could be encoded into an X and Y deflection position, and the beam would be directed to a starting point on a low-persistence phosphor screen in the CRT. Behind the CRT would be placed a photographic plate, a condensing lens, and a photodetector (see Fig. 9-7). The plate would have an array of transparent and opaque sites representing ones and zeros. From the starting address, the beam would be scanned along a row of these sites, and the resulting stream of ones and zeros would be read from the photodetector and an associated amplifier into a register of transistor flip-flops. The register would then contain the desired equipment number. This use of a "flying spot" scanner as a binary memory store provided a bulk memory device. It would contain all the information for lines and trunks and would include both translation of equipment location to directory number (calling number identification) and translation of directory number to equipment number (location of the called number's connection to the switching equipment).

Other electronic memories were considered for use in the control and accounting systems. These included magnetic tape, magnetic drums, and acoustic or electric delay lines. As pointed out above,

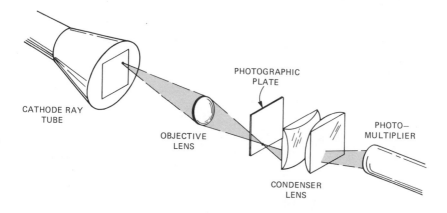

Fig. 9-7. Basic plan of the flying-spot store, about 1954. Information is stored in the photographic plate.

the system required fast access (tens of microseconds or less) and large capacity (tens or hundreds of thousands of bits); at the time, this combination of requirements was practically achievable only with the CRT systems with their rapid random access.

Equipment number to directory number translation would be stored in flying-spot scanners at the accounting center to identify the directory number to be charged. This is obtained by using as the memory address the equipment identification number transmitted from the transistor switching system to the accounting center. A barrier grid tube memory would be used to collect the information needed to determine call charges. Once the charge and billing numbers for a call were completed, the information would be moved to magnetic tape to make room for new call data entering the barrier grid store.

The central office would access the translation data in the accounting center as needed by request over the data link. For example, the completion of incoming calls requires a translation of the directory number to an equipment number. The central office would transmit the directory number, and the accounting center would use the directory number to address the flying-spot scanner. The response would be the readout of the equipment number, which would then be sent to the central office to allow the completion of the call. (Centralized computers of this type have since been used in non-Bell commercial switching systems.)

With these models, the transistor switching system appeared economically attractive for a 9,000-line office in New York City and a 2,000-line office in Morris, Illinois. However, more studies were undertaken to refine the requirements of the system and gain better understanding of the choices of apparatus. Market studies of both replacement offices and new wire center applications were to be undertaken along with a look at the tandem and toll switching applications. The development of a remote line concentrator for the No. 5 crossbar system was already under way (as described below, section 4.3.1) and would contribute to better understanding of that part of the transistor switching system.

4.2 1952—1954 Studies

Additional system studies continued to define more completely how the transistor switching system would operate and included fairly detailed considerations of apparatus, equipment, and cost effectiveness. The point was reached where development was considered the next logical step. A prospectus was prepared by Bell Laboratories and transmitted in May 1954 to AT&T.

This prospectus recommended that Morris, Illinois be the location of the first office. A good deal of engineering data had been generated for this location, and its modest size would enable engineers to obtain the experience needed with minimal expenditures. The outside plant included enough pairs so that a remote concentrator would not be required, and a smaller gas tube diode network could be used rather than wait for a transistor network. The transistor network was then proposed to make its appearance in larger offices subsequent to Morris. The flying-spot scanner memory store (later to be called the flying-spot store) was estimated to require 76,000 bits of information, and the barrier grid tube was calculated to require 14,000 bits of changeable memory.

The earlier system studies assumed every line would be scanned repetitively every five milliseconds. This fast rate was required for properly detecting dial pulses but was not necessary for detecting call originations or disconnects. The proposal was changed to scan idle lines every 100 milliseconds; only those lines in the state of dialing would be observed every five milliseconds. The same scanner would be addressed at different speeds to carry out the two functions.

It was thought that the speed of operations of the system would be so fast that dial tone signals would no longer be required to tell the originating customer when to start dialing. In prior systems the customer would be connected through the network to a digit receiver with a dial tone generator attached. The scanning at the line and the elimination of dial tone obviated the need for the "dial tone call." However, it was subsequently realized that dial tone provides very useful feedback to the customer—the line is working properly, another party or extension phone is not already using the line, and so on. Therefore, the idea of eliminating dial tone was abandoned.

The 1954 prospectus estimated the Morris control to be 100 flip-flops and 2000 semiconductor logic gates. The prospectus also noted a number of customer services and operating features that could be added subsequently by making modest changes in the control logic. It was recognized that a good deal of the control complexity had been transformed into words of data stored in the bulk CRT memories, and changes in the memory contents would be far easier to make than rewiring of individual circuits. (See Fig. 9-8 for a 1954 conception of the electronic central office.)

The system would largely comprise plug-in units, and test sequences would exercise the control logic and connecting subsystems to locate troubles. Lamps would automatically be lit to point to the location of the circuit fault. Duplicate subsystems would provide stand-by capability until faulty plug-in units could be replaced.

In July 1954, Bell Laboratories was authorized to develop an electronic central office, a major goal of the systems studies. In the meantime other systems studies and exploratory development continued as the transistor switching system evolved into the Morris system.

4.3 Exploratory Development

In the early 1950s a number of Bell Laboratories development and research engineers were applying electronics to modernizing electromechanical switching systems or functional parts of the systems. This included work on magnetic core logic and memories, cathode ray tubes, magnetic drums, cold-cathode gas tubes, transistors, and diodes. These were being assembled into working systems that were tested in the lab or underwent field trials. Four such projects are described below.

4.3.1 An Experimental Remote Line Concentrator

It would appear economical to concentrate telephone traffic close to a group of customers and so reduce the number of pairs of copper wire that must be brought to a wire center for interconnection. The

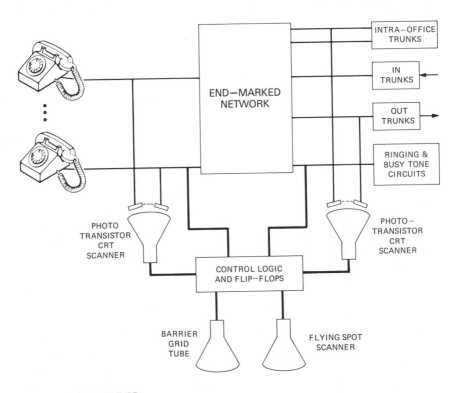

CRT – CATHODE RAY TUBE

Fig. 9-8. View of the Morris electronic central office as of 1954. The control system was then estimated to be 100 flip-flops and 2000 semiconductor logic gates.

economics involve a trade-off on the cost of remotely locating the switch, including its distributed power and maintenance, versus the savings in the loop plant. If, for example, a concentrator could be used to avoid adding new underground ducts, then a substantial material and cost saving could be realized.

In 1953, under the supervision of A. E. Joel, Jr., exploratory development of a remote concentrator was started using a variety of electronic components and techniques.[12] The design objectives included: compatibility with existing standard dial telephones; the ability to work with one- and two-party lines, but not with coin or PBX lines; a minimum of associated per-line central office equipment; and a design to work with No. 5 crossbar, since No. 5 was the newest local switching system at the time. Also, maintenance of the equipment was to be simplified by making a modular design with plug-in units in the remote equipment—a first for Bell Telephone switching equipment. Other "firsts" included the use of high-speed pulsing (500 bits per second) between the central and remote units, and a dedicated magnetic tape in the central office for recording usage and call delay measurements for several concentrators. The use of a high-speed line scanner not only saved two relays per line but also aided in generating the data for the magnetic tape measurements. The per-line portions of the scanner and gas tube reed relay concentrator for a single line were assembled into a plug-in unit that was encapsulated to protect against humidity. As shown in Fig. 9-9, it was designed for plug-in operation.

Fig. 9-10 shows a concentrator serving 60 lines over ten trunks. The pole-mounted unit uses two additional trunks as data links between control circuits in the concentrator and the central office. The concentrator acted as another stage of switching, but it basically replaced the "build out" of the first stage of the line link frame in the serving No. 5 crossbar office. Accordingly, the central control unit, which could handle a number of remote line concentrators, operated two stages of switches. This "fooled" the marker, which had sent a command to operate only one stage of the line link frame. Fig. 9-11 shows how the control is interposed to carry out the "fool-the-marker" method of operation. This minimized the wiring changes in the No. 5 crossbar office when the remote line concentrators were to be added or moved.

Three concentrators were built, and field trials were conducted in LaGrange, Illinois, Englewood, New Jersey and Freeport, Long Island. Although these trials were operationally successful, additional hardware would have been required for maintainability in a production model. Subsequent cost estimates indicated an insufficient market to warrant design development for manufacture at that time. The inherent advantages of speed and reliability offered by semiconductors had yet to win the day.

4.3.2 *The Distributed Line Concentrator*

Based on the experiences with Joel's experimental concentrator, switching systems engineers, headed by C. E. Brooks, investigated an alternative approach called the distributed line concentrator.[13] This approach was based on several important principles that were intended to "turn the corner" but which relied on similar technologies.

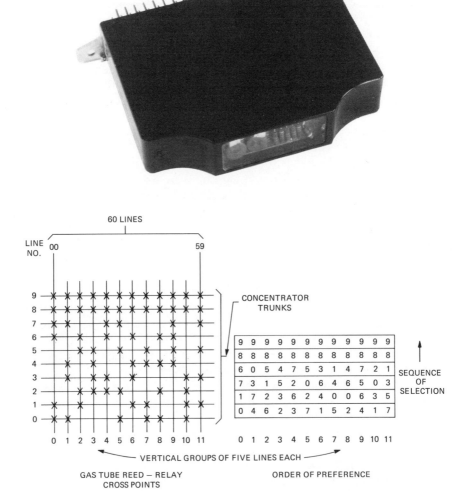

Fig. 9-9. Plug-in design of crosspoints for experimental line concentrator.

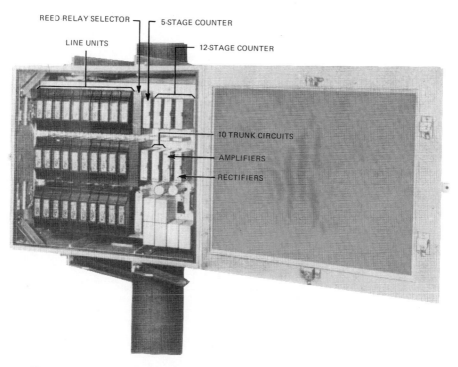

Fig. 9-10. Experimental remote line concentrator. This unit, development of which began in 1953, used ac power from the central office to drive rectifiers supplying power at the pole.

With the distributed line concentrator, most of the control complexity and associated maintenance was to be kept in the central office. The distributed per-line equipment was designed to have a minimum of autonomous control; for example, no repetitive scanning was provided as part of the remote equipment. Also, the per-line equipment was to be distributed in very small units that would have been connected at the points where cable pairs were spliced to individual line drops. Fig. 9-12 shows the arrangement described.

The distributed system was also based on the fact that most of the lengths of telephone loops were to be found as pairs in a multipair cable. Each and all per-line units would share a number of pairs in the cable, thereby concentrating traffic on a smaller number of pairs in that cable. Additional pairs in the cable would have served as signal leads (or number group) to communicate between the central office control and the individual customer telephones. By wiring each customer line unit to unique combinations of three out of eight number group leads, individual access to up to 56 lines was possible with the 15-pair cable.

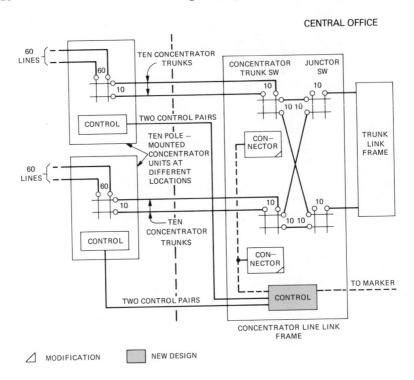

Fig. 9-11. Modification of No. 5 crossbar to accommodate remote line concentrators.

The central office control unit was intended to "fool-the-marker," as in the earlier concentrator design, but the distributed concept also envisaged intraconcentrator call connections with the aid of special customer line units. This technique removed unnecessary traffic load from the central office and reduced blocking on the concentrator trunks. With reasonable levels of a community of interest in the calling patterns within the concentrator group, significant increases in the effective concentration were possible.

The concentrator crosspoints distributed in each customer line unit were to be the combined gas tube reed relay type similar to those previously described. A second type of customer line unit was also proposed wherein the reed crosspoint was magnetically latched instead of requiring a hold current. Other gas tubes, semiconductor logic diodes, and relays comprised the remainder of the components of the customer line units. A paper design of two configurations of the concentrator was described in July 1963 and test models were operated in several No. 1 crossbar central offices, but like its predecessor the distributed line concentrator was not

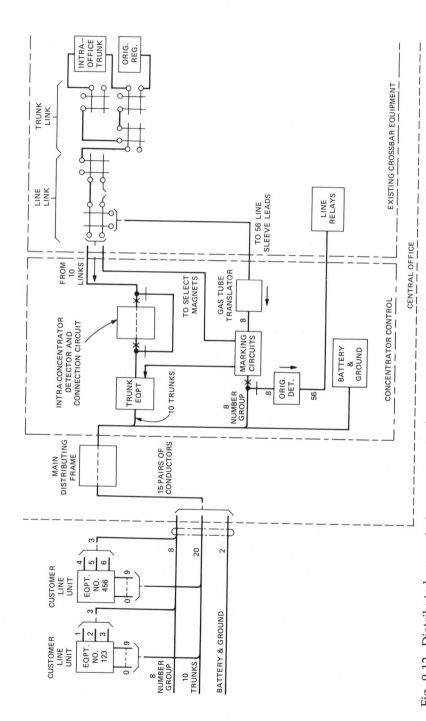

Fig. 9-12. Distributed concentrator concept: per-line equipment (left) would be at intersections of cables and loop connections to customers' telephones. Control equipment (center) would be housed at site of the crossbar office (right). (*AIEE Transactions on Communications and Electronics*, Vol. 82, July 1963.)

deemed practical for commercial production. An electromechanical concentrator using specially designed magnetically latched crossbar switches was introduced in 1961, and over 4000 of these systems were installed (see Chapter 11, section 2.10). Electronic concentration did not prove in until the late 1970s.

4.3.3 *Magnetic Drum Translator*

Beginning in the early 1950s, large-capacity magnetic drum memories were tried in applications of electronics to various switching functions. The first of these was the route translating function for the 4A crossbar toll switching system. The 4A card translator using point-contact phototransistors was originally designed for this task, as described in Chapter 8, section 1.2.

Magnetic drums offered speed and memory capacity appropriate to the task and, as will be explained, would have reduced the amount of equipment required and simplified the administration of the translations records of the card translator. A working model of the magnetic drum translator was built and was operated with a skeletonized No. 4A crossbar office for over a year.[14] It used a variety of electronic components including vacuum tubes, cold-cathode gas tubes and point-contact transistors and diodes.

Fig. 9-13 is a block diagram of the magnetic drum translator. It is associated with a relay decoder—another functional element in the 4A crossbar system. The decoder passed requests for call routing translation from the marker to the translator in the form of from three to eight decimal digits encoded in a two-out-of-five redundant code. The decoder accepted encoded route information from the translator in return.

As shown, the magnetic drum translator was designed to operate in the same way as the 4A card translator; thus, the drum translator could be added to a working 4A system with no changes. A 4A toll office can be equipped with up to 18 decoders and associated 4A card translators. Since the magnetic drum reads out all of its translation data in serial fashion with each 35-millisecond revolution, a single drum memory assembly could have been multipled to a number of delivery and selecting units to serve all 18 decoders. A second drum would have served as a maintenance and administrative spare. The magnetic drum would be updated via an administrative frame, which could be connected to the read/write heads of the drum. Thus, one or two update operations would serve to reliably update the entire translation facility.

The magnetic drum translator was carried to the point of demonstrating that the drum would retain the translation information over long periods of time without deterioration. The design was not a

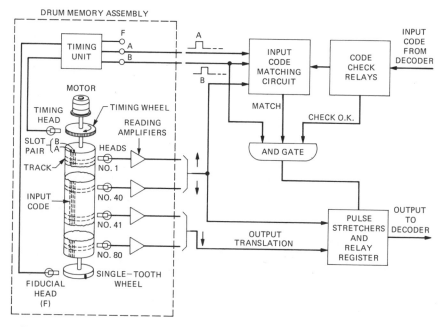

Fig. 9-13. Design of experimental magnetic drum translator, intended for use with No. 4 toll crossbar.

production design, and it was not carried further inasmuch as the choice of the card translator for the No. 4A crossbar development had already been made. The magnetic drum translator was reviewed again in the early 1960s for application to the 4A and 4M toll crossbar systems, but was once more dropped in favor of a more powerful stored-program control approach.

4.3.4 Magnetic Drum Auxiliary Sender

The beginning of direct distance dialing (DDD) in 1951 required that switching systems accept, process, and forward to connecting central offices more digits (typically 10 instead of 7) from the customer. This meant that local switching systems comprising step-by-step, panel, and crossbar had to register more digits and "send" or transmit more information to other nodes in the DDD network. Thus, the capacity of a substantial number of registers and senders needed to be increased in each central office in order for that office to be a part of the DDD network. The magnetic drum sender was proposed as an electronic means to meet this need.[15]

Fig. 9-14 shows a block diagram of the magnetic drum auxiliary sender as arranged for a laboratory model of a No. 1 crossbar office.

The scanner used diode logic for sequentially scanning 156 senders every ten milliseconds for dial pulses. The scanner was synchronized with the magnetic drum read/write circuits and therefore to corresponding memory slots on the drum. By comparing the scan result with the contents of the drum memory, the sender space control would determine the number of pulses in the digit, the interdigital times, and the completion of the digits received. When all the digits had been received, the sender space control would then assign one of six transmitters to the sender and convert the readout of the digits in sequence to select the proper train of two-out-of-five multifrequency tones to be transmitted to the distant office.

The apparatus included a narrow drum rotating at 1500 revolutions per minute. Fig. 9-15 is a photograph of the drum and Fig. 9-16 is a pictorial of the drum layout. The latter figure shows the memory for one "sender space"—occupying approximately one quarter of one square inch of the drum recording surface, but providing the equivalent of more than 50 relays of conventional digit registers.

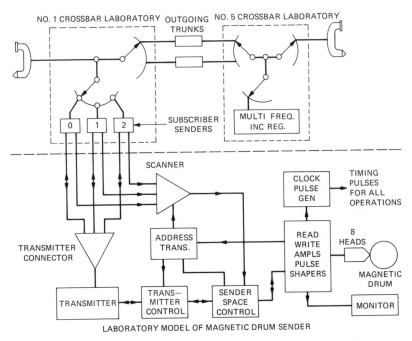

Fig. 9-14. Magnetic drum auxiliary sender (drum at lower right in diagram), an attempt to apply electronics to problems of expanding direct distance dialing. (*AIEE Transactions on Communications and Electronics*, Vol. 77, March 1958.)

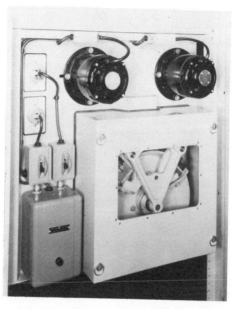

Fig. 9-15. Magnetic drum unit of the auxiliary sender, about 1953. (*AIEE Transactions on Communications and Electronics*, Vol. 77, March 1958.)

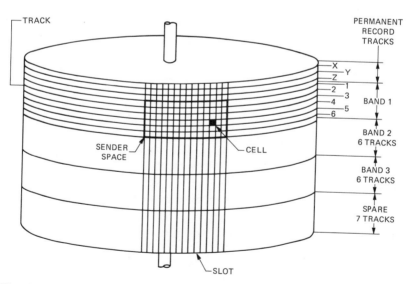

Fig. 9-16. Allocation of space on the drum. The sender space as indicated was equivalent to more than 50 relays. (*AIEE Transactions on Communications and Electronics*, Vol. 77, March 1958.)

The relative simplicity of the system logic is due to the ability to write back into a drum slot several microseconds after the readout from that same slot has been obtained. A partial digit can be read from the drum and updated when indicated by a scan result and the new value of the digit written back, all within 17 microseconds.

Although the magnetic drum auxiliary sender used transistor and diode logic extensively, it still required vacuum tube read/write circuits for the drum itself. Its engineers had intended the design for production, but the economics were not promising and specific development plans were dropped early in 1954 in favor of an electromechanical design (see Chapter 8, section III).

Included in the effort on the magnetic drum auxiliary sender was the work by W. Ulrich and B. J. Yokelson on the design of diode logic and diode scanners, which was used in the next step of the application of electronics to central office switching systems.[16]

4.3.5 *Conclusion*

Systems studies had suggested that high-speed electronics should provide smaller and less expensive centralized switching systems. Electronic replacements for several functional pieces of electromechanical switching systems were designed, built, and tested in the laboratories or in field trials, but were not cost effective. Questions regarding reliability and maintainability had not been fully answered. Hot-cathode, high-vacuum electronic components had useful lifetimes of only a few years, even when operated conservatively. The bearings of magnetic drum memories had lifetimes of only a few years.

During the early 1950s the junction transistor began to be manufactured, and techniques were developed for growing single crystals, for zone refining, and for ion implantation. These factors led toward electronic elements that, compared to vacuum tubes, were less expensive, smaller and more reliable, and used far less power. Cathode ray tubes to store information, which otherwise would have required tens of thousands of wires or relays, also provided powerful technology for considering the next step: the building of an entire switching system principally from electronic components. Theoretical work on the analysis and synthesis of combinational and sequential circuits, and the development of more powerful error-detecting and error-correcting schemes, allowed the designers of electronic switching circuits to economize their designs and to make the circuits more dependable and maintainable. The laboratory models and field trial systems provided a background of experience with some of the earlier devices from which the performance of newer technologies could be projected.

4.4 Towards an Electronic Central Office—Pre-Morris

Although application of electronics had not yet achieved production status, the designs were getting closer to the point of proving in, and work was authorized in July 1953 to build laboratory models of parts of an electronic central office and eventually to put the parts together in a skeletonized central office in the laboratory. The work was initiated by AT&T because the proposed system involved much that was radically new, both in circuitry and apparatus elements. The possibilities for the electronic central office with respect to existing switching systems were seen to be (1) substantially lower first cost, (2) large space savings, (3) less maintenance, and (4) greater flexibility in meeting changing service requirements.

Bell Labs development of a specific system was authorized by Western Electric one year later to develop a system for field trial from which a first production system could be attained. Initially, A. E. Joel's department in C. A. Lovell's laboratory was assigned to this task, and work began at the West Street, New York City location. Lovell's laboratory relocated to the Whippany, New Jersey Laboratory in the fall of 1954. By May 1955 the work had progressed to the "breadboard" stage, and the effort had expanded to the building of a field trial model using the technology of the laboratory model.

The apparatus for the laboratory system included germanium alloy junction transistors (complementary npn and pnp types) and germanium point-contact diodes.[17] Although these devices were not used in the production version of an electronic switching system (ESS), the discipline of limiting the variety of transistors and diodes for manufacturing economies was followed. Fig. 9-17 shows typical plug-in circuit packs and the mating connectors to which wire wrap connections would be made to construct functional units from these building blocks. On these packs were placed the diode AND and OR gates, the transistor inverting and noninverting amplifiers, and flip-flops. These building blocks were interconnected to construct the logical functions needed in the various equipment types. Figure 9-18 shows a typical rack-mounted array of the logic packages.

The other components of the system included the previously described barrier grid store and the photographic or flying-spot store suggested by C. E. Brooks and others (see above, sections 4.1.2 and 4.1.3). In June 1954, a radical change in the use of the flying-spot store was suggested in an internal memorandum written by W. Keister. The diode and transistor control circuits being designed were complex sequential circuits. Keister knew that the complete behavior of the circuits could be represented by a table of numbers whose entries would be binary numbers representing the

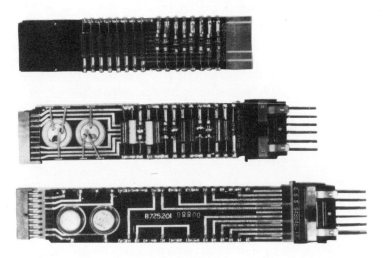

Fig. 9-17. Plug-in circuits and connectors used in mid 1950's laboratory model electronic switching system. Logic circuit boards are 1½ inches wide by 7 to 9 inches long and connect to 12 terminal wire-wrap connectors.

outputs of the control circuit and its next internal state. By placing the total description of the control circuits in memory, the control circuit complexity would appear in the table rather than in the diode and transistor logic circuits. Keister noted: "Detailed engineering of large numbers of logic circuits would be eliminated. To change a sequence of actions, add new functions, or modify old [ones] it would be necessary only to change the program in the permanent memory."

By June 1955, W. A. Budlong and A. H. Doblmaier were designing the sequential control circuits for the electronic central office. They were finding that the size and complexity of the circuits were straining the limits of design rules of the semiconductor diode and transistor logic circuitry. Furthermore, relatively minor changes in the requirements often resulted in extensive changes in the circuit design, which did not augur well for the subsequent addition of new features to meet evolving customer or operating company needs. At that time, Budlong had read an article in the journal of the Institute of Radio Engineers describing a digital computer and was struck by the similarity of what the computer could do and the actions required of the control circuits. He began devising instructions that suited the task of processing telephone calls and writing sample programs. This approach was dubbed Stored Logic in Memory (SLIM) by A. E. Joel, Jr. and underscored the circuit savings to be gained with this technique of implementing common control.

Fig. 9-18. Rack-mounted array of logic packages.

The idea began to gain momentum; however, the new technique required much more storage in the flying-spot store, and the speed of operation had to be increased materially. R. W. Ketchledge and R. E. Staehler learned of this proposal and began working on ideas to improve the performance of the memory system. This resulted in several inventions by these engineers that used servo techniques to sufficiently improve the performance of the flying-spot store. In September 1955, Lovell and Ketchledge decided to switch to stored-program control, and the revolution in the design of telephone switching systems was under way. The first reauthorization of the Western Electric funding in early 1956 noted this change of events.

The laboratory model was assembled, and the first telephone switching programs were written for this model.[18] Fig. 9-19 is a view of the laboratory model constructed at the Whippany, New Jersey Laboratory. By that time Morris, Illinois had been selected for the field trial location, and the model system came to be known as "pre-Morris." The first telephone call was placed through this system in March 1958. For reasons given earlier, the pre-Morris and later the Morris systems used the gas tube network. This required the new low-power telephone using an electronic tone ringer, which

Fig. 9-19. The stored-program "pre-Morris" laboratory model electronic switching system. The first telephone call through this system was placed in March 1958.

was field-tested in Crystal Lake, Illinois prior to its use in the Morris trial.

4.5 Electronic PBX

In 1955, several proposals were made to provide a modern private branch exchange PBX in the smaller line sizes—some to serve as few as 20 to 50 lines. One proposal used relays and crossbar switches but added transistors, semiconductor diodes, and magnetic cores to exploit their smaller size and much faster speed in a self-contained system. A second proposal was to adopt the previously described gas diode reed relay concentrator as a customer premises switch; the central office would contain one or more control units that would be shared by a number of customer-based switch units. The control would communicate with the switches via a data link, and PBX trunks from the switch would terminate at the central office containing the control unit. On the basis of these ideas, fundamental development was funded in March 1956 and continued through 1958.

A third proposal for the network of the new PBX called for placing electronically gated speech samples onto a "talking bus." Two telephones could be connected by arranging their electrical signals to be sampled at the same time. Other conversations could be interleaved in the same manner. The time-division switch approach was eventually favored over the space-division proposals inasmuch as the network switch elements would grow as the number of lines served, instead of as the square of that number.

Fig. 9-20 shows the basic configuration of switch and control circuits for the Electronic PBX (EPBX). Two talking buses are shown in the block diagram to provide capacity greater than that available with a single-bus system. To interconnect line A to line B requires the use of the interbus connection via gates 4 and 5.

The fundamental development effort focused on the design of the time-division switch elements, the memory systems appropriate for the electronic memories for the switch, and the requirements and logic for the control unit. Laboratory breadboard and brassboard models demonstrated technical feasibility, and in September 1958, specific development of the EPBX production was authorized by Western Electric. As in the Morris project, the design of the control unit of the EPBX was changed from wired logic to stored logic prior to its field trial.

4.6 The Morris Field Trial

With the successful design and construction of the pre-Morris laboratory system, the development of the Morris system was continued, applying the same or very similar devices and apparatus. An end-marked gas tube network provided the concentration and distribution functions, and a line scanner detected the off-hook/on-hook state as well as dial pulse signals and switchhook flash signals. Germanium diode and transistor logic comprised the logical building blocks for the central control and other functional units, and the barrier grid store and the flying-spot store provided the scratch pad and program memories.[19]

The organization of the system is shown in Fig. 9-21.[20] The marker executed the network order transmitted from the central control and provided a buffer between the 3-microsecond operating speed of the central control and the milliseconds required for the marker to find and mark a connection in the gas tube network. The signal distributor served as another buffering device which accepted encoded address information at microsecond speeds and selected relays to be operated and released. Most of the relays were associated with the various trunk circuits.

The crosspoint element for the switching network, the cold-cathode gas tube, is depicted in Fig. 9-22. It is a neon tube that requires 200 volts to be applied to cause ionization and conduction. When the tube conducts, its voltage drops to 110 volts, and 10 milli-amperes of current flows. In this state, the device possesses a nega-

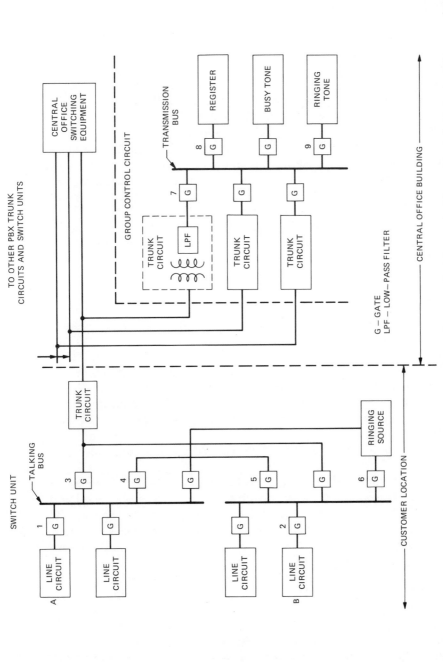

Fig. 9-20. Block diagram of the electronic PBX, which used a time-division switching network and a two-bus configuration. Control circuits in the central office accessed up to 32 switches at various customer locations.

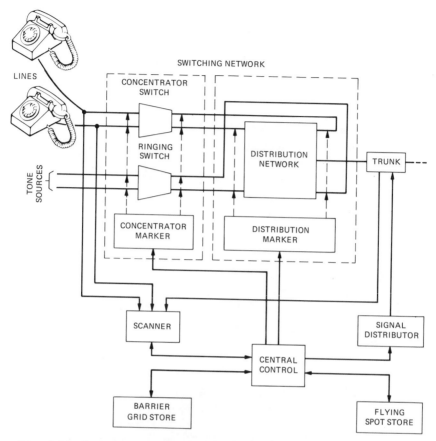

Fig. 9-21. Organization of the Morris, Illinois system. Most of the devices and apparatus were similar to those used for the pre-Morris system.

tive ac resistance that amplifies small signals (talking currents) transmitted through it. This gain offsets the losses in the transformers and other circuits in the network. A single path through the Morris network is shown in Fig. 9-23.

As indicated in Fig. 9-24, the network marker (only the distribution portion is shown for simplicity) was provided with terminal addresses of the desired connection and used this information to apply marking voltages at each end of the network. The voltage signals propagated towards the center or junctor stage of the network. The signals would not travel through busy crosspoints and thus were "locked out" from possible double connections. The marking signal fanned out through idle crosspoints, and the marking signal from each end of the network propagated to a number of terminals on each side of the junctor stage at the middle of the network.

The junctor stage comprised a set of junctor circuits which were sequentially interrogated or enabled to find a junctor circuit which had the marking signal present at both terminals. When that condition was obtained, a special gas tube tetrode would ionize, and the selected gas diodes turned on and remained on after the marking

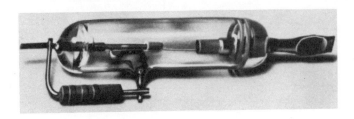

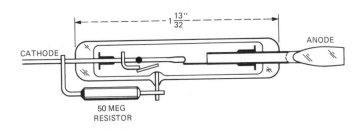

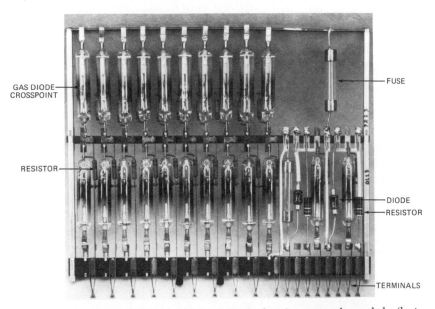

Fig. 9-22. Gas tube crosspoint (top) and plug-in network module (bottom) for the Morris system. In addition to its switching function, the device amplified voice signals.

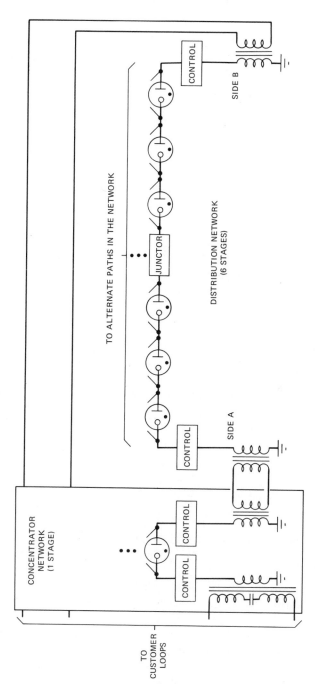

Fig. 9-23. Path through the gas tube switching network of the Morris system.

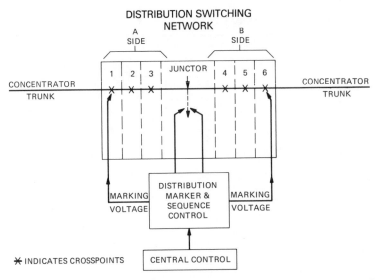

Fig. 9-24. Morris system talking connection showing marking voltages which caused connection control signals to propagate to the junctor stage of the network.

and junctor enabling voltages had been removed. The unselected paths deionized, and only the desired connection remained. The many possible connections which were sequentially tested with the junctor circuits provided the network with its redundancy to operate with occasionally failed network elements and to meet the low blocking requirements for its engineered traffic.

Once a path had been established, the "memory" of the connection was the conducting state of the gas diodes. To release the connection, a negative marking voltage was applied to the terminal of the customer for which the hang-up signal had been detected first. This signal propagated through the gas diodes and the junctor circuit, and released the connection. The release operation generated a pulse on the terminal of the second customer's connection. This pulse was detected and translated (in an identifier circuit not shown in Fig. 9-24) into the terminal's address. This information was subsequently read by central control so that it could update its busy-idle memory to reflect the disconnecting of the second customer.

Fig. 9-25 shows the concentration and distribution networks at Morris. Fluorescent lamps inside the cabinets excited a photoelectric material deposited inside each diode. This served to provide a sufficient number of free electrons in the gas to assure rapid ionization of the gas in response to the marking voltage signals.[21]

The ringing signal was a low-level audio frequency voltage that could be passed through the gas tubes and line transformers. (The normal 90-volt ringing signals were too great to pass through the gas

Fig. 9-25. Concentration and distribution networks of the Morris system. Fluorescent lamps excited enough free electrons for the gas tubes to operate. D. T. Osmonson checking the operation of a gas tube module in the network.

diode network.) The telephone shown in Fig. 9-26 used two transistors in a tuned amplifier to detect a particular ringing frequency and amplify the signal to drive the miniature horn shown in the photograph. This electronic substitute for the electromechanical

Fig. 9-26. Telephone set used in the Morris trial. Transistor circuit provided amplification for both tone ringing and speech.

bells is known as a "tone ringer." The tuned amplifier detected different frequencies for different party line telephones and thus provided full-selective ringing for up to eight parties. When the receiver was removed, switchhook contacts reconfigured the transistors into a speech amplifier. This reduced the line power required, and the reduced current permitted the use of a smaller line transformer connecting the customer's loop to the switching network.[22]

The flying-spot store for Morris was substantially larger and faster than the laboratory model.[23] The switch from wired logic to stored-program control resulted in the design of more sophisticated drive and feedback circuits to reduce the access time and increase the number of data channels. Figure 9-27 shows the multiple array of lenses, photographic plates, and detecting photomultipliers which, with the cathode ray tube, provided a 2.2 million bit store. To gain the high accuracy and speed of operations required of the flying-spot store, a number of channels accessed photographic plates, which were code plates giving a unique response for each of 256 values of vertical and horizontal deflection of the beam. As shown in Fig. 9-28, this information provided the error signal for a feedback deflection system, which achieved an accuracy of beam deflection otherwise unattainable. By combining the direct and feedback drive, the speed of operation of the store was increased so that successive 25-bit instruction words could be read by central control every 2.5 microseconds. To operate with occasional imperfections in the photographic plates (the information density was approximately 42,000 bits per square inch in a 256 by 256 array of opaque and clear spots), each instruction word included a 5-bit Hamming

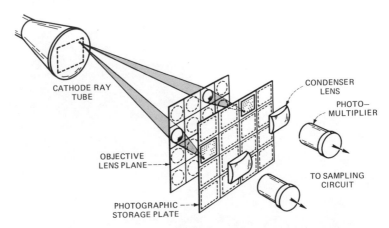

Fig. 9-27. Morris flying-spot store, which provided a memory of 2.2-million bits. (*Proceedings*, General Fall Meeting, IEEE, October 1960.)

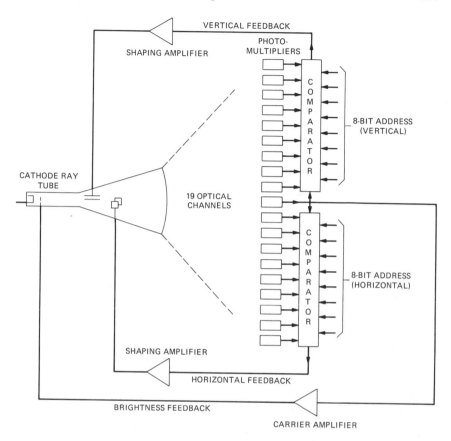

Fig. 9-28. Horizontal and vertical deflection feedback systems used to increase beam accuracy to levels previously unattainable. (*Proceedings, General Fall Meeting, IEEE, October 1960.*)

code and a parity bit to correct single-bit errors and detect double errors.

The Morris program required 50,000 instructions, of which one third contained the telephone operating functions and the remaining two thirds were used for maintenance and administration.[24] This amounted to 1.2 million bits of random access high-speed memory for the program alone. Translation memory also was stored in this memory. As can be seen from Fig. 9-29, which depicts the state of the art in late 1956, the flying-spot store best met the needs for large semipermanent stored programs.[25]

The Morris field trial began with part-time service on June 1, 1960 and was built up to 24 hours a day service on November 11, 1960. By June 1961, a peak of 434 main telephones (total about 650 main

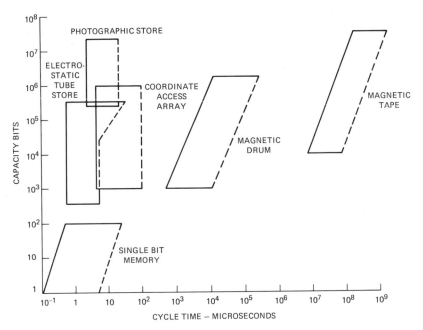

Fig. 9-29. In 1956, photographic store provided easily changeable, electronic read-only memory with the best combination of capacity and speed.

and extension telephones) were in service and continued at or near this level for the remainder of the trial, which was completed in January 1962.[26]

Morris proved the basic soundness of stored-program control for telephone switching systems and provided the necessary experience and background for the production design of ESS. Once the system was shaken down, Morris was able to operate with an uptime of close to 99.99 percent. By the end of the trial, customer trouble reports were dropping below the national average for several weeks at a time. Excluding vacuum tube and gas diode failures, the semiconductor logic circuit packs failed at a rate of fewer than two packs of 11,000 per month, and for the last six months of the field trial there was only one logic package failure.

The Morris maintenance plan was designed to simplify maintenance by having the system itself perform the bulk of testing, analysis, and trouble reporting. For most cases, the task of the maintenance personnel was only that of looking up a printed trouble report in a maintenance dictionary to find out the location of a defective plug-in package and replace it.

This technique was successfully employed by craftspersons who had been given various levels of training in the administration and maintenance of Morris.

Customers were provided with the new low-current telephones which included a faster, 20 pulse-per-second dial. In addition, many customers had new calling features nowhere previously available. Abbreviated dialing allowed the customer to dial a two-digit code; the memory contained the corresponding seven-digit office code and number, which was used to complete the call. The customer gave central office administrative personnel a list of seven-digit numbers corresponding to four available two-digit codes. Another feature was the ability, under customer direction, of automatically transferring calls to another telephone number, specified by dialing command codes and the designated second number. The system would automatically store the requisite information and forward calls to the new number until the feature was canceled by the customer's dialing a second specified command code. Not only did stored-program control provide the new features with no additional hardware, but these capabilities were added with relatively modest changes and additions to the program and space in memory. Making the same changes in the prior-art systems would have been much more extensive and costly. This advantage, along with the high degree of automation of maintenance through the use of stored-program control, were the driving forces for the revolution in the design of telephone switching systems.

4.7 New Devices

During the exploratory development of the electronic PBX and the Morris electronic central office, there were many innovations made in memory systems, network devices, and logic elements. The various enhancements were investigated and tried; some were adopted, others rejected. By the time the Morris system was in operation, a revolution in technology had made obsolete all its major components. This revolution resulted in large magnetic memories, newer network elements, and the introduction of silicon transistor and diode circuits. A short review of some of the new or improved devices follows.

4.7.1 Memory Systems

Both pre-Morris and Morris used two high-speed random access memories, which were accessed independently and concurrently by the common control in executing its program. The flying-spot store contained the program and data that remained constant over a period of time, ranging from a few weeks to many years. It was known as a semipermanent memory inasmuch as it required human intervention to change its contents; the program was thereby protected from inadvertently destroying itself. A second memory provided the scratchpad for rapidly changing information such as dial pulse counts and traffic data. This was referred to as a temporary memory, and in the Morris system the barrier grid store was used for this purpose.

It is interesting to note that this dual storage arrangement was not employed in general-purpose computers of that time, since they did not have the stringent dependability requirements placed on the stored-program control used in central office switching systems. An added benefit of the arrangement is the concurrent reading of program instructions and the reading or writing of data, which results in data processing speeds higher than those obtainable with a single memory.

The permanent magnet twistor memory—announced by Bell Laboratories in 1959[27]—provided a store that was as fast as core memory, reliably retained its data, and was substantially cheaper than equivalent core memories. The twistor memory is based on magnetic properties of permalloy tape helically wound around fine copper wire, as shown in Fig. 9-30. At that time, the twistor memory offered performance superior to that available from coincident-current access magnetic cores. To operate an equivalent-size core memory at the speeds attainable with the twistor would have required much more operating power.

The permanent magnet twistor or PMT memory was first employed in military systems in relatively small memory capacities,

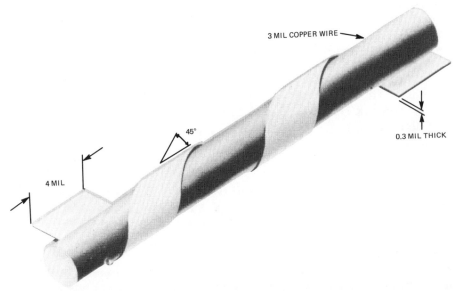

Fig. 9-30. Construction of twistor memory, 1963: a permalloy tape wound helically around copper wire.

but much larger memories were built and reported shortly thereafter. The PMT memory became a contender to the flying-spot store for the production model of ESS.[28]

Another contender developed by Bell Labs engineers was the capacitive memory store or "capstore." It was simply a matrix of capacitors to which input pulses were applied on word lines and the individual capacitors connected to output bit lines.[29] As shown in Fig. 9-31, the binary value of the word was determined by the presence or absence of coupling capacitors between the input word lines and the output bit lines. Fig. 9-32 shows a batch-fabricated submatrix of 32 words with 18 bits per word. Etched copper patterns

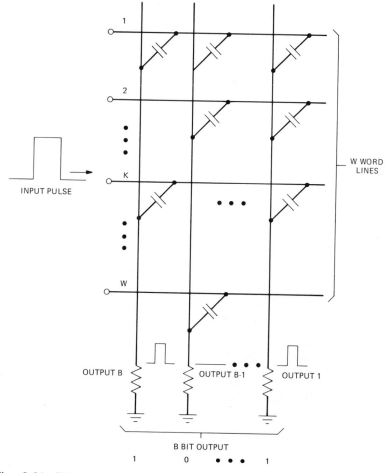

Fig. 9-31. Diagram showing concept of the capstore memory: words were constructed of patterns of coupling capacitors. (*IRE Transactions on Electronic Computers,* EC-10 September 1961.)

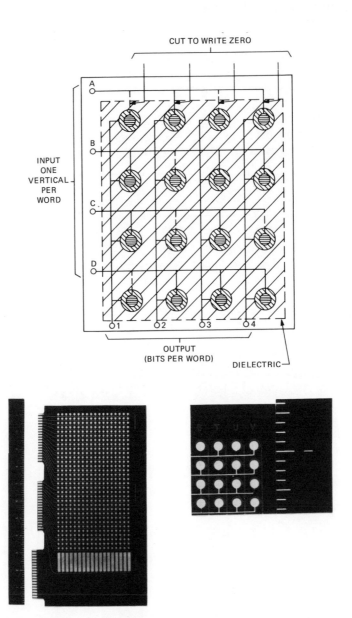

Fig. 9-32. Top: layout of copper and dielectric patterns forming capaci-tors. Bottom: photograph of capstore with capacity of 32 words of 18 bits each. *(IRE Transactions on Electronic Computers, September 1961.)*

separated by a thin layer of mylar formed the capacitors and the word and bit lines. By selectively cutting the connections between the vertical bit lines and the individual capacitor anodes, zeros are formed at those bit and word locations. The remaining uncut leads represent binary ones. A zero can be reconverted to a one by the application of conducting paint.[30] A 1024-word by 34-bit store was constructed and used in the brassboard model of the EPBX.

The awkwardness of changing the memory and the linear nature of the circuit access, which severely limited any substantial growth of the size of the store, foreclosed its use in the production model of the EPBX. However, years later the capstore served very well in scientific computers as high-speed microprogram stores.

In the area of temporary memories, the magnetic core memory had become the dominant memory in business and scientific computer systems. Coincident-current access techniques allowed the design of memories for which the size and cost grow as the square root of the total size of the memory. However, the speed of operation in the coincident-current mode was limited, and various approaches to overcome this limitation were explored in the development of the EPBX and the production ESS. One technique was to bias the coincident-current core matrix so that larger drive currents could be applied to speed up the switching action on the cores. Biased core access techniques were also used with core matrices which drove the solenoid windings of the PMT access circuits.

Another approach was the ferrite sheet store. The ferrite sheet, shown in Fig. 9-33, was a batch fabrication means to overcome the high cost of the then-used technique of manually threading a large core matrix. By the time the production design of ESS was started, it was understood that the smallest office would require hundreds of thousands of bits of temporary memory. The result was that the ferrite sheet had an economic advantage over conventional core memories.[31]

4.7.2 Network and Scanning Devices

Although the gas tube network performed satisfactorily in the Morris field trial, there were enough problems with it to warrant exploration of alternate technologies. As expected, the failure rate of gas tubes was significantly higher than that expected of transistors and diodes. Even during the earlier planning stages transistors were considered as the production device for the network, and gas tubes were accepted for use in Morris as an interim approach.

One arrangement of two junction transistors in a "hook connection," as shown in Fig. 9-34, yields a bistable switch that can be end-marked like a gas tube. The same operating characteristics can

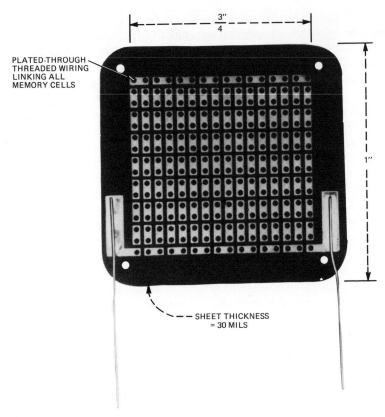

Fig. 9-33. Ferrite sheet memory which used batch fabrication to avoid manually assembling and threading magnetic matrices of cores.

be obtained in a single four-layer device—the pnpn diode—also shown in Fig. 9-34. Unlike the gas diode, the solid state bistable switches have some loss in the "on" state, so that networks made from these elements would degrade transmission more than the gas tube. Similarly, the "off" impedance of the pnpn and the hook connection was less than that of gas tubes. The reduced "off" impedance would degrade crosstalk margin. On the other hand, the pnpn offered not only a more reliable device but one that operated on much lower voltages, consumed much less power, and was far more compact.

One of the major limitations in electronic network elements had been their inability to directly handle some of the conventional telephone signaling and test voltages and/or currents. For example, in crossbar switching systems a telephone is rung by connecting its loop through the switching network to a ringing generator.[32] The ringing signal required to operate the bell is nominally 86 volts r.m.s. at 20 hertz superimposed on 48 volts dc. To collect or return coins, a 130-volt dc signal is sent through the network to coin telephones. Test circuits also require electrically transparent dc connections through the switching network to the customer's loop. Special access and protection circuitry had to be added to each line to accommodate electronic networks, regardless of whether the electronic network was one of space division or time division.

The Morris system addressed the handling of ringing with a new telephone containing a low-voltage ringer, but other requirements for coin and PBX lines and loop testing were not resolved in the field trial.

Although the use of the pnpn diode as a network crosspoint was pursued vigorously, the invention of the ferreed (a contraction of ferrite and magnetic reed) switch by A. Feiner, C. A. Lovell, T. N. Lowry, and P. G. Ridinger quickly became the economic choice. It was based on a small dry reed switch, to which was added a magnetic latching structure which could be operated and released with electronic controls. At the same time, it provided metallic contacts which could handle the wide range of existing signaling and test

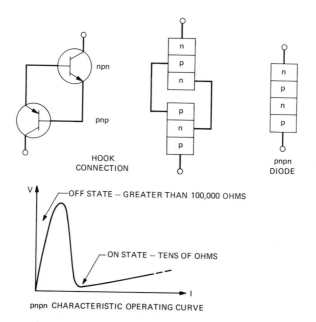

Fig. 9-34. Solid state alternatives for network switches: top left, the "hook" configuration of transistors; top right, the pnpn diode. Below, on-off characteristic curve of the pnpn diode.

voltages and currents without special circuitry. This avoided the extra cost of special access and protection circuits and eliminated the need to change to the new telephones.[33] Fig. 9-35 shows an earlier (1960) version of the ferreed which used powdered sintered ferrite; Fig. 9-36 shows the production model, which used Remendur as the magnetic latch.

The ferreed crosspoints were assembled into matrix switches, and networks were built up from these switches in a manner topologically similar to crossbar switch networks. In operating a crosspoint in a ferreed matrix switch, however, very different techniques are used for control. Simultaneous currents through the horizontal and vertical windings of the crosspoint are needed to operate it. Current through only one winding will knock down a closed crosspoint or leave it unaffected if it is open. The individual switches were arranged in a matrix so that all the horizontal windings of a row were connected in series, and all the vertical windings of a column were also connected in series. Simultaneous current through a row and column thus operated the crosspoint at the intersection and released any other operated points on the same row and column. This was known as "destructive marking" and eliminated the need to open closed crosspoints at the end of a connection with little risk

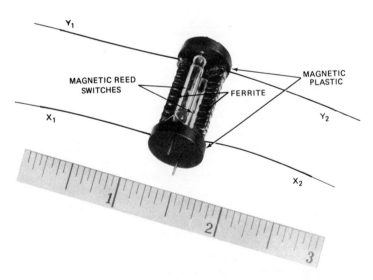

Fig. 9-35. Experimental ferreed switching using powdered, sintered ferrite rods and disks to latch glass-enclosed magnetic-reed switches. Differential windings (X1, X2, Y1, Y2) are pulsed simultaneously to close contacts; pulsing of either winding alone causes the contacts to open.

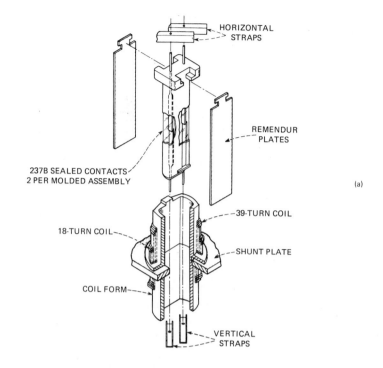

Fig. 9-36. (a) The production model ferreed switch with Remendur plates. (b) An 8 × 8 switch with covers removed.

of double connections, while greatly simplifying the control of setting up and taking down connections.[34]

The size of switch was chosen by considering the cost of control, the network configurations, the size of resulting frames, and switch cost. No. 1 ESS uses primarily an eight-by-eight switch. A binary number is most efficiently handled by a stored program, and the other factors determined the preference for 8 instead of 4 or 16.[35]

In previous networks a third lead, the sleeve, was switched along with the tip and ring to form the memory of the state of connections in the network. Rather than using this technique, the state of the ferreed was retained in bulk temporary memory, called a "map," and maintained in step with the actual state of the network through the program. This reduced the cost of the total system and allowed the program to "reserve" paths in memory in advance of the actual connection to be made.[36]

To scan lines and trunks for originations, disconnects, dial pulses, etc., the associated on-hook and off-hook voltages biased semiconductor diode elements in the Morris field trial scanner. Interrogation pulses would correspondingly be transmitted or blocked. Although simple in concept, elaborate component networks were associated with each diode to protect it from high voltages and currents and to balance out longitudinally induced ac signals. This led to the invention of the "ferrod" by J. A. Baldwin and H. F. May.[37]

With the ferrod on-hook and off-hook loop currents were magnetically coupled through windings to a stick of ferrite material, which was the size of a large paper match. The difference in currents would selectively allow or inhibit the coupling of pulses from an interrogation winding to a sensing winding. Balanced windings canceled the longitudinally induced interfering signals, and the magnetic rather than direct coupling of the loop to the interrogating and sensing electronics protected the latter from power line crosses or lightning strikes. Fig. 9-37 shows the ferrod in its most ubiquitous applications.

4.7.3 Logic Elements

The logic elements in the Morris ESS were point-contact diode AND and OR gates with germanium transistor alloy junction stages to provide gain and/or logical inversion. A catalog of "universal" circuit packs provided the logic building blocks for that system.[38] A different approach to providing "universal" logic elements was proposed for the EPBX and the production ESS. The PBX designers elected to use a single gate made up of resistors and silicon diffused junction transistors; the basic NOR gate could be used in combination to generate the needed AND, OR, and INVERT functions. The ESS circuit designers in going to the production design opted for the more expensive but faster NAND gate requiring silicon diodes and transistors. Its lesser power consumption and higher fan-in and fan-out capabilities made it attractive to the No. 1 ESS designers.[39] The logic families described are indicated in Fig. 9-38.

V. THE DEVELOPMENT OF ELECTRONIC SWITCHING

By 1958, ESS development at Bell Labs in Whippany, New Jersey consisted of two major efforts. The primary effort, in terms of personnel, was completing the hardware and software designs for the Morris system. This included writing and using simulators to test software before it could be tested in the system laboratory. The system laboratory was a full working replica of the Morris, Illinois system, and was used to test hardware and software working together as a system. And, while the development of the Morris system was being completed, a second and parallel Whippany effort was started on the design of the first production system, the No. 1 ESS.

5.1 From Morris to the Start of No. 1 ESS

Authorization to develop ESS was approved by Western Electric in March 1958, the same month that the first call was placed in the pre-Morris system. At that time it was recognized that the gas tube would probably be replaced, and that higher-performance, diffused-junction silicon transistors and diodes were more suitable for the production design. The serial operation of the barrier grid store was also seen to be too slow for high-speed processor operation.

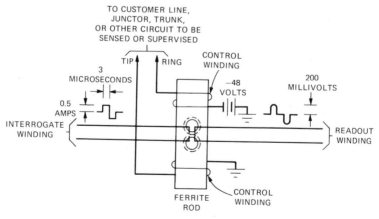

Fig. 9-37. Ferrod scanning point used in ESS. Typical devices used in line scanning would saturate at 10 milliamperes loop current and provide maximum coupling of interrogate and readout windings for 5 milliamperes or less.

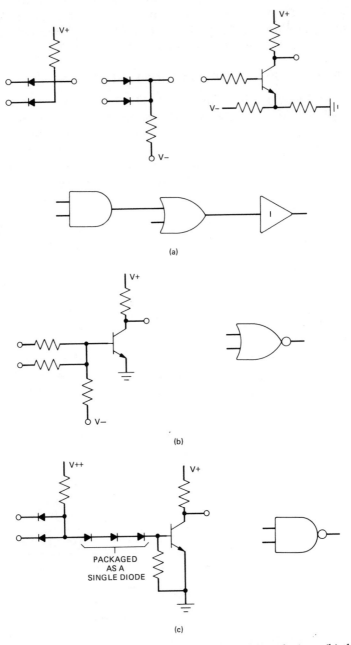

Fig. 9-38. Logic elements as used in (a) the Morris design, (b) the electronic private branch exchange, and (c) the production electronic switching system.

In 1959, the ferreed switch was being studied as an alternative to the pnpn diode as the network crosspoint.[40] By 1960, all the major hardware components had been selected. This included the ferreed crosspoint, the permanent magnet twistor store for program and translation data, the ferrite sheet store for transient data, and the silicon diode and transistors for the logic circuit. It is interesting to note that all the choices represented the better choice in power consumption. There was great concern over the use of "reliable" air conditioning to meet the range of operating temperatures required in a normal central office environment. Reliable air conditioning required expensive standby power generation equipment to back up commercial power.

The Morris field trial system provided many fundamental insights for the production system.[41] Foremost was the feasibility of the stored-program control to operate reliably in real time, 24 hours per day. The major functional units were duplicated, and the system included operational checks for both hardware and software. Special programs, known as fault-recovery programs, were initiated in response to failures of these operational checks. The programs quickly determined the faulty piece of equipment (network, memory, control unit, etc.) and automatically switched it out of service, allowing the duplicate to take over. The system could automatically isolate and remove faulty units, and thus could keep Morris running even though components might fail or operate intermittently. The wisdom of this design philosophy was confirmed by an unprecedented uptime for such a complex electronic system—better than 99.99 percent over a period of many months.

A "Final Report" on Morris, dated March 1963, states: "Excluding the outages due to the failure of air conditioning plant, outages for the last 11–1/4 months averaged 4 seconds per day or less than 0.005 percent." This was attained with an experimental system that contained about 75,000 semiconductor diodes, 12,000 transistors, 30,000 gas tubes, and 2,000 vacuum tubes. The Morris system proved that complex electronic switching systems could be kept in essentially continuous operation for long periods of time. Special customer services that were found to be relatively easy to implement with stored-program control were included in the Morris trial. The "Belltronic Services," as they were called, included abbreviated dialing, code calling, dial transfer, and others. Customer response was assessed and found to be very positive.

The Morris trial demonstrated the value of remedial maintenance techniques, by which a faulty unit was diagnosed to determine the repair, and the repair was made by replacing a few plug-in packs. The trial also demonstrated the value of generating a "dictionary" of failure patterns and of having adequate test access for the diagnostic programs. Overall, the use of stored programs to assist craftspeople in operating and maintaining the central office equipment was to be a key benefit in subsequent system designs.

Although changes due to technological evolution were widespread in the hardware of the system, the soundness of the fundamental architecture and of the stored-program approach was proven in Morris, Illinois. The extensive field trial comprised a year of dependable, full-time, around-the-clock service to more than 400 customers.[42]

5.2 The No. 101 ESS Development

The electronic PBX was renamed No. 101 ESS to indicate that it was to be part of a Bell System family of electronic switching systems.

As described previously, the review of new technologies sometimes took different directions for the No. 1 ESS and No. 101 ESS projects, but where economies of development and manufacture were indicated, common choices prevailed. Thus, the permanent magnet twistor and ferrite sheet store were selected for the common control for both the No. 1 and the No. 101 ESS. In going from the brassboard model to the production design, the No. 101 ESS also adopted the stored-program approach, since the flexibility of design to obtain new, sophisticated features and aids to operation and maintenance were important to the PBX design as well as to No. 1 ESS.

The No. 101 ESS included a pulse-amplitude modulation (PAM) time-division network. This was selected for use in the switch units to exploit the high speed and small size of semiconductor components. The offsetting complexity of interfacing with signaling voltages and currents was confined to providing special ringing controls in each line circuit and dial pulse-detecting circuits in each digit-receiving trunk. The pulse-detecting circuits pass TOUCH-TONE® signals directly and convert dial pulses into bursts of audio frequency tones that are detected by the control unit. Other special signals and switched test access, considered essential in central offices, were not required in PBX applications.

The No. 101 ESS development laboratory under the direction of W. A. Depp was one of the first technical organizations to be moved to the new Holmdel, New Jersey Bell Laboratories building in the spring of 1962. There a full-scale lab model was built and operated for the completion of the system design. A field trial installation was operated, beginning in March 1963 at New Brunswick, New Jersey prior to the first commercial installation. The trial included two commercial customers and New Jersey Bell.[43]

5.2.1 Initial Design

A No. 101 ESS, the first commercial installation of electronic switching, using stored-program control, went into service in Cocoa Beach, Florida on November 30, 1963.[44] At that time, each switch unit handled up to 200 lines, and the control unit had a capacity of 3200 lines and 32 switch units.[45]

Each 200-line switch unit has two buses of 25 time slots each; all lines and trunks have access to both buses, as shown in Fig. 9-20. The dual bus serves 3- and 4-way conference calls. If one bus fails, there are still 25 time slots available for all lines and trunks. The call-carrying capacity with only one bus is sufficient to handle all but the heaviest of traffic loads. Fig. 9-39 depicts the 200-line switch unit and shows the ease of access for additions and replacement of line and switch circuit packages.[46]

The No. 101 ESS control unit is functionally organized as shown in Fig. 9-40.[47] The line information store contains class-of-service information and data for vertical services, such as abbreviated dialing lists

Fig. 9-39. A 200-line No. 101 ESS switch unit with doors open to show easy access for maintenance. (*IEEE Transactions on Communications and Electronics*, Vol. 83, July 1964.)

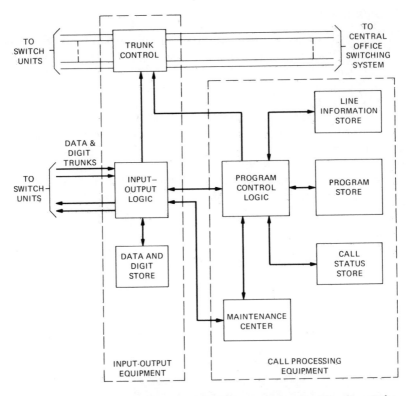

Fig. 9-40. Diagram of the No. 101 ESS control unit. The line information store and program store are permanent magnet twistor memories; call
status store and data and digit store are ferrite sheet memories. *(IEEE
Transactions on Communications and Electronics,* Vol. 83, July 1964.)

for each line served. The line information store is the only unduplicated functional unit. The system is designed to provide basic service
when the line information store is out of service, and the added cost
of a duplicate memory for vertical features was considered to be
unwarranted. Both the program store and the line information store
are permanent magnet twistor memories.

The call status store contains successive 4-word blocks associated
with each time slot in each switch unit. The first word of each block is
the "call progress mark." The call progress mark indicates the state of
the call in its associated time slot. The call progress mark can be idle
(no call in that time slot), originating (a line has just gone off-hook
and has been connected to an available time slot), dialing, ringing,
talking, and so on. As the call is advanced by action of the call-
processing program, the call progress mark is updated accordingly.

The data and digit store contains change in supervisory status or
signaling information transmitted over data and digit trunks from

each of the switch units and collected by the input-output logic. The input-output logic periodically scans all the data and digit trunks to collect the signaling and supervisory information in real time. Both the call status store and the data and digit store are ferrite sheet memories.

The call-processing program deals with each switch unit in succession. It first collects any new inputs for that switch unit from the data and digit store and readies that information for further action. It then proceeds to scan each progress mark in succession to determine if new inputs will permit a call to be advanced. If a call can be advanced, the program transfers to a call progress routine associated with that state of the call. Upon completion of the appropriate call progress actions, the scan of succeeding call progress marks associated with the same switch unit is resumed.

Fig. 9-41 shows a control unit which indicates that it can be provided in 7- or 11-foot bays according to the ceiling height and floor space needs. To grow to its capacity of 3200 lines, only digit data and trunk equipment need be added.

5.2.2 Additional Switch Units

Over 90 percent of the PBX installations were 200 lines or fewer, so the 200-line switch unit (the 1A) would handle a large segment of the market. There was also a recognized need for larger switch units to provide for larger PBX customer needs, and three additional units were designed and manufactured to provide capacities of 340, 820, and 4000 lines (see Fig. 9-42). The largest, the 4A switch unit, combined space-division ferreed switches and PAM time-division buses to provide the necessary terminal and traffic capacity.

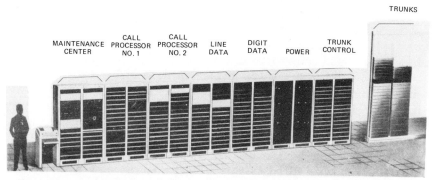

Fig. 9-41. Arrangement of No. 101 ESS control unit, 1000 lines. For growth to 3200 lines, only digit data and trunk units are added. *(IEEE Transactions on Communications and Electronics,* Vol. 83, July 1964.)

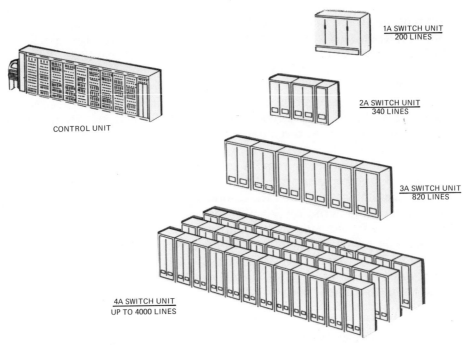

Fig. 9-42. Options available with the No. 101 ESS, starting with a 200-line switch unit.

The No. 101 ESS switch units offered Centrex-CU (for Customer Unit) service. Centrex-CU provided its customer with direct inward dialing to individual extensions in the PBX and automatically identified outward dialed calls to furnish billing details to the PBX customer. Calls between extensions were switched with equipment on the customer's premises, thereby reducing the number of trunks required between the customer and the central office.

In this application, the No. 101 ESS superseded the 701A PBX and saved floor space on the customer's premises.[48] The first 4A switch unit was placed in service in February 1967, at the newly completed Indian Hill Bell Laboratories location in Naperville, Illinois. The control unit for this switch was located in the nearby town of Wheaton.[49] This system provided the convenience of modern PBX features, such as call forwarding to another extension, three-way calling where one of three parties could be on one outside line, and a group pick-up feature to allow calls to extensions in a given office to be picked up by other extensions in the same office.

In 1969, the No. 101 ESS was arranged to provide main-satellite operation. In this arrangement several switch units for a single customer would be located in separate buildings, but all calls requiring an attendant would be routed to a common group of attendants at one location—the site of the "main" switch.[50] At its peak, the No. 101 ESS served 300,000 extensions from more than 200 control units.

5.3 Initial Development of No. 1 ESS

In 1958, several steps were taken to initiate the development of No. 1 ESS. Development leading toward manufacture was authorized in March of that year, and production design work started at the Whippany, New Jersey laboratory. A new systems engineering center was formed at the West Street, New York City, location with W. Keister as its director. This center was responsible for defining the requirements for the No. 1 ESS and the requirements for the field trial system at Morris, Illinois. The ESS development laboratory at Whippany was by that time staffed by over 200 people in five departments. It was headed by C. A. Lovell as director and R. W. Ketchledge as assistant director. The engineers and scientists in these departments were gradually shifted over a period of time from work on Morris to the production design.

At the time of the authorization for work, the first call had just been successfully completed in the pre-Morris laboratory model, and the actual field trial would not begin for more than two years. However, production design during this period resulted in the invention of the ferreed (initially for use in the line concentrator portion of the network), the invention of "low level logic" or "LLL" silicon diode-transistor logic gates by W. B. Cagle and W. H. Chen, and the invention of the basic architecture of the central control by J. A. Harr. Decisions were also made to drop the barrier grid store and the flying-spot store in favor of magnetic core memory (in the form of the batch-fabricated ferrite sheet array) and the permanent magnet twistor. These milestones were all reached by the end of 1959. At that time the paper design of the central control included the "autonomous call module," a subsidiary processor which was the forerunner of the "signal processor." Subsidiary processing would be provided in those offices requiring call-carrying capacity beyond that obtainable without a signal processor.

By January 1960, the development organization had grown to 240 and was divided into two laboratories. C. A. Lovell headed the systems and software laboratory, and R. W. Ketchledge had been appointed director of a laboratory responsible for all circuit and equipment design for production. In 1960, work continued on refining the hardware design and determining software requirements. An improved version of the ferreed was developed using a metal sleeve of Remendur to replace the more fragile rods of sintered ferrite material. In addition, the Bell Labs epitaxial process for transistor fabrication allowed the use of silicon transistors to obtain higher breakdown voltages, reduce the collector-to-emitter saturation voltage, and gain better reliability of operation. Laboratory models of ferrod scanners, ferrite sheet and twistor memories, central control logic units, and network control units were assembled and operated in 1960 and 1961. On the system and software side, program planning and development was under way. The system architecture was based on the expected size and capacity of the subsystems. The program order structure was evaluated by coding typical telephone sequences, and work was started on support programs both to generate and to debug actual ESS instructions. Planning of a system lab was started.

The flexibility of stored-program control was also extended to the trunk circuits designed for No. 1 ESS. The physical equipment in a trunk circuit is in most cases limited to that necessary for detecting and generating the signals required on these circuits and for performing basic switching operations such as loop closure or loop reversal. All sequencing of these operations, including timing the duration of signals, is performed by central control under instructions from the program. This has the effect of minimizing the variety of trunk circuits required and of reducing their cost, since changes in timing or sequence of operation can be made through changes in the program.

During 1961, the development teams were reassigned to a separate division dedicated to electronic switching. It was led by W. H. C. Higgins as executive director and included more than 300 people working on No. 1 ESS, as well as W. A. Depp's center at Murray Hill, New Jersey, which was developing No. 101 ESS, and J. A. Baird's center at Whippany, New Jersey, which was responsible for military applications. This last group had started development, in 1959, of an integrated (voice and data, analog and digital) system for the Signal Corps. This system, to be described later, adopted much of the No. 1 ESS hardware and software.

During the remainder of 1961 and 1962, the hardware designs were completed and given to Western Electric for manufacture. In the summer of 1962, the electronic switching division was relocated to a new laboratory location at Holmdel, New Jersey, and shortly thereafter systems lab models were assembled for the three major projects. W. Keister's switching engineering center had moved first to Whippany to work more closely with development engineers. This center also accompanied the development organization to Holmdel in 1962. Keister remained in charge of ESS switching engineering until after the cutover of the first No. 1 ESS in Succasunna, New Jersey in 1965.

Fig. 9-43 shows the early milestones for the first No. 1 ESS systems lab. Although the units were tested at the factory, the equip-

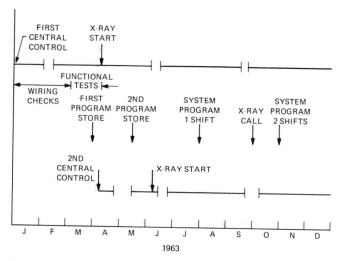

Fig. 9-43. 1963 status of No. 1 ESS systems laboratory tests.

ment was subjected to extensive tests with "X-ray" programs in the systems lab. These test programs were executed by the central control to test itself and the remaining functional units of the system. (These X-ray programs became the major element of installation testing, which minimized the need for testing hardware in the field.) By August of 1963, debugging of the system was under way, and effort was increased to two shifts by November of that year. With specially written X-ray programs, the first call was placed in the Holmdel lab on September 30, 1963. Although this did not use the system program, it demonstrated the working of all the functional units (networks, scanners, distributors, ringing circuits, and trunks) needed to place such a call and to confirm the readiness of the system lab to operate as a debugging tool for system programs.[51]

In addition to the system equipment, there was supporting hardware and software designed and built for the Holmdel laboratory. A program test console shown in Fig. 9-44 displayed the internal registers of both central controls and various other registers and flip-flops in other ESS units. With this hardware, the program could be stopped at selected points in its execution, and the state of the system could be read from the display. Geared to these points was a utility program operating high-speed punched card readers and line printers. Test conditions were inserted, and the results were printed out. The programmer could read the console display to help determine the nature of an elusive problem and use a utility program card reader and printer to get test results quickly from the test lab. Then the programmer could analyze the printout and make program changes without further tying up the valuable test facility.

Fig. 9-44. R. S. Cooper using the No. 1 ESS program test console, which displayed the execution of the ESS program and aided debugging.

The program changes could be made with punched cards, and the correction could be entered and tested in the systems lab. In this way, many programmers could "time-share" their debugging efforts in the Holmdel system lab.[52]

The first commercial installation of No. 1 ESS was a 4,000-line office at Succasunna, New Jersey. The equipment for Succasunna was installed in the summer and fall of 1963, and system program testing began at this location in January 1964. Also, there were tests using specially designed load boxes, and teams of test operators placed special calls to provide traffic well in excess of the busy-hour demand at Succasunna. The operators also tried as many combinations of unusual call sequences as reasonably possible to stress the program design. On May 27, 1965 a dedication ceremony was held,[53] and on May 30 Succasunna began providing commercial service to 4,000 customers.

The second No. 1 ESS, placed in service in January 1966, at Chase, Maryland was very similar in size and program requirements to the first. Despite extensive testing, program problems caused a number of brief interruptions of service at Succasunna in the first three months of operation. These problems were identified and the programs were corrected before the Chase office went into service.

The result was that the Chase office did not experience these interruptions and, soon after its cutover, was left unattended much of the time.

More general application of ESS required additions to the program used for Succasunna and Chase. This, the first of a series of "generic" programs, called CC1 for central control-1, was first applied to the Beverly Hills, California office, which followed the Chase installation into service in January 1967. It represented the first metropolitan-size ESS office, and handled a greater variety of calls. For this purpose, 33,000 words were added to the Succasunna program. Sixteen offices with the CC1 generic program went into service in 1967.

The flexibility of No. 1 ESS in incorporating new features has been amply demonstrated. When the first No. 1 ESS was placed in service in 1965, it provided 187 features, including (1) local automatic message accounting (LAMA), (2) custom calling services, (3) arrangements for numerous operator service trunks and interoffice signaling, and (4) various types of coin features including local overtime charging capability. The first program had 11 features not then available to No. 5 crossbar. By 1976, the number of No. 1 ESS features had increased to more than 500.

To provide both Western Electric installers and operating telephone company expertise in the operation and maintenance of the new system, a special school was set up and operated by Bell Laboratories. Engineers from Bell Labs, Western Electric, and the operating companies served as instructors to provide material for an extensive 34-week course that was run twice in succession starting in January 1964. One hundred and thirty-one trainees from various operating companies, Western Electric, and the Long Lines Department of AT&T completed the course, which included "hands-on" operating experience. Those trained in this special school returned to manage and maintain their early installations and to establish training schools within their own operating companies.

The principal of the school was M. Raspanti, who also designed two classroom demonstration units to represent the stored-program control of first the Morris system and then the No. 1 ESS. The latter unit was used extensively to introduce operating company operating personnel to the new techniques of switching system control. The students could write special programs for Raspanti's demonstrator and then debug and run them in the classroom. The demonstrator could be made to walk through its programmed sequence slowly enough to allow the class to visually follow every step.[54]

Western Electric installation personnel also had to acquire a working knowledge of No. 1 ESS software since the testing of No. 1 ESS installations was done largely with programs loaded into twistor memory. First the X-ray programs were loaded and run to assist the basic debugging of the equipment and interconnecting buses and cables. When all of the X-ray programs could run without errors being detected, the generic program was loaded and run. The operational programs attempted to run the system as a switching office, and the maintenance programs were also exercised to find and fix more errors of manufacture and installation.

Among the last tests performed were special pre-cutover tests of lines to which the No. 1 ESS would be directed during periods of light traffic, connecting each line, one after the other, to the network and to test circuits. ESS would then test and measure each line to verify that it was properly connected to the new system. Any faults detected would be noted on the teletypewriter for remedial actions. At the completion of each brief test, the line would be returned to the old central office by automatically disconnecting it from the No. 1 ESS. With these powerful new tools a "flash cut-over" of many tens of thousands of lines could be accomplished with the assurance of virtually no wiring errors and bother to telephone customers.

5.4 UNICOM

The advent of stored-program control ESS was of interest to military switching system planners. The Signal Corps began studying improvements to their strategic communications with a thought toward serving both the three military departments and other government traffic vital to the national interest. A systems study was made to define a UNiversal Integrated COMmunications system—UNICOM. The system study included new transmission facilities, a new family of station equipment, and the interconnection of various modes of telecommunications into a single integrated switching system. By 1958, the feasibility of such a system had been established, and in June 1959, the Signal Corps and the Bell System as prime contractor entered into an agreement for development.[55]

Bell Laboratories was the contractor of the system with ITT and RCA as major subcontractors for portions of the system. The system included a time-division network, which operated with either circuit connections for secure voice or switched data on a store-and-forward basis. The system also included a space-division network and a stored-program control to operate both the time-division and space-division networks as an integrated switching office. The space-division network was a 4-wire version of the ferreed network developed for No. 1 ESS, and the common control was a direct adaptation of the No. 1 ESS central control, twistor program store and ferrite sheet call stores. The time-division network was also designed by Bell Labs using the low level logic circuits designed for No. 1 ESS. Fig. 9-45 shows the block diagram of the central office.

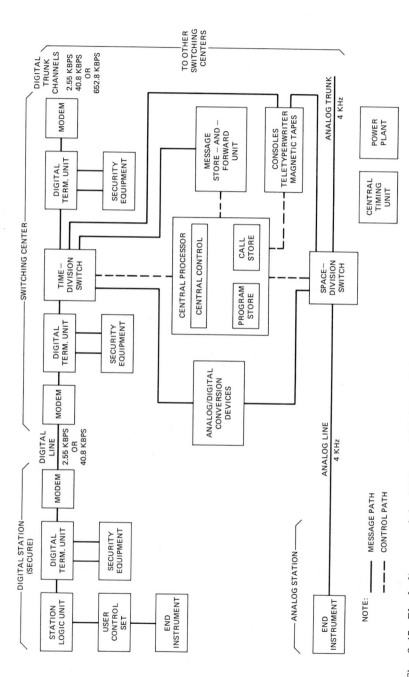

Fig. 9-45. Block diagram of the UNiversal Integrated COMmunications (UNICOM) 4-wire system for the Signal Corps. UNICOM uses both time-division and space-division switching. The end instrument could either be a telephone for voice, a facsimile terminal for graphics, or a teletypewriter or other terminal for data.

The contract called for the development and operation of a test model to demonstrate both the equipment operation and a large number of operational features obtained from special ESS programs written for this application.

Several departments in a military systems development laboratory under J. A. Baird were assigned to the UNICOM project. The development efforts for UNICOM started at the Whippany, New Jersey laboratories, collocated with the ongoing ESS development. Both projects moved to the new location in Holmdel, New Jersey in 1962, and there the UNICOM test model was built and operated. At that time, over 100 engineers and programmers were working on the UNICOM project.

Fig. 9-46 shows a view of one part of the UNICOM test model with the switching center consoles and the analog and digital station control sets.[56] The digital station encoding, encryption, and control required substantial additional circuitry to handle all the forms of encoding required. With discrete components, two seven-foot high bays of equipment were required to serve ten digital stations. The stored program was an adaptation of the No. 1 ESS program to handle the different network and features required for this system. The total program was estimated to require 200,000 words as compared to the 110,000 words provided in the Succasunna program.

Fig. 9-46. Part of the UNICOM test model—switching center consoles and digital and analog station control sets.

The equipment units were almost electrically equivalent to their No. 1 ESS counterparts, but substantial physical redesign was needed to meet military environmental requirements. Fig. 9-47 is a photograph of one aisle of the UNICOM test model at Holmdel. Grills at the bottom of several of the frames are for forced air conditioning required in approximately fifteen percent of the equipment. In October 1963 calls were placed in the system using simplified test programs. By 1964, the scope of the project had been curtailed to the test model itself, and the project had been redesignated (Defense Automatic Integrated Switch—DAIS).[57]

Although the UNICOM test model was destined to be one of a kind, its capabilities were successfully demonstrated to the Signal Corps, and much of the development effort saw fruition in other ESS projects. Fig. 9-48 shows a 4-wire version of the ferreed switch that was developed for UNICOM and the AUTOVON project (see

Fig. 9-47. Row of UNICOM switching equipment which employed forced air cooling, an example of special design to meet military requirements.

below). Engineers working on the time-division switch were later able to apply their knowledge to the design of the time-division switch for No. 4 ESS. Many unique features of the UNICOM system are described in Chapter 12 of the volume of this series subtitled *National Service in War and Peace (1925–1975)*.

5.5 AUTOVON

The Defense Communication Agency (DCA) in the early 1960s established a 4-wire worldwide telecommunications network. The new network (which superseded the UNICOM proposal) combined the Air Force's NORAD/ADS (NOrth American Air Defense Command/Automatic Dial Switching System) network and the U. S. Army's SCAN (Switched Circuit Automatic Network) into a single network designated CONUS AUTOVON (CONtinental U. S. AUTOmatic VOice Network). SCAN was activated in 1961 and NORAD/ADS in 1963, both using specially designed 4-wire No. 5 crossbar systems developed by Bell Labs starting in 1959 (see

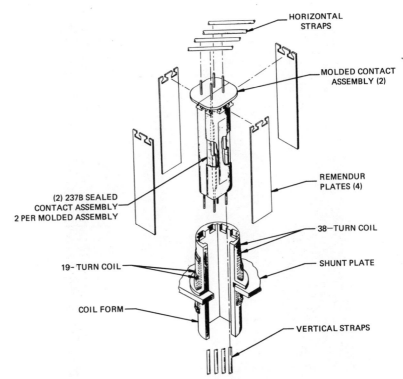

Fig. 9-48. Special 4-wire ferreed switch designed for UNICOM and subsequently used in the AUTOmatic VOice Network (AUTOVON) system.

Chapter 11 section 1.9). AUTOVON was to be a 4-wire end-to-end switching network. The Defense Communication Agency had learned of the ESS development and wanted to introduce stored-program control as soon as practicable into AUTOVON.[58] The DCA expected that they would have rapidly changing and evolving needs, and recognized that stored-program control would provide them with a system that had the necessary design flexibility.

AUTOVON was primarily to serve the Department of Defense, but it included other government communications and would switch voice, encrypted voice, and data. Fig. 9-49 shows one of the air defense command posts to be served by AUTOVON. The network was to be "survivable" in the face of nuclear attack. The switching centers were to be situated away from metropolitan centers and were in "hardened" sites, usually underground. In addition, the network links were to be arranged in a "polygrid" fashion much more redundant than the hierarchical Bell toll network. Fig. 9-50 shows the grid of AUTOVON trunk circuits across the Continental U.S. (see ref. 59). Even with the loss of many links and centers in the network, calls could be connected to those centers surviving a nuclear attack.

Development for AUTOVON electronic switching systems started in two areas at Bell Laboratories. In September 1963, development was authorized for a 4-wire version of No. 1 ESS for AUTOVON.

Fig. 9-49. Air defense command post served by AUTOVON.

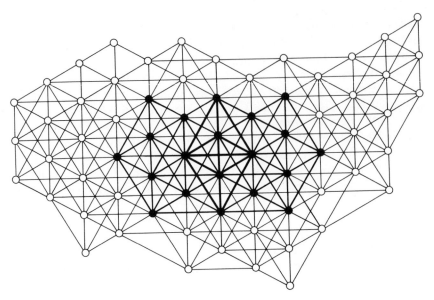

Fig. 9-50. Polygrid network concept for AUTOVON, which provides greater redundancy than commercial networks and therefore greater survivability in the face of nuclear attack.

Another development effort was authorized in July 1964 for a smaller ESS to be used in AUTOVON. The latter system was based on a new processor intended to extend the capability of the No. 101 ESS beyond 3200 lines. The new design was intended to provide small 4-wire and 2-wire central office systems using switch units similar to those already being designed for No. 1 ESS 4-wire and 2-wire projects. This system was later named No. 2 ESS.

The No. 1 ESS AUTOVON development was formed in 1963 under H. N. Seckler as department head, and with a supporting group for equipment design. This team comprised approximately 50 engineers and programmers. By January 1964, the development team had grown to 100 people in three departments under the direction of R. E. Staehler. A systems lab was established at Holmdel, New Jersey and moved to Indian Hill, Illinois in 1966. At the Indian Hill lab, two test models were required to meet the ongoing testing needs of engineers and programmers.

In May 1966, four No. 1 ESS 4-wire systems were simultaneously cut into service, followed by a fifth installation in July. In the meantime the No. 2 ESS 4-wire project faced technical problems with the processor stores, which were estimated to have delayed the availability of the system until the end of 1968. Consequently, the 4-wire portion of small office development was dropped, and No. 1 ESS 4-wire systems were used to meet all of the AUTOVON needs.

By 1971, a total of 45 No. 1 ESS 4-wire AUTOVONs were in service, including three in Canada. By that time the ongoing software needs had been met with the fifth AUTOVON generic (AV-5). Studies had already been started to determine the Bell System needs for its own toll network, and the development effort shifted to that project.

VI. EXPANSION OF NO. 1 ESS APPLICATIONS

By the end of 1967, No. 1 ESS had been successfully introduced in eighteen offices in eleven Bell operating companies, and one in Montreal for Bell of Canada. The Montreal system, in service January 1967, was the first of eight built and installed by The Northern Electric Company for Bell of Canada under licensing and manufacturing agreements with the Western Electric Company.

Much work remained to be done on the metropolitan 2-wire applications and capabilities; a suburban office was under development (No. 2 ESS), and the No. 101 ESS also required additional hardware and software to extend its range of application with the larger switch units already described. To this end, a new major laboratory—the Indian Hill Laboratory—opened its doors in the summer of 1966 in Naperville, Illinois. The entire electronic switching division of more than 800 engineers, technicians, and supporting staff was relocated, beginning in July 1966, from Holmdel and Columbus, Ohio to Indian Hill, with R. W. Ketchledge as executive director.

The new building included one section devoted to lab test models of the various systems. Until they were fully operational, the No. 1 ESS test model was retained at Holmdel, and a team of some fifteen engineers and programmers continued work in that lab until it was shut down in July 1968.

In setting up the labs at Indian Hill, additional facilities were provided to meet the increased demand for system testing. By mid-1968, the following test models were in operation: two No. 1 ESS 2-wire systems, two No. 1 ESS 4-wire systems, No. 2 ESS, No. 101 ESS, and No. 1 ESS Arranged for Data Features (ADF). (No. 1 ESS ADF is described in section 6.3.)

All of these labs were operated by groups whose responsibilities were (1) to plan the design and operation of the test models and supporting test equipment, (2) to direct the installation and bringing into service of each of these central office systems, (3) to maintain smooth operation and good up-time of the laboratory facilities, and (4) to plan, design, build, and operate new test adjuncts to increase testing effectiveness and efficiency. This type of large effort requires dedicated people and generally both a wide and deep range of knowledge of the total system. Of course, the systems test models were augmented by many smaller laboratories devoted to circuit, frame, and physical design. In addition, a large computer center was established to provide the necessary support for the generic software and engineering support programs required by the various systems.

This period saw an increased emphasis on the use of the support computers to enhance the productivity of the designers and testers of both software and hardware. It was recognized that the development of administrative methodology[60] was paramount to being able to meet the needs of the operating telephone companies.

Computer aids to various aspects of ESS design were developed. Some of these were based on experience starting in the 1950s with the Morris system. Others were adopted from other sources and refined for use in ESS development. These included (1) simulation of operational programs, (2) simulation of logic designs, (3) circuit analysis programs, (4) diagnostic test synthesizers and analyzers, (5) circuit board layout synthesizers, (6) thermal analysis programs for equipment design, (7) compilers and assemblers, (8) office engineering programs, and (9) time-shared interactive software to work with some of the programs listed above.[61]

In addition, the integration of computers in the test models to streamline the testing and to obtain test results was provided in all the test model labs. These small- and medium-size computer installations included interactive keyboard terminals, magnetic tape transports, disk memories and high-speed line printers, and punched card readers to facilitate the entire testing procedure. Fig. 9-51 shows a typical lab test model support system.

One of the important tests involves load testing to determine the call-carrying capacity of each ESS system. Load testing was performed on each of the systems with "load boxes," which provided call originations, dialing (or keying TOUCH-TONE* telephone) calls, answering on terminating lines and hanging up of calling and called lines, and repetition of the process. These load boxes could generate ten different numbers for 50 originating lines. Fig. 9-52 shows a load box capable of providing up to 6000 calls per hour. An actual installation was exercised with load boxes prior to its cutover into service when new programs or hardware improvements in processor capacity were being introduced. The limited network and/or terminal capacity of the test models, especially of the larger systems, precluded a full load test in the laboratory.

As the capacity of the No. 1 ESS was increased, ten or more load boxes were required for fully testing the call-carrying capacity of the systems. Additional hardware and ESS software aids were employed to double the load offered by the load boxes.[62] More powerful load box techniques were designed, using minicomputers to increase offered load capacity.

---

*Trademark of AT&T Co.

Fig. 9-51. Computer facility used in support of the No. 1 ESS laboratory test model.

A programmable electronic call simulator (PECS), including a commercial computer, was designed and built for automatically generating telephone traffic on both line and trunk terminals in the laboratory. It could generate, and repeat if necessary, unusual call

Fig. 9-52. Load box used to test No. 1 ESS developmental and installed systems. Unit placed up to 6000 simulated telephone calls per hour. *(Proceedings, Fall Joint Computer Conference, IEEE Vol. 41, 1972.)*

sequence patterns to test any call processing feature. In another instance, test calls were generated in one test model to provide an offered load to a second test model. In the development of No. 4 ESS, a computer was programmed to simulate the networks, terminals, and the offered traffic.[63]

6.1 Signal Processor and Capacity Improvement

While the cutover of the first offices in 1965 and 1966 was the culmination of a very large effort, further work was needed to bring No. 1 ESS to full maturity. One task was to provide the call-carrying capacity needed in very large metropolitan installations.

The call-carrying capacity of a stored-program control system is usually limited by the complexity of the program, the power of the repertoire of instructions to carry out the steps of the program, and the speed with which the common control can execute the stream of instructions to carry out its tasks. To increase call-carrying capacity in larger offices, the No. 1 ESS was to have added to it one or more pairs of signal processors to relieve the central control of the more routine program tasks such as line scanning and the setting up and taking down of connections in the ferreed network.[64] It was later decided to provide only one pair of signal processors in the larger offices, in keeping with other limitations imposed by the maximum size of the switching network. In this configuration, the No. 1 ESS was estimated to attain a peak capacity of 100,000 calls per hour. The capacity of the system with only the central control was estimated to be from 42,000 to 53,000 calls per hour, depending on the mix of call types handled. These estimates were obtained in 1962 using early predictions of the number of operating cycles (at 5.5 microseconds per central control instruction) required to execute call-processing programs. The estimates, which represented the design objectives, were revised in late 1964 when the program for Succasunna was much nearer to completion. The capacity was then calculated to be 80,000 calls per hour with a signal processor and 37,000 for a central control office.

The signal processor, plus the program changes and additions to allow the central control to share the work load cooperatively, were planned first for a New York City office within a year after the cutover of the Succasunna, New Jersey office. The ESS was to replace the first three-digit office code panel system serving the PEnnsylvania-6 office—the same office serving the telephone number made famous by bandleader Glen Miller's hit tune.

The first installations of No. 1 ESS were in limited environments that did not handle a great variety of trunk signaling. The Beverly Hills office in the Century City section of Los Angeles included the connection to adjacent step-by-step offices, which required more central processor work to detect the initiation of incoming trunk calls (the stored-program control equivalent of by-link operation described in Chapter 6). Because of this and other feature requirements, the first generic program went into service at Beverly Hills in January 1967. It was known as CC-1 (central control-1) and required over 140,000 words of program, substantially more than the 111,000 used in the Succasunna and Chase, Maryland installations.

The generic program concept was adopted to serve many installations rather than tailoring the program for each installation. This greatly simplified the tasks of writing and testing the rather complex programs to provide for the large variety of features demanded of No. 1 ESS.[65]

The Beverly Hills ESS was two to three times larger than its predecessors, serving approximately 11,600 customer lines, and was selected to obtain measurements of the call-carrying capacity of the central control with the CC1 programs. A Bell Laboratories and Western Electric team was stationed at Beverly Hills to carry out the on-site feature debugging and testing of call-carrying capacity. In the fall of 1966, a number of test-call load boxes were connected to the ESS, and the capacity was determined to be 27,000 calls per hour—sufficient for Beverly Hills at cutover but below earlier expectations.

The Succasunna program was designed and written to conserve the amount of both program and temporary memory required, and this objective was accomplished at the expense of requiring more program execution cycles to process calls than previously estimated, and the first generic program inherited this characteristic. It was also recognized that a corresponding reduction in capacity would be reflected in the installations using the signal processor. The developers of ESS began investigating the ways of increasing call-carrying capacity.

Fig. 9-53 shows the history of improvements in call capacity, including "quick fixes" to the CC-1 generic program provided early

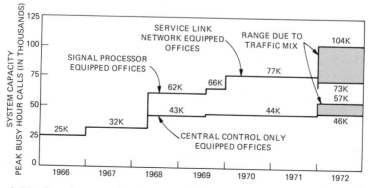

Fig. 9-53. Steady growth of No. 1 ESS call-carrying capacity, 1966–1972.

in 1967. The central control office improvements were principally software and, as can be seen, attained the early objectives by 1973. The signal processor data show the enhanced capacity obtained in 1968, when the PEnnsylvania-6 installation went into service. Its generic program, the SP-1 or signal processor-1, was substantially larger than CC-1. The No. 1 ESS signal processor doubled the call-carrying capacity to around 70,000 calls per hour, and software improvements that applied to the central control configuration also enhanced the signal processor offices.

Fig. 9-54 is a simplified block diagram of No. 1 ESS showing the interconnections of the signal processor. All the routine line and trunk scanning operations were transferred to the signal processor. The results of its operations were stored in its own temporary memory, and the central control accessed those memory locations (signal processor call stores) to fetch those results to carry out its call processing. Central control transmitted output information back to the signal processor, so that the latter would carry out commands to set up network connections, operate the necessary service circuits, and carry out trunk supervisory and signaling operations.[66]

It was planned that many installations could begin service with the central control only and have the signal processor added whenever the office customer lines and call needs grew beyond the initial capacity. Growth to larger sizes (instead of starting a second ESS at that point) provided efficiencies in switching and trunking and greatly conserved telephone company expenditures. This complex growth procedure of hardware and software was carried out in field trials in offices in service in Philadelphia, Detroit, and Denver. It then became available as a standard installation procedure in 1971.

An additional hardware improvement was applied to the signal processor offices to reduce the network reconfiguration required during the successive stages of setting up calls. The service link network, or SLN, streamlined the call-processing and signal-processing operation at an added cost to the No. 1 ESS switching network.[67] Addition of the SLN initially boosted the capacity of the largest offices by 15 percent.

An example of SLN simplification in setting up the connection required for ringing, followed by the transition to a talking connection, is depicted for an incoming call in Fig. 9-55. On incoming trunk calls, the service link network saves 10 network operations and 25 percent of processing time in setting up a ringing connection. Instead of three paths—ringing, caller-audible ringing, and talking—only two paths are needed because a single path serves both the ringing and talking connections. The ringing/talking path is split at the SLN. The number of network operations required for a ringing connection is thereby reduced from the 19 required

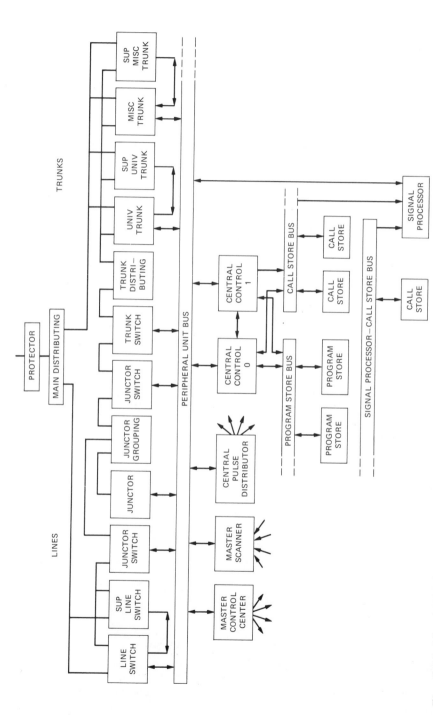

Fig. 9-54. No. 1 ESS block diagram showing the interconnections of the signal processor to double the call-carrying capacity of the system (January 1963).

without the SLN to 9. The first SLN was placed in service in the Chicago Calumet No. 1 ESS in April 1970. Later software improvements complemented the gains due to the SLN. Consequently, the service link network, with its added hardware, is no longer needed or offered. By 1973, the original call-capacity objectives for No. 1 ESS had been met and exceeded by software refinements alone.

6.2 Centrex

Centrex is the name of a set of PBX-like business services that were first offered in 1962 to customers served by No 5. crossbar (see Chapter 11, section 1.4 and Chapter 13, section 3.1). It was

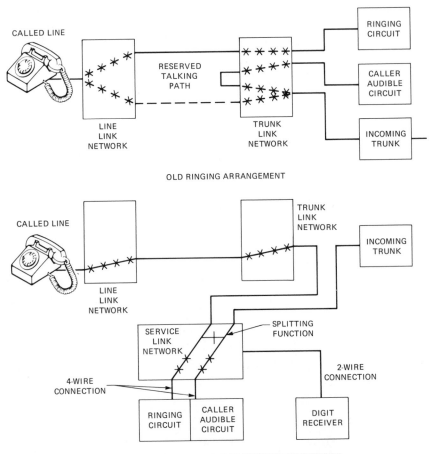

Fig. 9-55. Example of how the service link network (SLN) increases No. 1 ESS capacity. With SLN (bottom) fewer network operations are needed to set up paths for ringing and talking than with earlier arrangement (top).

designed to permit direct inward and outward dialing to a group of telephones, thereby reducing the attendant workload for the business customer and allowing more rapid completion of incoming and outgoing calls. Accountability of usage per telephone can be provided through detailed billing.

With Centrex-CO, instead of providing a switching system on premises, all telephones and attendant loops are returned to the central office, which carries out the various switching functions required. This reduces the amount of equipment on the customers' premises and the number of visits required to maintain and reconfigure the customers' telephone equipment.[68] Thus, an economic trade-off is made among more customer loops and less attendant workload and the sharing of central office switching equipment and operations. The central office switching system can serve a number of Centrex customer groups, each with its own set of selected services and operating features. As a consequence, since No. 1 ESS was designed to serve metropolitan needs, it was important that Centrex be included as a service offering.

A set of 20 telephone, attendant, and trunking features required some 30,000 words of program for No. 1 ESS, and the generic program, Centrex-1, was first placed in service in the Philadelphia, Locust exchange in April 1968. The features included 4-digit station-to-station dialing, transfer of calls from one telephone to another with the assistance of the attendant, dial "0" calls to the attendant, and access to special trunk groups such as foreign exchange (FX), wide area telephone service (WATS) and Common Control Switching Arrangements (CCSA). Features were added to the Centrex offerings with succeeding program issues. Table 9-1 shows the major features provided and added in the sequence of program issues from Centrex-1 to Centrex-7. With the relative ease of such feature additions, No. 1 ESS became the more attractive vehicle for Centrex. In December 1969 a No. 1 ESS Centrex was placed in service in the Pentagon in Arlington, Virginia. By 1971 it served 17,000 Centrex telephones and required 74 attendants.[69]

For some of the more sophisticated attendant features, a data link was provided for two-way communication between the No. 1 ESS and the attendant's console. A control cabinet, located on customers' premises, was required, as shown in Fig. 9-56, to provide the interface between the console and the data link. In smaller, less complex configurations, the attendant's console would be replaced by a multibutton key telephone.[70] A newer console, the 50A customer premises system, featured direct station selections (DSS) and a busy line field (BLF). The 50A was first placed in service in 1973 and provides, for smaller Centrex groups, another alternative to the data link controlled console.[71]

Table 9-1. Evolution of Major Features, No. 1 ESS Centrex.

Centrex-1 Generic Program:	Centrex-3 Generic Program:
Console features for attendant operation	Multilocation service
Direct inward dialing	Attendant-established conference calls
Automatic identified outward dialing	Interface with AUTOVON network
Station-hunting arrangements	**Centrex-4 Generic Program:**
Toll restriction on outward calls	Tandem tie-line operation
Individual/attendant ability to transfer calls to another line	TOUCH-TONE® calling on incoming calls
Ability to hold and consult with party on another extension and to add a third party to the connection	**Centrex-5 Generic Program:**
	Call forwarding and call waiting
	Additional attendant call and testing capabilities
Dial-controlled automatic dictation capabilities	**Centrex-6 Generic Program:**
Ability to access foreign exchange lines, tie-lines, WATS lines or portions of the public network acting as a corporate private network	Automatic call distribution capability
	Additional station-hunting capabilities
	Extension user able to establish conference calls
Ability to route certain incoming calls to the first idle one of a designated list of extensions	Variable assignment of connection of off-hour calls
	Centrex-7 Generic Program:
Paging	Additional capabilities for automatic call distribution
Routing of off-hour calls to a fixed location, usually the attendant's station	Features for use of Centrex in a hotel/motel or hospital

6.3 No. 1 ESS ADF

The No. 1 ESS Arranged for Data Features (ADF) is a store-and-forward data switching system designed to handle messages among low-speed teletypewriters and computer ports. It was the first electronic system to handle TWX traffic in the Bell System, and at the time of its first service for the Long Lines Department of AT&T in February 1969, it was unique in its traffic-handling capacity and

Fig. 9-56. Jack Leidy, Pennsylvania Bell, checking a Centrex attendant's console controller.

operating services and features. It serves over 1,250 four-row (ASCII) teletypewriters and low-speed computer ports. No. 1 ESS ADF prioritizes, queues, receives, and delivers up to 100,000 messages with more than 120 million characters per day to teletypewriters having different operating speeds and different characters sets (Baudot or ASCII). It provides for multiple message delivery based on a single originating message, orders the delivery of messages according to a four-level precedence code designated in the originating message, and stores delivered messages on a magnetic tape file for subsequent retrieval. These and many other features are in daily use at the single installation in New York City, which handles all of Long Lines administrative messages, commercial services orders, traffic service orders, service results, payroll, plant circuit orders, and expense analysis reports.[72]

By basing the ADF design on No. 1 ESS technology, development and manufacturing efforts were minimized, and the high reliability of telephone switching systems was achieved. Sixty percent of the

ADF hardware and 25 percent of the 250,000 words of program are standard No. 1 ESS design already in use.

The block diagram in Fig. 9-57 indicates the new equipment designed for the No. 1 ESS ADF. The message store is a high-speed magnetic disk memory that was later adapted for use in the Automatic Intercept System (see Chapter 10, section III).

Fig. 9-58 shows the connection of terminals to the system. As indicated, a number of teletypewriters may share the same narrow band line. In this instance, ADF recognizes the "party line," polls

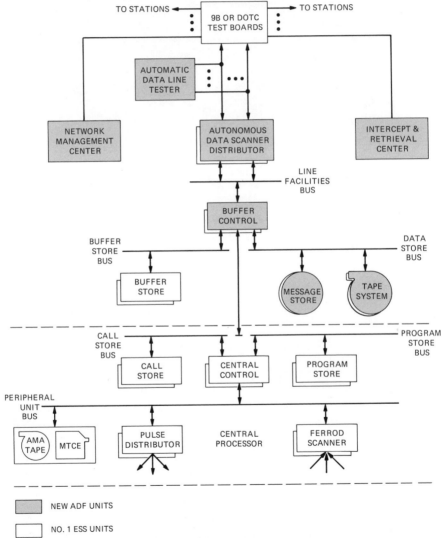

Fig. 9-57. New equipment designed for No. 1 ESS ADF (Arranged for Data Features).

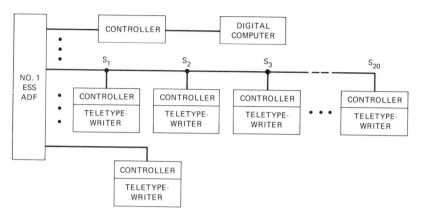

Fig. 9-58. Connection of terminals to No. 1 ESS ADF.

individual stations in turn for incoming messages, and queues outgoing messages for sequential delivery.

The reliability of the initial installation was monitored and reported to be far superior to that of prior electromechanical data switching systems. After the first week of service, ADF proceeded to deliver over ten million messages in the next seventeen months without loss or misdirection.[73]

At the time of deployment of the ADF installation, AT&T had agreed to sell its dial teletypewriter network (TWX) to Western Union (see Chapter 13, section 5.4). This obviated the need for additional installations, and future deployment ceased.

6.4 32K Call Store

The temporary memory initially provided with No. 1 ESS was the ferrite sheet, which used batch-fabricated arrays of 256 magnetic cores along with simplified wiring techniques (see this chapter, section 4.7.1). Bell Laboratories circuit engineers in the research and development areas continued to search for smaller and faster temporary memories by investigating new materials, circuits, and assembly techniques. As part of this ongoing effort, individual magnetic core memory arrays were surveyed, and a number of modules were purchased for use in one of the Indian Hill systems laboratories in the late 1960s.

Simpler wiring of core arrays (two-dimensional instead of three-dimensional), automatic techniques for assembling and wiring of core mats, and the ability to manufacture smaller and faster sintered ferrite cores had been developed by the computer memory industry. To these contributions Bell Labs added new ways of testing cores to assure minimization of core shuttle noise and novel access circuits that allowed more practical memory sizes for ESS application and faster operating speeds than previously obtainable from two-dimensional array core memories.[74] The result was a new temporary memory for use in No. 1 ESS. Fig. 9-59 shows the dramatic improvement in memory frames used in the largest ESS installations.

The memory module is 32,000 words (hence the name 32K) of 24 bits each, four times the number of words of its predecessor. Fig. 9-60[75] shows the economic analysis that led to selecting the new module size.

The first 32K memories were placed in service in a No. 1 ESS installation in Alton, Illinois in 1971. By 1972 all new No. 1 ESS systems shipped by Western Electric used the 32K temporary memory exclusively.

The 32K memory is less expensive for the operating telephone companies to buy and maintain. Through the use of integrated circuit techniques in the memory access and control circuits, far fewer plug-in circuit packs are required. This allows improved diagnostic resolution of circuit faults. In addition, the core memory module can operate, with different access circuits, at four times the speed required for No. 1 ESS. This fact permitted a module common to No. 1 ESS and another project described below in section 6.9 of this chapter.

6.5 Generic Programs and Feature Additions

As previously indicated, the complete set of programs for call processing, operation, administration, and maintenance are relatively

Fig. 9-59. Improvement in the size and power of No. 1 ESS memory frames obtained with the 32K call stores. (*Symposium Record, International Switching Symposium*, Kyoto, Japan, October 1976.)

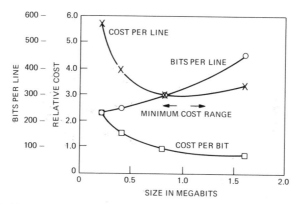

Fig. 9-60. Economic analysis leading to an optimum size of No. 1 ESS temporary memory. Bits per line multiplied by cost per bit implied a module in the range of one million bits. (*Proceedings, IEE Conference on Switching Techniques for Telecommunications Networks*, April 1969.)

large and complex—over 200 functional programs totaling from 150,000 to over 300,000 words for No. 1 ESS. The decision was made relatively early to design a single program that would cover all applications or major segments of applications, hence the term "generic program" for ESS. It was recognized that such programs would require more memory and take more time to execute (and therefore reduce the processor call-handling capacity) than programs tailored to each installation. The result was reduced development effort and better debugged programs for all installations. (These factors reduced the cost of the programs to the operating companies, thereby compensating for the additional memory and processing real time required.) The use of the generic program with a table of office parameters as contrasted to tailored programs is depicted in Fig. 9-61.

One of the significant advantages of the stored-program approach is the relative ease of adding features and services. Almost annually the generic program has been updated to provide a steady stream of enhancements to No. 1 ESS. The frequency and size of these enhancements are regulated by the work required to define and document (with AT&T) the features and services, write the programs, debug them first in the laboratory, then in a "first application" system in the field, and with Western Electric, make the new issue of the generic program generally available to the field.[76] There are always more candidates for added features and services than can possibly be developed in a single program update. A priority or so-called "grocery list" is established, and decisions have to be made as

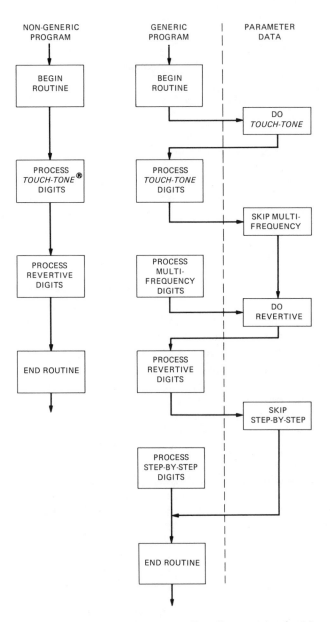

Fig. 9-61. Generic programs versus tailored programs for No. 1 ESS.

to what items to include in each new generic program development. Bell Labs systems engineers estimate the savings or revenues for various enhancements, development teams gauge the amount of effort and the number of program words required, and AT&T prepares a priority list for each new issue of a generic program for ESS. Fig. 9-62 shows the distribution of features and program store required for No. 1 ESS.[77] The growing set of features for Centrex customers, only a part of the growth in the generic program, was detailed above in section 6.2.

Fig. 9-63 shows the varieties of generic programs and the growth in memory required. Since it was necessary for most No. 1 ESS installations to provide Centrex service, the non-Centrex generic programs were not continued beyond issue 3. Later, the generic program concept was reexamined in light of large additions to the program for use in more limited applications. In 1976 the generic programs were separated into a base program, with features used in almost every application, and feature packages, which could be optionally selected and loaded into individual installations as needed. Large programs (e.g., ESS-ACD and mobile telephone service or AMPS) are provided on an as-needed basis. This containment of program size has relieved operating companies of the purchase of unnecessary storage of unused programs. By this time, techniques for debugging and integrating new software had advanced sufficiently to make this approach more practical.

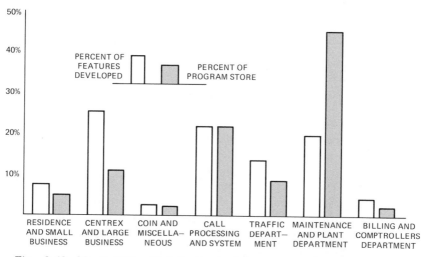

Fig. 9-62. No. 1 ESS—Distribution of features and program storage requirements. (*Symposium Record, International Switching Symposium,* Paris, April 1979.)

6.6 Remreed Network

When the ferreed was first proposed in the late 1950s, the idea of using the reeds themselves as the latching magnetic structure was proposed by R. L. Peek. At the time, however, the reed switch could not be fabricated consistently with the necessary magnetic properties. This problem was overcome in 1970, when it was realized that stamping the reeds from annealed remendur provided the necessary cold-working of the metal.[78]

By making the metal blades of the reed switch of remendur (hence the name remreed), the entire switch structure can be reduced in volume to one-fourth the size of the corresponding ferreed switch. The scanner ferrods were also reduced in size, and wire spring access relays were replaced by pnpn transistors and access diodes. These components are directly mounted in a package of two eight-by-eight switches.[79] Integrated circuits were also introduced into the network controllers. When first introduced, small scale integration (SSI) was achievable. Fig. 9-64 shows the initial size reductions and the further reduction in components and interconnections with the use of large scale integration (LSI).[80]

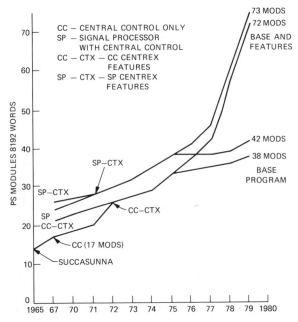

Fig. 9-63. Varieties of generic programs and growth in memory requirements. The non-Centrex generic programs were not continued beyond issue 3. *(Symposium Record, International Switching Symposium, Paris, April 1979.)*

As shown in Fig. 9-65, the reduction in size of the components resulted in a reduction in the No. 1 ESS network frame's size to one third or one fourth, depending on the network type. This allowed a complete trunk link network (TLN) serving 1,000 trunks to fit into a single 6-foot 6-inch equipment frame. The TLN is completely assembled and tested in the factory, then shipped as a single unit to the installation site. The ferreed TLN consisted of eight frames and

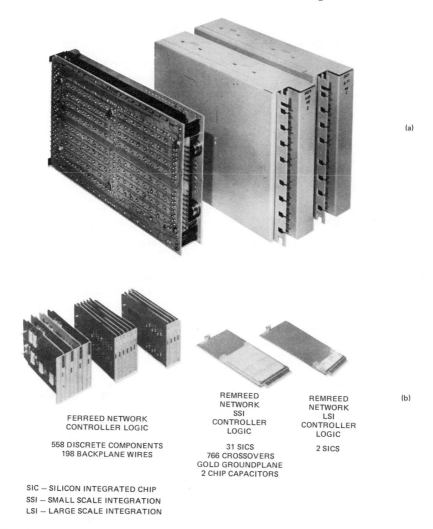

(a)

(b)

FERREED NETWORK
CONTROLLER LOGIC

558 DISCRETE COMPONENTS
198 BACKPLANE WIRES

REMREED
NETWORK
SSI
CONTROLLER
LOGIC

31 SICS
766 CROSSOVERS
GOLD GROUNDPLANE
2 CHIP CAPACITORS

REMREED
NETWORK
LSI
CONTROLLER
LOGIC

2 SICS

SIC — SILICON INTEGRATED CHIP
SSI — SMALL SCALE INTEGRATION
LSI — LARGE SCALE INTEGRATION

Fig. 9-64. Size reduction of remreed switch compared to the equivalent two ferreed switches (a) and corresponding reduction in control circuits and their wired and bonded interconnections (b). (*Symposium Record, International Switching Symposium*, Kyoto, Japan, October 1976.)

required substantially more installation wiring to interconnect these frames. It also required more testing of the assembled functional unit, since factory testing of the separate frames was more limited.

The actual remreed switch element, as distinct from the equipment frame, is in several respects only slightly smaller than its ferreed predecessor. This allowed the reuse of much of the ferreed assembly machines, thereby reducing the retooling cost of the new design. Also, the remreed network was designed to be electrically similar enough to the ferreed network so that operational programs would encounter no differences, and testing programs a minimum of differences. Remreed networks could be added as extensions to in-service No. 1 ESS's operating with ferreed networks.

The first remreed trunk link network (TLN) went into service in Detroit, Michigan in June 1973. Beginning in 1974, the remreed line link networks (LLNs) went into production and were placed into service. The remreed network not only offers a price advantage over ferreed but reduces the floor space of an ESS office by thirty percent. By October 1976, shipments of remreed networks to serve 6 million lines and 3 million trunks were reported.[81]

6.7 Centralized Maintenance

The interface between No. 1 ESS and maintenance craftspeople is at the master control console (MCC). At this location is a maintenance typewriter over which trouble messages are printed out and

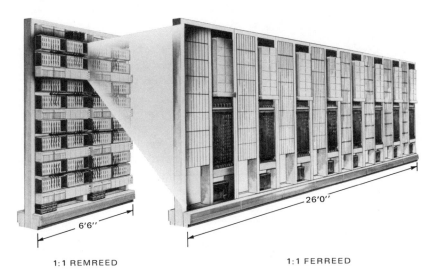

1:1 REMREED   1:1 FERREED

Fig. 9-65. Dramatic reduction in size of the No. 1 ESS trunk link network components made possible by the remreed switch and integrated circuits. *(Symposium Record, International Switching Symposium,* Kyoto, Japan, October 1976.)

interrogatory and corrective messages are typed in. So long as the ESS is operable enough to communicate over this link, it can be considered the primary channel of maintenance communications. As backup in the event the system becomes inoperable, the display and control panel operates independently of the ESS to monitor the status of major functional units and to allow manual reconfiguration of duplicate units. With these controls, the craftsperson can try to build an operable system when the ESS cannot automatically do so.

Experience with early ESS installations showed troubles to be infrequent enough that the continuous presence of the more skilled craftspeople was not required, and that adequate troubleshooting would frequently be beyond the training of lesser skilled craftspeople. This led to the centralization and concentration of skills in the technical assistance center (TAC).

6.7.1 Technical Assistance Center (TAC)

The maintenance teletypewriter could be remotely operated over a data link on a dedicated or a switched loop for unattended operation, and various alarms could be operated in conjunction with the teletypewriter to sound the alert for minor or major difficulties. When the number of ESS installations in an operating telephone company increased, these remote connections could be placed in a single location, which came to be known as a TAC. The TAC would be staffed with highly skilled craftspeople who would then be much more frequently exposed to problems and would become adept in relating problems to previous experiences and in quickly correcting them. The craftspeople would guide the less experienced person over the telephone as to the troubleshooting and repair actions to take, or would dispatch a repair person if the office were unattended. This improvement successfully reduced the number and extent of office difficulties that required the still more skilled efforts of Western Electric product engineering control or Bell Labs development engineers.

However, situations still existed that required access to the maintenance control and display panel; if a difficulty occurred that could not be remedied by the teletypewriter link, then dispatching a craftsperson might extend a total office outage for several hours. This led naturally to the next step—the ability to remotely observe and operate the control and display panel over a voice-grade data link.

6.7.2 Switching Control Center (SCC)

Experiments in Chicago in 1972 using the remote control and display led to the Switching Control Center (SCC), which replaced the TAC and stimulated the planning for additional analytical tools. The next step was the addition of a minicomputer to aid SCC craft personnel. The minicomputer would monitor incoming messages, log them on magnetic tape for later retrieval, and detect and highlight messages that required SCC personnel attention. It also allowed craftspeople to browse through messages on a cathode ray tube display by scrolling commands and to chronologically sort and filter messages to help detect patterns among long sequences of trouble printouts. Brief teletypewriter messages can be expanded with more self-explanatory messages as a further aid to the craftsperson, and specific analysis programs automatically determine patterns in network failure messages. By incorporating a minicomputer into the SCC, it became possible to serve many other types of stored-program control systems, such as TSPS, No. 2 and 3 ESS, Automatic Intercept System (AIS), No. 101 ESS, etc. The first SCC with the minicomputer system began operation in Miami, Florida in June 1974.

The introduction of stored-program control into the central office provided automatic trouble detection and default location superior to that attained for non-SPC switching systems. ESS achieves a substantial advantage in maintenance expense over No. 5 crossbar and earlier electromechanical systems. The concentration of skilled craftspeople and further automation of testing and test analysis provided with the SCC further reduces maintenance expenses, improves trouble locating, and provides more expert assistance in recovering central office outages.

In Chapter 11, section 3.3.4 a description of an SCC for No. 5 crossbar is given, but enhancements in its maintenance efficiency are limited by the test access built into No. 5 crossbar.

6.8 Improved Trunk Circuits for No. 1 ESS

Even though many trunk circuit functions had been placed into software for No. 1 ESS, new miniaturized relays, coils, and transformers, along with better semiconductor devices, allowed further dramatic improvements in size and cost of the No. 1 ESS trunk circuits. The associated distributing and scanning circuits were also improved to gain a threefold to sevenfold size reduction and a reduction in cost and installation interval.[82] These improvements were introduced into the field beginning in the spring of 1976 in Salt Lake City, Utah.

Fig. 9-66 shows the improved Universal Trunk (UT) circuit frame. The UT frames reduced the floor space required for an ESS by 25 percent.

6.8.1 HiLo Trunk Circuits

Although 4-wire ferreed networks were designed and are in use in the No. 1 ESS AUTOVON network for toll transmission, they are relatively large, and production was limited to this application. To meet the need for 4-wire service, therefore, an innovative alternative was provided for use with the remreed network. The remreed network, being less than one-fourth the size of the ferreed network, substantially reduced the inherent capacitive and magnetic coupling between tip and ring and among pairs in the network voice paths. The new trunk circuit (see Fig. 9-67) segregated the pair into separate one-way paths. By using a high impedance in the transmitting end, inductive crosstalk is inhibited; a low-impedance receiver inhibits capacitively coupled crosstalk—hence the name HiLo. This technique reduces crosstalk due to unbalanced transmission to a level comparable with that obtained with 4-wire balanced transmission.[83] The HiLo approach introduced 4-wire switching for tandem and toll applications in No. 1 ESS, beginning in April 1977 in Sioux Falls, South Dakota.

6.9 The 1A Processor

During the late 1960s and early 1970s, several efforts were started to increase the call-carrying capacity of No. 1 ESS. One approach was to rewrite those portions of the program that were large users of processor real time. Another was to increase the efficiency of the network interconnection with the service link network (see section 6.1 of this chapter). The third was to explore the possibility of providing a new processor for the No. 1 ESS using newer technologies—a faster central control and faster memory-accessing schemes. During this study it was also recognized that a powerful

Fig. 9-66. Universal Trunk frames for No. 1 ESS. Technological innovations resulted in smaller unit (left) replacing its predecessor (right) to reduce the floor space required by 25 percent. (*Symposium Record, International Switching Symposium,* Kyoto, Japan, October 1976.)

enough processor could serve the proposed toll ESS, and thereby avoid the need for a complex multiprocessing array of No. 1 ESS processors (see Chapter 12). Several processor architectures were considered, including variations of memory technologies. Development of this processor for several applications was authorized by Western Electric in 1970.

A block diagram of the 1A processor is shown in Fig. 9-68. Although not shown in the figure, redundancy is provided for all major subsystem units and interconnecting buses. A pair of central controls are microsynchronized, and each instruction's execution is matched. Each central control is made up of 50,000 integrated circuit gates and can execute instructions four to eight times faster than its predecessor, the No. 1 central control. The main memory consists of two arrays of the previously described 32,000-word magnetic core memory modules for the program store and call store. The core store memories operate in a system cycle of 1.4 microseconds, and the backup is provided with one or two roving spares (except for certain critical information where full duplication is retained). The more flexible roving spare scheme is inherently more dependable than the fixed full duplication scheme. Since the core memory modules do not retain their information when power is removed and the programs can be overwritten, the backup of the program is provided on high-speed, fixed-head disk memories.[84]

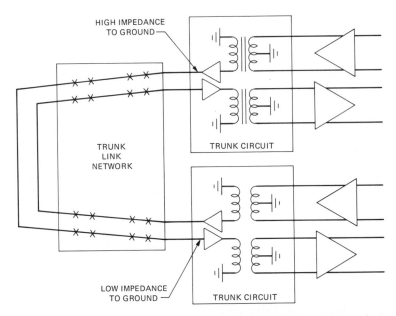

Fig. 9-67. HiLo trunk circuit, introduced in 1976, permitted 4-wire switching in No. 1 ESS tandem and toll applications. *(Symposium Record, International Switching Symposium, Kyoto, Japan, October 1976.)*

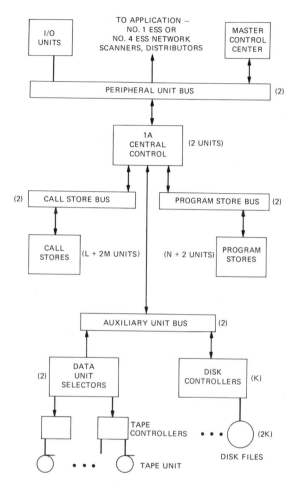

Fig. 9-68. Block diagram of the 1A processor, which executes instructions four to eight times faster than the earlier No. 1 ESS central control.

The 1A processor with magnetic core memories occupies only 40 percent of the floor space of its predecessor. Its compact size and connectorized interunit cabling allow complete processor assembly and test in the factory, and a fixed floor plan simplifies office engineering.

The 1A processor was designed for two applications: as a successor to the No. 1 ESS central control and signal processor in its local and tandem applications, and as the processor for the very large new toll office—the No. 4 ESS. The 1A processor order structure is designed to operate directly with the No. 1 ESS peripheral program through a software conversion process. This allows the extensive reuse of No. 1 ESS software with a minimum of additional writing, debugging and documenting. A new common processor program is required, but this software is used in both No. 1A ESS and No. 4 ESS. The No. 4 ESS first went into service in January 1976, and the first No. 1A ESS in October, 1976, both in Chicago, Illinois. In the latter application, the 1A processor has a peak call-carrying capacity of 240,000 calls per hour, more than twice that of the No. 1 ESS.

Since the 1A processor is directly compatible with the No. 1 ESS peripheral system, the 1A processor can be retrofitted into existing No. 1 ESS installations. Since the 1A processor can handle more than twice as many calls per busy hour as its predecessor, a 1A processor of a retrofit can extend large No. 1 ESS offices much further before a second entity is required. The large capacity of the No. 1A ESS is estimated to reduce the total number of large ESSs required by 1990 from 1600 to 1300. A large No. 1A ESS can replace several older systems, thereby saving up to 25 percent of the trunking. Work on this project began in 1973, and the first retrofit was carried out in the San Francisco Folsom Street office on January 20, 1978.[85] The replaced processors are then reused as part of new No. 1 ESS offices in other locations.

To match the increased processor capacity, the line link and trunk link networks were increased in their maximum number and size. Fig. 9-69 shows the relationship between processor and network as a function of busy hour call holding time. The processor and net-

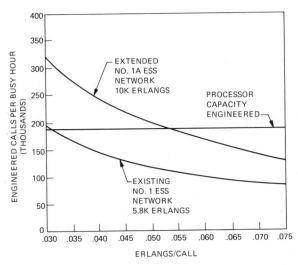

Fig. 9-69. The line link and trunk link networks were extended to handle additional telephone traffic (top curve), thus matching the greater capacity of the 1A processor. (*Symposium Record, International Switching Symposium*, Kyoto, Japan, October 1976.)

work are matched for three-minute calls, which is the average for local calls in the Bell System.[86]

Both the No. 1 and No. 1A ESS use the remreed network with the HiLo trunk circuits to provide space-division 4-wire interconnections. Accordingly, both No. 1 and No. 1A ESS are designed to provide combinations of local/tandem/toll service in those areas where a modern central office is needed and for which the No. 4 ESS is too large to be economical.

6.10 Improved Memory Systems

As noted above in section 6.4, a 32,000-word magnetic core memory was introduced in 1971 to reduce the cost for the No. 1 ESS call store. When connected to faster access circuits, that same memory served, beginning in 1976, as both program store and call store module for the 1A processor. The core memory achieved substantial size, power, and cost reductions over the ferrite sheet predecessor. Technology had advanced by the early 1970s to the point where a much smaller core memory appeared able to achieve another reduction in size and cost. However, semiconductor memories were also becoming more attractive (one third the space and one fifth the power of the 32K core) and won the competition to be the next generation of main memory for ESS.[87] The semiconductor memory was first used in a No. 1A ESS in July 1977, in the Wilmington, Delaware office.

Magnetic bubble memories were also investigated as a possible replacement for the disk memories in the 1A processor in the early 1970s, but at that time they did not have an economic advantage. Interest remains in finding an economic semiconductor mass memory to compete in cost with rotating disk memories; the inherent higher reliability of devices that have no moving parts is a motivating factor.

The use of laser beams in a very large holographic memory was also explored—basically a photographic memory with the potential for very large storage and high-speed random access. This work was started in the early 1970s, but did not progress to the stage of being economically competitive.

6.10.1 The Role of SPC in Mobile Telephone Service

Significant use of private mobile radio systems dates back to 1921, beginning with the Detroit police department. Over the years, the Federal Communications Commission has granted additional radio spectra to increase private licenses to over eight million users (and another eight million on CB). These systems for the most part do not connect to the telephone network. Beginning in 1946, the Bell System inaugurated a three-channel system in St. Louis. Over the succeeding years, additional frequencies were allocated, improvements were made in changing service from manual to automatic, and trunking was added between mobile units and available channels. However, only 143,000 customers are served by Bell and the radio common carriers (RCC). There are tens of thousands of held orders for carrier-connected mobile telephone systems, even though the tariff is ten to twenty times that of residential telephone service. Because the waiting time is so long, there are many others who need this type of service but have not bothered to add themselves to the waiting list.

Since 1947, the Bell System has expressed to the Federal Communications Commission, in a number of review dockets, its interest in a large-scale mobile telephone system. In docket 19262, Bell introduced in 1971 a new version of the cellular system, which reuses a basic group of frequencies in nonadjacent hexagonal cells. As the mobile unit roams from cell to cell, its connection is moved from transceiver to transceiver under control of a central office switching system. No. 1 ESS was chosen to be the mobile telephone switching office (MTSO), since it has the software capability to allocate cells and frequencies as a call is "handed off" from cell to cell. In addition, the MTSO has to locate the cell for originations and provide additional conveniences for mobile customers. Initially the intent was to combine local and mobile services in the same switching office. In 1975, the FCC gave the Bell System the go-ahead for a development field trial of the cellular system but the switching office would be limited to handling only calls to and from mobile units. A No. 1 ESS, located in Oakbrook, Illinois was set up to operate a few cells and mobile units. Success of the trial is expected to lead to a larger service test and, with FCC approval, commercial service.[88]

VII. NO. 2 ESS LOCAL SYSTEM DEVELOPMENT

The No. 2 ESS development was an evolutionary extension of the No. 101 and No. 1 ESS developments. In July 1961, during the development of No. 101 ESS, the possibility was noted of extending that system to provide improved central office services. The early ideas included a redesign of the No. 101 processor and an increase in memory capacity to enable it to have a broader range of application, including the serving of larger PBX switch units and also main telephones, via remote switch units.

7.1 The Initial System

In response to inquiries from AT&T engineering, a study was undertaken in 1963 by A. Feiner, W. Ulrich, and F. S. Vigilante of a small electronic switching system for use in the Bell System in

2-wire arrangements and as a 4-wire office for use in CONUS AUTOVON. The processor design included single- and half-word instructions to conserve program memory, special instructions for efficiently nesting subroutines, and an autonomous input/output unit to perform scanning and other repetitive operations interleaved on a cycle-stealing basis with the call program. The periphery used No. 1 ESS network and trunk circuit apparatus in a smaller and more economical configuration than that of the No. 1 ESS. For example, the number of network controllers was reduced, the network was simplified into a four-stage, single-sided network where lines and trunks appeared on a combined line-trunk network frame, and the variety of network concentrations was reduced, which simplified both hardware and software. Further simplifications were proposed with the use of the electrically writable piggy-back twistor (PBT) program store to avoid the cost of a magnetic card writer and the associated ongoing expense of the card writing required of the permanent magnet twistor (PMT) used in No. 1 ESS. Additional proposals included simplified communication buses, since the physical size of the office would be much smaller than No. 1 ESS and, because of fewer total components, simplified reconfiguration arrangements for the communication bus and functional units. The No. 2 ESS, as the system was later named, was to provide service for use to 10,000 lines and 25,000 calls per busy hour and to serve up to 2,000 trunks in the AUTOVON application. Price comparison studies showed that the No. 2 ESS compared favorably with No. 5 crossbar from 600 lines on up, with substantial savings between 3,000 and 10,000 lines.[89]

At that time, PBT stores encountered severe design problems, and eventually it was decided that the No. 2 ESS AUTOVON application would not be economically attractive. Work on that part of the project was stopped in December 1966. The 2-wire office design continued, using the PMT and ferrite sheet memories.

By 1968, a 2-wire system lab model was in operation at the Indian Hill, Illinois Laboratories, and in November 1970 the first office went into service at Oswego, Illinois. A block diagram of the production version of No. 2 ESS is shown in Fig. 9-70. By the summer of 1976, 200 installations of No. 2 ESS equipped for one million lines were in service. The No. 2 ESS processor also served as the control unit for another application, the Automatic Intercept System (AIS), which is described in Chapter 10, section III.

7.1.1 Transportable Version (No. 2A ESS)

Recognizing that building costs were rising rapidly, Bell Labs engineers designed transportable modules of No. 2 (designated No. 2A ESS) for quick installation in rural or suburban locations.

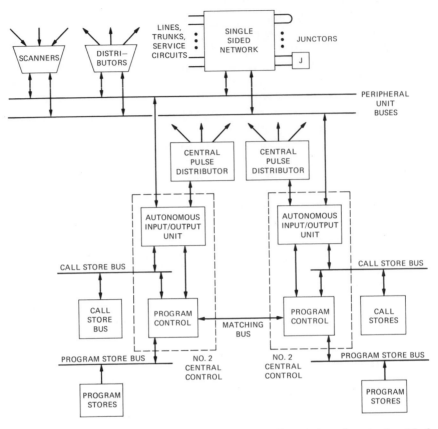

Fig. 9-70. Block diagram of the No. 2 ESS illustrating the single-sided network with common network terminal arrays for lines, trunk circuits and service circuits.

Fig. 9-71 shows No. 2A ESS modules under way from the factory to the installation site. Three such equipment modules, each 12 feet wide by 48 feet long, can contain the switching equipment and batteries for a 3000-line office. Additional modules provide capacity to 15,000 lines, power service, and an optional administration center. The complete system is assembled in the factory with connectorized cables between modules. The module can be quickly set on a precast foundation and plugged together for quick, efficient site installation. Facade panels[90] can be installed to provide a more pleasing exterior. The first No. 2A ESS went into service in Sun Valley, Nevada in November 1972.

7.2 The 3A Central Control and No. 2B ESS

Although successful, the No. 2 ESS was not economical below several thousand lines in comparison with step-by-step community

Fig. 9-71. Transportable No. 2A ESS. Units are assembled at the factory with connectorized cables. Set on a precast foundation, system quickly provides service for 3000 lines.

dial offices, even though the No. 2 ESS offered much more capability. The No. 2 ESS processor, to meet its development schedules, had to forego monolithic integrated circuit logic and the PBT memory. Furthermore, the No. 2 ESS network could expand beyond 10,000 lines to 20,000, but the call-handling capacity of the No. 2 ESS processor limited the practical size in almost all offices to 10,000 lines or fewer.

Several independent exploratory design efforts were undertaken to provide the control for a very small office. The design ideas were coalesced into a single microprogrammed control that became the 3A CC (central control), the processor for No. 3 ESS. The microprogramming capability of the new processor, along with price and size advantages gained through the use of integrated circuit logic and semiconductor memories, made it attractive for several switching applications. Although redundant controls were usually used, these processors had extensive self-checking capabilities and did not employ matching techniques for error detection.

An integrated circuit version of the autonomous input/output logic of the No. 2 ESS was added to the 3ACC, extending the width of the data words from 16 to 24, and the microprogram memory was set to emulate the No. 2 ESS processor instructions. With these changes, the No. 2 ESS was both substantially reduced in cost and increased in capacity. The new configuration, the No. 2B ESS, first went into service in Acworth, Georgia in February 1976. The Acworth system was actually a No. 2C ESS—a transportable arrangement of the No. 2B. The first No. 2B ESS was placed in service in Elgin, Illinois in June 1976.

Since the new processor emulates the No. 2 ESS programs directly, much of the software investment in No. 2 ESS is conserved with a minimum of additional testing effort to incorporate it into the No. 2B ESS. The 2B processor can be retrofitted in a No. 2 ESS so that the existing No. 2 ESS's have the option of doubling their capacity before exhausting. The first retrofit of a 2B processor was carried out in Northbrook, Illinois in April 1977. The 2B processor resulted in rating as manufacture discontinued (MD) the No. 2 ESS processor by 1977. Again, one can note the shortening of the life cycle of telephone switching processors in this case to less than a decade.[91]

The 3ACC also was employed, beginning in 1976, in a special private network which handled credit card transactions. This application is noted in Chapter 13, section 5.4. A third application was for the No. 5 Electronic Translator System, which provided some stored-program capability for No. 5 crossbar. (See Chapter 11, section 1.14.2 for a description of the No. 5 ESS.)

7.3 Centrex and Other Feature Developments

The first generic program for No. 2 ESS was the LO-1 (Local Office-1), which went into service in 1970 with 182 residential, business, call-processing, maintenance administration, and traffic and billing features. This compares favorably with 124 features in the initial No. 1 ESS program. The second generic program, EF-1 (Extended Features-1) went into service in February 1974, in Naperville, Illinois. EF-1 added 128 features, most of which were Centrex operating and maintenance features. Centrex service from the No. 2 ESS was first provided to the AMOCO research center in Naperville, Illinois in April 1974.

Because of the difference in operating environment between No. 1 ESS and No. 2 ESS (longer loops, more T carrier development), several features appeared on No. 2 ESS that had not been added to No. 1 ESS by the end of 1976. Special range extension amplifier and battery boost circuits were placed in the network B links to be connected to long loops. By concentrating the range extenders inside the network, the number of extenders was reduced from that required if attached to each long loop. A more powerful extender, which adapted its compensation according to the condition of the loop, was later added. These circuits, later known as CREG (concentrated range extension with gain), were first used in the North Madison, Connecticut office, which went into service in August 1976. A second feature is the combining of T carrier D3 channel banks and No. 2 ESS trunk circuits into a single functional unit to eliminate redundant signaling, components, and cabling. This feature went into service at Lake Villa, Illinois in November 1977.

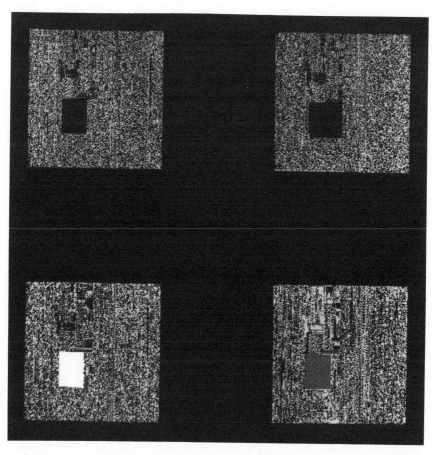

Section of photographic plate used in the Morris system flying-spot store (see pages 236 and 237). In the actual plate, each square is 1-3/8 inches on a side. Overall 2.2 million-bit store allowed the central control to read 25-bit instruction words every 2.5 microseconds. The rectangular areas within each square were for test purposes.

REFERENCES, CHAPTER 9

1. Malthaner, W. A. and Vaughan, H. E. "An Experimental Electronically Controlled Automatic Switching System." *Bell System Technical Journal* **31**, May 1952, p. 443.
2. Depp, W. A. and Townsend, M. A. "Cold Cathode Tubes for Transmission of Audio Frequency Signals." *Bell System Technical Journal* **32**, Part II, November 1953, p. 1371.
3. Moll, J. L., Tanenbaum, M., Goldey, J. M. and Holonyak, N. "P-N-P-N Transistor Switches." *Proc. of IRE* **44**, September 1956, p. 1174.
4. Murphy, O. J., McGuigan, J. J. and Lovell, C. A. "An Experimental Polytonic Signaling System." *Bell System Technical Journal* **34**, July 1955, p. 783.
5. Malthaner, W. A. and Vaughan, H. E. "DIAD—An Experimental Telephone Office." *Bell Laboratories Record* **32**, October 1954, p. 361.
6. Keister, W., Ketchledge, R. W., and Vaughan, H. E. "No. 1 ESS: System Organization and Objectives." *Bell System Technical Journal* **43**, September 1964, p. 1831.
7. Schneckloth, H. H. "Some Basic Concepts of Translators and Identifiers Used in Telephone Switching Systems." *Bell System Technical Journal* **30**, July 1951, p. 588.
8. Vaughan, H. E. "Research Model for Time-Separation Integrated Communication." *Bell System Technical Journal* **38**, July 1959, p. 909.
9. Newby, N. D; U. S. Patent 2,679,551; filed September 21, 1950; issued May 25, 1954.
10. Hines, M. E., Chruney, M. and McCarthy, J. A. "Digital Memory in Barrier-Grid Storage Tubes." *Bell System Technical Journal* **34**, November 1955, p. 1241.
11. Horton, A. W., Jr. and Vaughan, H. E. "Transmission of Digital Information Over Telephone Circuits." *Bell System Technical Journal* **34**, May 1955, p. 511.
12. Joel, A. E., Jr. "An Experimental Remote Controlled Line Concentrator." *Bell System Technical Journal* **35**, March 1956, p. 249.
13. Brooks, C. E., Henry, J. L., Markthaler, G. E. and Sand, W. C. "Distributed Line Concentrator with Unique Intraconcentrator Completion Circuits." *AIEE Transactions on Communication and Electronics* **82**, July 1963, p. 435.
14. Buhrendorf, F. G., Henning, H. A. and Murphy, O. J. "A Laboratory Model Magnetic Drum Translator for Toll Switching Offices." *Bell System Technical Journal* **35**, May 1956, p. 707.
15. May, H. F. "Magnetic Drum Storage System Considered for Use as a Common Sender in Nationwide Dialing." *AIEE Transactions on Communication and Electronics* **77**, Part 1, March 1958, p. 5.
16. Yokelson, B. J. and Ulrich, W. "Engineering Multistage Diode Logic Circuits." *AIEE Transactions on Communication and Electronics* **74**, Part 1, September 1955, p. 466.
17. Yokelson, B. J., Cagle, W. B. and Underwood, M. D. "Semiconductor Circuit Design Philosophy for the Central Control of an Electronic Switching System." *Bell System Technical Journal* **37**, September 1958, p. 1125.
18. Joel, A. E., Jr. "An Experimental Switching System Using New Electronic Techniques." *Bell System Technical Journal* **37**, September 1958, p. 1091.
19. Joel, A. E. and Quirk, W. B. "Field Trial of an Experimental Telephone Switching System." *Conference Record*, General Fall Meeting of the AIEE, Morris, Illinois, October 12, 1960.
20. See ref. 18 above.
21. Dunlap, K. S. and Simms, R. L., Jr. "A Gas-Tube Space-Division Network for an Electronic Telephone Switching System." *Conference Record*, General Fall Meeting of the AIEE, Paper No. 3, Morris, Illinois, October 12, 1960.
22. See ref. 18 above.

23. Greenwood, T. S. "A 2.2 Megabit Photographic Store for an Electronic Telephone Switching System." Part of the General Fall Meeting of the AIEE, Morris, Illinois, October 12, 1960.

24. Harr, J. A. and Smith, R. B. "Logical Design and Programming an Electronic Telephone Switching System." Part of the General Fall Meeting of the AIEE, Morris, Illinois, October 12, 1960.

25. Joel, A. E., Jr. "Electronics in Telephone Switching Systems." *Bell System Technical Journal* **35**, September 1956, p. 991.

26. Haugk, G. "Report on Morris ESS." *Electronic Switching Symposium*, Holmdel, New Jersey, January 21–24, 1963.

27. DeBuske, J. J., Janik, J. Jr. and Simons, B. H. "A Card Changeable Nondestructive Readout Twistor Store." *Proc. of the Western Joint Computer Conference*, San Francisco, California, March 3–5, 1959, p. 41.

28. Barrett, W. A., Humphrey, F. B., Ruff, J. A. and Stadler, H. L. "A Card-Changeable Permanent-Magnet-Twistor Memory of Large Capacity." *IRE Transactions on Electronic Computers* EC-10, September 1961, p. 451.

29. MacPherson, D. H. and York, R. K. "Semipermanent Storage by Capacitive Coupling." *IRE Transactions on Electronic Computers* EC-10, September 1961, p. 446.

30. MacPherson, D. H. "Information Storage Arrangement." U.S. Patent No. 3,011,156; filed May 28, 1959; issued November 28, 1961.

31. Genke, R. M., Harding, P. A. and Staehler, R. E. "No. 1 ESS Call Store 0.2-Megabit Ferrite Sheet Memory." *Bell System Technical Journal* **43**, September 1964, p. 2147.

32. Goddard, M. C. "Ringing Selection in No. 5 Crossbar." *Bell Laboratories Record* **20**, April 1950, p. 168.

33. Feiner, A., Lovell, C. A., Lowry, T. N. and Ridinger, P. G. "The Ferreed—A New Switching Device." *Bell System Technical Journal* **39**, January 1960, p. 1. The ferreed invention is covered by U.S. Patent 2,992,306 applied for July 1, 1959; issued July 11, 1961.

34. Danielson, D., Dunlap, K. S., and Hofmann, H. R. "No. 1 ESS Switching Network Frames and Circuits." *Bell System Technical Journal* **43**, Part 2, September 1964, p. 2221.

35. Feiner, A. and Hayward, W. S. "No. 1 ESS Switching Network Plan." *Bell System Technical Journal* **43**, Part 2, September 1964, p. 2193.

36. See ref. 34 above.

37. Feiner, A. and Goeller, L. F. "A High-Speed Line Scanner for Use in an Electronic Switching System." *Bell System Technical Journal* **37**, November 1958, p. 1383; Freimonis, L., Guercio, A. M. and May, H. F. "No. 1 ESS Scanner, Signal Distributor and Control Pulse Distributor." *Bell System Technical Journal* **43**, September 1965, p. 2255.

38. Yokelson, B. J., Cagle, W. B. and Underwood, M. D. "Semiconductor Circuit Design Philosophy for the Central Control of an Electronic Switching System." *Bell System Technical Journal* **37**, September 1958, p. 1125.

39. Means, W. J. "Hardware and Packaging for the No. 101 ESS." *1963 Electronic Switching Symposium*, Holmdel, New Jersey, January 1963, p. 25–1; Staehler, R. E. "No. 1 ESS Logic Circuits." and Ross, I. M. "Semiconductor Devices." Ibid.

40. Howard, L. A., Jr. "ESS—4 Years Old. An Interview with R. W. Ketchledge." *Bell Laboratories Record* **47**, August 1969, p. 226.

41. See ref. 26 above.

42. See ref. 26 above.

43. "Electronic Telephone System to get New Jersey Field Test." *Bell Labs News* **3**, February 28, 1963, p. 4.

44. Averill, R. M. and Stone, R. C. "No. 101 ESS: The Time-Division Switch Unit." *Bell Laboratories Record* **41**, December 1963, p. 425.

45. Williford, O. H. "The No. 101 Electronic Switching System." *Bell Laboratories Record* **41**, November 1963, p. 374.

46. Herndon, J. A. and Tendick, F. H. "A Time Division Switch for an Electronic Private Branch Exchange." *IEEE Transactions on Communication and Electronics* **83**, July 1964, p. 338.

47. Seley, E. L. and Vigilante, F. S. "Common Control for an Electronic Private Branch Exchange." *IEEE Transactions on Communication and Electronics* **83**, July 1964, p. 321.

48. Breen, C. "Expanding the No. 101 ESS." *Bell Laboratories Record* **44**, May 1966, p. 150.

49. "Indian Hill is First Customer for Its Own ESS." *Bell Labs News* **7**, March 1, 1967, p. 1.

50. Carlson, R. G., Weber, N. D. and Wolf, R. B. "New Switching Concept for Multilocation Customers." *Bell Laboratories Record* **49**, September 1971, p. 230.

51. Haugk, G., Tsiang, S. H. and Zimmerman, L. "System Testing of the No. 1 Electronic Switching System." *Bell System Technical Journal* **43**, September 1964, p. 2575.

52. Cooper, R. S. "Testing the System." *Bell Laboratories Record* **43**, June 1965, p. 268.

53. "Story of No. 1 Electronic Switching System from Pre-Morris, Illinois to Succasunna, New Jersey." *Bell Labs News* **5**, May 28, 1965, p. 2.

54. Raspanti, M. "Training for No. 1 ESS." *AFIPS Conference Proceedings* **27**, Part I, 1965 Fall Joint Computer Conference, November 1965, Las Vegas, Nevada.

55. Foster, H. F., Jr. "UNICOM Objectives." *1964 International Symposium on Global Communications, Digest of Technical Papers*, New York: June 1964, p. 48.

56. "DAIS (UNICOM) Defense Automatic Integrated Switch—Concept and Test Model." Report for U.S. Army Economics Laboratory, December 31, 1964.

57. Baird, J. A. "The UNICOM Test Model." *1964 International Symposium on Global Communications, Digest of Technical Papers*, New York: June 1964, p. 49; see ref. 55 above.

58. Gorgas, J. W. "AUTOVON—Switching Network for Global Defense." *Bell Laboratories Record* **46**, April 1968, p. 106.

59. Gorgas, J. W. "The Polygrid Network for AUTOVON." *Bell Laboratories Record* **46**, August 1968, p. 223.

60. Ketchledge, R. W. "Administration of Generic Programs." *IEE Conference on Switching Techniques for Telecommunications Networks*, London, April 1969, Conference Publication No. 52, p. 451.

61. Ketchledge, R. W. "Development of Development Methods." *International Switching Symposium* **74**, Munich, September 1974, p. 412/1.

62. Jones, W. C. and Tsiang, H. S. "Field Evaluation of Real-Time Capability of a Large Electronic Switching System." *AFIPS Conference Proceedings* **41**, Part I, 1972 Fall Joint Computer Conference, December 5–7, 1972, Anaheim, California.

63. Howard, L. W., Sellers, G. A. and Zweifel, K. W. "Traffic Simulator for Load Testing ESS." *International Conference on Communications* 1972, p. 32–15.

64. Ketchledge, R. W. "Outline of No. 1 ESS." Electronic Switching Symposium, Holmdel, New Jersey, January 21–24, 1963.

65. Phillips, S. J. "Generic Programs for No. 1 ESS." *Bell Laboratories Record* **47**, July 1969, p. 210.

66. Doblmaier, A. H. and Neville, S. M. "The No. 1 ESS Signal Processor." *Bell Laboratories Record* **47**, April 1969, p. 120.

67. Liss, W. A. "Service Link Network Simplifies No. 1 ESS Call Handling." *Bell Laboratories Record* **49**, June/July 1971, p. 171.

68. Spiro, G. "Centrex Service with No. 5 Crossbar." *Bell Laboratories Record* **40**, October 1962, p. 327.

69. Johannesen, J. D. and Staehler, R. E. "What's New in No. 1 ESS." *Bell Laboratories Record* **49**, June/July 1971, p. 166.

70. Liss, W. A., McGowan, J. K. and Wickham, T. F. "Centrex Service in No. 1 ESS." *Bell Laboratories Record* **46**, November 1968, p. 332.

71. Baker, D., Horenkamp, J. J. and Nickerson, C. "A Versatile Attendant Console for Smaller Businesses." *Bell Laboratories Record* **52**, May 1974, p. 152.

72. Ewin, J. C. and Giloth, P. K. "No. 1 ESS ADF: System Organization and Objectives." *Bell System Technical Journal* **49**, December 1970, p. 2733.

73. Barney, D. R., Giloth, P. K. and Kienzle, H. G. "No. 1 ESS ADF: System Testing and Early Field Operation Experience." Ibid, p. 2975.

74. Chevalier, J. G. and Rolund, M. W. "New Memory Reduces No. 1 ESS Cost and Size." *Bell Laboratories Record* **50**, April 1972, p. 121.

75. Irland, E. A. "Reoptimization of Call Stores for No. 1 ESS." *Conference on Switching Techniques for Telecommunications Networks, April 21–25, 1969.* London: IEE.

76. See ref. 66 above.

77. Joel, A. E., Jr. and Spiro, G. "Bell System Features and Services." *International Switching Symposium*, Paris, May 7–11, 1979, p. 1247.

78. Archer, W. E., Olsen, K. M. and Renault, P. W. "Remreed Switching Networks for No. 1 and No. 1A ESS: Development of a Remanent Reed Sealed Contact." *Bell System Technical Journal* **55**, May-June 1976, p. 511.

79. Gashler, R. J., Archer, W. E., Wassermann, N., Yano, D. H. and Zolnoski, R. C. "Remreed Switching Networks for No. 1 and No. 1A ESS: Remreed Switches." Ibid, p. 537.

80. Haugk, G. and Walsh, E. G. "Remreed Switching Networks for No. 1 and No. 1A ESS: System Overview." Ibid, p. 503.

81. Haugh, G. "The New Peripheral System for No. 1 and No. 1A ESS." *International Switching Symposium*, Kyoto, Japan, October 25–29, 1976, p. 131–2–1.

82. See ref. 82 above.

83. See ref. 82 above.

84. Staehler, R. E. "1A Processor: Organization and Objectives." *Bell System Technical Journal* **56**, February 1977, p. 119.

85. Orcutt, S. E. "A Central Office Steps Up." *Bell Laboratories Record* **59**, December 1981, p. 298.

86. Nowak, J. S. "No. 1A ESS—A New High-Capacity Switching System." *International Switching Symposium*, Kyoto, Japan, October 25–29, 1976, p. 131–1–1.

87. "Semiconductor Stores Replace Magnetic Cores in 1A Processors." *Bell Laboratories Record* **55**, October 1977, p. A.

88. Young, W. R. "Advanced Mobile Phone Service: Introduction, Background, and Objectives." *Bell System Technical Journal* **58**, January 1979, p. 1.

89. Vigilante, F. S. "General Description of No. 2 Electronic Switching System." *IEE Conference on Switching Techniques for Telecommunication Electronics*, London, April 1969, p. 479.

90. "Modular ESS Offices Shorten Installation Interval." *Bell Laboratories Record* **50**, April 1972, p. 129.

91. Mandigo, P. D. "No. 2B ESS: New Features from a More Efficient Processor." *Bell Laboratories Record* **54**, December 1976, p. 304.

Installation of TSPS (traffic service position system) consoles provides an opportunity for a pleasant work environment. Even with direct distance dialing, many calls require operator assistance. TSPS was invented and developed at Bell Labs to bring to these calls the maximum benefits of stored program control and solid state electronics. Within seven years of its introduction in 1969, TSPS served over half of all Bell System operator-assisted calls. TSPS was successful in part because it incorporated many circuits and devices produced for No. 1 ESS.

Chapter 10

Completing the Electronic Switching Family

Stored-program control and solid-state electronics, which together caused a revolution in switching systems design, suggested many services beyond those of No. 1 ESS. The traffic service position system (TSPS) automated many parts of operator-assisted calls and introduced overseas dialing from electromechanical offices. Hotel/motel services, automatic intercept, and automated coin-telephone service were important applications, as were the addition of the electronic translator system and common channel interoffice signaling to 4A crossbar. Stored-program control and modern electronics also allowed the design of a very large ESS for toll applications and the development of additional local electronic switching systems for the smaller communities.

I. TRAFFIC SERVICE POSITION

The success of the No. 101, No. 1, and No. 2 local electronic switching systems led Bell Labs development engineers to explore ways to apply the stored-program principle to other systems that comprise the Bell System network.

1.1 Early Studies

With the introduction of customer direct distance dialing, an important category of traffic being handled at cord switchboards gradually disappeared. Studies made at Bell Laboratories in the early 1950s anticipated these changes and explored methods for reducing or eliminating much of the remaining traffic.

From these studies it was recognized that DDD automated only a maximum of 60 percent of the toll traffic under the existing tariffs. Therefore, starting in 1949, a committee in the toll switching engineering group was assigned to study methods for "operator AMA"—that is, the implementation of AMA recording at operator switchboards. These studies included proposals for customer dialing of the called number on operator-assisted calls. Among the results of these studies was the conclusion that the remaining traffic was becoming more specialized and that a new form of cordless switchboard with associated AMA could speed service and reduce the operator work time per call. Projected estimates of this type of traffic indicated that the need for operators would again grow once DDD with automatic number identification was fully available, thereby eliminating the need for operators on station-to-station toll calls from non-coin telephones and for calls requiring line identification (operator number identification). See Fig. 10-1.

A key element in the plan was proposed in 1947 by C. E. Brooks of Bell Laboratories. Special operator-assisted calls such as person-to-person and collect calls would be placed into the system by dialing a distinctive prefix such as "0." This prefix could be used not only to route calls to operator positions arranged to handle the traffic, but also to avoid the necessity for the operator to key the called number into the system.

Throughout the 1950s these suggestions were intensively studied by G. H. Peterson and others, with the conclusion that customer dialing of these calls was feasible and that a more efficient switchboard for serving this type of traffic would be an automatic call-distributing, cordless position arrangement much like the CAMA-ONI position that had proved itself during this same period[1] and the cordless "B" boards of an earlier period (see Chapter 3, section IV). Fig. 10-2 shows an early model of the proposed cordless position.

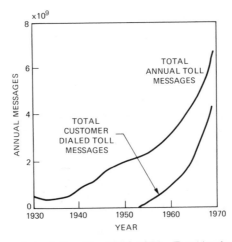

Fig. 10-1. Growth in toll calls, 1930–1970. Despite increased customer dialing, such growth indicated need for more operator services, hence more efficient operator systems.

Fig. 10-2. Early (1960) model of cordless switchboard developed in anticipation of increased customer dialing of person-to-person, collect, and coin-phone toll calls.

1.2 Person-to-Person, Collect, Special Positions (PPCS)

During 1956 and 1957 Bell Laboratories made arrangements for a field trial of the operator AMA concept with the New York Telephone Co. This company was chosen since it then carried 10 percent of the special operator-handled calls and agreed to provide the people and equipment for a trial of the new services. This equipment was placed in service in 1959 in two No. 5 crossbar offices, one in New York City and one in Poughkeepsie, New York.[2] The operator positions were operator number identification (ONI) positions modified with extra keys and lamps (see Fig. 10-3). Cordless switchboards could be used for this service since the associated crossbar switching system provided the equivalent of plug-and-jack switching. The systems had the acronym of PPCS for person-to-person, collect, special (special included credit card calls). No. 5 crossbar offices were used since they were already arranged for CAMA operation for recording charge information on paper tape, instead of requiring handwritten tickets. With CAMA the systems could serve selected customers in nearby offices.

1.3 TSP on Crossbar Tandem

In the meantime, a plan was devised to provide a new cordless switchboard position on the crossbar tandem system arranged for

Fig. 10-3. New York Telephone Company trial in Poughkeepsie, New York of positions allowing operators to service many types of customer-dialed calls.

CAMA operation.[3] The position, later known as the "traffic service position" (TSP) and coded 100A, provided keys for the operator to indicate the type of call to the AMA recording equipment. It also had a numerical display for recalling the calling or called numbers, and other numerical information from the system, and included the ability to hold three calls associated with the position so that more than one could be served at a time (see Fig. 10-4).

Considerable attention was paid in the design of the position to the human factors aspect.[4] Several different designs were built. Fig. 10-5 shows the first installation.

Advanced installations of this system, made in cooperation with the New York Telephone Co., were placed in service in Manhattan and Forest Hills, New York in October 1963. The first of twenty-one standard installations was in Cleveland, Ohio in August 1964.

The standard TSP arrangement permitted the servicing not only of special calls but also of toll coin calls. For the first time, some of the advantages of DDD were brought to coin telephone customers. This required development of a circuit using a Dimond ring translator (see Chapter 7, section 1.1) for computing the charges on these calls in real time, based on the calling and called numbers.[5] A unique cir-

Fig. 10-4. In developing the traffic service position, Bell Labs engineers paid close attention to the human factors aspects of the design.

Fig. 10-5. First installation of traffic service positions (TSPs), New York City, 1963.

cuit function provided in this subsystem was a data transfer circuit for the parallel movement of call data between the senders, markers, and positions (see Fig. 10-6).

The operator consoles, in groups of 33 positions, could be located remote from the serving crossbar tandem office[6] using five cable pairs per position. Polar duplex signaling was used, thereby limiting the range to a few miles. Operators found the new console operation a most attractive work situation and, since the consoles were free-standing, two-position desks (consoles), they could be attractively arranged in carpeted operating room environments (see Fig. 10-7). Also, a computerized training arrangement—using positions appearing and operating the same as those used in service—was developed to improve the proficiency of operators.[7]

1.4 Traffic Service Position System (TSPS)

The TSP for crossbar tandem systems provided for a maximum of only 500 trunks and 60 positions. Similar developments were studied in the early 1960s for application to the No. 4A and No. 5

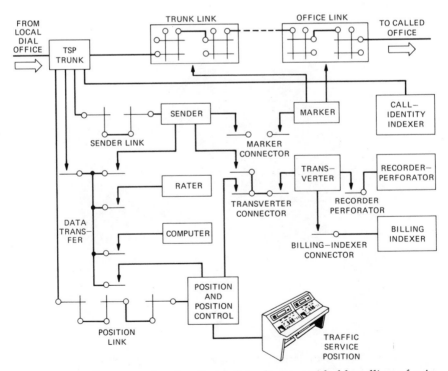

Fig. 10-6. Data transfer circuit at left in diagram aided handling of coin toll calls from traffic service positions.

Fig. 10-7. Traffic service positions, with their desk-like consoles, allowed a more attractive environment for operators.

crossbar and step-by-step offices equipped with the CAMA features. However, the synergy and advantages of the electronic switching stored-program concept, and the desire to avoid undertaking and maintaining at least four different TSP subsystem designs, led to the invention of the Traffic Service Position System (TSPS) by R. J. Jaeger, Jr., and A. E. Joel, Jr. in 1963.[8] For this invention they received the Outstanding Patent Award for 1972 of the New Jersey Council for Research and Development.

This concept consisted of a separate stored-program controlled electronic switching entity supporting groups of traffic service positions. The trunk circuits are located between local offices and toll or tandem offices. The positions are accessed through a four-stage ferreed link network (see Fig. 10-8). Several different processors were considered before it was decided to use the No. 1 ESS circuit packages in a new processor known as the "stored-program control 1A" (SPC No. 1A). A different processor from that in No. 1 ESS was required because of the need for remotely and electrically writable nonvolatile stores. These stores retain for immediate recall the call charge rating information for a large number of originating and terminating rate centers. The same need also existed for simple and rapid route translation changes when adding the stored-program control concept to the No. 4A crossbar system, particularly in conjunction with real-time network management (see below, section II).

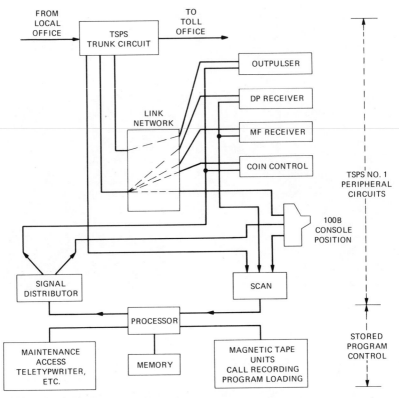

Fig. 10-8. Traffic service position system: instead of separate designs for various switching systems, TSPS uses stored-program control to support groups of positions and trunks between local and toll offices.

Studies showed the new system, TSPS No. 1, to be competitive with the previous electromechanical switching plans since, except for the new store, it used circuits and devices being produced in large quantity for the No. 1 ESS. The piggyback twistor store,[9] invented at and developed by Bell Laboratories, was used in the SPC No. 1A to store all information: call data, system, maintenance and administrative programs, office parameters, and translations. The SPC No. 1A was the first Bell System switching processor to use a single store subsystem for all memory requirements: program, translations, and data base. It was also the first common systems processor system designed for application in several different systems.[10] A unique feature of the SPC 1A central control is its ability to use identical equipment units and to maintain short wires between units used to match their operations by physically reversing one with respect to the other (see Fig. 10-9).

The No. 1 TSPS has a capacity of 3000 trunks and 320 positions in a maximum of five separate operator groups of 64 positions. These position groups may be located remote from the base unit where the trunks between local and toll offices, the links to the positions, and the SPC No. 1A are located.[11] The TSPS base unit may be located in any telephone building with or without operator units. Remote units are served over T1 digital carrier facilities that provide the speech paths and data links for receiving lamp lighting signals and transmitting key closure indications back to the base unit. A center for force administration and chief operator functions is provided with extensive real-time traffic and operator force data.

The first TSPS was placed in service in Morristown, New Jersey on January 19, 1969. To the end of 1976, 114 systems, including almost 20,000 positions, had been placed in service. The success of this important member of the ESS family is indicated by the fact that within seven years after its introduction, it served over 50 percent of the operator-assisted calls originating in the Bell System.

Fig. 10-9. Duplicated processor frames for the stored-program control No. 1A used with the traffic service position system. One processor is physically reversed from the other, with the wiring side of the right-hand unit adjacent to the apparatus side of the left-hand unit.

1.5 Hotel/Motel

Most calls originating in hotels and motels require charge information in almost real time, so that they can be billed by the hotel or motel. With the deployment of TSPS, arrangements were developed for better serving these customers. Calls originating at hotels and motels were identified at local offices, and this identification was sent to the TSPS with the other ANI information. Such calls are specially indicated to the TSPS operators, who ask for and record room numbers along with the other details of the calls.

When hotel/motel calls are completed, the details are typed out on a special teletypewriter at the TSPS administration center. Hotels and motels with heavy traffic or those desiring the most modern service are provided with teletypewriter links directly to their premises. In this way, Bell Laboratories engineers have greatly increased the efficiency of service provided with this source of operator-assisted calling. By year-end 1976, over 10,000 hotels and motels were served in this manner by TSPS. In 1976, a new development was undertaken to provide a computer-supported record base for the accessing and transmission of this information to hotels and motels. The system, known as No. 1 HOBIS (HOtel Billing Information System), is used to keep track of time and charge data for both voice and teletypewriter transmitted quotations.[12] The first installation was in Boston, Massachusetts in September 1977.

1.6 IDDD

The TSPS enjoys a unique position in the Bell System nationwide network. It is providing a most important bridge and buffer between electromechanical and electronic offices of the Bell System and accelerating the availability of new services to all customers. For example, it provides international direct distance dialing (IDDD) service on calls from local electromechanical switching offices, as described in Chapter 8, section V. Fig. 10-10 shows how the TSPS is used in placing calls into the international gateway or transit center that acquires an overseas sender through a loop-around trunk. The first calls of this type were served by TSPS in 1975.

1.7 Integrated Circuits

In 1971 TSPS became the first Western Electric switching system to use integrated circuits in dual in-line packages. Each chip included the transistor, shifter diode and logic diodes for as many as four NAND gates of the low-level-logic type used in No. 1 ESS. (See Chapter 9, sections 4.7.3 and 5.3.)

The piggyback twistor (PBT) stores served the SPC No. 1A well but were relatively slow compared with those using the more volatile magnetic cores or integrated circuit arrays. Experience with the

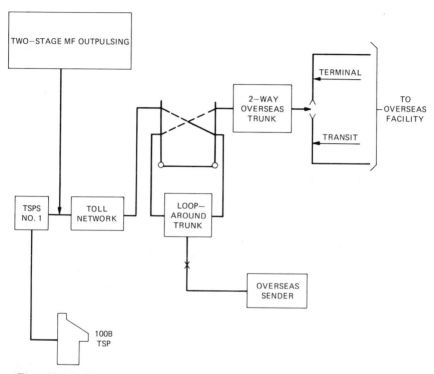

Fig. 10-10. Diagram indicating how TSPS serves overseas calls from electromechanical offices. First service of this type was in 1975.

SPC No. 1A in TSPS indicated that, with programs and data stored on a magnetic tape and always ready for entry into the system, the special protection offered by the PBT could be traded for the increased speed and capacity and lower space requirements of a volatile semiconductor store. TSPS became the first Bell switching system to use semiconductor storage. It began service in Macon, Georgia in April 1975. The large scale integrated (LSI) memory chip contained nearly 4,000 insulated-gate field-effect transistors (IGFETS) and stored 1,024 bits of information.[13]

1.8 Remote Trunk Arrangement No. 1A and Position Subsystem No. 2A

With the use of T1 digital carrier, the distance of operator groups remote from the TSPS base unit was limited to about 50 miles. With T2 carrier, one installation in Texas in 1974 extended over 200 miles. In many places where this distance or greater was desired, digital carrier was not available or contemplated. For this reason, a development was undertaken to permit the remote operator groups to function over longer distances, by permitting service over analog carrier and radio systems.

At the same time, studies indicated that to bring the advantages of TSPS to smaller communities and to eliminate small, relatively inefficient switchboards at these locations, a new TSP development was needed. As a result, work was undertaken in 1973 to locate TSPS trunk groups and/or positions remote from the base unit,[14] the system to be served by analog facilities.

A new operator group data link was designed to serve both the new No. 2A position subsystem, as it is called, and the "remote trunk arrangement" (RTA) (see Fig. 10-11). New remote-to-base trunks connect the remote TSP trunks with the base unit through a two-stage concentrator using new small crossbar switches. An RTA unit serves a maximum of 496 trunks with a maximum of 64 remote-base trunks. This use of concentration required an unusual design to achieve low blocking.[15] The longer distances between the served trunks and the operators required special transmission considerations.[16] The data from position keys and the data to light the lamps as well as control the trunks and concentrator flows over 2400 bit-per-second data links. A maximum of 1000 miles might separate positions and RTA from the base unit.

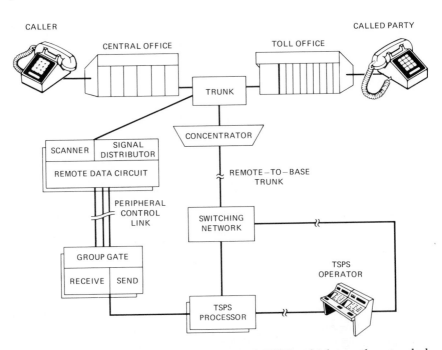

Fig. 10-11. Remote trunk arrangement with TSPS, which greatly extended the range (up to 1000 miles) over which TSPS can serve customers.

The first system of this type was placed in service in Utica, New York in May 1976 with the base unit 60 miles away in Syracuse, New York.

1.9 Automatic Coin Telephone Service (ACTS)

Another development started during this period was an arrangement for further automating DDD coin service. The automatic intercept system (see below, section III) had proved the ability of customers to respond to machine-generated audio messages. The new development used the TSPS stored-program control in combination with an audio response unit (ARU) to provide recorded messages from a prerecorded vocabulary. Such messages indicate the required deposit on DDD coin calls. Coin telephones so served are modified to generate machine-detectable audio signals when coins are deposited, and the received signals are used to calculate whether the deposit matches the required amount. (This idea was first proposed for extending the coin zone service concept in 1952.[17]) The stored-program control and ARU provide announcements as the depositing and call progresses. A TSPS operator is called in if the required deposit is not eventually detected.

The first installation of this system was in Phoenix, Arizona in November 1977.[18] It is another example of a service provided by the TSPS-SPC base unit due to its unique position in the nationwide network.

II. NO. 4A CROSSBAR ELECTRONIC TRANSLATOR SYSTEM (4A/ETS)

One of the most successful and least known accomplishments of the Bell System in electronic switching has been the development of stored-program control capability for the 4A toll crossbar systems. These systems were used at the most important nodes in the nationwide toll switching network, these nodes representing only 10 percent of the offices but serving (in 1976) 50 percent of the total carried traffic. For many years, as the complexity of administering six-digit translations at controlled switching points (CSP) grew, particularly with the introduction of wide-area telephone service (WATS), studies were made of applying new technology to the translation functions in the No. 4A crossbar system.[19] Fig. 10-12 shows how the 4A crossbar system was modified to include the electronic translator.

Even before the card translator had originally been adopted for this system, research experiments were conducted using a magnetic drum for the translation function (see Chapter 9, section 4.3.3). With reduced cost and increased reliability, the use of magnetic drums was again studied in the early 1960s, but the new concept of stored-program control proved more flexible and useful. After several further studies, the SPC No. 1A, also used in TSPS No. 1,

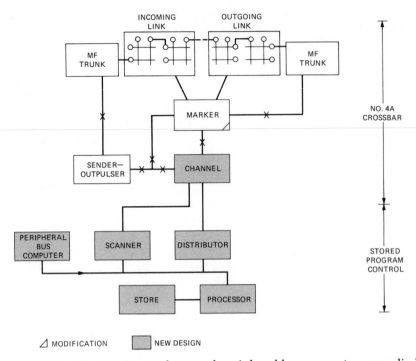

Fig. 10-12. Electronic translator and peripheral bus computer as applied to No. 4A crossbar. This new technology enabled No. 4A crossbar to provide WATS and other modern services more efficiently.

was adapted to replace the card translators of the No. 4A crossbar system. This resulted in greater call capacity and faster call-completion time at lower cost, since the production of the metal translator cards was no longer required. Also it provided means for more rapidly adjusting the routing information in real time to the changing network capacity. For the first time, the rapidly growing toll traffic (then growing at approximately 11 percent per year) could be made to flow smoothly through the network with automatic, semiautomatic, and manual network management controls.[20]

With the growth of long distance calling, the number of trunk groups in the network was greatly increased. A larger portion of the traffic was switched at the class 3 and 4 levels, with less switching through regional and sectional centers. The control of traffic required more sophisticated techniques. This called for detecting focused overloads to specific destinations, such as where disasters and other significant events caused abnormally high calling. It also required detecting excessive delays due to faulty trunk groups (carrier failures). The use of stored-program controls permitted the automatic detection and invoking of controls under these circumstances.

The first of these modified No. 4A crossbar installations was placed in service in Grand Rapids, Michigan on June 1, 1969. The last new No. 4A crossbar (No. 152 in the Bell System) office was installed in Madison, Wisconsin in 1976. By that time 132 No. 4A crossbar offices had been equipped with electronic (SPC No. 1A) translators.

2.1 Peripheral Bus Computer

During the era when minicomputers were being applied to improve the gathering of maintenance, traffic, and charging data in electromechanical switching systems (see Chapter 11, section III), a minicomputer was added to the peripheral bus of the SPC No. 1A associated with No. 4A crossbar offices (see Fig. 10-12).[21] In this capacity it is used to provide improved traffic and maintenance data. Most (107) electronic translator-equipped offices have had peripheral bus computers (PBC) associated with them since they were introduced in Akron, Ohio in November 1973.

2.2 Common Channel Interoffice Signaling (CCIS)—Signal Transfer Point (STP)

The No. 4A crossbar system equipped with stored-program control was ready for the introduction of many new features into the toll network. Perhaps the most important feature is the new standard method of interoffice signaling over separate data links not associated with the trunk groups. This out-of-band signaling method, known as "common channel interoffice signaling" (CCIS), was the subject of much study for over a decade from the late 1950s to the late 1960s. Indeed, the idea of CCIS dates back to early manual switching "call wire" methods.[22] By the late 1960s the CCIS method was being studied, with the cooperation of Bell System engineers, by the Comité Consultatif International Télégraphique et Téléphonique (CCITT) as a standard method, later adopted (1968) as CCITT Signaling System No. 6 for international signaling.

From 1970 to 1972 the Bell System participated in international trials of this new signaling method from the Columbus, Ohio Bell Laboratories location.[23] By this time, much attention was being given to the new services and features possible with electronic switching offices. The new form of interoffice signaling such as CCIS would enable the post dialing to ringing time to be reduced by a factor of five or ten (to about 1–2 seconds from 10–13). But more importantly, this form of signaling permits the interchange of much call data in addition to the more conventional supervisory and address signals. Data about the call may be sent from toll office to toll office and eventually from the originating office to and from the terminating office. The data may include the number of the calling telephone and class of service information for the calling and called lines.

The most expeditious method for introducing CCIS into a switching office is with a stored-program control processor. Since No. 4A crossbar ETS offices rapidly blanketed the toll network, it was natural that this would be the first system to include this important forward-looking feature (see Fig. 10-13).

A plan for CCIS in the U.S. toll network was devised at Bell Laboratories (see Chapter 12, section III). The plan called for establishing 10 signaling regions, coincident with the toll switching regions, each with two independently located (in different cities) SPC processors known as "signal transfer points" (STP).[24] These STPs were to be fully interconnected with data links. Each toll office with one or more trunk groups served by CCIS will have their processors connected over data links to both STPs in their signaling regions. These planning studies indicated that the economic success of CCIS would be facilitated by the greatly reduced need for relatively expensive in-band single-frequency signaling units (see Fig. 10-14).

In 1976 the toll CCIS network became operational. The first 4A-ETS offices provided with CCIS were in Madison, Wisconsin (the last new 4A crossbar office) and in Waukesha, Wisconsin (the first retrofit office). No. 4A crossbar ETS offices in Omaha, Nebraska and Indianapolis, Indiana were provided with the STP features (see Chapter 12, section III). Most of the 4A crossbar offices equipped with the No. 4A ETS and the peripheral bus computer have been modified to serve as STPs or as serving offices (SOs) that communicate via CCIS. Despite this extensive relatively recent modernization of these offices, studies show that even with the development and deployment of No. 4 ESS (see Chapter 12, section I) there is still considerable advantage to the application of these features in No. 4A crossbar offices prior to their accelerated replacement.

III. AUTOMATIC INTERCEPT SYSTEM

During the early 1960s studies were made to improve number services, such as intercept, and directory assistance (formerly called "information"). To automate intercept services, arrangements using electromechanical switching in combination with a magnetic drum storing audio vocabulary were studied, starting in 1962 with methods of announcing newly assigned directory numbers on intercepted calls.

Not until the advantages of time-division switching, taken from the No. 101 ESS, and the advantages of stored-program control

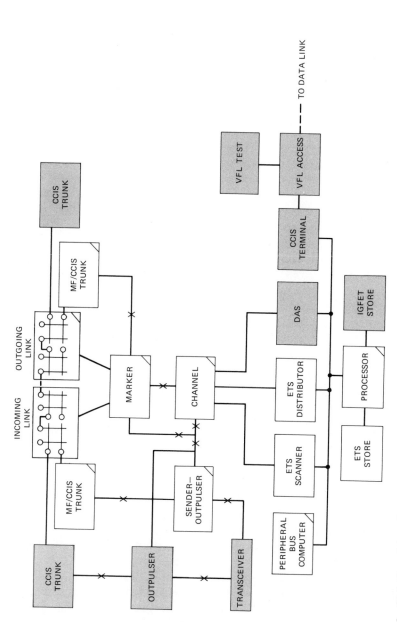

Fig. 10-13. Relationship of common channel interoffice signaling equipment to No. 4A crossbar electronic translator. CCIS opens up a wide range of service possibilities.

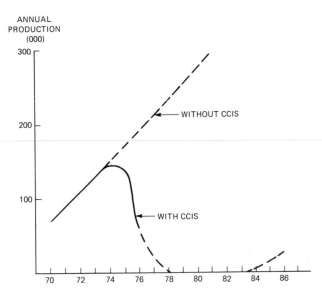

Fig. 10-14. Study showing fall-off in need for single-frequency in-band signaling equipment as a result of CCIS.

from No. 2 ESS were applied to this problem did a viable solution appear. In 1967 this became the Automatic Intercept System No. 1A (AIS) development.[25] Semiautomatic systems, developed by others, were placed in service in 1965 (e.g., ref. 26). These systems required operators to key in the number the caller was attempting to reach (ONI) and did not give the caller the assurance that the number reached was the number dialed.

To be most effective, the called local offices sending calls to the AIS are equipped with automatic number identification so that the number actually reached can also be forwarded. Economically adding this capability to electromechanical switching offices was as challenging as the development of the equipment for the automatic intercept center (AIC). Table 10-1 shows the type of vocabulary used with a sample announcement. A special 96-track magnetic drum was designed by Bell Laboratories to provide the vocabulary.

Fig. 10-15 shows the basic plan of the automatic intercept system. The system included remote cordless operating positions, similar to TSP, for calls where announcements could not satisfy the caller. (These positions are also used for ONI calls where local offices do not have ANI.) An idle operator is connected by the time-division network while a display of the input number, announcement, if any, and other information on the call is simultaneously displayed on the console (see Fig. 10-16). The first AIS was placed in service in Hempstead, New York in September 1970.

Table 10-1. Announcements on Magnetic Drum for No. 1A
Automatic Intercept System.

Track No.	Phrase or Digit
1	The number you have reached
2	has been changed
3	the new number is
4	the customer
5	not to give out
6	in the
7	has been disconnected
8	has instructed us
9	is temporarily disconnected
10	at the customer's request
11	is being changed
12	the new number
13	is not yet connected
14	please call information for
15	calls are being taken by
16	is not in service
17	is a working number
18	please check the number
19	and dial again
20	if you need assistance
21	repeat
22	please stay on the line
23	and an operator will answer
24	thousand
25	hundred
26 to 35	(digits 0 to 9 with neutral inflection)
36 to 45	(digits 0 to 9 with falling inflection)
46	(recorder tone)
47	area
48	will you dial it again please
49 to 96	(new location name as required)

Sample announcement:

"The number you have reached, 368 11 hundred, is not in service in the 201 area. Please check the number and dial again. If you need assistance, please stay on the line, and an operator will answer."

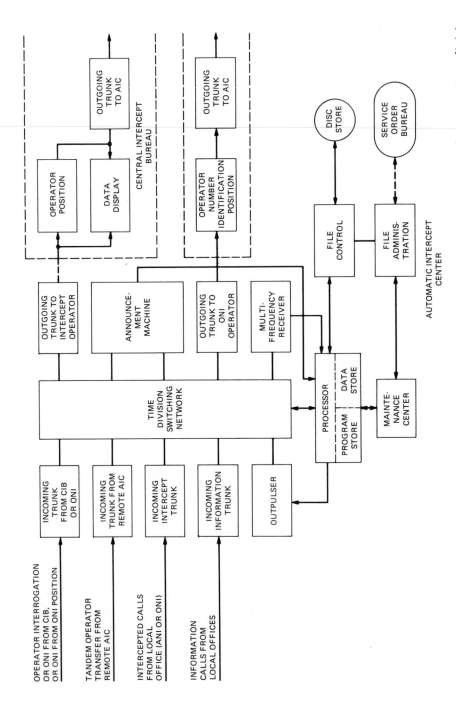

Fig. 10-15. Block diagram of automatic intercept center. All switching is done through an electronic time-division switching network, which connects incoming calls to the processor, the announcement machine, or other equipment.

Fig. 10-16. Model of operator position used as backup to automatic intercept system. AIS was introduced into service in 1970.

Originally, the translations from the intercepted to the new numbers were stored on a magnetic disk similar to the one developed for the No. 1 ESS ADF.[27] This file could store up to a half million numbers, enough for a suburban area. Numbers were added to or subtracted from the file by a program internal to AIS.

3.1 File Subsystem No. 2A

Telephone operating people, impressed with the advantages of AIS, wished it to be expanded in capacity. First the switching network was expanded from 415 trunks to double that number. (The first system of this size went into service in Cleveland, Ohio in October 1971.)

For AIS to serve complete numbering plan areas or metropolitan areas required a larger and more elaborate administration system. While the original (No. 1A) file subsystem[28] provided many facilities for administration, the larger file system had several times the capacity and a separate off-line minicomputer complex for administration.[29] It could also accept number changes from customer record changes distributed by other than the Business Information System (BIS). The first No. 2A file subsystem with a capacity of 900,000 numbers was placed in service in Hammonton, New Jersey in August 1975.

By the end of 1976 twenty-eight automatic intercept systems were in service, serving about 40 percent of the Bell System.

IV. TOLL FEATURES ON ESS

From the start of the ESS development, it was expected that the ESS family would include toll switching capability.[30] Indeed, early in the ESS development a special situation arose where the system elements were combined with a 4-wire ferreed switch to provide 4-wire toll switching for the AUTOVON leased network (see Chapter 9, section 5.5).

The No. 1 ESS was called upon early to provide local tandem (trunk-to-trunk) switching capability, the first being in Nashville, Tennessee in 1968. The No. 1 ESS was designed initially with special attention to transmission range compensation and balance.[31] As a result, 2-wire installations of No. 1 ESS have provided superior transmission capability to crossbar tandem when used for toll switching. Starting in 1971, the No. 1 ESS was used in toll switching, first for toll connecting or completing tandem and then for full intertoll switching. By 1976, more than 23 installations provided toll switching.[32]

To make No. 1 ESS more useful in tandem and toll switching, a new trunk link network was developed with 2048 rather than 1024 trunk and service circuit terminations. The first 2048 terminal trunk link networks were placed in service in Williamsburg, Brooklyn, New York in September 1974.[33] This gave it a capacity of approximately 28,000 trunks. While this was more capacity than that of 4A crossbar (latest capacity 21,500 trunks), studies starting in the 1950s showed that many metropolitan areas would need more toll capacity than was available with either the modified No. 1 ESS or the 4A crossbar. As a result, with the successful introduction of local electronic switching, studies were begun to find a systems architecture for a large toll switch, one postulated as at least three times the size of the 4A crossbar system.

Initial studies at Bell Laboratories in 1966 and 1967 assumed that a version of No. 1 ESS with expanded trunk network and multiple No. 1 ESS processors would provide a capacity of 200,000 busy-hour calls or more. But, in view of the state of the art at that time, the software problems of multiprocessing were believed to be too great to solve satisfactorily. Instead, the integrated circuit technology had advanced so that a new technology for a new more powerful processor, later called the 1A processor, was postulated and investigated.[34] As a result, it was decided to move in this direction and develop a system processor to support a toll ESS, after which it was determined that a digital time-division switch (see Chapter 12, section I) would be used for the network portion of the system.

As a result of the development of features for toll ESS, both space and time-division, the rapid replacement of electromechanical toll switching systems with stored-program controlled systems is expected. Fig. 10-17 shows the expected rapid toll traffic as measured by intertoll trunk terminations. While the number of No. 1 ESS systems will be large, No. 4 ESS will account for a large portion of the toll trunk terminations, due to its large capacity. (See Chapter 12, section IV and Fig. 12-5 for corresponding information on systems.)

4.1 HiLo Transmission

Despite the advance in large toll systems, the No. 1 ESS is an excellent system when the demand for toll switching is fewer than 28,000 trunks. While 2-wire toll switching has been used with No. 1 ESS with less expense than the crossbar tandem system it replaces, still to obtain further operational savings, and particularly to avoid any office balance consideration,[35] a new concept called "HiLo" was developed (see Chapter 9, section 6.8.1). HiLo (see Chapter 9, Fig. 9-66) gave No. 1 ESS an effective 4-wire capability by providing ground-return, constant-voltage transmission over each conductor of a 2-wire remreed network (see Chapter 9, section 6.6), thereby giving the equivalent of 4-wire toll service. This development which was started in 1973 and first applied in 1977, will also be useful for private network switching where 4-wire transmission is a requirement.

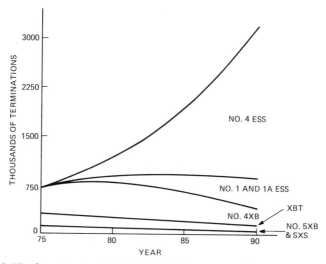

Fig. 10-17. Starting in 1976, No. 1 ESS with equivalent 4-wire transmission (HiLo) and No. 4 ESS were expected to rapidly dominate the needs of toll terminations in the Bell System network.

V. SMALL ELECTRONIC SWITCHING SYSTEMS

With the development of No. 1 and No. 2 ESS, stored-program control switching became available to more than 85 percent of the Bell System lines (see Fig. 10-18). However, more than half of Bell System offices are small, containing fewer than 2000 lines. Studies and exploratory developments showed that providing switching with modern electronic technology for small systems is viable; indeed, other administrations successfully introduced such systems as early as 1966. However, attaining stored-program capability economically in this size range proved more difficult. An exploratory development experiment known as ECDO (for "electronic community dial office") was carried out from 1969 to 1972.[36] This system included a new network and control technique, each taking advantage of the latest integrated circuit technology.

In 1972, development was started on the No. 3 ESS, the first stored-program control system to compete economically with electromechanical switching below 4500 lines.[37] This system used the 3A central control. The 3A central control is also used in the 2B ESS (see Chapter 9, section 7.2), the transaction switching network,[38] and the No. 5 crossbar ETS (see Chapter 11, section 3.3.4). A semi-

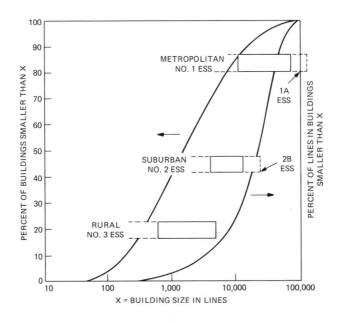

Fig. 10-18. Local stored-program controlled ESSs were developed and extended to cover the entire range of Bell System requirements for all size buildings, starting with the No. 1 ESS for large metropolitan buildings to the No. 3 ESS for rural buildings.

conductor network using pnpn crosspoints, originally postulated for the No. 3 ESS from the ECDO experiment, proved at the time development started to be too costly. It was therefore replaced with a remreed network. Fig. 10-19 shows a rough layout of the system. This development was successfully completed in 1976, with the first installation placed in service in Springfield, Nebraska on July 31, 1976. It permits customers and telephone administrations in smaller communities to attain the same service and feature advantages as for the larger cities and towns.

For very small switching center needs (fewer than 2000 lines) a remote switching system was announced as being "under serious consideration" in 1976,[39] and was subsequently developed as the 10A remote switching system.

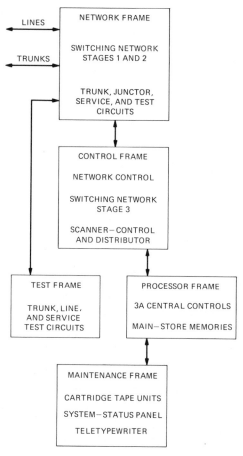

Fig. 10-19. General arrangement of No. 3 ESS, first placed in service in 1976. No. 3 ESS brought the advantages of stored-program control to small offices.

REFERENCES, CHAPTER 10

1. Peterson, G. H. "Current Experiments in Person-to-Person DDD." *Bell Laboratories Record* **38**, August 1960, p. 299.
2. Fredericks, L. "Special Positions for Person-to-Person, Collect, and Credit Card Calls." *Electrical Engineering* **79**, October 1960, p. 814.
3. Morris, R. M. "Crossbar Tandem TSP." *Bell Laboratories Record* **42**, May 1964, p. 146.
4. Funck, R. H. "Designing the Traffic Service Position Console." *Bell Laboratories Record* **42**, June 1964, p. 208.
5. Many, C. J., Ilmberger, E. H. K. and Irwin, C. G. "A New Look for Long-Distance Coin Calling." *Bell Laboratories Record* **44**, July-August 1966, p. 218.
6. McGuinness, T. P. "TSP Circuits." *Bell Laboratories Record* **42**, July-August 1964, p. 258.
7. Kroning, R. D. and Gale, D. H. "Automatic Training for Operators of the 100A TSP." *Bell Laboratories Record* **41**, September 1963, p. 314.
8. Jaeger, R. J., Jr. and Joel, A. E., Jr.; U.S. Patent 3,484,560; filed January 10, 1966; issued December 16, 1969.
9. Baker, W. A. "The Piggyback Twistor—An Electrically Alterable Nondestructive-Readout Twistor Memory." *IEEE Transactions on Communication and Electronics* **83**, November 1964, p. 829.
10. Durney, G. R., Kettler, H. W., Prell, E. M., Riddell, G. and Rohn, W. B. "TSPS No. 1: Stored Program Control No. 1A." *Bell System Technical Journal* **49**, December 1970, p. 2445.
11. Jaeger, R. J. and Joel, A. E., Jr. "TSPS No. 1: System Organization and Objectives." *Bell System Technical Journal* **49**, December 1970, p. 2417.
12. "Columbus Group Develops Billing System 'On Location.'" *Bell Labs News* **18**, December 5, 1977, p. 1.
13. Green, C. W. "Checking Out Semiconductor Memories for Electronic Switching Systems." *Bell Laboratories Record* **55**, May 1977, p. 131.
14. Arnold, T. F. and Jaeger, R. J., Jr. "TSPS/RTA—An Overview of the Remote Trunk Arrangement." *International Conference on Communications Record* III, San Francisco, June 1975, p. 46-1.
15. Bulfer, A. F. "Blocking and Routing in Two-Stage Concentrators." *National Telecommunications Conference, New Orleans, Louisiana, Conf. Record* I, December 1-3, 1975, p. 19–26.
16. Brune, W. L. and Frank, R. J. "TSPS/RTA—Transmission Considerations." *International Conference on Communications Record* III, San Francisco, June 1975, p. 46–17.
17. Joel, A. E., Jr.; U.S. Patent 2,676,209; filed September 1, 1949; issued April 20, 1954.
18. "ACTS Debuts in Phoenix." *Bell Labs News* **17**, December 12, 1977, p. 1.
19. Fought, B. T. and Funk, C. J. "Electronic Translator System for Toll Switching—System Description." *IEEE Trans. on Communication Technology* COM-18, June 1970, p. 168.
20. Snare, R. C. and Croxall, L. M. "Electronic Translator System for Toll Switching—Routing Strategy and Network Control." *IEEE Trans. on Communication Technology* COM-18, June 1970, p. 175.
21. Crawford, K. E., Funk, C. J. and Snare, R. C. "A Peripheral Computer System for Maintenance and Administration of No. 4 Crossbar Toll Offices." *Proceedings of the National Electronics Conference* **30**, October 6–8, 1975.
22. Fagen, M. D., ed. *A History of Engineering and Science in the Bell System: The Early Years 1875–1925.* Bell Telephone Laboratories, Inc., 1975, p. 637.
23. Sipes, J. D. and Funk, C. J. "CCITT Signaling System No. 6 Field Trial United States Installation." *Telecommunication Journal* **41**, February 1974, p. 114.

24. Nance, R. C. and Kaskey, B. "Initial Implementation of Common Channel Interoffice Signaling." *International Switching Symposium*, Kyoto, Japan, October 25–29, 1976, p. 413–2.

25. Winckelmann, W. A. "Automatic Intercept Service." *Bell Laboratories Record* **46**, May 1968, p. 138.

26. Abbott, G. F. and Bence, R. L. "An Automatic Telephone Intercept System." *IEEE Transactions on Communication Technology* COM-13, December 1965, p. 395.

27. Aitcheson, E. J., Ault, C. F. and Spencer, R. G. "No. 1 ESS ADF: Message Store—A Disk Memory System." *Bell System Technical Journal* **49**, December 1970, p. 2887.

28. Hopkins, J. W., Hunter, P. D., Machol, R. E., Di Salvo, J. J. and Piereth, R. J. "Automatic Intercept System: File Subsystem." *Bell System Technical Journal* **53**, January 1974, p. 107.

29. "Automatic Intercept System Grows." *Bell Laboratories Record* **53**, October 1975, p. 385.

30. Hough, R. R. Testimony under cross examination, FCC Docket No. 19129, Phase II, May 24, 1974, tr. 7072.

31. Feiner, A. "Transmission Aspects of No. 1 ESS." *Conference on Switching Techniques for Telecommunications Networks*, April 21–25, 1969. London: Inst. of Elec. Engrs.

32. Jacobsen, C. R. and Simms, R. L. "Toll Switching in the Bell System." *International Switching Symposium*, Kyoto, Japan, October 25–29, 1976, p. 132–4–1.

33. Johannesen, J. D. "No. 1 ESS Local/Toll/Tandem." *International Switching Symposium Record*, Munich, Germany, September 9–13, 1974, p. 526.

34. Ritchie, A. E., and Tuomenoksa, L. S. "No. 4 ESS: System Objectives and Organization." *Bell System Technical Journal* **56**, September 1977, p. 1017.

35. Klosterman, C. H. and Unrue, J. E. "Remreed Switching Networks for No. 1 and No. 1A ESS: Transmission Design and Environmental Protection of Remreed Networks." *Bell System Technical Journal* **55**, May-June 1976, p. 637.

36. McKay, K. G. Supplement to Rebuttal Testimony, FCC Docket No. 19129, Phase II, Bell Exhibit No. 190, July 14, 1975, pp. 3A-6 through 3A-9.

37. Foster, R. W. "No. 3 ESS Improves Telephone Service for Country Customers." *Bell Laboratories Record* **55**, October 1977, p. 231.

38. Irlend, E. A. and Stagg, U. K. "New Developments in Suburban and Rural ESS (No. 2 and No. 3 ESS)." *Proceedings of the International Switching Symposium*, Munich, West Germany, September 13, 1974, p. 512.

39. Pamm, L. R. "Transaction Network: Data Communications for Metropolitan Areas." *Bell Laboratories Record* **55**, January 1977, p. 8.

40. Fleckenstein, W. O. "Development of Telecommunication Switching in the United States of America." *Proceedings of the International Switching Symposium*, Kyoto, Japan, October 25–29, 1976, p. 121–6–1.

The "Hi-bay" laboratory at the Holmdel, New Jersey location of Bell Laboratories, 1967. In such labs, engineers developed many of the services and features which we today take for granted. Familiar examples include direct distance dialing by customers, TOUCH-TONE® dialing, automatic number identification, and 911 emergency numbers. Businesses benefited from direct inward dialing to extensions, automatic identified outward dialing, automatic call distributors, and WATS and INWATS. Custom calling features like speed calling and call forwarding were introduced. Also important were new developments to improve the efficiency and economy of the internal operations of switching offices, such as systems for maintenance, trouble recording, and traffic measuring.

Chapter 11

The Service and Feature Era

The tendency and practice in the Bell System network are to continuously add new services and features. This began in the earliest days of networking, and it accelerated with the introduction of dial systems. In this sense, the network continuously grows more "intelligent" and more serviceable to customers. Moreover, the growth, while continuous, is nonuniform. Two events stand out: the development of No. 5 crossbar, which offered an enhanced level of switching flexibility on which new services and features could be built, and the invention and rapid expansion of stored-program control, which has in recent years found applications of even greater power and versatility in both electronic and electromechanical systems. Many of these applications impact the customer directly and many aid the internal management of the network; but directly or indirectly, all aim at better service at reasonable cost.

One of the primary motives for introducing stored-program control switching over the entire range of Bell System office requirements was the need for flexibility to meet the growing number of sophisticated services and features for customers. Each generation of switching equipment introduces new features and services, and few are discontinued unless they are improved upon or no longer needed. The days of panel switching saw services and features such as interfaces with manual offices, prepay coin service (originally with dial-tone-first), free official numbers, automatic overtime message charging, and automatic sender test circuits. The No. 1 crossbar system offered most of these, plus automatic trouble detecting and recording, larger nongraded trunk groups, PBX jump-hunting, number-checking, etc. The step-by-step system included such features as digit-absorbing selectors, service code and preliminary "1" correction (see Chapter 3, section II) combined selector repeaters, intertoll transmission, and pulse-correcting repeaters.

The development of the No. 5 crossbar system, however, introduced a new era. The No. 5 system not only improved upon earlier features, its architecture offered a degree of flexibility not previously known. Advantage was taken of this capability for over two decades while the telephone business grew and while electronic switching was being explored to improve even upon this advance. The No. 5 crossbar system made the organization of the basic switching and signaling functions more flexible and also improved the ability to add other features and services. Because of its flexibility, the No. 5 crossbar system was the first to be designed to include most new services or features. This was due to the skill of the Bell Labs team, one of the most capable ever assembled for electromechanical switching development. So high was their *esprit de corps* and the demand for their services that it was difficult for those developing electronic switching to recruit them and to build upon their expertise.

During the 1950s, the thrust toward new features meant expanding the application of No. 5 offices to permit their operation with various systems and switchboard interconnections, and to offer direct distance dialing. In the 1960s, the growth was primarily in new customer services. Moreover, the expansion of design was not confined to the No. 5 crossbar system. Although the No. 5 design was the leader, even panel and step-by-step were modified to accommodate changing and expanding service needs.

I. INTRODUCTION OF NEW SERVICES

The most important new service since World War II was direct distance dialing, DDD. By 1960, DDD was available to 54.4 percent of the Bell System. By 1965, 47.9 percent of the DDD calls included Automatic Number Identification (ANI). With full automation of station-to-station calling well under way, automation improvements and the offering of other services proceeded.

1.1 TOUCH-TONE* Service

From the beginning, the use of pushbuttons has been the preferred method of remotely controlling automatic switching systems (see Fig. 11-1). The efficiency of pushbuttons had proved itself for operator control (see Chapter 3, section IV), but cost and electrical problems[1] made such control for each telephone unattractive. The invention of the transistor, however, brought the cost to a point where the service might be offered at an attractive price. Much experimental work was carried out, including the study of different pushbutton arrangements (see Fig. 11-2).

Pushbutton dialing was tried in the initial No. 5 crossbar office in Media, Pennsylvania in 1948 (see Chapter 7, section II), using vibrating reeds with 2-out-of-6 frequencies—similar to that used for

_____
*Registered service mark of AT&T Co.

Fig. 11-1. Pushbuttons were always the preferred method of placing calls automatically, but widespread application had to await the cost-reduction potential of solid-state electronics.

interoffice pulsing[2] (see Chapter 7, Fig. 7-6). An improvement, less prone to detecting false signals when speech signals reached the receiver, was an arrangement of 2 frequencies, each frequency 1-out-of-4. This system was developed in the late 1950s. Technical trials were held in a step-by-step office in Hamden, Connecticut and in a No. 5 crossbar office in Elgin, Illinois in 1959.[3] Fig. 11-3 shows the trial results comparing the dialing times with rotary dials and pushbuttons as people learned to use the new "dials."

Further technical trials focusing on central office equipment, revised on the basis of the previous year's trials, were held in 1960 in a step-by-step office in Cave Spring, Virginia and in a No. 5 crossbar office in Hagerstown, Maryland. Marketing trials were held in 1961 in Findlay, Ohio and in Greensburg, Pennsylvania. The economic provision of TOUCH-TONE capability in each type of local central office[4] (see Fig. 11-4) and customer switching system was a development challenge not unlike the challenge of providing

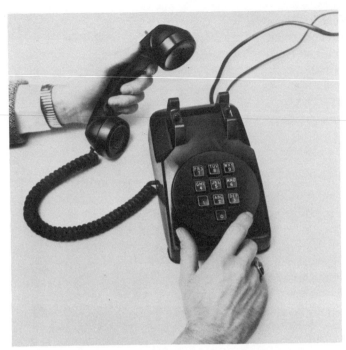

Fig. 11-2. Experimental pushbutton telephone using transistor circuits to send multifrequency dial signals to the central office.

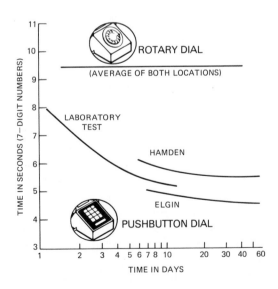

Fig. 11-3. Time to dial seven digits, comparing conventional rotary dialing with pushbuttons, 1959 technical trials in Hamden, Connecticut and Elgin, Illinois.

DDD in toll switching. A tri-company committee (AT&T, Bell Labs, and Western Electric) was formed in 1959 to insure that problems encountered during the introduction of TOUCH-TONE® service were dealt with promptly. The first commercial application was in the Switched Circuit Automatic Network (SCAN) project (see below, section 1.9). The first Bell System public offering was in the fourth quarter of 1963.

1.1.1 Panel and No. 1 Crossbar Systems

For these systems, subscriber sender designs were modified to include TOUCH-TONE™ receivers. To avoid modifying all senders in an office, lines originating TOUCH-TONE traffic were segregated.

1.1.2 Step-by-Step Systems

Two approaches were used to adapt TOUCH-TONE calling in step-by-step systems. Until this time, most step-by-step systems were directly controlled. To adapt them for TOUCH-TONE calling requires the addition of a form of indirect control to register the TOUCH-TONE dialing digits and then, at a slower rate, to outpulse them as dial pulses. This amounts to a very simple form of register-sender without translation, code-conversion, etc. For years Bell Labs engineers had considered "senderizing" the step-by-step system for its application in metropolitan areas, and one early design in 1940 reached the laboratory stage. However, due in part to the adoption of the automatic ticketing system in the Los Angeles area (see Chapter 6, section 5.1) and in part to the interruption of Bell System development work during World War II, this project was dropped. After the war, "full senderization" was undertaken. In addition to the need for register-senders for TOUCH-TONE calling, there was also a need in some situations for more efficient interfaces between local originating step-by-step offices and other systems, both local and toll, using multifrequency pulsing. Further, there was a need to introduce a degree of flexibility into step-by-step systems.

Therefore, in 1961 two TOUCH-TONE service projects were undertaken simultaneously, one called "noncompatible,"[5] and the other "compatible"—that is, the common arrangement where the register-senders could, at a later time, be readily adapted to (1) access added common decoders for office code translations and (2) outpulse multifrequency once an outgoing trunk was reached.[6] Telephone companies contemplating later conversion to full common control could initially order the converters for the more expensive "compatible" system. The first of approximately 250 installations of the compatible TOUCH-TONE calling arrangement was in Kokomo, Indiana in March 1965.

The first nonconvertible system was the equipment field-tested in 1960 in Cave Spring, Virginia. This system used step-by-step

            Engineering and Science in the Bell System

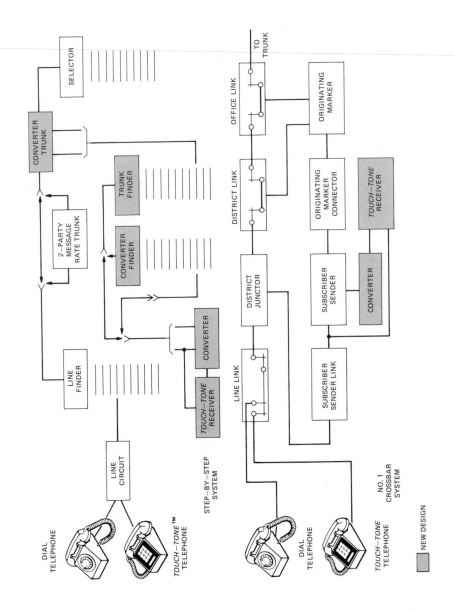

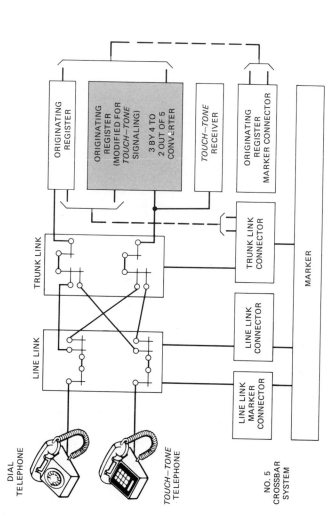

Fig. 11-4. TOUCH-TONE® arrangements for (top to bottom) step-by-step, No. 1 crossbar, and No. 5 crossbar.

switches as the access link to connect the line finders to the TOUCH-TONE register-senders. In this application, the step-by-step switches received about ten times the usage of the regular switch train service. As a result, the design was changed in 1967 to use a crossbar switch link, since the high usage of the step-by-step switch caused excessive wiper wear.

The equipment arrangement of the original designs was in the Bell System tradition designed for the long term, for ease of growth, and for efficient maintenance. Later, as the end of life in these offices was predictable, because of their eventual replacement by electronic switching, a new lower-cost design, TOUCH-TONE D, was developed without the long-term growth provisions and with cost-reduced TOUCH-TONE receivers. (TOUCH-TONE A was the original common-control system, TOUCH-TONE B was the non-compatible system, and TOUCH-TONE C was the crossbar switch link arrangement.) The first TOUCH-TONE D was installed in Montevideo, Minnesota in 1974.

TOUCH-TONE calling was the first of the post World War II optional services introduced that required specific local central office provisioning and customer premises equipment. By the end of 1976, about 70 percent of the Bell System lines could be provided with TOUCH-TONE service and more than 30 percent of the customers served by these lines had subscribed (see Fig. 11-5).

1.2 Wide Area Telephone Service (WATS)

To encourage broad usage of the telephone, flat rates for local exchange service were introduced in most areas. As dial service expanded to the suburbs, an expanded flat rate service to contiguous exchanges was offered as "extended area service" (EAS).

When direct distance dialing became widespread, a new bulk rate plan for long distance service was offered, starting in 1961. This became known as WATS, for Wide Area Telephone Service. The rates vary, based on filed tariffs and depending upon the geographic area to which the customer wants to place calls. For its introduction, the local or tandem switching equipment had to be modified (1) to measure total (monthly) connect time of the WATS line, and (2) to screen calls so that they would be completed only to areas subscribed to by each customer. To simplify this process, the geographical "bands" to which calls may be completed according to the tariff are represented by groups of area codes. Customers subscribe to one or more bands. The switching equipment must thus match the area codes of the band(s) to which customers subscribe against the dialed area code. Total connect time is measured, since some rates allow only a certain number of hours at the base rate. This service was so successful (180,000 lines by year-end 1976) that a new version, INWATS was introduced.

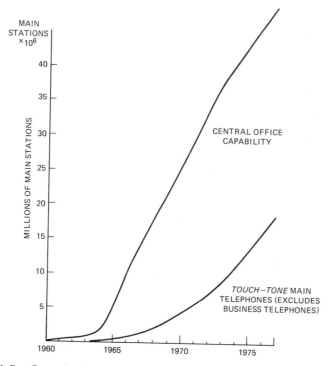

Fig. 11-5. Growth of central office TOUCH-TONE capability and main telephone TOUCH-TONE lines.

1.3 INWATS

Inward WATS, or INWATS, is a toll service with a bulk measured rate that automatically reverses the charge to the called customer. The rates are for a measured period but apply to intrastate or interstate with the latter accepting calls by originating band(s), again identified by area code. This popular service is identifiable by the prefix code "800" dialed ahead of a telephone number. The called telephone numbers are specially assigned for 800 service. For interstate INWATS, the toll switching systems are arranged to use code-conversion and screening capabilities. A toll office near the originating point makes a six-digit translation of the dialed 800 NNX. The NNX represents an area (usually an area code), so that 10,000 INWATS numbers associated with an NNX code may be assigned in each area (a few areas are represented by more than one NNX). As a result of code-conversion, a new NNX that includes a representation of the band of the calling line is forwarded to a principal city toll office in the Numbering Plan Area (NPA) of the called line. A unique area code that includes the calling band number is generated for calls not routed directly to the principal city in the terminating NPA. At the terminating toll office, the received office code and three of the four numerical digits are used to determine the actual terminating directory number and to match the bands to which the called customer subscribes against the source of the call. The call is thereby screened to determine if it should be completed.

This service was first offered intrastate in 1966 and interstate in 1967. By 1976 it was provided to 108,000 interstate and intrastate lines.

1.4 Centrex (also see Chapter 13, section 3.1)

During the post World War II period, dial PBX service was increasingly leased to businesses, especially for customers with large numbers of telephones. With dial service, therefore, more sophisticated and costly features could be offered.

A basic new service idea, later called Centrex-CO, was studied and explored at Bell Laboratories in the late 1950s. This provided service from a nearby central office to telephones that would otherwise be served by a PBX (see Fig. 11-6). (An early name for the concept was Customer Group Service.) For this purpose, the central

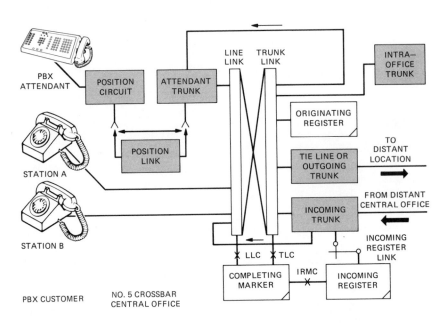

△ MODIFICATION

Fig. 11-6. Centrex-CO service as supplied by No. 5 crossbar. Customers (left) dial business extensions just as if PBX switching equipment were on premises.

office switching system is arranged to recognize and complete calls within a group of lines representing a customer when four or five digits are dialed (except specific initial digits such as 0 and 9). Several different customers may be served by the same central office equipment.[7]

Attendants' consoles are generally provided at the customer's premises for answering calls incoming to the listed directory number of the customer and for other features requiring judgment in rendering the service to meet customers' needs. Centrex service may be provided at several customer locations called "satellites." Bell Labs developed an arrangement for the attendants to be centralized for these several Centrex serving vehicles[8] (see Fig. 11-7).

Among the outstanding features of Centrex service are (1) the ability to offer customers bills listing calls by extension number, known as Automatic Identified Outward Dialing (AIOD), and (2) inward dialing to specific extensions instead of only to an attendant answering calls to the base or directory number. This is known as Direct Inward Dialing (DID). Later AIOD and DID were generically identified together as Centrex service, and the equipment for

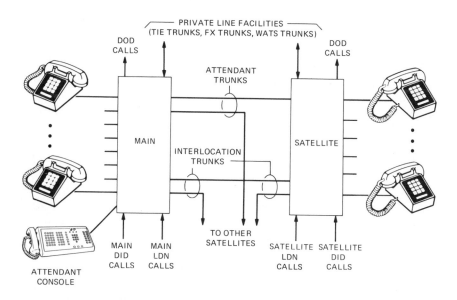

DID — DIRECT INWARD DIALING
DOD — DIRECT OUTWARD DIALING
LDN — LISTED DIRECTORY NUMBER

Fig. 11-7. Arrangement allowing attendants to be centralized at a location serving several Centrex customers.

the service could be offered by dial PBX equipment located on the customer's premises together with cooperative modifications in the central office (see Chapter 13, section 3.1).

Centrex service was first offered on a trial basis with a modification of the No. 5 crossbar system in Colorado Springs, Colorado in 1958. The first commercial installation was for the Dow Chemical Corporation in Detroit, Michigan in 1959. At about the same time, a step-by-step 701 PBX was modified for placement in quarters leased by the telephone company to serve two customers with Centrex service. When Centrex service was offered by PBXs on customer or leased premises, it was known as Centrex-CU.

Centrex service increased the number of telephones identified by a regular 7-digit directory number and therefore increased the use of central office codes. However, office codes may be shared by both a plurality of Centrex and regular customers. The crossbar tandem system was modified to outpulse station codes directly to Centrex-CU installations (initially these were step-by-step PBXs). Centrex-CO service was made available with No. 101 ESS in 1963, No. 1 ESS in 1968, and No. 2 ESS in 1971. As of the end of 1976, almost 6.5 million Bell System telephones were served with Centrex service, with 70 percent served directly from a central office.

1.5 Automatic Identified Outward Dialing (AIOD) and Direct Inward Dialing (DID)

Centrex-CU service to provide charging on an extension basis requires the PBX to be equipped with a form of automatic number identification (ANI). Studies at Bell Laboratories in the early 1960s showed that transmitting this information over PBX trunks would be inefficient, costly, and time-consuming. As a result, it was decided that Automatic Identified Outward Dialing (AIOD) would be provided using a separate data link to transmit ANI information from the PBX to the serving central office at the time the central office PBX trunk was seized.[9] There the extension number and trunk numbers would be stored in a magnetic memory and held until the central office ANI equipment attempted to obtain the calling line number. Upon discovering the number represented by a Centrex-CU trunk, the ANI equipment would refer to the AIOD store for the extension number associated with the identified trunk (Figs. 11-8 and 11-9.)

The first AIOD equipment was placed in service in Princeton, New Jersey in 1965 serving the Western Electric Engineering Research Center. Later that year, the first standard system was installed in the Newark, New Jersey office serving the Prudential Life Insurance Co. This was known as AIOD-A1 and could serve a maximum of 1800 Centrex-CU trunks from 60 PBXs. Later a smaller version known as AIOD-A2 using a magnetic delay line store, ser-

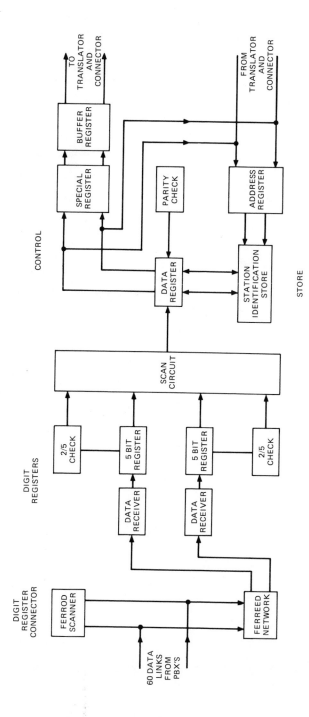

Fig. 11-8. Arrangement used to obtain and store identification of calling extension numbers from as many as 60 PBXs. With this information, obtained from data links (left), telephone companies can provide detailed billing by PBX extension. See Fig. 13-36 for connections to and from translators and connectors. (*AIEE Transactions*, Vol. 80, 1961.)

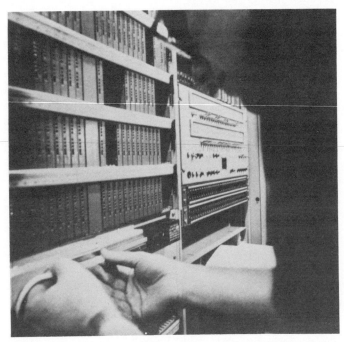

Fig. 11-9. Mr. C. Kuehner, Jr. examines the paper tape printout of the trouble recorder located on the station identification frame adjacent to its test panel.

ving a maximum of 220 Centrex-CU trunks from nine PBXs, was placed in service[10] in Wilmington, Delaware in 1970. The AIOD equipment was designed to work with all forms of ANI as well as the automatic message accounting translator in No. 5 crossbar systems. The AIOD data line can also terminate in the No. 1 and No. 2 ESS. In addition, the No. 101 ESS information identifying extensions may be transmitted over a data link to the AIOD equipment or to an ESS central office.

This project demonstrated the complexity of introducing a new service and the development coordination required among the many older and new generations of switching system designs. These characteristics of new service developments became increasingly commonplace in the late 1960s and 1970s. Each new service and many feature developments had an impact on the design of many central office systems.

Direct inward dialing (DID) to a Centrex CU also requires central office modifications since Centrex (PBX) extensions are identified by the same 4-digit codes used by regular lines. Local office and tandem systems (such as step-by-step, No. 5 crossbar and crossbar tandem) that provide for dial pulsing on trunks may treat these Centrex service PBXs as central offices. Except for very large PBXs, this is very inefficient service since it uses valuable central office (NNX) codes. It is most desirable to share central office codes with regular customers as well as other Centrex customers. This is readily accomplished in step-by-step. For ESS and crossbar offices, it is necessary to determine that on calls to particular directory numbers, outpulsing of the number to the PBX is needed and means must be provided for this function.

A method developed for the No. 5 crossbar system completes the call to a PBX in the usual manner but with a central office PBX trunk circuit that is connected by the marker to a dial pulse sender to which it supplies the directory number (see Fig. 11-10). This feature, known as "line link pulsing,"[11] was first installed in December 1962 in Michoud, Louisiana.

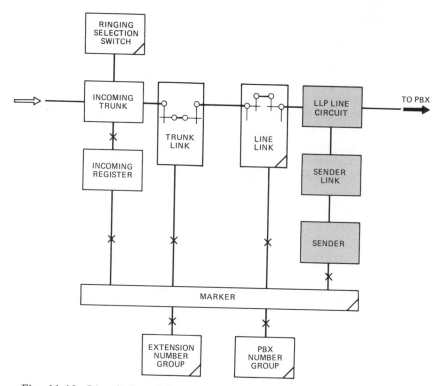

Fig. 11-10. Line link pulsing arrangement used with No. 5 crossbar to avoid wasting central office (3-digit) codes. System distinguishes between a PBX customer and a regular customer, even though both have the same CO code.

1.6 Data Services

One little-known development for the No. 5 crossbar system was an arrangement for the switching of wideband data, starting in 1967 and known as "Dataphone* 50" data communications service.[12] Until 1976, the only customer for this was the Long Lines Department of AT&T, which uses it daily for the interchange of toll call charges between itself and other operating companies. This service is known as CMD, for Centralized Message Distribution. (Since 1976, other customers have been added.) Special frequency-shift pulsing senders and receivers (with 200 digits per second capability) were developed for the No. 5 crossbar system for this and other data services, thereby adding another pulsing language to this system and again demonstrating its flexibility in this regard. The frequencies used for this type of pulsing were 1170 and 2125 hertz. Another data service used transmission with a bandwidth of about one quarter of that required for speech. Special narrow-band trunks using the B1 data system (see Fig. 11-11) to carry this traffic were selectable on a class of service basis. A No. 2A remote line concentrator (156 lines on 32 trunks) was developed for this service.[13] This crossbar concentrator could operate at high speed over long analog and telegraph carrier (up to 1000 miles) channels (see Fig. 11-12). This development also used frequency-shift pulsing over the data link for control of the remote and central office terminal.

Teletypewriter (TWX) exchange service was transferred from manual to automatic service in 1962 by providing a dial and data modem at each TWX station and assigning the line to a central office with a regular directory number.[14] Only a small number of No. 5

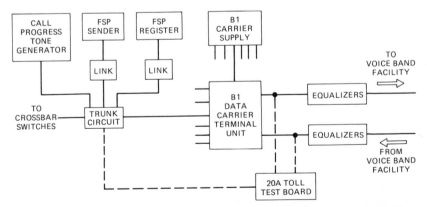

Fig. 11-11. Narrow-band B1 data system. Six data trunk circuits from the No. 5 crossbar system may be served by one 4-wire voice channel.

---

*Registered service mark of AT&T Co.

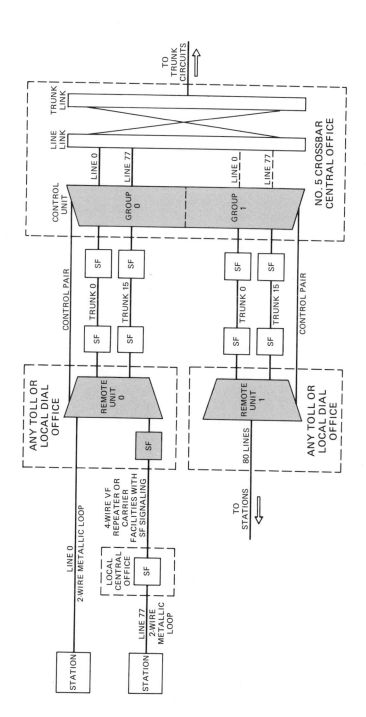

Fig. 11-12. The 2A remote line concentrator developed for use with No. 5 crossbar offices to concentrate narrow-band data traffic.

crossbar offices were arranged for this service. Access to them was through No. 2A remote line concentrators. The No. 5 offices were modified for this service with frequency-shift pulsing to access narrow-band trunks, thereby forming a subnetwork of the DDD network for TWX service. Furthermore, the service started with teletypewriters with three rows of keys (32 characters), and later four-row (64-character) sets were introduced.[15] Different area codes (X10 series) were assigned to the lines with 4-row formats. The No. 4A crossbar offices used in this network were arranged with equipment to convert between three- and four-row signal formats and also different speeds (100 instead of 75 baud). These converters were inserted into the connection by loop-around trunks (trunk circuits with an appearance on both the incoming and outgoing link frames).

To permit billing for dial TWX calls, No. 5 crossbar offices equipped with local automatic message accounting were chosen for this service. However, since these offices were not always located where they could serve the lines directly, a divided access line circuit was developed for proper charging on terminating calls. Originating calls could reach the No. 5 crossbar office where billing records are made, but calls terminating to these numbers could be routed through their regular step-by-step or crossbar office (Fig. 11-13).

Another data switching development was the application of No. 1 ESS for store-and-forward switching. This arrangement, described in Chapter 9, section 6.3, was known as the No. 1 ESS Arranged for Data Features (ADF). More recently, the 758 PBX was modified to provide switched digital data services (SDDS) of varying bit rates from 1.2K to 56.5K using registers that receive data signals, translate them into addresses that may be used by the marker to establish the desired connection, and relate the address information to the required data bit rate. This service has not been tariffed to date.

1.7 Emergency Service—911

By mid-1955 the Bell System introduced the idea of special telephone sets with enclosed heavy duty housings, placed in outdoor or other public locations, for use in reporting crimes, fires, or other civil emergencies.[16] Calls from these boxes were automatically routed through switching systems to one of several centralized headquarters. By 1960 the service was also made available to cities for direct termination at police headquarters.[17] With the low calling rate characteristic of this type of service, it was natural that in large cities concentrators would be developed and used to provide the service more economically.[18]

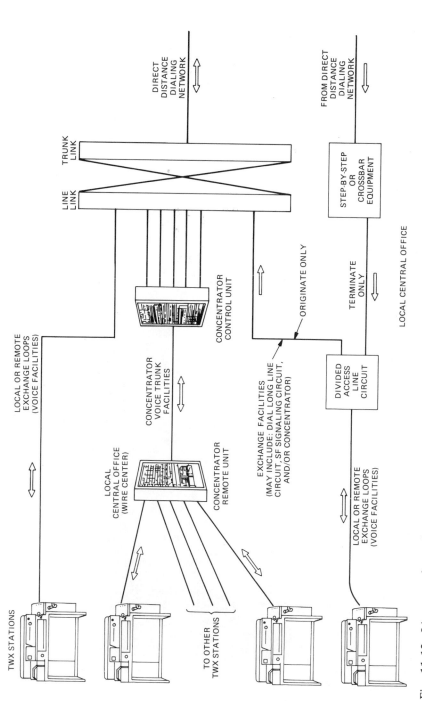

Fig. 11-13. Line, trunk, and concentrator arrangements to provide originating service for teletypewriter stations using specially equipped No. 5 crossbar offices and terminating service through the nearest local central office.

This was the status of emergency reporting when, on January 15, 1968, the Bell System announced the dedication of the service code 911 for emergency calling within an exchange.[19] Initially, regular telephone equipment, including an earlier design emergency-service manual switchboard,[20] was used to offer this service. Later, based on experience with this service, special central office and emergency bureau equipment was designed. With this special equipment, calls to the bureau could be held and rung back, since callers sometimes failed to give their identity.[21] Also, arrangements were required to force the release of connections by the bureau to prevent emergency lines from being tied up by malicious callers and otherwise. Fig. 11-14 shows an emergency service console for 911 service.

While 911 service served almost 50 million people with almost 600 installations by the end of 1976, it has spread more slowly than desired by public officials. Among the difficulties is the lack of coincidence between the telephone exchange and political (town, city, etc.) boundaries. As a result of a study conducted by Bell Labora-

Fig. 11-14. A 911 emergency position. Special provisions are made to call back the caller and to force the release of emergency call connections.

tories at the request of the Law Enforcement Assistance Administration telecommunications officials,[22] a comprehensive method for overcoming these deficiencies was devised, using the memory access and program flexibility of electronic switching. With ESS, calls can be routed to the proper bureau. Furthermore, ESS call-forwarding facilities can be used to move emergency calls to more appropriate bureaus (hospital, rescue, fire, etc.). Also, by identifying and routing these calls via an ESS tandem with a minicomputer, the address associated with a calling number can be determined for use in providing better service. A trial of some of these features was held in Philadelphia in 1974.[23] A trial of all features that were developed took place in Alameda County, California starting in July 1978. The service is known as expanded 911 (see Fig. 11-15).

1.8 Coin Service

Since the early 1920s, automatic switching systems were designed to serve coin telephones, some on a postpay (deposit and collection of coins upon call answer with no coin return) and others on a prepay (coin before call establishment) basis. For the initial charge on local answered calls, coin circuits were provided for automati-

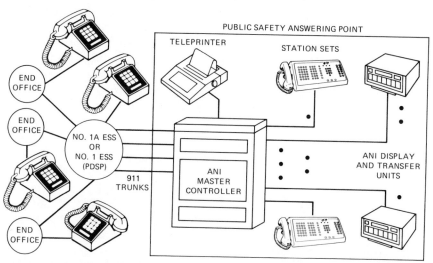

Fig. 11-15. Expanded 911 calls from local end offices are routed through the No. 1A ESS or No. 1 ESS with or without a Peripheral Data Storage Processor (PDSP), serving as the Expanded 911 tandem to the Public Safety Answering Point. The ANI master controller routes calls to answering attendants at station sets, and displays the calling number. Display and transfer units show the calling number, and are used for transferring calls. A teleprinter is used to record information about emergency calls.

cally collecting coins and, with prepay service, for automatically returning coins on unanswered calls. Circuits were also developed for dial system A switchboard (DSA) operators to collect and return coins on calls from prepay coin stations.

Early panel system developments provided for prepay coin service (coin had to be deposited before call was completed), but dial tone was given without a check of the deposit at coin telephones. The coin test was made by the sender at the completion of dialing. This was known as dial-tone-first operation. Provision was made for free (and coinless) calls to operators, service codes, and selected "official" numbers. If coins were not deposited by the time the dialing was completed, the sender "stuck" and lighted a lamp before the DSA operator monitoring the sender, who asked the caller for the deposit. By 1930 it was decided[24] to require a coin deposit on prepayment coin operation before giving dial tone. This became known as coin-first operation. It reduced false usage of equipment and made the service and meaning of dial tone more consistent with noncoin service.

The early panel systems, and later the No. 1 crossbar system, included provision for accepting a separate charge for coin service during each overtime period in excess of the period covered by the initial charge (at that time 5 cents). A few exchanges, mainly in New York City, had tariffs that provided for overtime charging. Equipment was developed for timing the initial period for a fixed period, usually 5 minutes. The initial deposit was automatically collected at the end of 4.5 minutes as a warning; then at the end of 5 minutes the district selector or junctor was connected to a DSA operator who would answer the call by requesting the overtime deposit.

By 1943 customer-dialed coin service was extended beyond the 5 cents initial deposit, so that more distant points in metropolitan (multizone) areas could be dialed directly.[25] An operator was called in, for both the initial and overtime deposits, by outgoing trunk circuits routed through panel sender or later (1953) crossbar tandem offices using panel call indicator pulsing.[26] With this type of pulsing, it was possible to delay completion of the call until the operator collected the correct amount of additional coins.

A unique system feature was designed into the No. 5 crossbar system in 1952 to provide coin service. For the panel, No. 1 crossbar and step-by-step systems, special groups of originating circuits (selectors and junctors) were required. In the No. 5 system, coin features may be inserted into a call using any outgoing trunk circuit by looping a call originating from coin telephones through a coin junctor[27] (see Fig. 11-16). Later, in 1959, coin zone features were added to No. 5 crossbar using the same principle.[28]

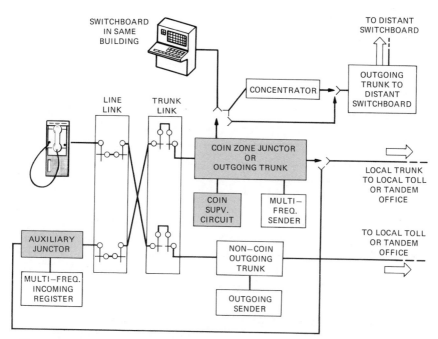

Fig. 11-16. Unique No. 5 crossbar arrangement for coin phone service improved on No. 1 crossbar and step-by-step methods, which required special groups of originating circuits.

Since operator positions may be located remote from the local office, special signals, both dc and ac,[29] were developed for controlling coin deposits. When the traffic service position (TSP) (1964) and traffic service position system (TSPS) (1969) were introduced (see Chapter 10, sections 1.3 and 1.4), zone and toll coin calls could be customer-dialed with operator intervention to request, verify, and collect the correct amount. A different "wink" signaling arrangement was later designed for TSPS coin operation. A most advanced coin service, automatic coin telephone service or ACTS, has been developed (see Chapter 10, section 1.9) using the TSPS.

The first increase in the initial local coin charge, from 5 to 10 cents, occurred in 1952, and by the late 1950s the 10-cent charge was common in many jurisdictions. Not only was the coin telephone design modified[30] by the addition of a totalizer to take care of different initial charges, but also single-slot telephones with electronic coin tone generators were developed to provide for returning single 5-cent deposits on abandoned calls.

A 911 service goal was to permit calls to emergency bureaus or to operators from prepay coin telephones without the deposit of a coin. Bell Laboratories studies indicated that development of this feature would be costly in some local switching systems. This particular service need—to arrange selected coin telephones to receive dial tone and to translate some digits before requiring the deposit of a coin—illustrated dramatically the differences in effort in developing features for electromechanical and stored-program control electronic switching systems. The effort for No. 1 ESS was one-third that required for the No. 5 crossbar system.[31] The differences in cost of implementation in the field were equally impressive.

For the first time, the panel system was omitted from a new local service development, since by that time (late 1960s) an ambitious panel replacement program was gaining acceptance, and since most panel offices were in buildings with more modern switching entities. Therefore, coin lines could be transferred from panel to other entities. The first dial-tone-first coin service was placed in operation on a trial basis in 1966 in a New York City No. 1 crossbar office and in Hartford, Connecticut on a No. 5 crossbar office. Standard arrangements were available in 1967 and 1968, respectively, for the No. 5 and No. 1 crossbar systems.

For dial-tone-first operation, the step-by-step system was modified with a new coin trunk between the line finders serving coin lines and the first selectors.[32] The first of these arrangements was placed in service in Cheyenne, Wyoming in October 1970.

As with many service developments, coin service has kept pace with other needs, e.g., the design of circuits to detect full boxes and to extend coin service over longer loops,[33] and the development of automatic test sets for use by coin telephone installers and repair forces.[34]

1.9 Common-Control Switching Arrangement (CCSA)

Growth in public switching was paralleled by expansion of private line services, and, as might be expected, this required special switching services and features. In particular, arrangements were developed for No. 5 crossbar[35] and No. 1 ESS so that the central office provided not only Centrex service for one or more customers but acted in nationwide two-level hierarchical private networks that served the telecommunication needs of large businesses. By dialing an access code, usually 8, the customer's employees could reach company or agency locations on the network. In order for the switching offices to be shared by several private networks, common-control switching was required, hence the name common-control switching arrangement, or CCSA. A special 4-wire version of the No. 5 crossbar system was developed in 1960 to serve as the first or higher-level (tandem) in these networks. Thirty-four of these offices, together with 54 2-wire and several other systems including No. 1 ESS, are used for this service. Networks for the federal government—such as the Federal Telephone System (FTS) for civilian use (cutover February 1963), Switched Circuit Automatic Network (SCAN) for the army (first service December 1961), and the Command Automatic Dial Switching System for NORAD (service November 1963), later combined into AUTOVON for the Defense Department's general needs—were among the first to be placed into service.[36] By 1971 more than 25 of these networks were established for commercial customers with some offices serving as many as 4 or 5 customers.

While the intention was for this to be a fixed-rate service, provision was added for recording automatic message accounting data on 10 percent of the calls. In 1975, the systems were modified so that the access to facilities, including intraoffice trunk circuits, could be limited to a number subscribed-to according to revised tariffs. This is known as a simulated facilities group.

In many cases, CCSA customer networks include not only PBXs but also Centrex service from the same switching systems. CCSA service includes not only access to private network switching and transmission facilities, but also local and distant (foreign exchange) access to the public network and direct or tie trunk facilities between PBXs connected to the network. Also added in 1975 were arrangements known as flexible or automatic route selection that permit the customer to choose the order and degree to which calls may be routed from particular telephones over the available facilities.

1.10 Expanded DDD

From a service point of view, direct distance dialing resulted in a great change in the public's dialing habits. Nevertheless, 40 percent of the toll calls, such as person-to-person, time and charge, etc., still required operator assistance. These calls were converted to customer-dialed calls with the development of the traffic service position (see Chapter 10, section I). Service with TSP was originally known as "expanded DDD."

The location of the stored-program controlled cordless positions in the telephone network makes the TSPS ideally suited for the introduction of many new services and the further automation of operator services. Since the service potentials of these systems are greater than expanded dialing of toll calls, this service name was dropped in the early 1970s. Some new services envisioned for expanded DDD are described under the name "Stored-Program Control (SPC) network" (see Chapter 12, section IV).

1.11 Automated Intercept Service

As described in the first volume of this History series,[37] calls to disconnected numbers were originally passed to special desks for the purpose of giving the caller information about the called number or party. With the introduction of dial service, it was possible to dial numbers that were unequipped. Initially, a vacant code tone was applied to these terminals, but with DDD service the number of office codes that could be dialed expanded greatly. It became desirable to indicate not only that an unequipped or unassigned number was reached, but where it was located.

Recorded announcements not only provided an indication that an unequipped or unassigned terminal or code was reached, but could also contain a code or phrase indicating to where the call progressed. The first of a series of magnetic drum recording systems, the 6A, was introduced in 1955[38] (see Fig. 11-17). Later, improved magnetic drum systems were introduced—the 9A[39] and 11A[40] in 1959 and 1963, respectively. These systems were used not only for intercept but also when abnormal congestion was encountered in the network, indicating with a plant code the location reached in the network.[41] This was an important part of the DDD improvement program (see below, section 3.1).

The later development and deployment of the automatic intercept system did not eliminate the need for routine plant announcements.

Fig. 11-17. A. R. Bertels (left) and H. F. Brueckner discussing the magnetic drums of the 6A recording system, introduced in 1955.

In 1977, one of the first applications of magnetic bubbles was in the 13A announcement system, which eliminated the need for rotating magnetic drums.[42]

With the introduction of the automatic intercept system No. 1A (see Chapter 10, section III), which by the beginning of 1977 served 40 percent of the Bell System, the quality of this aspect of rendering telephone service has been greatly improved. In the United States, at that time, the mobility of telephone subscribers was very great. In many locations, to gain one telephone required 10 to be removed and 11 to be installed. This has been called "churning." When such changes occur, the practice in the United States is temporarily to suspend the use of the number and route calls to "intercept." Therefore, the volume of intercepted calls and the quantity of directory numbers being intercepted may be large. The automation of this service not only greatly improved the speed of service but also added an important new ingredient. With manual service, callers give the operators the numbers they believe they dialed. With automatic intercept service (AIS), the number reached is automatically identified, and therefore does not depend upon the recollection of the caller. Automatic intercept service in 1977 handled more than 3.3 million calls per day on this improved basis.

To use the automatic intercept system most efficiently, not only was a larger file developed (see Chapter 10, section 3.1) but intercept trunks from local offices were concentrated so that the traffic could be brought over longer distances from within a numbering plan area. The No. 23 call distributor used in some locations for intercept operator access prior to the introduction of the AIS (see below, section 2.7.1) was modified so that it could be used as a concentrator for traffic to an AIS location. In addition, a new trunk concentrator (No. 1A) was developed for use in more remote areas where surplus No. 23 concentrators were not available.[43] This system, introduced in Marietta, Georgia in January 1975, provides switching to concentrate a maximum of 200 incoming intercept trunks to 60 outgoing trunks using the smaller crossbar switches. The switch can also be used to concentrate directory assistance traffic.

1.12 Mechanization of Service Evaluation

To insure the quality of service as seen by the customer, it has been the practice since 1915 to provide equipment to observe calls in progress. With the development in 1949 of the No. 12 service observing desk (see Fig. 11-18), it was possible to centralize these activities for many types of central office systems and switchboards.[44] The No. 12 system provided loops to observing points at

Fig. 11-18. New York City installation of No. 12 service observing desks, developed in 1949 to centralize this function for various central office systems and switchboards.

switchboards or switching offices and included automatic call distribution to a team of service observers (see Fig. 11-19).

In 1973, development was started on a semiautomatic system for service evaluation. Recognizing in the mid-1960s the need for automatically detecting call progress tones, such as dial, reorder, busy and ringing, a precise (machine-detectable) tone plan[45] was developed and implemented. The service evaluation system (No. 1A) was first placed in service in Dallas, Texas in July 1976[46] and takes advantage of the precise tones to gather statistics on call attempt originations, completion, and charging with only a minimum need for operators. With this development, one can be more selective in specifying which types of calls are to be observed and can free operators from making written records on all calls.

1.13 Switching for PICTUREPHONE* Visual Telephone Service

In 1969, development was completed on a wideband switching network for the No. 5 crossbar system (see Fig. 11-20).[47] This switching network can serve a 1-MHz bandwidth signal on a 4-wire basis. Special care was taken to balance the wiring between the two directions of transmission and to ground. The three-stage crossbar

---

*Registered service mark of AT&T Co.

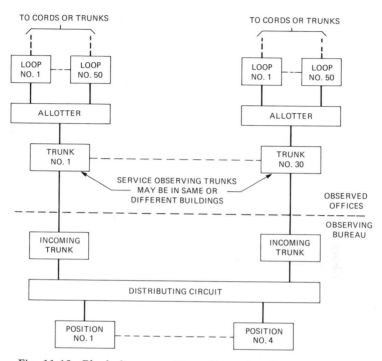

Fig. 11-19. Block diagram of No. 12 service observing system.

switch network had a maximum capacity of 3200 lines and 400 trunks. The regular No. 5 crossbar network carried the audio, and the control was modified to recognize PICTUREPHONE calls and to switch both audio and video.

In addition to developments for the No. 5 crossbar system, key systems (1P1), the 850 PBX, and No. 101 ESS were arranged to provide wideband data or PICTUREPHONE service, the latter two using the 4-wire ferreed switches developed for the AUTOVON No. 1 ESS (see Chapter 9, section 5.5). Unfortunately, the PICTUREPHONE developments were ahead of their time from an economic point of view, but these and other exploratory switching developments proved the feasibility of using space-division switching for this type of service.

1.14 Electronics in Local Electromechanical Switching

As new electronic devices appeared, efforts were made to apply them to electromechanical switching. In fact, the use of the transistor in the 4A crossbar translator (see Chapter 8, section 1.2) was its first commercial application.[48] Other applications were in signaling and timing circuits.

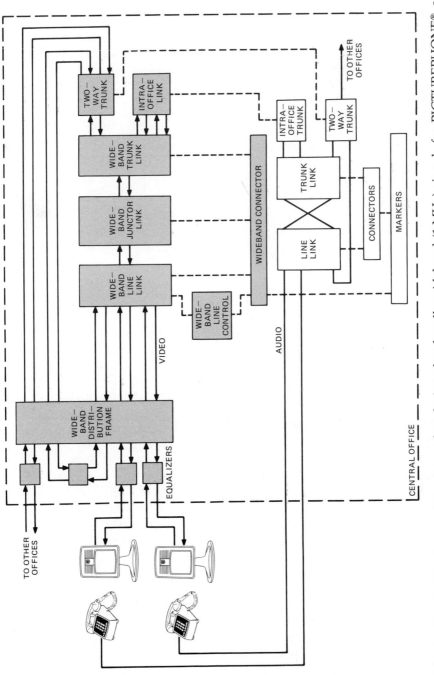

Fig. 11-20. Modifications to No. 5 crossbar designed to handle wideband (1 MHz) signals for PICTUREPHONE® service or data.

None of these had the impact of complete new switching systems using electronics with stored-program controls. Studies were made more or less continuously in attempts to apply subsystems from ESS in electromechanical systems. A popular application was for translators (see this chapter, section 2.6, and Chapter 10, section II). But most important was their application in attempts to provide the new service, administrative, and maintenance techniques that ESS generated.

1.14.1 Custom Calling Services

Stored-program control electronic switching opened a new era of services and feature implementation, including a new category of services known as custom calling services (see this chapter, section 4.1), which were implemented and tariffed for the electronic switching system. This created a need to explore methods for implementing them in electromechanical systems. The principal development efforts in this regard were made in the No. 5 crossbar system. A trial of the four custom calling services—abbreviated dialing (now called speed calling), call transfer (now called call forwarding), three-way calling, and call waiting—was held in a Columbus, Ohio central office between 1963 and 1965.[49] The first two services were the first to use the piggyback twistor memory in commercial telephone service.[50] Marketing trials of these services were conducted in Sioux City, Iowa and Wellesley, Massachusetts in 1966. The results indicated that in particular the call-waiting service appeared popular. A further trial of this service was conducted in Upper Arlington, Ohio in November 1971.[51] While the service was well received, it proved to be too expensive in the No. 5 crossbar system. Many arrangements were studied in efforts to reduce costs, but none proved economically viable.

1.14.2 Modernization

As electronic switching systems evolved, additional effort was expended in attempts to introduce their services and techniques into electromechanical systems. In 1970 a committee studied the possibilities of modernizing the No. 5 crossbar, step-by-step, and crossbar tandem systems by adapting stored-program control techniques. (The 4A crossbar system had already been successfully modified with an SPC electronic translator system; see Chapter 10, section II.) At that time, electronic technology was not low enough in cost for the new services to be provided at tariffs comparable with the ESS family and for administration cost reductions.

1.14.3 No. 5 Crossbar ETS

By 1975 the electronic technology for stored-program control had advanced to a point where it was possible to demonstrate that the 3A central control (see Chapter 9, section 7.2 and Fig. 11-21), could be applied in No. 5 crossbar offices where local AMA recording is required for most calls (see below, section 2.8 on usage-sensitive pricing). At the same time, it could replace the number group, route relay, and AMA translator frames, thereby eliminating all cross-connection operations. Fig. 11-22 shows some of the considerable cross-connection activity these frames require. (In 1958 a feature was added to the system to enable an automatic cross-check of these translators' on-line service order activities.[52])

This modification of the No. 5 crossbar system, known as the No. 5 crossbar ETS for Electronic Translator System, was installed in Tarrytown, New York and became generally available in 1977.[53] While the principal purpose of No. 5 crossbar ETS is to reduce routine effort in executing service orders, it also provides for improved AMA magnetic tape recording as measured service is applied to a greater portion of local calls.

1.15 Other New Services

In Chapter 7 the tremendous growth of features and services for the No. 5 crossbar system was indicated. As discussed in this

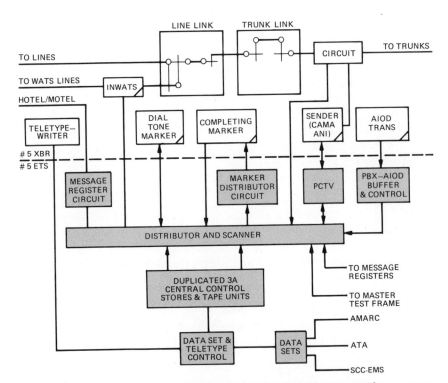

Fig. 11-21. Electronic translator system for the No. 5 crossbar system adds duplicated 3A central controls and high-speed electronic memory in place of number group and translator frames.

Fig. 11-22. Checking cross-connections in number group frames and AMA frames of a No. 5 crossbar-ETS.

chapter, many of these services had an impact on other local and toll switching systems as well. In addition, some new services such as Centrex and AIOD (see above, section 1.5) required the simultaneous development of customer premises equipment, such as attendants' consoles and automatic number (station) identification facilities for PBXs.

In this volume it would be difficult to include a description of how every new service evolved. However, below are some that should be mentioned, particularly since they involved close cooperative development of switching with other parts of the plant.

1.15.1 Group Alerting

Group alerting is an arrangement for simultaneously calling a number of lines in an emergency.[54] This is widely used by volunteer fire and rescue squads.

1.15.2 Rate Quote System

Another development was the rate quote system, a centralized audio response arrangement for operators to obtain rate and routing information.[55] Operators would key in the area and office codes and receive an announcement of the required information.

1.15.3 BELLBOY* Radio Paging Service

Step-by-step, crossbar tandem, and No. 5 crossbar offices were modified in 1964 to permit outpulsing of called numbers representing paging receivers served by J1 control terminals.[56]

---

*Registered service mark of AT&T Co.

1.15.4 *Mobile Radio Service*

Switching arrangements were developed to permit mobile telephones (including those on railroads) to originate and terminate
calls without operator intervention—in particular the MJ dial mobile
radio system.[57] This system also provided operator access for mobile
telephones roaming beyond their normal service area where dial
service for them was not available.

Starting in the late 1950s, research was initiated at Bell Laboratories on methods for expanding mobile service beyond acquiring
new frequency bands. In response to an FCC question in 1968, the
Bell System proposed to respond with respect to the feasibility and
characteristics of high-capacity mobile systems. After an 18-month
study, the FCC permitted development to proceed on a proposed
cellular system under an experimental license with marketing and
technical trial service in the Chicago area. This service started in
late 1978. The important role of switching in this development is
described in Chapter 9, section 6.10.1.

II. GROWTH OF SERVICE

Not only were innovative services growing in our systems, but the
services that had been long offered were also growing. As a result,
continual study at Bell Laboratories and among the operating companies indicated new and changing requirements for the services
and features of existing systems.

2.1 Unigauge

As the suburban and rural areas expanded, service was needed
over longer loops. Initially, dial long line circuits were used.[58] With
electronics, it was possible to miniaturize such circuits to take care
of their ever-growing numbers. In 1966, a new outside plant concept was conceived that recognized the economic trade-off between
small (26) gauge cables in the distribution plant and the use of central office range extension such as used in dial long line circuits.
This also avoided the necessity for introducing loading into the new
plant.

Instead of dial long line circuits being placed on specific lines, a
common set of long line or "range extenders with gain" was
designed into the "B" links of some line link frames of the No. 5
crossbar system (see Fig. 11-23). Other portions of the system were
also modified so that higher voltages could be used on these calls to
obtain minimum required loop current. This is a good example of
the complexity of a switching system development; while the concept is simple, its execution requires modification of many portions

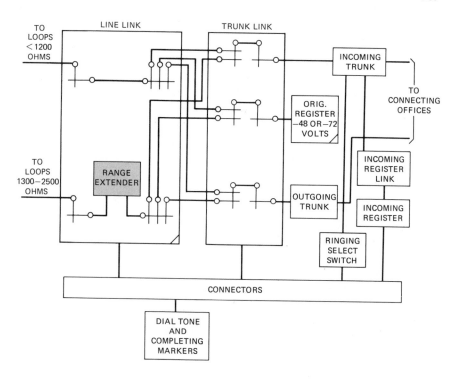

Fig. 11-23. No. 5 crossbar modifications for Unigauge, including the addition of range extenders to links in the line link frame. *(IEEE Transactions on Communication Technology,* April 1968.)

of the system. This 1966 development, known as Unigauge, was of help in offices experiencing rapid growth distant from the wire centers.[59] A field trial was held in Rockford, Illinois in October 1966. The first standard office was in Dubuque, Iowa in June 1969. The Unigauge concept was also applied to No. 2 ESS and was initially used in 1971[60] in the second No. 2 ESS office to go into service, in North Madison, Connecticut, in August 1971. A similar loop range extension feature was later developed for the No. 1 ESS.

2.2 Foreign Area Translation

When direct distance dialing was introduced, the ability to route according to the dialed area code was assigned to control switching points (CSPs). At these points the six digits comprising the area code and office code could be translated (see Chapter 8, section I). In most cases the area code is for an area different from that of the caller. This is known as foreign area translation (FAT).

As direct distance calling increased the need for more direct inter-toll trunking, calls to adjacent numbering plan areas increased. Therefore, a limited foreign area translation capability was designed into No. 5 crossbar,[61] crossbar tandem,[62] and step-by-step CAMA common-control systems, as well as into No. 1 and No. 2 ESS.

2.3 All Number Calling

With the expansion and acceptance of direct distance dialing, it was discovered fairly early that local central office names, particularly their spelling, made nationwide universal calling more difficult. Customers at distant locations were not familiar with these names and made dialing errors.

It became obvious that the two-letter, five-number system of office identification, in use since the late 1940s, could no longer be preserved. The letters represented local names, the spelling of which was not always understood by the distant caller. But, more important, the letters appeared only in pronounceable combinations, thereby restricting the number of usable codes. The original three-letter, four-number directory numbers required three letter combinations from central office names (see Chapter 2), severely restricting the useful codes in large cities among the possible 512 codes. By going to two letters and five numbers, this was expanded to 640. As the metropolitan areas grew, there was a need to use all of the $9 \times 8 \times 10 = 720$ central office codes. Therefore, eventual conversion to all number calling (ANC) was made part of the Bell System policy in the late 1950s.

In Wichita Falls, Texas in January 1958, for the first time the telephone numbers were all changed to seven numerical digits without letters or names.[63] Earlier, steps were taken to introduce digit dialing locally. This required the introduction of digit-absorbing selectors into the step-by-step offices (see Chapter 3, section II). The trial in Wichita Falls showed that the accuracy of dialing was not affected by all number calling (ANC). The public had become used to dialing, a far cry from the time, 40 years earlier, when the letters were originally introduced. The trial also showed that ANC was faster. Now each area could support 720 central office codes.

The conversion has taken some time, primarily because of public resistance to losing favorite office names. As of 1977, however, better than 74 percent of the Bell System numbers are ANC. While the process has been slow, with mixtures of 2–5 and 7 in the same area, the conversion process is now in its final stages.

2.4 New Numbering Plan

The 10-digit nationwide dialing established in 1945 has stood up well.[64] However, confining area codes to the 152 that have only 0 or

1 in the second digit (such as 201 or 312) results in the danger of a shortage of these numbers. In 1947, only 86 area codes were assigned. By 1960, due to expanding service needs, 117 codes had been assigned. A plan was devised to enable the use of three-digit area codes without restriction.[65] The consequence is that area codes may be identical with office codes. Therefore senders and registers have to time after the seventh digit is received to determine when dialing is completed. Also, preceding the 10-digit called numbers by 1 or 0 could help distinguish toll calls from local 7-digit calls. The new area codes could be unique if these central office codes were not assigned in all areas. A complementary development was the development of arrangements to use area codes as office codes by timing for the end of dialing.

Changes were developed from 1961 to 1964 for all switching systems to enable their operation with conflicting area and office codes. All systems were also modified for 0+ dialing to reach TSP operators. In 1970, the step-by-step local SAMA equipment in Los Angeles, California was also modified to accept the 0+ calls.[66]

2.5 Local/Tandem/Toll

As mentioned in connection with the need for foreign area translation (FAT) in local offices (see above, section 2.2), the growth of toll calling, both interstate and intrastate, made it economical to establish more class 4 toll switching offices. One of the most economic and popular ways of doing this was to provide the class 4 functions—particularly two-way intertoll trunks, facilities for testing them, and FAT—in offices already established for local service. For the No. 5 crossbar system, these provisions were made in 1955.[67] Also, the No. 5 system was provided with complete CAMA and local tandem features in 1958[68] so that it could act as an outward class 4 toll point. Similar arrangements were made for the No. 1 ESS with first service in Wichita Falls in October 1974.[69]

The crossbar tandem system is used extensively for toll operation with features developed in 1956.[70] Crossbar tandem was also modified to act as an end office on direct inward dialed (DID) calls for Centrex service, for radio paging on inward calls (see above, section 1.15), and for WATS outward calls.

An early application of the No. 1 ESS in Nashville, Tennessee in November 1968, was as a local tandem office. Later, to accommodate more trunk terminations for tandem service, a 2048-termination remreed trunk link frame was developed and first placed in service in Brooklyn, New York in 1975.

The growing need for tandem offices in metropolitan areas to distribute incoming toll calls to the growing number of local offices made special "sector" and "high volume" tandems economically attractive (see Fig. 11-24). The first No. 4 ESS was applied as a selective routing tandem in January 1976.[71]

From the above it may be observed that multipurpose switching centers serving local, tandem, and/or toll traffic became commonplace. The flexibility of the common-control and stored-program architectures made it possible to provide these many services and features.

2.6 No. 5 Crossbar Route Translator

The complexity of serving a number of Centrex, AUTOVON, common-control switching arrangement (CCSA), and other special services on the same No. 5 crossbar system, in addition to many other services, has been discussed. Each of these services, as well as the many improvements in features such as CAMA and dial TWX, reacts on the translation functions. The intertwining of the translation requirements for these services and features indicated the advantage of developing an electronic route translator.[72] This equipment was not deployed since it was not cost-effective. Later, a stored-program version was developed and placed into service (see Chapter 11, section 1.14.3).

2.7 Directory Assistance

2.7.1 Automatic Call Distributor

The TSPS development inspired telephone companies to request an equally efficient arrangement for distributing calls to directory

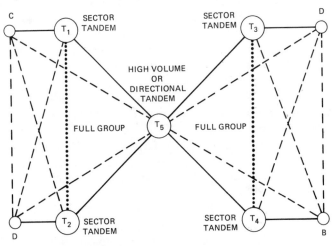

A, B, C, AND D ARE END OFFICES
PREFERRED ROUTES ARE IN THE
ORDER DASHED, DOTTED, SOLID.
NOT ALL ROUTES SHOWN.

Fig. 11-24. Arrangement of tandem offices for high-volume service in metropolitan areas. (Minutes: DDD Subcommittee meeting with AT&T representatives, February 2, 1968.)

assistance (DA). The growth of DDD as well as extended area dialing had greatly increased DA traffic (13,600 positions in 1970). The step-by-step call distributors, No. 2 from 1929 and No. 3 from 1941[73] and the No. 23 crossbar call distributor from 1950,[74] then standard, served only a maximum of 66 positions. All positions had to serve the same type of traffic (e.g., local or toll). The No. 23 operating room desk system could connect 140 trunks with 40 operator positions (see Fig. 11-25). Many different physical arrangements were possible; Fig. 11-26 shows one of them. The controls were unduplicated. The No. 23 system was modified in 1969: (1) to provide greater reliability, since by then it was serving 12,000 operator positions through the Bell System; (2) to be used as a concentrator for intercept trunks ahead of the No. 1A automatic intercept system; and (3) to serve on a preferential basis four different classes of traffic.

To attain an expanded-size call distributor, a version of the No. 2 ESS was first considered. While its stored-program control offered attractive flexibility, the additional development effort requirement came at a time when the No. 2 ESS initial development was peaking. Therefore, with the assistance of New York Telephone, a new version of the No. 5 crossbar system was developed in 1968 to serve a maximum of 2400 trunks with up to 500 positions (see Fig. 11-27). The positions may be remoted to six operator locations, each with no more than 100 positions.[75] Special gating was added to the line link frames, on which the incoming trunks appeared, to insure calls were served in strict order of arrival. Five classes of service could route calls to preferred operator groups.

The first of 91 No. 5 automatic call distributors (ACDs) was installed[76] in New York City, starting in 1969. The first 42 entities served 82 percent of the positions. By 1973, phase II of the development was completed.[77] This included announcements of origins to the operators when their positions are seized by calls, gradual closedown of operator groups, geographical groupings, and call transfer, as well as new auxiliary service positions. More than 49 of the No. 5 ACDs of the phase II type were installed, starting with an installation in Omaha, Nebraska in September 1973.

2.7.2 *Information Retrieval*

The operation of directory assistance positions developed using printed directories with a bulletin showing frequently called numbers and daily or weekly addenda. Starting in the summer of 1958 in Washington, D.C. a trial was conducted using cards with microfilm frames of directory pages and a special reader (see Fig. 11-28). In 1961, experimental installations used microfilm projector methods, with sticks supporting film frames replacing

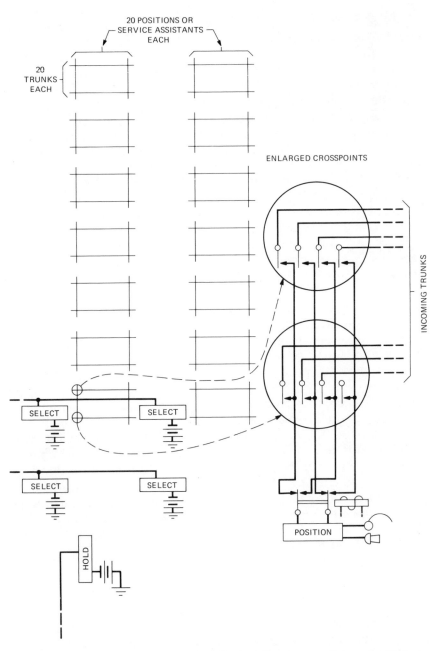

Fig. 11-25. Arrangement for distributing directory assistance calls from 140 trunks to 40 operator positions, as used in the No. 23 crossbar call distributor, which was then one of three standard call distributors.

Fig. 11-26. No. 23 system directory assistance installation. Many different office configurations were possible.

directory pages (see Fig. 11-29). This arrangement saved part of the time to use and file microfilm images.[78] However, a trial in Brooklyn, New York showed insufficient savings in operator work times to pay for the film-handling equipment.

Computer developments made many think of computer retrieval of directory information, with keyboard input and a display on a cathode ray tube. Generally this took too much input information to save operator work time that would pay for the computer installation and operation time. In 1963, R. L. Deininger of Bell Laboratories came up with an idea that made computerized DA (DA/C) attractive. It was an algorithm indicating that the use of as few as four characters could result in only a limited number of listings being retrieved. The set of four characters was termed a "combination of details" and consisted of such elements as two letters of the last name, a first initial, and an address letter or number.[79] A simulation of this method, known as MECHSIM, was held in East Orange, New Jersey in 1968 (see Fig. 11-30), and a full trial was conducted in Oakland, California in 1971.[80] Later, improved computer DA/C and microfiche DA/M[81] systems were developed by the general trade under the auspices of the business information systems area of Bell Laboratories[82] and adopted by most Bell operating companies.

2.7.3 Directory Assistance Charging

The growth of directory assistance resulted in intensive studies to identify the manner in which this service is used. Details of long distance DA calls (NPA + 555–1212) were AMA recorded with listing made and charging nullified at accounting centers. To study

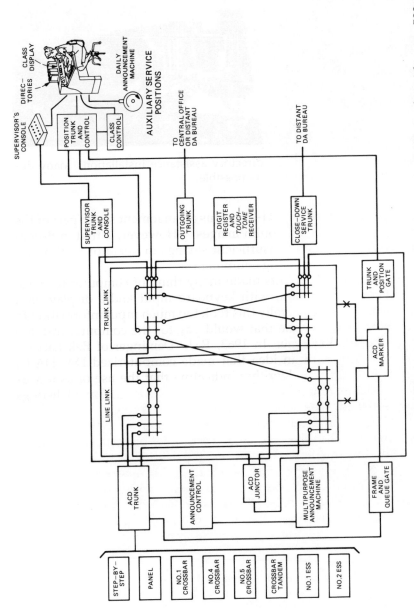

Fig. 11-27. No. 5 crossbar automatic call distributor, developed in 1968 to serve up to 2400 trunks with up to 500 operator positions.

Fig. 11-28. Experimental directory assistance positions, Washington, D.C., 1958. Telephone numbers on microfilm replaced directories.

Fig. 11-29. Trial in 1961 of microfilm-strip based directory assistance system. Expense of film handling and replacement proved excessive.

local calling habits, similar modifications were made to record and screen 411 DA calls.

Directory assistance calls increased 93 percent in 10 years from 1963 to 1973. Only 10 to 15 percent of the customers accounted for 50 percent of the calls. In March 1974, the Cincinnati and Suburban Telephone Co. started charging 20 cents for all DA calls over the first three per month. Calls decreased by 74 percent.[83] Other companies have now introduced similar plans. As usual, to effect such plans required switching developments at Bell Laboratories. All systems with AMA recording were arranged to record 411 and 114 DA calls on a regular basis. In some locations, charge keys were added to DA positions to control whether there would be a charge indication for the call.

2.8 Charging

Initially, charge recording was for short haul toll calls, as described in Chapter 8, section 3.1. Paper tape recording for these calls was adequate. Magnetic wire recording was studied at an early stage but was rejected because of the uncertainty and cost of the technology. As charge recording was required for DDD, the same paper tape method was employed.

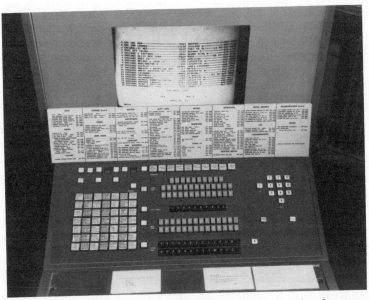

Fig. 11-30. MECHSIM 1968 trial position layout. As few as four alphanumeric characters produced a limited number of telephone listings from which the directory assistance operator could choose.

With the growth of traffic, there was a greater advantage to placing AMA recording in the local office (LAMA), since here there was more freedom in call routing and, here, records from fewer locations containing calls from the same line needed to be correlated in the accounting process. While paper tape LAMA was applied to a few step-by-step (SAMA)[84] and No. 1 crossbar offices,[85] the principal LAMA application was in No. 5 crossbar offices. The ESS[86] and TSP systems were already using magnetic tape recording, so magnetic tape recording was examined for No. 5 crossbar in 1966. A system of magnetic tape recording (MTR) was developed and applied in about 60 new offices. This highly integrated arrangement was found too costly as a general replacement for paper tape AMA.

Eventually a system known as LAMA-C was developed in 1974 (first service Buffalo, New York, March 1975), and 21 No. 5 crossbar systems were so modified. It was applicable most economically where most of the trunk circuits were already arranged for AMA and would therefore facilitate conversion to magnetic tape recording.

In the meantime, a different approach to paper tape replacement was proposed by the International Business Machines Corporation (IBM). This approach, using duplicated IBM System 7's, was based on minimizing changes in the switching system by electronically scanning the control and data wires of the paper tape recorders. An added feature was scanning the trunk supervisory relays directly to obtain answer and disconnect time. As a result, the determination of the total connect time was made more precisely by the electronic computer techniques than formerly possible with relay equipment. Also, in this manner the expansion to trunks not originally arranged for AMA was made easier.

This equipment was first installed in Cincinnati, Ohio in 1974, and was highly successful. It showed that within the approved tariffs, greater revenues were obtainable. The development was applied to centralized AMA offices that were already equipped with large numbers of paper tape recorders and where maximum benefit could be obtained at least cost. As of January 1, 1977, 155 of these systems, known as CAMA-C, were installed in crossbar tandem and No. 4A crossbar offices. Later the programs for these offices were modified to seek out potential troubles and suspected fraud situations, based upon the detected supervisory signals.

As a result of the CAMA-C experience, improved call timing was developed for application to the paper tape and LAMA-C systems. The LAMA-C system mentioned above was similar to the CAMA-C, but utilized Digital Equipment Corp. (DEC) PDP 11/30 computers programmed by, and with scanners and other interface equipment developed by, Bell Laboratories.

The growth of AMA recording also required changes in the programming and provision for additional AMA tape recorders in No. 2 ESS. By this time (1974), it became obvious that the growth of charge recording had only reached a plateau and that future tariff trends would require charge recording on all calls as the Bell System moves from flat rate to "usage sensitive pricing" (USP) plans. Furthermore, the growth of recording has required tapes to be picked up more frequently at central offices. The natural trend, therefore, was to consider data links to replace manual handling of even the magnetic tapes.

In March 1975, the first AMA recording center (AMARC) was placed in service in Buffalo, New York.[87] This system, initially using duplicated commercial computers, is used to record AMA call data transmitted from the local offices, generally in real time (see Fig. 11-31). The first systems modified to work with the AMARC were quite naturally the local step-by-step systems that generally have not included LAMA capability and did include ANI. This required a "call data accumulator" (CDA) to be developed (and ANI modified) for the step-by-step system.

For crossbar systems a billing data transmitter (BDT) was developed to interface the former paper tape AMA equipment with the new AMARC. By January 1, 1977, 22 AMARCs were in service and many more are expected. The trend to this method of recording is indicated by developments to transmit AMA data from No. 2 and No. 3 ESSs to AMARC.

Originally, to flash supervisory lamps on switchboards on calls to busy lines or busy trunk groups, short reversals of the dc current were sent over the loop 60 or 120 times per minute. To avoid false charges, 2 seconds were allowed for answer supervision. This timing was performed by mechanical interrupters with a 50 percent tolerance. With the availability of electronic timing circuitry and the elimination of lamp flashing, it was possible in 1973 to introduce more precise answer supervision timing. This resulted in more accurate charge time recording.

Finally, another development resulting from growth of traffic was the provision of charge recording arrangements for directory assistance calls (see above, section 2.7.3). This affected all systems, as described, including provisions for routing these calls. Of particular interest was the addition of CAMA provisions on the No. 5 crossbar ACD system in 1975 when optional charging for DA was introduced.

While systems were developed to improve AMA recording, the New York Telephone Co. initiated a development with the VIDAR Company for a system that automatically recorded message unit charges for local calls in metropolitan areas. The system scanned these leads in panel and No. 1 crossbar offices, recording the pulses

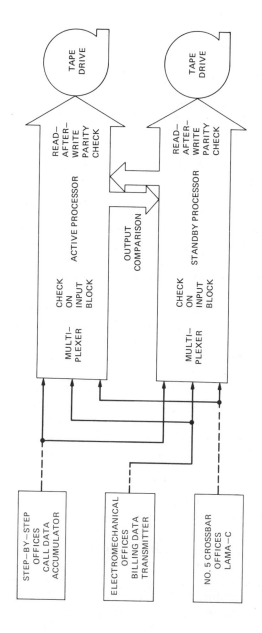

Fig. 11-31. Diagram of AMA recording center (AMARC), introduced in 1975, showing redundancy used to protect billing data.

that appeared on the message register leads together with the line
number and time of day.[88] This system, known as Electronic Local
Message Metering System, was installed in about 100 offices by the
end of 1973.

2.9 Increased Crossbar System Capacity

The development of new processors for electronic switching systems (see Chapter 9, sections 6.9 and 7.2) was symptomatic of the
growth of service needs as well as the rapid cost reductions possible
with the new electronics developments. However, electromechanical switching systems were also being modified to meet the growing
service needs being encountered where these systems were
deployed.

The No. 5 crossbar system originally provided for 40 line link
frames. Later it was modified to accommodate 60 line link frames,
giving it a capability of 35,500 lines. (So far as is known, no No. 5
crossbar office has attained this size.) To improve efficiency in serving traffic among several No. 5 crossbar offices in the same building, an "intermarker" group operation arrangement was developed
so that interoffice pulsing over the trunks is not necessary[89]
(see Fig. 11-32). The call-carrying capacities of all crossbar systems
were increased by the use of a higher-voltage surge (+135 volts) to
operate the hold magnets of crossbar switches more quickly, one of
the actions contributing to a considerable portion of marker holding
time.[90] The system was also redesigned to use the faster wire spring
relays and the smaller crossbar switches to gain trunk capacity (see
Chapter 7, section IV).

Similar increases were made in the trunk and call-carrying capacity of the No. 4A crossbar system.[91] From the introduction of DDD
to the present, and with the electronic translator, the 4A capacity
has increased from 84,000 to 130,000 busy-hour call attempts and
from 16,000 to 19,200 incoming trunk terminations.

2.10 Party Lines and Concentrators

Immediately after World War II, the demand for service was so
great that party line service (some lines with as many as eight parties) continued to be commonplace. With several customers on one
line, the outside plant requirements would be reduced if they could
be served by the same cable pair. All switching systems were
arranged for this service, including improvements in the panel and
No. 1 crossbar systems.[92] For the most part, the arrangements to
provide these services were developed prior to the war to meet
depression needs. While party line service has been declining
(see Fig. 11-33), it was extensive enough for this capability to be
included in the No. 1 ESS in 1970.

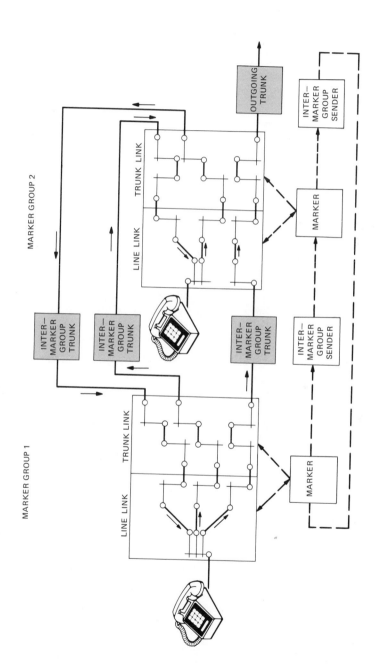

Fig. 11-32. Intermarker group trunking, used to improve traffic-handling when several No. 5 crossbar offices are in the same building.

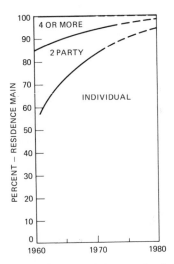

Fig. 11-33. Forecast, early 1970s, of the gradual disappearance of party lines, which were developed to meet depression needs.

The possibility of moving the first stage of switching closer to the customer has always seemed attractive for reducing the amount of cable required to render service. Therefore much research and exploratory development work has been done by Bell Laboratories in trying to find economically viable solutions (see Chapter 9, sections III, 4.3.1, 4.3.2, and 4.6). The first Bell System production remote line concentrator was the No. 1A.[93] It provided service to 50 or 100 lines over 10 or 20 trunks, plus control pairs (see Fig. 11-34). To reduce power requirements at the remote terminal, special magnetic-latching crossbar switches were developed. The system was called a universal concentrator since expansion was provided in the central office so that each line had an identifiable termination and could be used with any switching system. The first concentrators were installed in Gulfport, Mississippi and Eau Claire, Wisconsin in 1961 (see Fig. 11-35). A total of 4300 systems were built, and at its peak no more than about one half were installed at any one time. They were used primarily to defer supplementing outside plant distribution cable. The No. 1A concentrator could not be fully utilized because of traffic limitations and lack of sufficient customers to fill the terminal, and because of maintenance costs higher than those of central offices.

More recently, with the reduction of the cost of applying modern electronics technology to the loop plant, a new universal concentrator system known as the loop switching system or LSS has been developed and was under field test in 1977.[94] Not only has the

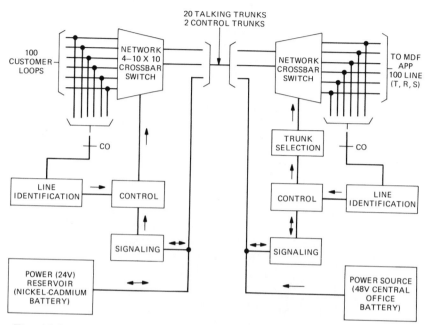

Fig. 11-34. Diagram of 1A concentrator, introduced 1961. By moving the first stage of switching closer to customers, expensive cable plant required to render service is saved.

technology reached the point where concentrators might be able to compete favorably with cable, but Bell Labs engineers now better understand how to provide suitable traffic capabilities in a concentrator.[95] As a result, graded line link multiples have been used to reduce the number of crosspoints required per line (see Fig. 11-36). These gradings (for the graded multiple concept, see Chapter 5, section 3.1) help make the concentration function more economical, not only in concentrators but also in ESS (see Chapter 9, section 5.3). The loop switching system, which uses miniature relay selectors, provides for 96 lines on 32 trunks, so that on the average it should have fewer traffic limitations and should render better service.

III. QUALITY OF SERVICE

Starting in 1970, service in some cities, particularly New York, deteriorated to a point where it was noticeable by a segment of the public. This "service crisis," as it became known, cannot be attributed to any one cause, nor was there a single "magic relay" solution. Commonly accepted major contributors were (1) poor main

Fig. 11-35. Pole-mounted 1A concentrator unit. Magnetic-latching crossbar switches reduced power requirements.

distributing frame administration due to the large number of service orders, (2) poor switching system and trunk maintenance and administration, (3) deficient installation of the many new features and growth additions to switching systems, (4) poor training of maintenance personnel, and (5) an unforecast surge in traffic in the business community, particularly in the New York securities market.[96] While the service crisis was repugnant to the very core of the Bell System's dedication to service, the System benefited greatly in the long run from the Bell Laboratories investigations and solutions that developed from the various service situations.

In particular, Bell Laboratories responded to the opportunity by making many corrective contributions. These contributions were not only of great immediate importance but they ushered in a new era of major developments now known collectively as operation support systems (OSSs).[97] While not all of these systems were solely switching oriented, many were inspired by those developed initially for switching systems.

3.1 DDD Improvements

Even before the service crisis, the rapid growth of DDD facilities and traffic gave some advance warning of things to come. Some cus-

NUMBERS AT INTERSECTIONS INDICATE ORDER OF PREFERENCE
FOR CUSTOMER – LINE ACCESS TO TRUNKS

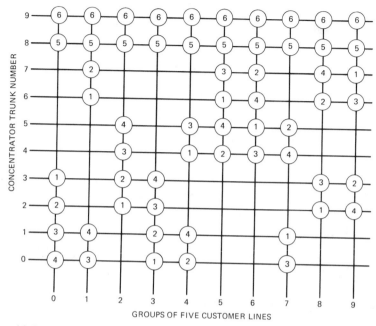

Fig. 11-36. Graded multiple concept as applied to concentrators. Grading results in fewer crosspoints, hence lower costs.

tomers and Bell System reports indicated that an unexpectedly high percentage of offered DDD calls were not reaching their destinations.

Bell Laboratories has for many years, particularly since the technology explosion of the 1950s, maintained project lists, better known as "grocery lists", of items identified as possible developments, in many cases requiring systems engineering studies to determine if a development is justified and has sufficiently high priority. As a result of the DDD service situation it was decided by executives at AT&T and Bell Laboratories that the many items on the list that had an impact on DDD service needed higher priority. To accelerate their development, operating company engineers were transferred to Bell Laboratories. These developments generally included improvements in existing or new test equipment (frames and portable sets), service evaluation arrangements, and call-progress signal improvements. They were accelerated at Bell Laboratories and by Western Electric, and in addition the Operating Telephone Companies were held responsible for their deployment and utilization.

Some other developments accelerated as a result of the DDD improvement program were precise tones (this chapter, section 1.12

above), recorded plant code announcements (see above, section 1.11), traffic control centers (Chapter 5, section 3.4.1) and automatic trunk test circuits (below, section 3.3). As a result, DDD service did indeed improve. In recent years the emphasis has shifted from the technical facilities to the increasing percentage of call attempts that result in revenue-producing messages, known as DDD call-completion. Among the features recently developed are automatic checking for completeness of translations in elec- tromechanical systems (that is, the ability to reach any number) and the noting of destination offices that are "hard to reach" based on offered traffic at stored-program controlled toll offices.[98] As an adjunct, TSPS operators, encountering difficulties on calls, key information about such calls into the system. These data are gath- ered nationwide by an operation support system known as NOTIS, for Network Operator Trouble Information System. The data are used as clues which, when correlated with other reports, direct maintenance forces to possible trouble sources in the public message network. This technique has now been extended to include other sources of information and is known as the Network Operations Trouble Information System II.[99]

3.2 Main Distributing Frame (MDF)

The main distributing frame (MDF) principle, patented in 1893,[100] had hardly changed in 75 years. Over the years, Bell Laboratories had improved the MDF by providing for growth in larger wire centers.[101] But perhaps no single item had contributed more to the service crisis in New York. This was due primarily to the large amount of telephone movement, or "churning," within wire centers. Instead of meticulously removing unneeded jumper wires on the MDF, many were left in place, so that after a while the sheer weight of the "dead" jumpers severely restricted the ability to "operate" the frame. Jumpers broke when others were pulled. Fig. 11-37 shows an example of one of the frames in trouble.

Bell Laboratories engineers became involved in this problem and proposed short- and long-range solutions. A new frame had already been designed for wire centers with only ESS[102] (see Fig. 11-38). A new version of this frame, turned 90 degrees, was proposed for general application (see Fig. 11-39). This was known as the COSMIC* (COmmon System Main InterConnecting) main distributing frame that computerized the assignment (and removal) of jumpers on main distributing frames in general.[103] How- ever, it was early recognized by A. E. Joel, Jr.,[104] that in the long term, the MDF functions of cross-connect and test access should be

*Trademark of Western Electric Co.

Fig. 11-37. Tangle of jumper wires on a main distributing frame—a source of trouble posing a major challenge to designers and administrators.

automated to cope with increasing labor costs and to permit remote operation. A proposed solution looked upon the MDF as just another switching center network. Another proposal, by J. G. Kappel, was a multistage manual switchboard.[105]

Therefore, Bell Laboratories engineers proposed many arrangements for automating the MDF. SARTS (Switched Access Remote Test System)[106] was a partial response to the remote test access, but its cost permits its application only for special service lines. In general, these proposals involved trading crosspoint costs for speed. An exploratory automatic MDF project was started in 1974 after a solution promising to achieve this trade was proposed by R. F. Bergeron and H. Southworth.[107] A laboratory model (Fig. 11-40) was built, but the initial cost was still too high to justify its application in all but a few very large and active wire centers. Efforts were directed to improved MDF administration with computerized systems such as COSMOS (COmputer System for Main frame Operations System). Congested frames have been sectionalized, and computerized data base systems have been designed to aid in their administration.[108]

3.3 Maintenance Improvement

From the very beginning of the introduction of the dial system into the Bell System, test sets and test frames were developed for use with each system.[109] In some cases these test arrangements—for

Fig. 11-38. Main distributing frame for No. 1 ESS, requiring one half or less of the space required for earlier MDFs.

example, sender test frames for tandem and toll offices—were quite comprehensive for testing most call combinations.[110] Indeed, they constituted some of the most complex relay and switch circuit designs, next in complexity to markers. They were the first circuits to be functionally subdivided (see Fig. 11-41, for example).

Initially, the test arrangements for automatic switching systems were designed to check only the circuits of the switching system of which they were a part. With each new generation of automatic switching, however, the environment of the system was tested to a greater extent. For example, to insure proper functioning of distant

Fig. 11-39. COSMIC variation of the No. 1 ESS main distributing frame proposed for general use. It used a minicomputer support system to aid in the administration of cross-connections.

Fig. 11-40. Laboratory model of an automatic main distributing frame, judged too expensive except for large, active wire centers.

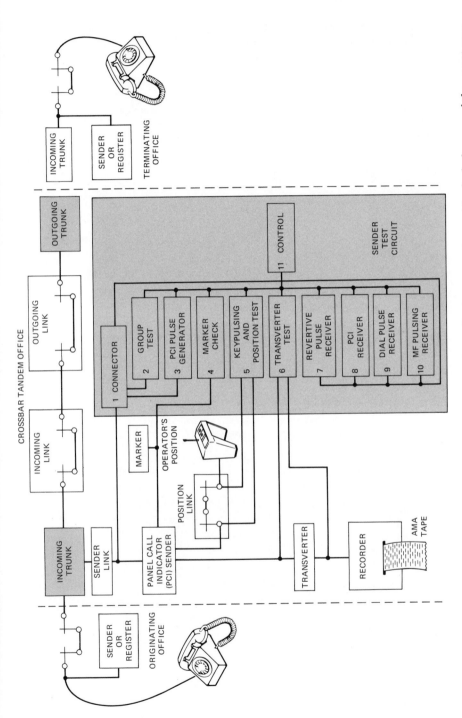

Fig. 11-41. Sender test circuit (right) applied to crossbar tandem. Such test equipment included some of the most complex relay and switch circuits ever designed at Bell Labs.

selectors, the panel system makes a trunk guard (TG) test of the trunk conductors. If the test fails, this means that the sender originally "stuck" (did not release), requiring an operator to release the connection (see discussion of the sender monitor in Chapter 3, section IV). In succeeding systems, more comprehensive tests were made of lines and trunks. Crossbar and electronic switching systems make false cross and ground tests and automatic line insulation tests (see below). ESS also checks for foreign potentials on call originations.[111] The sensitivity of ESS to its environments has been responsible for stimulating improvements in the outside plant when an ESS replaces an electromechanical switching system.

Maintenance centers were established with the introduction of crossbar offices. At a maintenance center, all frame-mounted routine test and trouble recorder equipment for a particular office was located together (see Fig. 11-42). Also at this location, manual access to trunk conductors and access to make trunks busy were

Fig. 11-42. Central maintenance facility of a No. 5 crossbar office. Grouping of a variety of automatic and manual test points improved maintenance efficiency.

made possible by manual outgoing trunk test frames. The many maintenance frames in a typical toll crossbar switching office are listed in Table 11-1.[112]

While circuits for routinely testing trunk circuits did detect some outside plant troubles, it remained for automatic trunk transmission testing to check more positively and completely the operational quality not only of the trunk facilities but also of the trunk circuits at the distant end and at its termination. The initial emphasis on automatic trunk testing came with the crossbar tandem and toll systems.

Table 11-1. Equipment Quantities for a Large No. 4A
Toll Crossbar Switching Office.

Automatic Outgoing Intertoll Trunk Test Circuit with Automatic Transmission Measuring Circuit, 17C Toll Testboard or Portable Tea-wagon Test Set*	1000 Tandem Trunk Circuits
	3500 Toll Completing Trunk Circuits
	1100 Service (Through Traffic, Inward & Information Operators, etc.) Trunk Circuits
Portable Tea-wagon Test Set*	1200 Incoming CAMA Trunk Circuits
Automatic Outgoing Toll Completing Trunk Test Circuit or Manual Outgoing Trunk Test Circuit*	20 Outgoing Senders
	240 Incoming Multifrequency Pulsing Senders
Automatic Incoming Trunk Test Circuit*	40 Incoming Dial Pulsing Senders
Automatic Outgoing Sender Test Circuit*	60 Incoming CAMA Senders
Automatic Incoming Sender and Register Test Circuit*	100 Incoming Dial Pulse Registers
Trouble Recorder, Decoder and Marker Test Circuit, Translator Verification Test Circuit*	10 Transverter Circuits
	3 Billing Indexers
	2 Position Link Frames
Master Timing Circuit	18 Decoders
Link Controller Test Circuit*	20 Markers
640 Outgoing Intertoll Trunk Circuits	27 Card Translators
	56 Incoming Link Frames
5600 Two-way Intertoll Trunk Circuits	56 Outgoing Link Frames
	40 Trunk Block Connectors
300 Incoming Intertoll Trunk Circuits	15 AMA Recorders and Associated Connector Units
	36 Link Controllers

*Test circuits.

To test an incoming trunk circuit required that the circuit be made busy manually at the outgoing trunk test frame at the distant end. The two techniques shown in Fig. 11-43 were developed so that automatic testing could be employed with a circuit in the terminating office such as shown in Fig. 11-44.[113] The trunk could be automatically "made-busy" if the originating office had an outgoing trunk circuit that could respond to a reverse battery make-busy signal (Fig. 11-43a), or a "reserve" trunk could temporarily take the place of the trunk under test (Fig. 11-43b).

The trunk circuits in No. 5 crossbar are quite complex and varied in features. To make automatic, definitive tests of outgoing trunks, an automatic progression trunk test was developed.[114,115] This test circuit used a punched paper tape to supply the test circuit with information to access the trunk and the types of tests to be made

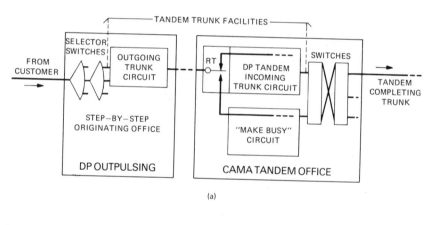

(a)

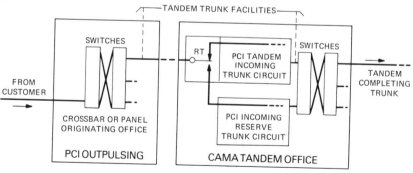

(b)

Fig. 11-43. Two ways of making a trunk busy, for test purposes, at a distant tandem office with trunks using: (a) "make-busy" circuit to signal the unavailability of the trunk during testing and (b) temporarily a reserve trunk circuit takes the place of the trunk circuit to be tested.

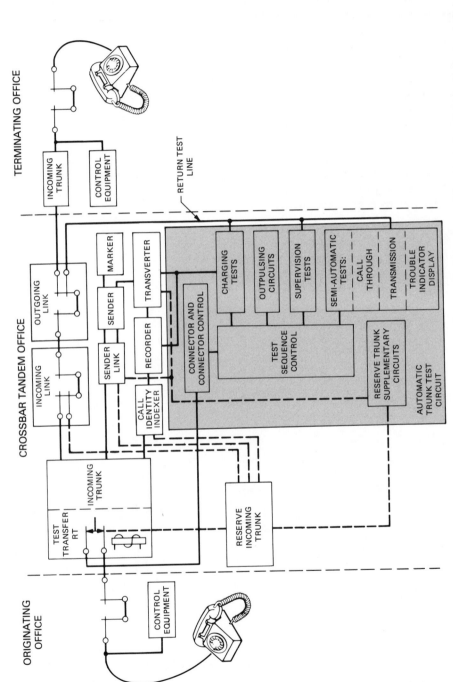

Fig. 11-44. Automatic trunk-test circuit associated with a crossbar tandem system. The test circuit simulates an originating and a terminating office.

(see Fig. 11-45). Since the tests varied with the features or characteristics of the trunk circuit, it was a precursor of the modern
computer-driven test circuits that test not only the switching equipment but also the transmission facilities.

Automatic progression testing of lines started in 1952, with a test
set known as the automatic line insulation test (ALIT) frame.[116,117]
This frame—through a no-test trunk and marker connector
appearances—gains access to lines on terminals one at a time. It is
used in the early morning hours when the lines are most likely to
show high leakage to ground and other incipient impairments. Initially, the lines showing measurements below threshold were
printed out (or used the trouble recorder) by line equipment
number. Later this was changed to directory number and the technique found much wider acceptance.[118]

While the stored-program technique was being introduced into
switching systems, large computers were becoming more powerful
and new small computers known as "minicomputers" were becom-

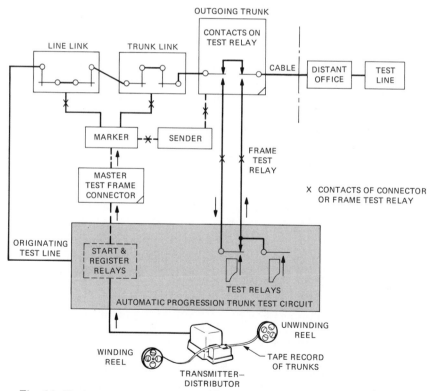

Fig. 11-45. Automatic progression trunk-test circuit with paper tape drive.
System was a precursor of modern computer-driven test equipment.

ing relatively low in cost. Minicomputers, such as the Digital Equipment Corporation PDP* series, found widespread application in the Bell System operations support systems.

3.3.1 Central Office Maintenance and Administrative System (COMAS)

Coincident with the New York service crisis, a special Bell Laboratories project was under way to help New York Telephone Co. rewire the ring translators used for route translation. These cross-connections had become abnormally congested in a crossbar tandem office. The Bell Laboratories solution was to introduce temporarily a PDP/8E computer in place of the ring translator, so that the latter could be stripped of its cross-connections and rewired. (Like the main distributing frame, as described above in section 3.2, the translator included some dead jumpers.)

The minicomputer was successfully introduced into this service in April 1971. Not only was it used in place of the ring translator, but it was also used to check the rewiring to make sure that it was complete and correct. This operation was so successful that Bell Laboratories engineers next considered applications of minicomputers to assist in the service crisis. By November 1971, a trial was started using a PDP 11 minicomputer in the New York City (Chelsea 2) crossbar tandem to record and correlate ineffective call attempts (by senders) and to improve the operation of the network as seen by this office. This system was known as the Central Office Maintenance and Administration System (COMAS). Minicomputers were added to a number of crossbar tandem and No. 4A crossbar offices in New York. The first standard phase I development—providing route verification, foreign area translation, and exception reporting on ineffective attempts—was placed in service in Boston (Franklin), Massachusetts in January 1972.

In 1972, a new version known as mini-COMAS was tried in Manchester, Massachusetts, and a standard version was first placed in service in 1973 in Manhattan. Eventually, three versions of this system were developed, and more than sixty were placed in service. The peripheral bus computer (PBC) as applied to the 4A crossbar ETS offices (see Chapter 10, section 2.1) also evolved from this effort.

3.3.2 Quick Tests

While COMAS was a boon to searching out troubles in the network, Bell Laboratories investigative teams noted that the pace of developments and growth in offices (see above, sections I and II), particularly new offices, had caused some of them to be performing

---

*Trademark of Digital Equipment Corporation.

poorly. In mid-1972, F. R. Wallace of the Columbus Laboratories devised a special set of manual tests for No. 5 crossbar offices. These tests rapidly checked the operational capability of the office, including the functioning of all markers, connectors, features, and options. They were dubbed "quick tests." Later they were documented, standardized, and offered as a service by the Western Electric Co. installation service forces. Still later (1975) they were extended to the No. 1, No. 4A, and tandem crossbar systems.

3.3.3 Automatic Trouble Analysis

As the ideas and advantages of ESS maintenance techniques permeated the Bell System, the electromechanical switching development area of Bell Laboratories also began using the new-found tools of minicomputers. The trend started with a minicomputer used to store the records issuing from the trouble recorder. Previously, these records had been placed on punched cards (see Chapter 7, section 1.2). Storing the results permitted programs to be written to analyze the trouble indications as they accumulated.

Initially these programs merely summarized the reports. Later, under the name Automatic Trouble Analysis (ATA) a more sophisticated program was written for the No. 5 crossbar system to perform the type of analysis carried out by the craft personnel. A number of the most experienced No. 5 crossbar craftspeople were brought to Bell Laboratories in 1975. They were then asked to devise a program strategy that represented the best of their techniques. These were then converted to ATA minicomputer programs by Bell Laboratories experts. The first standard ATA program for No. 5 crossbar was applied in Warren, Michigan in January 1976. For the No. 1 crossbar system a similar program was first placed in service in New York City in the second quarter of 1976.

3.3.4 Switching Control Centers for Electromechanical Switching Systems

Initially the minicomputers used for ATA were used locally with the trouble recorders in No. 5 crossbar offices. This was in contrast with the centralization of maintenance administration in electronic switching which progressed with the No. 1 and No. 2 switching control centers (see Chapter 9, section 6.7.2).

While alarms for community dial offices had always been remoted to operator switchboards, the systematic collection of alarm monitoring and control and trouble recording at a central point for the other electromechanical switching systems was needed. The need became apparent as more offices were unattended for longer periods, and as the administration of craft personnel was centralized. Known as Centralized Status, Alarm and Control System (CSACS), this single telemetering system was developed for application to all step-by-step and crossbar offices. The first, placed in service in Atlanta, Georgia in July 1974, served three remote offices, and the second, in Wheaton, Illinois in December 1974, served four remote offices. The CSACS has recently been replaced by the Telecommunications Alarm Surveillance and Control (TASC) system.

Eventually a more encompassing concept of a switching control center for electromechanical offices, Switching Control Center-EMS (electromechanical switching), emerged by bringing together ATA, TASC, and various computerized administrative systems. The first of these centers was established in Clinton, Michigan in January 1977.

3.4 Traffic Measurement Systems

As described in Chapter 5, section 3.3, the history of traffic measurements goes back to the days of the early manual switchboards, when operators kept track of calls served by moving small wooden pegs[119] in cribbage board-like counters, hence the well-known traffic term "peg counts." Electromechanical registers were used in increasing numbers with the more sophisticated manual and electromechanical switching systems. These counters, or registers as they were called, were read by clerks, and later recorded by cameras, periodically, during the busiest periods of the day. Statistics were collected on the volume of traffic served and the volume denied service due to lack of facilities.

3.4.1 Traffic Usage Recorder (TUR)

The measuring of only peg counts presented a problem in administering and engineering trunks and switching equipment because the most appropriate measure of traffic flow, which is the total call-seconds of use, or usage, had to be computed by multiplying peg count times an estimated holding time. In the late 1940s, a portable scanning device, then known as the Trunk Group Usage Equipment (TGUE) and later known as a Traffic Usage Recorder (TUR) was developed. It measured the use of each trunk by examining whether it was busy or idle each 100 seconds. A grouping arrangement was provided in which all of the "busies" in each selected trunk group were fed to a corresponding traffic register, which then recorded hundred call-seconds of use (CCS) for the group. This development and the theoretical studies behind it[120] proved that the data collected in this manner would be satisfactory to indicate whether the size of the trunk group was adequately engineered for the traffic offered during the busiest hour of the busiest season.

The traffic usage recorder was developed in 1953 for this purpose, and is extensively used in electromechanical offices.[121] A separate lead is cabled to each circuit to be measured. These leads are scanned by crossbar switches and relays at the rate of 36 tests per hour (once every 100 seconds). Typically, as with the TGUE, these leads are the sleeve leads of trunk circuits (see Fig. 11-46). The development of the TUR opened the door to better and routine traffic measurements and, in turn, improved service by revealing the adequacy of trunk circuit provisioning. The TUR No. 4A provided for scanning 3600 circuits in as many as 1200 groups. The first TUR No. 4A was placed in service October 1953 in the Newark, New Jersey No. 4A toll crossbar office.

A smaller portable TUR unit was developed to serve up to 800 inputs and 100 groups[122] (see Fig. 11-47). The counts were still recorded on a register provided per trunk group.

3.4.2 Traffic Data Recording System (TDRS)

While the frame-mounted version of the TUR was a great step forward in obtaining the basic information for engineering the nationwide toll network, it was still quite labor-consuming since, each time a trunk assignment was changed, a change was also required in the cross-connection field. Furthermore, the registers still required reading by clerks, either directly or from photographs. This entire process, including the computation (subtracting the previous reading from the current reading), was subject to inaccuracies. To overcome these disadvantages, a new system known as the Traffic Data Recording System (TDRS), began to be developed in the early 1960s.[123] It was the first attempt at centralizing the recording of administrative information in the Bell System.

The TDRS consisted of a terminal in the central office that took the place of the TUR registers (see Fig. 11-48). The terminal sent coded digital signals over a data link to a centrally located magnetic tape recorder for each count pulse received. Similar data links were established to all offices in an area or region. The recorder consisted of a special magnetic tape with 40 tracks. The raw data were recorded during busy hours and then, during off hours, the same equipment was used to summarize the data—that is, to take all "peg counts" of each code and add them together by trunk group for a traffic-engineered period. The system could be programmed to indicate the association of specific trunks within a group. The summary information was then printed. Magnetic tape output was also provided for further data processing in connection with the traffic engineering and provisioning process.

Fig. 11-46. Traffic usage recorder frame. By replacing peg counts with usage measured in call-seconds, TURs greatly aided the engineering and administration of trunks and switching equipment.

Fig. 11-47. S. J. Brymer, left, and G. E. Linehan inspecting circuits of a traffic usage recorder No. 3B designed for smaller installations.

Some 23 of these systems were installed throughout the Bell System. The initial network consisted of one for each Long Lines region, and could be used not only to summarize traffic data but also to provide traffic usage information on a quasi real-time basis. This means that the data were recorded and summarized within a 15-minute period, so that traffic administrators, located at network control centers remote from the TDRS location, could use the data in managing the network by recognizing unusually heavy usage and overflow traffic. Such a network was in place feeding data to the Holmdel, New Jersey Bell Labs installation of the TDRS in November, 1963 (see Fig. 11-49). The first field installation of the TDRS took place in Washington, D.C. in 1968.

While the TDRS showed the feasibility of gathering traffic information in this manner, it was, for a number of reasons, slow in its implementation. First, it used electronic technology which was rapidly changing and, therefore, the initial design was almost out of date before the system could be deployed. It was through this system, however, that traffic administrators learned that the quality of their efforts was only as good as the data they could collect. The records of cross-connections in the central office generally were not maintained accurately, so the collected data did not keep pace with

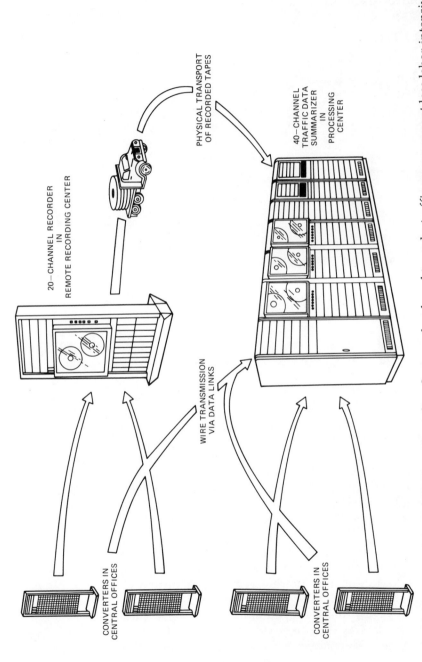

Fig. 11-48. Elements of the Traffic Data Recording System, developed to make traffic measurement less labor-intensive and more accurate.

the changes and rearrangements of actual facilities they were intended to measure. Much effort was expended to improve this process.

3.4.3 *Engineering and Administrative Data Acquisition System (EADAS)*

By 1971, commercially available minicomputers became attractive enough that a more efficient processing system could be implemented. The summarizing and subsequent engineering of summarized data could also be included and made much more efficient. As a result, the Engineering and Administrative Data Acquisition System (EADAS) was developed.[124] EADAS extended the concepts of the TDRS but used a commercial minicomputer for central processing and control. While it could use the TDRS terminals, new, more efficient terminals were designed to reduce costs and improve features. Real-time (30 to 15 minute) data availability was a prominent feature. The first installation of EADAS used a PDP11/40 DEC minicomputer, and was placed in service in Kansas City in October 1973. EADAS was also designed to include data link inputs from program-controlled systems such as electronic switching systems and traffic service position systems.

The EADAS system was extended, in a manner similar to that described for TDRS, to provide information collected in quasi real

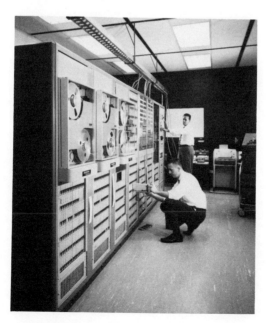

Fig. 11-49. J. L. Mollica (foreground) and V. L. Ransom operating the Bell Labs Holmdel, New Jersey installation of TDRS.

time (5 minutes) for use in network management.[125] This system, EADAS/NM, was placed in service in Milwaukee, Wisconsin in September 1975. The second EADAS/NM was placed in service in Wayne, New Jersey in December 1975. It was the first regional network operations center to benefit from this system. A special version of the EADAS/NM was developed for the national control center, operated by the Bell System's Long Lines department, initially located in Netcong, New Jersey and later moved to Bedminster, New Jersey, where it was placed in service in July 1977 (Fig. 11-50).

3.4.4 Total Network Data System (TNDS)

At the same time that EADAS was developed, a number of large programs for batch processing of administrative data for traffic, maintenance, and billing from switching systems were also being developed. The name, Total Network Data System, was given to the collection of systems (such as EADAS), and these programs had to act together to give information to telephone company engineers and administrators based upon processed data.

The TNDS has three basic stages: data acquisition, provided by EADAS as well as by general trade systems or by manual methods; data storage, verification, and distribution provided by a batch computer program called the Traffic Data Administration System (TDAS); and a number of applications programs to process data for

Fig. 11-50. AT&T Long Lines national control center, Bedminster, New Jersey, used to monitor and administer the functioning of the nationwide network. *(Long Lines Magazine, AT&T, March 4, 1977.)*

use in central office and trunk engineering administration. In the switching area, the Load Balance System assists traffic loading of central offices. Two Central Office Equipment Report systems (COERs) prepare data for use in central office engineering. No. 5 crossbar offices are served by their individual COERs, while all of the ESSs are served by ESS COER. (ESS COER was originally known as PATROL, Program for Administrative Traffic Reports On-Line.) ESS COER uses both batch processing and interactive communication with its users.

Another part of TNDS is network management. Extensive network management features were built into the No. 4A crossbar ETS and No. 4 ESS stored-program controlled electronic switching systems (see Chapter 10, section II and Chapter 12, section I).[126] These features not only automatically controlled traffic in real time, but the data on the imposition of these controls were sent to the network managers. This reporting function is an additional feature of the network management portion of TNDS. The network management control center using EADAS/NM can command these systems to implement the various preprogrammed controls in these stored-program control toll offices.

Finally, to round out the traffic measurement administrative systems developed as part of TNDS, there are systems that deal with the operator force at switchboard and position system installations, such as the Traffic Service Position System (TSPS), the Automatic Intercept System (AIS), the No. 5 Automatic Call Distributor (ACD), and other directory assistance system installations. These were known as Force Administration Data Systems (FADS).

The purpose of the FADS traffic measuring system is to inform administrators, in real time, of the average holding time per call and other pertinent information. These administrators supervise operators or attendants interfacing a telephone network at positions or consoles. The information helps insure good and efficient use of the human resources.

The first FADS was a combination of a TUR, a unique electronic circuit called a totalizer to count calls arriving at a high rate, and electrically resettable registers. It was used with an airlines ACD in 1967. Later, it was widely used with manual switchboards. Fig. 11-51 shows the plan of the system and what it measures.[127] Fig. 11-52 shows the register cabinet of the system, used here in association with a telephone company business office. A computerized system known as Automatic Force Administration Data System (AFADS) was developed after experience with the less-sophisticated FADS equipment.

TNDS was the first attempt to bring together the burgeoning software revolution in operation support and administrative systems being developed at Bell Laboratories. Toward the close of the

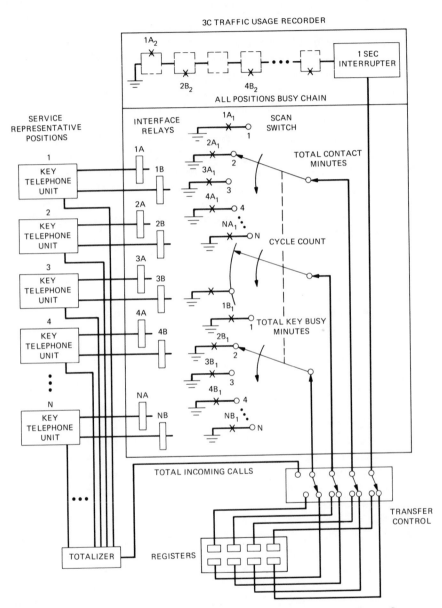

Fig. 11-51. Plan of the Automatic Force Adjustment Data System (AFADS). Registers at lower right keep track of traffic and inform supervisors in real time.

Fig. 11-52. AFADS installation. Display of information aids supervision in administering the workforce.

period covered in this book, broader views were being taken of these systems to include not only traffic data acquisition and administration but also the operation of the network as a whole. This system is known as TNOP, for Total Network Operations Plan.

3.5 New York Fire

On February 27, 1975, a serious fire started in the cable vault of a large central office building at 204 Second Avenue, New York City. Before the fire was extinguished it ravaged the equipment, including the main distributing frame in the lower three floors of the 10-story building. Fig. 11-53 shows fire-damaged panel switching equipment. Much of the remaining equipment in the building was damaged by heat, smoke, and water. The building was serving 170,000 lines and also acted as a tandem point for switching many calls through New York City to Long Island. The fire was the biggest disaster in telecommunication history.[128]

Fig. 11-53. Panel switching equipment damaged in the disastrous February 1975 fire in New York City. Large Bell System resources were employed to restore service quickly.

Bell Laboratories engineers, along with large groups from the entire Bell System, were called upon even before the fire was extinguished to aid in the restoration of service. The Bell Labs force, led by J. E. Mack and W. B. Macurdy, was organized to study the smoke, particulate, and chemical damage to the electromechanical (principally crossbar) switching system equipment in the upper floors of the building. Bell Laboratories chemists recommended cleaning procedures and studied the possible long-range effects of the damage to the equipment. Simultaneously, plans were made to route traffic intended for the tandems in the building via an ESS tandem in Brooklyn. However, before this could be done, a change had to be made in the system program, since the rerouted traffic required different charge treatment (CAMA for calls from panel offices) than the traffic it was handling. Network management features and systems all over the country performed in blocking, near their sources, calls intended for the out-of-service offices. Network managers implemented reroutings, some based on earlier Bell Labs studies of off-peak traffic, so that some calls originating from the Atlantic coast area were completed via midwest and California switching centers back to Long Island.

Plans were made to restore local switching capacity in the burned-out areas of the building, using a new No. 1 ESS that included the latest remreed network frames. It was manufactured by Western Electric and tested at the Indian Hill (Illinois), Bell Laboratories prior to its rapid installation and cutover within only four months of the fire. Prior to the cutover, most of the lines had been cabled to electronic switching systems located elsewhere in New York City. These offices were programmed to serve the affected customers without number changes, which enabled service to be restored within three weeks. Bell System people were proud of the contributions they could make assisting the New York Telephone Company recover from this disastrous event.

IV. NEW FEATURES MADE POSSIBLE BY ELECTRONIC SWITCHING

Almost from the very beginning and prior to the invention of stored-program control, it was realized that the bulk memory available in electronic switching systems could be used to offer many services and features. One of the first, suggested by W. A. Malthaner,[129] was to build into the memory in the central office a listing of numbers called frequently by the customer. These numbers could be accessed by having the customer dial a short or abbreviated code. This was particularly important as one looked forward to 10-digit nationwide dialing.

After the invention of stored-program control, and as plans matured for the Morris trial (see Chapter 9, section 4.6), many additional new services were conceived. These included what is now known as add-on service, automatic call transfer (now call forwarding), and distinctive ringing to permit intra-calling among extension telephones. All of these except the last were successful. Almost from the beginning they were called custom calling services.[130]

4.1 Custom Calling Services

The No. 1 ESS program used in the first commercial office in Succasunna, New Jersey included abbreviated dialing, call transfer, and add-on. The marketing department later changed these names to speed calling, automatic call forwarding, and dial conference. The call-transfer feature is provided so that the customer can change the number to which calls are forwarded. In Succasunna a preset arrangement was also tried. There is a fixed monthly charge for these services, although in 1973 in Trenton, New Jersey a trial was conducted with a No. 1 ESS program modification to charge casual users on the basis of usage.

A call-waiting feature was initially implemented and market tested in the No. 5 crossbar system (see above, section 1.14.1). This service proved so popular that it was added to the No. 1 ESS programs in 1969. When the No. 2 and No. 3 ESSs were developed, the same features were included in their initial programs.

Since these features were available only in ESS, it was difficult to advertise them widely; they were then available to only a small percentage of customers in the Bell System. With the growth of availability of ESS in the 1970s, custom calling services grew in popularity, as shown in Fig. 11-54. The growth rate of these services by the early 1970s exceeded the rate of growth of ESS lines in the Bell System.

In developing and standardizing these services, stored-program control proved to be of considerable value. It was possible to try different rate treatments for these services by engineering temporary program changes. For example, call-forwarding, rather than being subscribed to on a monthly basis, could be offered generally to all customers in the office on a usage basis. With electronic switching well embedded in the message network, it is expected that many new services will be added to the original list to take advantage of bulk memory and stored-program control (also see Chapter 12, section IV).

4.2 Feature Growth

Once ESS became standard in the Bell System, the many services and features covered elsewhere in this chapter were built into the programs of ESS systems so that these offices could become full members of the switching family. (It has been traditional in switching that each new generation eventually include most of the features and services available in previous-generation systems, although the

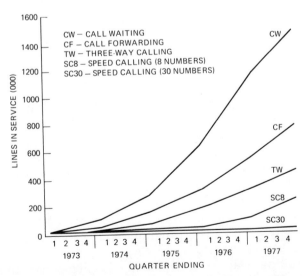

Fig. 11-54. Growth in the use of custom calling services, 1973–1977. Such features were made possible by the bulk memory and stored-program control used in ESS.

reverse is not always the case.) Furthermore, the flexibility of stored-program control enabled many more features to be added to electronic systems than the electromechanical systems, and the services were offered in more variety. For example, it was possible to add many different types of call transfers in Centrex service, more in keeping with the similar features being provided in stored-program control PBXs. It was also possible, when offering 911 emergency service, to record in the line class of service a coded indication of the town in which a given telephone line was located, so that such calls could be routed to the proper 911 bureau (see above, section 1.7). With ESS it was also possible to have these numbers located in a centralized memory in an ESS tandem office used for extending the 911 service.

Many other examples of new services for No. 1 ESS could be given. The list of features is impressive since it includes those that were of great benefit in unattending and remotely attending switching systems once the basic concept of automatic trouble-locating was available with ESS. Fig. 11-55 shows the growth of features and service in No. 1 ESS since its initial service in 1965. The illustration also shows that the rate of growth of features in No. 2 ESS follows the same rate of introduction of new features as in No. 1 ESS. Plotted on the same graph is the corresponding feature and service growth for the No. 5 crossbar system, which grew over a longer period. With the establishment of the stored-program control network (see Chapter 12, section IV) the rate of growth of features is expected to further accelerate in the years to come.

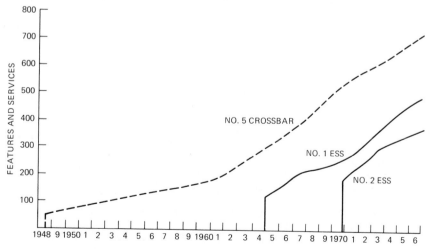

Fig. 11-55. Numbers of services and features offered with No. 1 and No. 2 ESS, 1965–1976.

REFERENCES, CHAPTER 11

1. Depp, W. A. and Meacham, L. A. "Station Apparatus, Power and Special Systems." *Bell Laboratories Record* **36**, June 1958, p. 216.
2. Hopkins, H. F. "Pushbutton 'Dialing.'" *Bell Laboratories Record* **38**, March 1960, p. 82.
3. Kimmich, W. L., Jr., "'TOUCH-TONE' Telephoning." *American Institute of Electrical Engineers Conference Paper 61–693*, 1961.
4. Laso, N. and Martins, A. S. "Central-Office Modifications for TOUCH-TONE Calling." *Bell Laboratories Record* **39**, December 1961, p. 436.
5. Anderson, H. P. "TOUCH-TONE Converter for Step-by-Step PBX." *Bell Laboratories Record* **42**, May 1964, p. 167.
6. Martins, A. S. "Common Control Features for the Step-by-Step System." *Bell Laboratories Record* **42**, May 1964, p. 167.
7. Shea, P. D. "Centrex Service: A New Design for Customer Group Telephone Service in the Modern Business Community." *Transactions of the American Institute of Electrical Engineers* **80**, Part I, 1961, p. 474.
8. Richardson, D. B. "Upgrading Multilocation Services with No. 1 ESS." *Bell Laboratories Record* **53**, June 1975, p. 264.
9. Comella, W. K., Backman, G. A., and Pina, R. F. "Central Office Facilities for Automatic Identified Outward Dialing from PBXs." *Proceedings of the National Electronics Conference* **22**, Chicago, Illinois, October 3–5, 1966, p. 342.
10. "A New Central Office Facility for Automatic Identified Outward Dialing." *Bell Laboratories Record* **48**, September 1970, p. 251.
11. Masucci, E. D. "Improved PBX Service with No. 5 Crossbar." *Bell Laboratories Record* **43**, July-August 1965, p. 303.
12. Kahl, H. "Evolution of Wideband Data Services." *Bell Laboratories Record* **49**, September 1971, p. 244.
13. Stagg, U. K. "2A Line Concentrator." *Bell System Technical Journal* **44**, October 1965, p. 1535.
14. Tyberghein, E. J. "TWX Goes Dial." *Bell Laboratories Record* **40**, July-August 1962, p. 232.
15. Minutes (dated April 1, 1961) of Bell-USITA DDD Subcommittee Meeting of February 23–24, 1961.
16. Michael, H. J. "Civil Emergency Reporting System." *Bell Laboratories Record* **34**, August 1956, p. 285.
17. Pearsall, F. M., Jr. "The Direct-Line Emergency Reporting System." *Bell Laboratories Record* **38**, July 1960, p. 256.
18. Wadsworth, P. W. "Emergency Reporting: The Concentrator System." *Bell Laboratories Record* **38**, September 1960, p. 342.
19. *New York Times*, January 13, 1968, p. 62, col. 3.
20. Greiling, W. R. "Municipal Alarm Systems Speed Emergency Calls." *Bell Telephone Magazine* **35**, Summer, 1956, p. 116.
21. Horlacher, R. L. "Key Telephone System Improves '911' Service." *Bell Laboratories Record* **54**, October 1976, p. 234.
22. Hovey, S. W., Jr. "Study for Alameda County 911." Law Enforcement Assistance Administration Grant 73-NI-99–0059 G, U. S. Dept. of Justice, October 1974.
23. Ovaitt, F., Jr. "911 at the Roundhouse." *Bell Telephone Magazine* **53**, November-December 1974, p. 24.
24. Mabon, P. C. "Public Telephones." *Bell Telephone Quarterly* **18**, October 1939, p. 246.
25. Brooks, C. E. and Flint, E. W.; U.S. Patent 2,356,576; filed December 20, 1941; issued September 5, 1944.

26. King, G. V. "Centralized Automatic Message Accounting System." *Bell System Technical Journal* **33**, November 1954, p. 1331.
27. Germanton, C. E. "Handling Coin Calls in No. 5 Crossbar." *Bell Laboratories Record* **30**, November 1952, p. 430.
28. Goddard, M. C. "Coin Zone Dialing in No. 5 Crossbar." *Bell Laboratories Record* **38**, March 1960, p. 106.
29. Minutes of the Bell-USITA DDD Subcommittee Meeting of September 29, 1960.
30. Pferd, W. "A New Coin Telephone." *Bell Laboratories Record* **37**, December 1959, p. 464.
31. Howard, L. A., Jr. "ESS—4 Years Old." An Interview with R. W. Ketchledge. *Bell Laboratories Record* **47**, August 1969, p. 226.
32. Peterson, G. H. "Improving Coin Service for Step-by-Step." *Bell Laboratories Record* **52**, February 1974, p. 40.
33. Schillo, R. F. "A Circuit That Stretches Coin Telephone Service." *Bell Laboratories Record* **51**, April 1973, p. 120.
34. Grandle, J. A. "A New Test Line for Coin Phones." *Bell Laboratories Record* **50**, May 1972, p. 150; " 'Dial-A-Test' for Public Telephone Repairmen." *Bell Laboratories Record* **49**, May 1971, p. 161.
35. Fisher, D. R. "Common Control Switching Arrangement." *Proceedings of the National Electronics Conference* **24**, Chicago, Illinois, December 9–11, 1968, p. 639.
36. "New Military Switching System Goes Into Operation." *Bell Laboratories Record* **40**, February 1962, p. 61.
37. Fagen, M. D., ed. *A History of Engineering and Science in the Bell System: The Early Years, 1875–1925.* Bell Telephone Laboratories, Inc., 1975, p. 511.
38. Bertels, A. R. "Intercepting with Recorded Announcements." *Bell Laboratories Record* **33**, September 1955, p. 331.
39. Gagne, D. J. "The New 9A Announcement System." *Bell Laboratories Record* **37**, February 1959, p. 49.
40. Banks, D. D. "The 11A Announcement System." *Bell Laboratories Record* **41**, July-August 1963, p. 287.
41. "Notes on the Network—Section 5." AT&T Publication, 1980.
42. Trupp, R. D. "Improving Recorded-Announcement Service with Magnetic Bubbles." *Bell Laboratories Record* **55**, October 1977, p. 249.
43. Tse, B. "A Trunk Concentrator for Centralized Automatic Operator Service to Rural Communities." *Western Electric Engineer* **21**, October 1977, p. 6.
44. Noweck, H. E. "A New Service Observing Desk." *Bell Laboratories Record* **31**, November 1953, p. 445.
45. Haefner, J. A. "The Precise Tone Plan." *Automatic Electric Technical Journal* **11**, April 1969, p. 255; "Standard Telephone Tones." *Bell Telephone Magazine* **41**, Summer, 1966, p. 63.
46. "SES Helps SW Bell Insure Quality." *Bell Labs News* **16**, May 24, 1976, p. 1.
47. Burgess, P. N. and Stickel, J. E. "The PICTUREPHONE® System: Central Office Switching." *Bell System Technical Journal* **50**, February 1971, p. 533.
48. Ritchie, A. E. "The Transistor: Applications in Telephone Switching." *Bell Laboratories Record* **36**, June 1958, p. 212.
49. Giesken, K. F. "Custom Calling Services with No. 5 Crossbar Switching." *Bell Laboratories Record* **44**, March 1966, p. 96.
50. "Piggyback Twistor." *Bell Laboratories Record* **42**, June 1964, p. 206.
51. "Crossbar Call Waiting Service." *Bell Labs News* **11**, November 24, 1971, p. 1.
52. Crane, E. G., Jr. "Line Verification in No. 5 Crossbar." *Bell Laboratories Record* **36**, April 1958, p. 137.
53. "N. Y. Tel Cuts Over No. 5 ETS." *Bell Labs News* **17**, October 24, 1977, p. 1.
54. Orost, J. and Seckler, W. H. "A New Group-Alerting System." *Bell Laboratories Record* **38**, December 1960, p. 46.

55. Bell-USITA Manufacturer Subcommittee Meeting Record, September 23–25, 1975.
56. O'Neal, E. L. "The Bellboy Switching System." *Bell Laboratories Record* **42**, September 1964, p. 281.
57. Douglas, V. A. "The MJ Mobile Radio Telephone System." *Bell Laboratories Record* **42**, December 1964, p. 382.
58. Pilkinton, D. C. "A New Family of Dial Long Line Circuits for the Bell System." *IEEE International Convention Record*, Part 1, March 21–25, 1966, p. 40.
59. Gresh, P. A., Howson, L., Lowe, F. A. and Zarouni, A. "Unigauge Design Concept for Telephone Customer Loop Plant." *IEEE Transactions on Communication*, April 1968, p. 32.
60. Beuscher, H. J. and Deisch, C. W. "No. 2 ESS Unigauge Range Extension." *IEEE Transactions on Communications* COM-21, April 1973, p. 271.
61. Knepper, C. F. "Foreign Area Translation in No. 5 Crossbar." *Bell Laboratories Record* **33**, February 1955, p. 54.
62. Adam, A. O. "Crossbar Tandem as a Long Distance Switching System." *Bell System Technical Journal* **35**, January 1956, p. 91.
63. Sinks, W. A. "New Numbers for Tomorrow's Telephones." *Bell Telephone Magazine* **38**, Winter 1959–60, p. 6.
64. Shipley, F. F. "Nation-wide Dialing." *Bell Laboratories Record* **23**, October 1945, p. 368.
65. Myers, O. "New Nationwide Telephone Numbering Plan." *AIEE Communication and Electronics*, January 1961, p. 673. See also Poole, J. F. "The New Numbering Plan in Panel Switching Offices." *Bell Laboratories Record* **41**, September 1963, p. 323.
66. Junkus, J. J. "Keeping Step in Place." *Western Electric Engineer* **18**, July 1974, p. 12.
67. See ref. 61 above.
68. Hurst, G. A. "Extending CAMA with No. 5 Crossbar." *Bell Laboratories Record* **36**, October 1958, p. 372.
69. Johannesen, J. D. "No. 1 ESS Local/Toll/Tandem." *International Switching Symposium*, Munich, September 9–13, 1974, p. 526/1.
70. Meszar, J. "The Full Stature of the Crossbar Tandem Switching System." *Transactions of the American Institute of Electrical Engineers* **75**, Part I., September 1956, p. 486.
71. Giloth, P. K. and Vaughan, H. E. "Early No. 4 ESS Field Experience." *International Switching Symposium*, Kyoto, Japan, October 1976, p. 241–4–1.
72. Busick, R. C. and Masucci, E. D. "Electronic Translator for Local Switching." *Proceedings of the National Electronics Conference* **25**, Chicago, Illinois, December 8–10, 1969, p. 622.
73. Abbott, H. H. "Modernized 'Information' for Large PBXs." *Bell Laboratories Record* **22**, January 1944, p. 218.
74. Sermius, W. T. "The No. 23 Auxiliary Operating Room Desk." *Bell Laboratories Record* **31**, May 1953, p. 161; Shafer, W. L., Jr., ibid., p. 169.
75. Laggy, W. J. and May, H. F. "Operator Arrangements in the No. 5 Crossbar Automatic Call Distributing System." *Proceedings of the National Electronics Conference* **24**, Chicago, Illinois, December 9–11, 1968, p. 684.
76. Malloy, P. E. Elliott, G. L. and May, H. F. "No. 5 Crossbar Automatic Call Distributor." *Bell Laboratories Record* **46**, December 1968, p. 370.
77. Kahn, R. W. "Redesigned ACD Improves Directory-Assistance Service." *Bell Laboratories Record* **53**, April 1975, p. 197.
78. Lewis, E. P. "What's Behind the Numbers Game." *Bell Telephone Magazine* **38**, Spring 1959, p. 28.

79. Deininger, R. L. "Human Factors Studies of Telephone Number Services." *Teleteknik* 9, 1965.

80. "Business Information Systems." *Bell Laboratories Annual Report*, 1971, p. 10.

81. Kubitsky, G. L. and Naughton, J. J., Jr. "An Experiment in Microfilm Directory Assistance." *Bell Laboratories Record* 50, October 1972, p. 316.

82. Thayer, G. N. "BIS in the Bell System." *Bell Laboratories Record* 46, December 1968, p. 354.

83. "Cincinnati Bell Finds Directory Assistance Fee Cuts Queries 74 Percent." *Telephony* 182, July 8, 1974, p. 90.

84. Martins, A. S. "Conversion of Automatic Ticketing to AMA." *Bell Laboratories Record* 35, March 1957, p. 89.

85. Pennoyer, D. H. "Basic AMA Central Office Features." *Bell Laboratories Record* 29, October 1951, p. 454.

86. Wickham, T. F. and Nolan, N. S. "AMA for No. 1 ESS." *Bell Laboratories Record* 44, September 1966, p. 271.

87. Byrne, C. J. and Pilkinton, D. C. "Towards Automated Local Billing." *Bell Laboratories Record* 54, April 1976, p. 104.

88. "Message Metering Unit Improves Telco Billing." *Communications News*, June 1972.

89. Goddard, M. C. "Intermarker Group Operation in No. 5 Crossbar." *Bell Laboratories Record* 35, October 1957, p. 431.

90. Mehring, A. C. and Erwin, E. L. "Dual Voltage Operation of Relays and Crossbar Switches." *Bell System Technical Journal* 34, November 1955, p. 1225.

91. Brymer, S. J. "Increased Traffic Capacity for the 4A and 4M Switching Systems." *Bell Laboratories Record* 42, November 1964, p. 375.

92. Green, H. C. "New Eight-Party Service for Panel and No. 1 Crossbar." *Bell Laboratories Record* 31, March 1953, p. 90.

93. Whitney, W. "The New Line Concentrator No. 1A." *Transactions of the American Institute of Electrical Engineers* 81, Part 1, 1962, p. 83.

94. Brown, J. M. "Loop Switching System Triples Cable Capacity." *Bell Laboratories Record* 56, May 1978, p. 127.

95. Hayward, W. S., Jr. "Traffic Studies of Line Concentration." *Bell Laboratories Record* 36, February 1958, p. 56.

96. Demaree, A. T. "The Age of Anxiety at AT&T." *Fortune* 81, May 1970, p. 156.

97. Sumner, E. E. "Operation Systems for the Local Telecommunications Network." *International Zurich Seminar on Digital Communications*, Zurich, Switzerland, March 7–9, 1978, p. F-6.

98. Mummert, V. S. "Network Management and Its Implementation on the No. 4 ESS." *International Switching Symposium*, Kyoto, Japan, October 1976, p. 241-4-1.

99. "NOTIS II Spots Troubles." *Bell Labs News* 17, August 22, 1977, p. 1.

100. Ford, W. S. and Lenfest, B. A.; U.S. Patent 507,424; filed March 31, 1892; issued October 24, 1893.

101. Noble, R. E. "A New Main Distributing Frame for Large Offices." *Bell Laboratories Record* 8, May 1930, p. 430.

102. Wetherell, D. H. "No. 1 ESS: Mechanical Design." *Bell Laboratories Record* 43, June 1965, p. 241.

103. Dale, O. B. and Levi, I. M. "A COSMIC Approach to Untangling Problems in Main Distributing Frames." *Bell Laboratories Record* 52, March 1974, p. 70.

104. Joel, A. E., Jr.; U.S. Patent 3,562,435; filed December 27, 1968; issued February 9, 1971.

105. Kappel, J. G.; U.S. Patent 3,763,325; filed June 29, 1971; issued October 2, 1973.

106. Gilmore, J. F. and Seifert, J. A. "A System for Remote Testing." *Bell Laboratories Record* **54**, June 1976, p. 155.

107. Bergeron, R. F. and Southworth, H.; U.S. Patent 3,978,291; filed September 9, 1974; issued August 31, 1976.

108. "COSMIC/COSMOS for Main Distributing Frames." *Bell Laboratories Annual Report* 1974, p. 18.

109. Fagen, M. D., ed. *A History of Engineering and Science in the Bell System: The Early Years, 1875–1925.* Bell Telephone Laboratories, Inc., 1975, p. 596.

110. Sims, R. Y. "CAMA—Sender Test Circuit." *Bell Laboratories Record* **33**, August 1955, p. 313.

111. Biddulph, R., Budlong, A. H., Casterline, R. C., Funk, D. L. and Goeller, L. F., Jr. "Line, Trunk, Junctor, and Service Circuits for No. 1 ESS." *Bell System Technical Journal* **43**, September 1964, p. 2321.

112. Nance, R. C. "Test Circuits for Toll Crossbar." *Bell Laboratories Record* **36**, April 1958, p. 137.

113. Dusenberry, R. F. "CAMA—Automatic Trunk-Test Circuit." *Bell Laboratories Record* **34**, June 1956, p. 223.

114. Cahill, H. D. "Automatic Progression Trunk-Test Circuit." *Bell Laboratories Record* **32**, August 1954, p. 313.

115. Nance, R. C. "Automatic Outgoing Intertoll Trunk-Testing Circuit." *Bell Laboratories Record* **32**, December 1954, p. 467.

116. Burns, R. W. and Dehn, J. W. "Automatic Line Insulation Test Equipment for Local Crossbar Systems." *Bell System Technical Journal* **32**, May 1953, p. 627.

117. Blount, F. E. "Line Insulation Test Circuit." *Bell Laboratories Record* **32**, October 1954, p. 393.

118. Hardaway, H. Z. "Computers and the Exchange Plant." *Bell Laboratories Record* **50**, February 1972, p. 36.

119. Hibbard, Angus. *Hello Goodbye.* A. C. McClurg & Co., 1941, p. 152.

120. Hayward, W. S., Jr. "The Reliability of Telephone Traffic Load Measurements by Switch Counts." *Bell System Technical Journal* **31**, March 1952, p. 357.

121. Barnes, D. H. "Measuring Telephone Traffic." *Bell Laboratories Record* **36**, March 1958, p. 107.

122. Linehan, G. E. "A Portable Traffic Usage Recorder." *Bell Laboratories Record* **36**, March 1958, p. 107.

123. Ransom, V. L. "Automatic Traffic Data Processing." *Bell Laboratories Record* **42**, October 1964, p. 302.

124. Machol, R. E. "Acquiring Data for Network Planning and Control." *Bell Laboratories Record* **52**, October 1974, p. 279.

125. "EADAS Monitors Traffic for Switching Systems in Real Time." *Bell Laboratories Record* **52**, February 1974, p. 64.

126. Haenschke, D. G. "Network Management Systems in the United States." *Proc. of the Ninth International Tele-traffic Congress,* Torremolinos, Spain, October 1979, Paper No. 632.

127. Deltuvia, A. A., Jr. and Faris, W. L. "Business Office FADS." *Bell Laboratories Record* **48**, May 1970, p. 150.

128. Allan, R. "The Great New York Telephone Fire." *IEEE Spectrum* **12**, June 1975, p. 34.

129. Malthaner, W. A. and Vaughan, H. E.; U.S. Patent 2,951,908; filed August 5, 1957; issued September 6, 1960.

130. Ketchledge, R. W. "Electronic Switching." *Bell Telephone Magazine* **39**, Autumn, 1960, p. 2.

Time multiplex switch of the No. 4 ESS lab, Indian Hill, Illinois location of Bell Laboratores, about 1975. As a result of intensive Bell System studies, a digital time-division switching network for toll ESS was decided upon in January 1970. Among the advantages of this ambitious project: an essentially nonblocking network, incorporation of common channel interoffice signaling, reduced floor space, lower installation costs, less processor time per call, plus all the advantages of stored-program control. The No. 4 ESS call processing program contains more than one million software instructions and diagnostic testwords, and the system by cutover date in 1976 achieved a capacity of 550,000 call-attempts in the busy hour. Over $400 million dollars were invested in No. 4 ESS before it entered service.

Chapter 12

The Integrated
Digital Toll Network

Recent years have seen a basic shift of emphasis in the development of switching systems. Planning is leading to an integrated, nationwide network controlled by stored-program control switching systems. Of great significance to this trend were the choice of time-division digital switching for No. 4 ESS and the development of common channel interoffice signaling. As a result, many new services for customers become possible, even to the extent of offering customers, in some instances, the choice of having telephone numbers independent of geographical location. Also important is the trend toward centralized, comprehensive testing and maintenance using modern techniques of accessing and processing data.

I. NO. 4 ESS—INTEGRATED TRANSMISSION AND SWITCHING

As indicated in Chapter 10, section IV, electronic switching for toll traffic was, from the beginning, considered to be an essential part of the ESS development program. Moreover, in the late 1950s it was recognized that some cities might require more than one switching system to serve all of their toll center needs.[1] As a result, studies were conducted at AT&T and Bell Labs, resulting in a system plan for multiple toll switching offices in metropolitan areas.[2] It was during this period that the capacities of both the crossbar tandem system used for toll and the 4A toll crossbar system were increased (see Chapter 11, section 2.9).

Toll service was growing rapidly. It was anticipated that by 1970, 15 metropolitan areas would require more than one 4A crossbar office, and that this figure would grow to 24 by 1975 and to 47 by 1980. It was obvious that a larger toll switching system was needed for the future.

Electronic switching techniques had always been assumed for future application to toll, and these techniques were maturing in the local and AUTOVON system applications. Bell Laboratories engineering studies indicated a need for a 4-wire toll system that would serve at least 40,000 trunks. This requirement could be met with switching networks of the type being built for local ESS. However, the call-attempt capability was estimated at 300,000 attempts per busy hour, a figure much in excess of the capacity of processors and software then being developed for local systems. Consequently, several system control architectures were examined, including multiprocessing with the No. 1 ESS processor. This was abandoned because of expected difficulties in coordinating software.[3] In the end, a proposal was accepted for a new processor, called the 1A processor, with signal processors and fast signal distributors. This proposal was considered to be the best way to meet the call-attempt requirement with a single processor, duplicated for redundancy requirements.[4]

There were a number of viable switching network alternatives. These included a ferreed network using the 4-wire AUTOVON switch (see Chapter 9, sections 5.4 and 5.5), new ferreed switches, solid-state switches, and electronic network controllers. However, studies indicated the growing use of digital transmission facilities among local offices and for toll-connecting and completing between local and toll offices. A digital time-division switching network for a toll ESS was therefore proposed in April 1968. As a result of the growing acceptance and applications of digital transmission, studies were accelerated to determine the cost effectiveness and the availability of technology for such a network. Networks of this type appeared attractive not only for their greater degree of integration with toll-connecting digital facilities, but also for expected floor space savings, lower installation costs, and reduced processor real time per call. Also, at little additional cost, the network could be made nearly nonblocking with an expense saving by reducing if not eliminating load balancing rearrangements. However, development of a time-division network would require a greater dependency on new technology and additional development effort and cost.

During the ensuing 15 months, much progress was made in defining a digital switching network. Many ideas developed earlier at Bell Laboratories during the ESSEX experiment[5] and the concept of time slot interchange were recast in modern technology. H. E. Vaughan, who in 1977 received the IEEE Medal of Honor for his work in this field, was the prime mover of this effort.

One of the most important decisions for this project was made in January 1970. After meeting with an intercompany committee known as the switching council, W. H. C. Higgins, vice president of the switching area at Bell Laboratories, decided, based on the exploratory development and study results at hand, that a digital time-division network would be developed for the toll system, which by that time had been coded the No. 4 ESS. At the same time, it was decided that the 1A processor then being developed for the expanded local system, No. 1A ESS, would also be used for the No. 4 ESS (see Fig. 12-1).

The No. 4 ESS project was the most ambitious development project undertaken at Bell Laboratories. Between Bell Labs and Western Electric, more than $400 million was spent before the first office was placed in service in January 1976.[6] A whole new technology, known as the 1A technology, was developed featuring small- and medium-scale integrated circuit chips on ceramic substrates. This technology was used in this and other concurrently developed switching systems, No. 1A, 2B, and 3 ESS[7] (see Fig. 12-2). In addition to the new technology, the development involved many other areas of Bell Laboratories, such as electron device groups and transmission development groups. The transmission area was responsible for the development of peripheral equipment that combined the signaling and terminal functions, including their maintenance, to interface with interoffice transmission facilities.

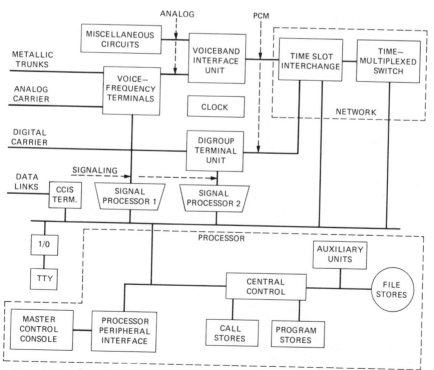

Fig. 12-1. Basic plan for a No. 4 ESS system. This $400 million development was the largest ever undertaken by Bell Laboratories.

While the initial time-division network proposal was for 65,000 terminations, the plan by March 1970 was adapted to have a growth potential of 107,000 terminations with a 0.9 erlang capacity per termination at a 0.001 blocking loss (nearly nonblocking). The principal reason for the increase in capability was the result of engineer-

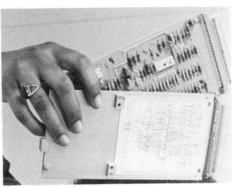

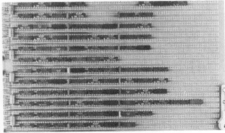

Fig. 12-2. Elements of the new technology developed for No. 4 ESS. Clockwise from upper left: integrated circuits, two types of circuit packs, special interconnection boards, and wiring backplanes.

ing studies predicting the possibility of longer holding times in the future. Since the network used many active devices and was vital to the provision of service, it was completely duplicated.

From the beginning, the network architecture used a technique called time slot interchange (TSI) followed by time slot permutation switching. The unit performing this latter function is called a time multiplexed switch (TMS).[8] With time-division switching, groups of digits are received in multiplex for a number of different connections. These digits are synchronized and stored in a TSI memory so that they may be placed in different time slots. They are passed through the TMS so that connections may be interchanged in each time slot between different multiplexed lines. Unique in the design of this network are the expansion and decorrelating features by which lower blocking is obtained among all inputs. Also, switchable spare voice interface and digroup terminals are provided on a 1 for 7 or 8 basis, respectively. The highly precise clock for this system is quadrupled for reliability.[9]

While the use of digital time division for the network was an important innovation, one must not forget that, as with other ESSs, the principal advantage of introducing No. 4 ESS into the plant besides its size is the fact that it is stored-program controlled. As a result, exciting new possibilities opened up, some of which were demonstrated to a lesser degree with No. 4A crossbar ETS (see Chapter 10, section II).

Having extensive experience with software development and having the capacity problems of the early No. 1 ESS much in mind (see Chapter 9, section 6.1), Bell Labs engineers initially estimated conservatively a 350,000 busy-hour call-attempt capability for the No. 4 ESS. The first call was completed in a laboratory model in May 1973. For the first time with the No. 4 ESS, a general-purpose computer was connected to the peripheral bus of the laboratory model for artificially creating a traffic load on the central processor and on the call-processing programs. This arrangement was called PETS, for programmable electronic traffic simulator.[10] While a contingency factor of at least 25 percent was maintained during the development, it was found through PETS that the engineered busy-hour call-attempts could be as high as 500,000. Just before the first cutover, a peak capacity of 550,000[11] was announced, making the system, by far, the most powerful to date.

The unique maintenance advantages are given below in section II, particularly as they apply to trunk facilities. As with all Bell System stored-program systems, automatic fault detection and location are inherent in the design, with the usual objective of no more than two hours downtime in 40 years.[12] Backup of the program memory was provided by a pair of memory modules, each of which serves as a roving spare standing by to replace any one of N active memory modules. Previous systems required a backup module associated with each active memory module (a total of $2N$ modules). The scheme with the roving spare modules required a total of only $N + 2$ modules and at the same time provided greater dependability of service.

Besides providing for dial pulse and multifrequency pulsing, the system is the first to be equipped from the beginning with common-channel signaling (see below, section III). Thus, calls between No. 4 ESSs and similarly equipped 4A crossbar ETS offices enjoy faster switching and the other advantages of CCIS. Wired logic signal processors are used for receiving and sending pulsing and supervision.[13] The ease with which trunks are assigned to the network is due in part to its nearly nonblocking character (see Fig. 12-3) and in part to the use of the circuit maintenance system (see below, section II) that includes an extensive translation and administrative data base. Call charge recording is provided as CAMA. Extensive traffic data are recorded, including provision for noting the origin and destination of calls to aid division of revenues between the toll and local companies. The program for call processing, containing more than 400,000 instructions, is one of the most extensive ever introduced into an initial system design.

The built-in network management features are also the most extensive.[14] Reorders encountered on calls are counted on the basis of attempts per called central office code. These results are analyzed periodically (e.g., every 5 minutes) to determine "hard to reach" codes. The more usual dynamic overload controls (DOC), such as traffic overload reroute control (TORC) and directional reservation equipment (DRE), are employed to deal with focused overloads. Selective trunk reservation is employed for traffic with a higher probability of completion. Finally, manual controls may be

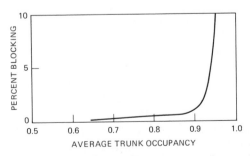

Fig. 12-3. No. 4 ESS network blocking. Curve shows that, below 0.9 occupancy, the network is virtually nonblocking.

instituted to cancel traffic on a code or route, and to reroute traffic out-of-chain (out of the hierarchial routing) (see Fig. 12-4).

II. MAINTENANCE AND ADMINISTRATIVE TECHNIQUES

While digital technologies were bringing about the merger of switching and transmission, the automation and integration of the maintenance of the network was also being integrated. In fact, the greatest savings from the application of electronics to switching have to date come as a result of the maintenance advantages realized by the use of modern data processing.

The No. 4 ESS has access to an extensive data base for all the trunks it serves. This data base, unlike translations, contains details for identification and maintenance of the facilities that carry the trunk groups as well as of the trunks themselves. It is known as the circuit maintenance system, or CMS. It comprises duplicated computer facilities and terminals used by crafts personnel.[15] At these

Fig. 12-4. Network management center in Chicago, Illinois where Bea Dellorto (left) checks routings with Chris Layden (foreground). Extensive network management features built into No. 4 ESS enhance ability to control traffic and avoid traffic congestion.

terminals, displays and keyboards are used to access trunks for tests and to place them into or take them out of service. The CMS 1A is used in No. 4 ESS to interconnect the trunk operation center (see below), terminal equipment center, and the ESS administrative center (see Fig. 12-5). In a sense it is the modern data processing version of the earlier toll test facilities (see Chapter 3, section IV). CMS uses the No. 4 ESS to access trunks and to connect measuring and functional testing equipment as required by craftspeople. With it, operators at cathode ray tube terminals in the various operating centers can perform routine tests of the internal system facilities to check signaling capability. They also can localize troubles between offices, in conjunction with remote telemetering systems.

The integration of test and maintenance facilities has always been an inherent part of switching system design. However, with the improved operations support system conceived and devised by Bell

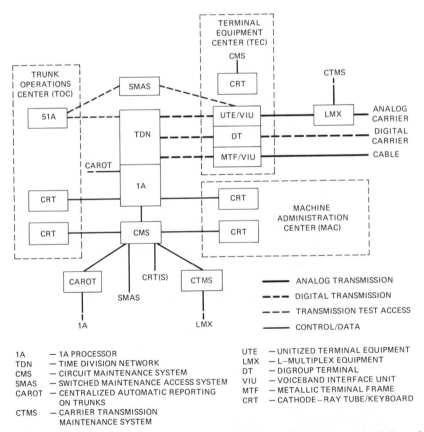

1A	— 1A PROCESSOR	UTE	— UNITIZED TERMINAL EQUIPMENT
TDN	— TIME DIVISION NETWORK	LMX	— L–MULTIPLEX EQUIPMENT
CMS	— CIRCUIT MAINTENANCE SYSTEM	DT	— DIGROUP TERMINAL
SMAS	— SWITCHED MAINTENANCE ACCESS SYSTEM	VIU	— VOICEBAND INTERFACE UNIT
CAROT	— CENTRALIZED AUTOMATIC REPORTING ON TRUNKS	MTF	— METALLIC TERMINAL FRAME
		CRT	— CATHODE–RAY TUBE/KEYBOARD
CTMS	— CARRIER TRANSMISSION MAINTENANCE SYSTEM		

Fig. 12-5. The circuit maintenance system (CMS, lower middle of diagram) is the trunk data base of No. 4 ESS. Such modern data processing facilities greatly enhance the efficiency of maintenance personnel.

Laboratories engineers, centralization and comprehensiveness of testing is now an integrated function of all systems, whether transmission, switching, outside plant, or other. Further, Bell Labs studies indicate that this integration and centralization of maintenance and administration will continue to be as important as the integration of the technical facilities that perform the service functions. This is particularly important as the first costs of these facilities are reduced and developments are implemented to take advantage of the new techniques by reducing annual expenses. Fig. 12-6 shows the unique way the CMS No. 1A interfaces with the many parts of the adjuncts to the No. 4 ESS.

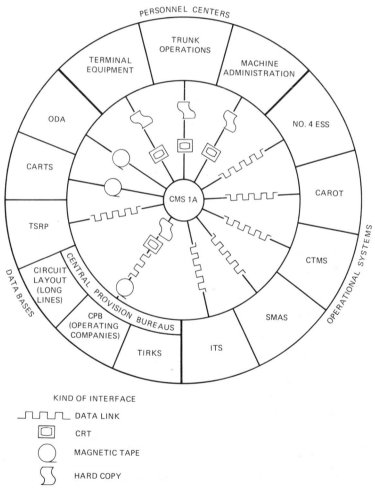

Fig. 12-6. Interaction of the circuit maintenance system (center) with No. 4 ESS and its adjuncts. The extent of such centralization and its comprehensiveness are new to telecommunications.

The circuit maintenance system provides the data base at the heart of the trunk maintenance of the No. 4 ESS. Operations or work centers for the system equipment (transmission and switching) are equipped with cathode ray tube and keyboard work stations. One of these, the 51A test position, is shown in Fig. 12-7. A group of these positions form the trunk operations center (TOC) (see Fig. 12-8). The master control center is located in the maintenance operations center as shown in Fig. 12-9.

With the liberal engineering of the time-division digital network, the trunk facilities may be directly assigned to the network without taking into account the average trunk occupancy. As a result, the size and number of distributing frames are greatly reduced, being required only for the nonswitched services that share transmission facilities with the switched channels. Furthermore, most internal trunk cabling is coaxial, since the channels are digitally multiplexed. This considerably simplifies installation cabling.

III. COMMON CHANNEL SIGNALING

In the early days of manual switchboard operation, one popular arrangement was separate but common "call wires" from the customer to the central office. Over these wires, customers "ordered up" the connections they desired.[16] The standard manual switch-

Fig. 12-7. Barbara Reed, Long Lines, at a 51A test position of the circuit maintenance system 1A, which gives craftspeople access to No. 4 ESS data bases and circuits for trunk maintenance.

Fig. 12-8.   No. 4 ESS trunk operations center in Jacksonville, Florida.

Fig. 12-9.   Maintenance operations center at the Chicago 7 No. 4 ESS office. The master control center is also located here.

boards had call or "order wires" between A and B switchboards for the originating A operators to order up terminating connections by the B operators.[17] In the 1920s a time-multiplexed asynchronous teletypewriter-like channel was used to signal trunk seizures between toll switchboards in New York and Philadelphia.[18]

In the late 1940s, switching researchers at Bell Laboratories took a renewed interest in call wire techniques as a way of speeding signaling between central offices. In the late 1950s, exploratory and engineering studies focused on arrangements to use one trunk in a group to carry the interoffice signaling for the entire group. The last idle trunk, or first to become idle, was used for signaling for the entire group.

By 1964, foreign administrations through the Comité Consultatif International Télégraphique et Téléphonique (CCITT) became interested in applying separate data link signaling to intercontinental operations that were just beginning a period of rapid growth. This form of signaling was promoted since it was much faster than the form of international signaling (system CCITT No. 5 and R2)[19] then being used. Furthermore, it was visualized that, in the future, additional information might need to be transferred.

A CCITT study was started in 1964, leading to a standard form of common channel signaling, later known as CCITT No. 6. The Bell System was an important contributor to this proposal. An international trial was agreed upon in 1968. Ten PTT administrations from nine countries participated: the United States, Australia, Japan, United Kingdom, Belgium, Netherlands, West Germany, France, and Italy (2), and the trial extended from 1970 to 1972. The Columbus, Ohio location of Bell Laboratories, the U.S. participant, used a modified version of the 4A crossbar ETS (see Chapter 10, section II).[20]

In the mid 1960s the Bell System became acquainted with fraudulent schemes for bypassing accounting equipment and, thereby, avoiding charges on certain toll calls.[21] To determine the extent of this practice at the time, special equipment was developed and built at Bell Laboratories to enable Bell System security forces to estimate the seriousness of the problem.[22] Since then, CAMA-C equipment (see Chapter 11, section 2.8) has been arranged to detect this so-called "blue box" type of fraud.[23]

Also during this period, the cost increased for ac signaling equipment designed to withstand inadvertent simulation of disconnect signals by speech. Further, electronic switching systems were being deployed that offered the potential of new services not only within systems but also between systems. The signaling capability of the nationwide network had not changed since the introduction of ac signals. Therefore, the need for better interoffice signaling in the coming era of electronic switching was apparent.

Fig. 12-10 compares over-the-channel or channel-associated ac signaling (single-frequency for supervision and multifrequency for pulsing) with digital signaling over a common (but separate) channel or data link for a group of trunks connecting two switching offices. Since the data link is connected to the same toll offices or end points as the trunk group it serves, it is said to be "associated" with the trunk group, and the method is referred to as associated common channel signaling. With ac per-channel signaling, the amount of information and the speed with which it could be conveyed between offices were limited in view of the data processing capabilities of the offices themselves. With common channel signaling, the rate of transfer of data is faster (initially 2400 bits per second), and much more information about each call may be transmitted in both directions. This is best implemented by using stored-program control.

Having a common channel signaling data link associated with each group of trunks for all trunk groups is not cost effective. There are many small trunk groups in most national telephone networks, and the older signaling methods are less expensive for such cases. CCITT

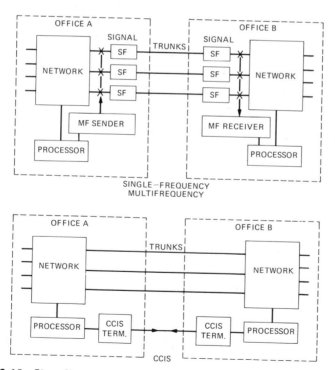

Fig. 12-10. Signaling can be over the communications channels (across top) or through a separate data network (through processors and common-channel interoffice signaling terminals).

planning studies of common channel signaling recognized this and included in their recommendations a "non-associated" approach where the data links did not necessarily share the same end points. Signaling and supervisory data traversing the common channel signaling links must also contain information to link that data to the proper trunk group by its end points or place in the network.

A further step, also included in the CCITT recommendations, was the routing of signaling messages from common channel signaling equipped offices to a signaling switch which routed the data between those offices according to part of the contents of the transmitted messages. This switch, a message switching system, was called a signal transfer point (STP). Processor-controlled switching offices would have access to STPs for collecting and conveying signaling information between two similarly equipped and directly connected offices.

In a large network, more than one STP would be required, and the common channel signaling links connecting toll offices and STPs form a message switching network communicating packets of data used to control calls through a nationwide toll network. This arrangement was the one adopted by the Bell System as the most economical and powerful means for modernizing its signaling network.

This arrangement was selected after intensive study by the Bell Laboratories switching engineering organization under the leadership of W. O. Fleckenstein and in conjunction with Long Lines. These studies showed great economies could be achieved by reducing and eventually eliminating the growth of ac signaling equipment in the toll plant (see Fig. 10-14). Furthermore, interoffice toll service can be speeded from an average of 10 to an average of 3 seconds from the end of dialing to the start of ringing. The possibility of "blue box" fraud will gradually be eliminated, and more information can be conveyed to stimulate the development of future new services (see below, section IV).

The specific implementation of the new signaling network was worked out by Bell Laboratories and AT&T Long Lines engineers to meet the needs of the nationwide network. A two-level signaling network structure was planned with toll offices and STPs in ten signaling regions corresponding to the network regions (see Fig. 12-11). Each region includes, for reliability, two STPs located in different cities. Each office serving some trunks using CCIS connects with data links to the STPs in their regions (see Fig. 12-12).

For Bell System use, the CCITT No. 6 signaling system was modified and called Common Channel Interoffice Signaling (CCIS).[24] Details such as the number of words in messages for trunk identification were modified, since trunk groups within the United States are generally much larger than those in other countries.[25]

Fig. 12-11. Plan of signal transfer points for common-channel interoffice signaling. Call information transmitted over CCIS offers potential for many new services. (*IEEE Symposium Record,* International Switching Symposium, Kyoto, Japan, October 1976.)

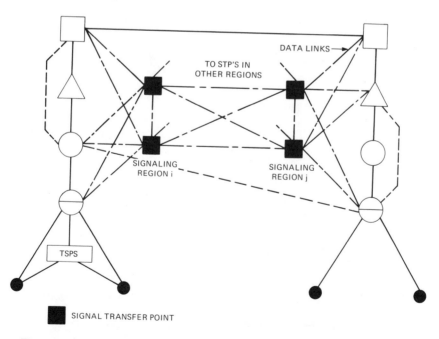

Fig. 12-12. CCIS switching plan. An office with trunks served by CCIS connects with signal transfer points in its region.

Implementation of this system was begun in 1976. Both the No. 4 ESS and the No. 4A crossbar ETS systems were provided with this capability. Selected No. 4A crossbar ETS offices were also arranged to be signal transfer points. The first signaling region was established to correspond with the Norway, Illinois region in the midwestern U.S. The toll CCIS network became operational with the first offices in Madison, Wisconsin (No. 4A-ETS crossbar) and Chicago, Illinois (No. 4 ESS) being served in the signaling region by No. 4A-ETS crossbar offices in Indianapolis, Indiana and Omaha, Nebraska as STPs (see Fig. 12-13). The No. 4 ESS was the first switching system to include CCIS capability in its initial design.

The cutover of the CCIS network represents the start of a new era for toll switching in the United States. Common channel signaling networks were placed in service in Japan to a limited degree prior to the start of CCIS in this country, but no nation matched the widespread and extensive deployment of common channel signaling provided by the Bell System in the 1970s.

By the end of 1976 three of the ten signaling regions were established serving two No. 4A ETS crossbar and four No. 4 ESS toll switching offices with a total of 700 trunks. All ten signaling regions were activated by the end of 1977.[26] Fig. 12-14 shows the extent of CCIS application expected (and achieved) by the end of 1979.

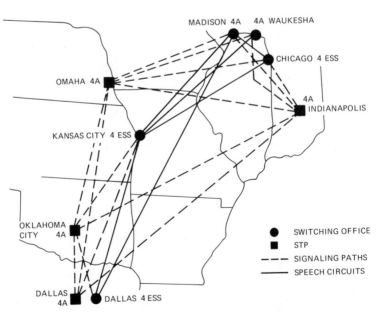

Fig. 12-13. Initial CCIS network, 1976. (*IEEE Symposium Record*, International Switching Symposium, Kyoto, Japan, October 1976.)

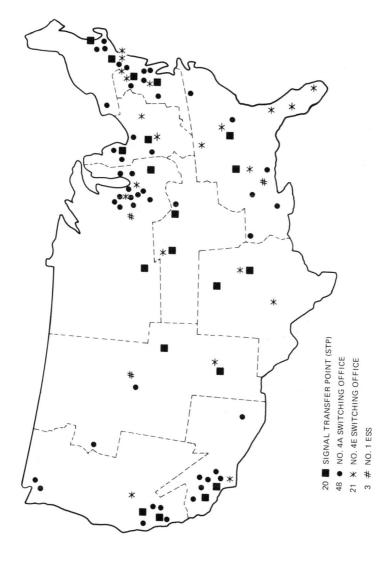

Fig. 12-14. Common channel interoffice signaling (CCIS) implementation, 1979. (*Conference Record*, International Conference on Communications, Chicago, Illinois, June 1977.)

20 ■ SIGNAL TRANSFER POINT (STP)
48 ● NO. 4A SWITCHING OFFICE
21 ✳ NO. 4E SWITCHING OFFICE
3 # NO. 1 ESS

Since signaling for toll calls involves the entire North American network, the independent telephone industry was kept informed of the plans for CCIS, starting in 1972.[27] Extension of CCIS into local ESS and TSPS offices is planned to obtain additional efficiencies and service capabilities.

IV. STORED-PROGRAM CONTROLLED NETWORK

With plans for the development and introduction of CCIS in the toll network well under way, Bell Laboratories switching engineers, under the leadership of R. L. Simms, started in 1973 to study in more detail other advantages this form of signaling could bring to the North American message network. From these studies it was realized that the sooner offices with stored-program control could be directly interconnected (trunked) using CCIS, the sooner the advantages, particularly improvements in call-completion times, would be discernible to the public. This led to an effort by Bell Laboratories switching engineers to find other reasons for planning such a subset of offices within the nationwide network.

As a result, the concept of a stored-program controlled network, or SPC network, was planned and implementation begun. It will offer new services and other improvements on calls between customers within this network.[28] This subnetwork will ultimately bring to the entire nationwide network what SPC has brought to the customers and administrators of individual ESS offices.

By 1976 studies of the SPC network concept demonstrated ways of accelerating the achieving of such a network by directly interconnecting SPC offices in the network hierarchy.[29] Other studies have shown that greater efficiency may be achieved in the installed trunk plant, particularly during overload, by taking into account the non-coincidence of busy hours in different parts of the network and by treating as one the separate trunk groups serving SPC entities between the same cities.[30]

With CCIS, it has been proposed to establish data bases that may be reached via the STP network to determine the destination and treatment of calls based upon the time and location of the call origination. With this ability, some telephone directory numbers need no longer be associated directly with specific switch terminations. Also, it will be possible to forward over the SPC network the class and calling line identity information to permit different service treatment at the terminating office according to the wishes of the called party. As an example, there can be automatic acceptance of collect and reverse-charge calls and a special form of ringing on calls from numbers specified by the called customer.[31] As shown in Fig. 12-15, by 1990 the number of toll switching systems should be reduced by 40 percent. This is expected despite an increase of more than 300 percent (see Fig. 12-16) in the growth of intertoll trunk ter-

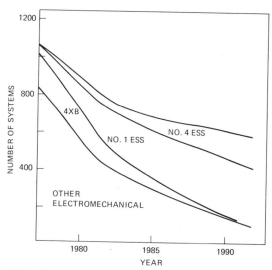

Fig. 12-15. Numbers of switching systems expected to 1990. The large capacity of No. 4 ESS makes such reductions possible. (*Conference Record, International Conference on Communications, Chicago, Illinois, June 1977.*)

minations. By that time the SPC network should be more than 90 percent implemented. This penetration is made possible by the use of the large-capacity ESS systems to replace all but a few small electromechanical toll switching systems.

As stated in reference 31: "What is essentially a new nationwide telephone network—the network of the future—is now evolving.

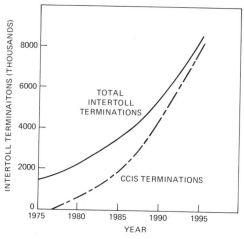

Fig. 12-16. Expected growth in toll terminations, to 1995. ESS replaces electromechanical systems, and CCIS grows to accommodate most trunks. (*Conference Record*, International Conference on Communications, Chicago, Illinois, June 1977.)

As it takes shape over the next quarter century, a variety of new customer services will become increasingly available. At the same time, greater operating efficiencies will be realized." It is appropriate that this history of central office switching end on these most exciting possibilities for the future. Without the basic principles and engineering foundations that were developed in large part by Bell Laboratories engineers during the past 50 years, they would not now be possible. These and many more innovations will be possible in the services and features to be included by Bell engineers in the design of switching systems for the future. From this history of public central offices, one does indeed come away with the impression that switching progress is the glue that holds together the many individual innovative service concepts in providing excellent community and nationwide telecommunications.

REFERENCES, CHAPTER 12

1. Federal Communications Commission Docket 19129, Phase II, FCC Exhibit No. 165.
2. Federal Communications Commission Docket 19129, Phase II, FCC Exhibit No. 167.
3. Federal Communications Commission Docket 19129, Phase II—Cross Examination of K. G. McKay, pp. 12954 to 12972.
4. "1A Processor." Special issue of *Bell System Technical Journal* **56**, February 1977, p. 119.
5. James, D. B. and Vaughan, H. E. "ESSEX-Continuing Research Experiment in Time-Separation Communications." *Proc. of IEEE* B107, Supplement 20, November 1960, p. 330.
6. Watson, G. F. "Getting No. 4 ESS on Line on Time." *Bell Laboratories Record* **54**, April 1976, p. 82.
7. Becker, J. O., Chevalier, J. G., Eisenhardt, R. K., Forster, J. H., Fulton, A. W., and Harrod, W. L. "1A Processor: Technology and Physical Design." *Bell System Technical Journal* **56**, February 1977, p. 207.
8. Cirillo, A. J., Jenness, R. V. and Rutkowski, P. J. "Switching and Signaling." *Bell Laboratories Record* **55**, December 1977, p. 310.
9. Leer, I. D. and Wiley, P. R. "Timing—Marching to the Same Drum." *Bell Laboratories Record* **65**, December 1977, p. 316.
10. McCabe, P. S., Otto, J. B., Roy, S., Sellers, G. A., Jr. and Zweifel, K. W. "No. 4 ESS: Program Administration, Test and Evaluation." *Bell System Technical Journal* **56**, September 1977, p. 1264.
11. Spencer, A. E., Jr. "No. 4 ESS: Prologue." *Bell System Technical Journal* **56**, September 1977, p. 1015.
12. Arnold, T. F. and Rohn, W. B. "Minimizing Downtime for Electronic Switching Systems." *Bell Laboratories Record* **53**, March 1975, p. 157. See also Clement, G. F., Jones, W. C. and Watters, R. J. "No. 1 ESS Processors: How Dependable Have They Been?" *Bell Laboratories Record* **52**, March 1974, p. 21.
13. Huttenhoff, J. H., Janik, J., Jr., Johnson, G. D., Schleicher, W. R., Slana, M. F. and Tendick, F. H., Jr. "No. 4 ESS: Peripheral System." *Bell System Technical Journal* **56**, September 1977, p. 1029.
14. Greene, T. V., Haenschke, D. G., Hornbach, B. H. and Johnson, C. E. "No. 4 ESS: Network Management and Traffic Administration." *Bell System Technical Journal* **56**, September 1977, p. 1169.

15. Giunta, J. A., Heath, S. F., III, Raleigh, J. T. and Smith, M. T. "No. 4 ESS: Data/Trunk Administration and Maintenance." *Bell System Technical Journal* **56**, September 1977, p. 1203.
16. Fagen, M. D., ed. *A History of Engineering and Science in the Bell System: The Early Years (1875–1925)*. Bell Telephone Laboratories, Inc., 1975, p. 484.
17. *Ibid.*, p. 502.
18. *Ibid.*, p. 639.
19. Johannessen, G. H. "Signaling Systems . . . An International Concern." *Bell Laboratories Record* **48**, January 1970, p. 13.
20. Sipes, J. D. and Funk, C. J. "CCITT Signaling System No. 6 Field Trial—United States Installation." *Telecommunication Journal* **41**, February 1974, p. 114.
21. Rosenbaum, R. "Secrets of the Little Blue Box." *Esquire* **76**, October 1971, p. 117.
22. *New York Times*, "AT&T Monitored Millions of Calls," February 3, 1975, p. 1:5 and 39:2.
23. "AT&T Device Detects Use of 'Blue Boxes.'" *Computerworld* 11, May 30, 1977, p. 7.
24. Dahlbom, C. A. "Common Channel Signaling—A New Flexible Interoffice Signaling Technique." *International Switching Symposium Record*, Mass. Inst. of Tech., Cambridge, Mass., June 1972, p. 421.
25. *Ibid.*, p. 421.
26. Johnson, J. L. "The DDD Network Goes Electronic—Logistics of Implementation." 1977 International Conference on Communications 3, Chicago, Illinois, June 1977, p. 35.3–8.
27. Bell-U.S. Independent Telephone Association Manufacturers Subcommittee Minutes, September 28, 29, 1972.
28. Richardson, D. E. "The DDD Network Goes Electronic: The Future of the Stored Program Control Network." *1977 International Conference on Communications* **3**, Chicago, Illinois, June 1977, p. 35.5–16.
29. Jacobsen, C. R. and Simms, R. L. "Toll Switching in the Bell System." *Proceedings of the International Switching Symposium*, Kyoto, Japan, October 1976, p. 132–4–1.
30. Bohacek, P. K. "The DDD Network Goes Electronic: Systems Engineering." *1977 International Conference on Communications* **3**, Chicago, Illinois, June 1977, p. 35.2–4.
31. "Network of the Future Taking Shape." *AT&T Shareowners Newsletter*, Third Quarter 1977.

DIMENSION® *Custom private branch exchange (PBX), Miami, Florida, 1977. PBXs in many ways paralleled central office switching systems by evolving from manual and early dial systems through crossbar to today's modern electronic systems, using the same techniques. In 1963 the Bell System introduced the first stored-program controlled, time-division, all-solid-state PBX (the No. 101 ESS). Thereafter, rapidly developing solid-state technology and stored-program techniques led to the DIMENSION system, introduced commercially in 1975. By early 1976, it had about 135 features grouped into packages to meet the needs of various businesses and industries.*

Chapter 13

Private Branch Exchanges, Key Telephone Systems, and Special Systems

Communications technology of necessity focuses on the vast community of individual telephone users, but not to the neglect of the many needs of businesses and other organizations, and of systems adapted to special purposes. Private branch exchange and key telephone systems have therefore been developed to cover the very wide range between small businesses with only a few telephones to large companies and government agencies with installations nationwide. Further, these systems have been constantly updated and improved with infusions of new technology and engineering innovations, some of these in response to business demands and some pointing the way toward new business potentials. The Bell System's sensitivity to the market, the full power of electromechanical switching, and later of solid state electronics and stored-program control have helped solve the problems of business communications needs.

I. BEGINNING THE SECOND HALF CENTURY

The second half century began with a fundamental program directed at meeting the extremely varied service requirements of the Bell System's private branch exchange (PBX) customers. In the first five years of this period (1925–30) there evolved from their predecessors not only a family of manual switchboards tailored to the requirements of installations of varying sizes, but also an array of dial PBXs for large and small installations.

As described in the first volume of this History series (subtitled *The Early Years: 1875–1925)*, the manual family of PBXs included the cordless 506A and 506B, which provided service for 7 to 12 lines for small businesses. Also available were the cord switchboards 551A and 551B for customers requiring up to 300 lines, and the large multiple cord switchboards 604C, 605A, and 606A for requirements up to 5000 lines.

443

Somewhat similar to the pattern of manual systems, the dial systems were designed for specific size segments in order to function as efficiently as the prevailing art permitted. The small relay-type 750 PBX was developed for customers having up to 15 lines; the step-by-step types 740A, B, and C served customers having up to 80 lines; and, for customers having very large numbers of lines, there were the step-by-step types 701A and 701/711 combinations.

It is interesting to note that almost as many PBX systems were introduced during 1925–30 as were developed in the previous 25 years. It is perhaps equally interesting that the added impetus given to PBX development during this period coincided with the formation of Bell Laboratories in 1925. Indeed, not only was a fundamental array of systems made available at that time but also a pattern was established which laid the groundwork for future improvement and innovation for many years. Further detail on systems made available during this period is shown in Table 13-1.

II. CONTINUED EVOLUTION OF PBX SYSTEMS

2.1 The Thirties

The great depression of the 1930s caused many social and economic problems, leading to severe effects on all of the nation's

Table 13-1. Private Branch Exchange Systems, 1925-1930.

System	Capacity (Lines)	Introduced	Characteristics
Manual			
506A	7	1928 ⎱	Key controlled
506B	12	1928 ⎰	cordless switchboard
551A	40	1927 ⎱	Non-multiple
551B	80,320	1927 ⎰	cord switchboard
604C	2,000	1925 ⎞	Multiple
605A	1,500	1928 ⎟	cord switchboard
606A	5,000	1929 ⎠	
Dial			
701A	3,200	1929	Step-by-step with cord switchboard
711A	10,000	1929	Step-by-step for "satellite" use
740A	88	1926 ⎱	Step-by-step with
740B	38	1928 ⎰	cordless switchboard
740C	38	1928	Similar to 740B but residence oriented
750A	15	1929	Relay logic

manufactured products. The PBX field was no exception, of course; it felt this directly through lower demand for new PBX equipment and indirectly through reduced development effort. Even so, two significant changes occurred in the art, one as a result of functional reevaluation and the other from efforts to try new technology to reduce costs and improve performance and demand.

The reevaluation process occurred in the small dial PBX field represented by the 740-type step-by-step equipment, which had cordless attendant positions. These systems were characterized by engineered and packaged equipment units, which reduced material and installation costs. In addition, these units were characterized by key-type cordless auxiliary switchboards instead of cord switchboards. While the cordless boards offered operating and aesthetic advantages, their success depended upon the acceptance of several compromises in operating functions. Among these were a need for the attendant to dial the telephone on incoming calls without a prior indication of busy, and the need for the telephone user to hang up and be called back on outgoing calls completed by the attendant. Experience with the 740 systems indicated that many customers preferred the flexibility of full cord switchboard operation such as was available with the larger 701A systems. Accordingly, such a combination, known as the 740AX, was made available in 1932. It consisted of 740A dial equipment with a cord switchboard (coded 552) composed of 605-type circuitry in a 551A framework, at which appeared the central office trunks, stations, and attendant trunks. However, the 740A and B cordless systems continued to be desired by many customers; their manufacture continued into the 1950s, at which time they were superseded by more modern systems.

The second and more forward-looking development of the depression years was the exploration and subsequent introduction of PBX crossbar switching in the latter half of the decade. Concurrent with the development of crossbar switching in the central office area (see this volume, Chapter 4), and leaning on the common system device and circuit technology, PBX development engineers ventured into this new method of switching, since it held the promise of escaping from the technological traditions of the past and of promoting better systems in the future. Two crossbar systems resulted from this effort, one a small system for customers having 20 lines or fewer, and the other a larger system for up to several hundred lines.

The small system, known as the 755, was introduced in 1938. Utilizing 10×10 crossbar switches and U-type relays, it functioned from the customer's standpoint in much the same manner as the earlier 750, and indeed it replaced that system. However, its capacity of 20 lines and 4 trunks provided a wider field of use than the 15-line 750, and the new apparatus provided greater reliability. The maximum capacity was made possible by a switching network consisting of two crossbar switches; one of these could be omitted along with some of the peripheral equipment to make an economical system for ten lines. A 6-button telephone set was used which functioned similarly to the 5-button set used with the 750. One button conditioned the system for station-to-station calls, four buttons provided access to each of the four trunks, and one button was used for holding connections while permitting use of the telephone for other connections. Telephone lines were connected to the verticals of the crossbar switch (10 lines per switch) with trunks and station-to-station junctors (called links in this system) connected to the horizontals. A maximum of three links were available for station-to-station calls. In addition to providing the transmission path, these links accepted dial pulses and decoded two digits for the use of the common control in setting up the connection to the called telephone. Outgoing calls were steered to the proper horizontal to which the button-selected trunk was connected; incoming trunk calls were indicated by a lighted lamp, and a user at any telephone could answer by depressing the proper trunk button. If another telephone was desired, the answering telephone could hold, call the other telephone, and identify the trunk to be picked up. Additional features of the system included line hunting and conferencing of up to three telephones.[1]

Block diagrams for station-to-station and trunk calls are shown in Figs. 13-1 and 13-2. A view of the equipment of this first crossbar PBX is shown in Fig. 13-3. The usefulness of the 755 was attested to by the fact that it continued to be manufactured for more than 25 years after its introduction.

The larger crossbar system developed in the 1930s, coded 745A, used a cord switchboard for completing incoming calls to telephones from central office trunks. The service features were essentially the same as those of the 701A and 740AX PBXs. It was intended that this system would cover the field of the 740 and small 701A PBXs. The 745A was developed to the point of field trial of a 200-line system in the late 1930s. Solutions of some circuit problems were worked out, but final development was not undertaken because of the onset of World War II, which diverted nearly all development effort to war projects.[2] After the war, technological concepts had been altered to the point where other embodiments of crossbar switching principles were undertaken. However, it is interesting to note that the 745 PBX pioneered some features that were used in other switching systems. For example, the 745 PBX employed the "call-back" technique, which dispensed with a separate register link and controller by causing the marker to connect a line to a register through the line-to-trunk

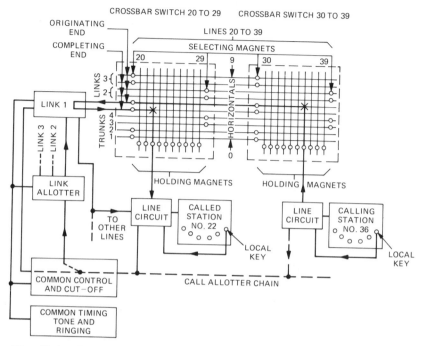

Fig. 13-1. Connections through two crossbar switches for a 755 private branch exchange station-to-station call. Telephone 36 (right) calls telephone 22 (left).

switching matrix. After dialing was completed, the register called back the marker and told it to connect the line to the trunk or telephone represented by the called digits. Some years later, this technique was used in the No. 5 crossbar design, the 756A PBX, and in other systems (see Chapter 7, section I).

2.2 The Forties—War and Post-War

As World War II approached, the use of dial PBXs increased and many installations grew in size enormously. For example, the Department of Agriculture PBX in Washington, D.C. grew from 400 lines to 6000 lines; another government agency grew to 12,000 lines. The Department of Defense in the then recently established Pentagon building in Washington grew to 16,000 lines, requiring a PBX switching system of a size suitable for a small city. The operating telephone companies, aided by Bell Laboratories, provided special equipment designs to accommodate these growth requirements. To reduce the station multiple for handling inward calls at the switchboard, the attendant was provided with trunks to groups of 100 tele-

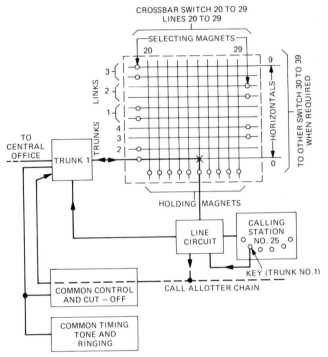

Fig. 13-2. Telephone 25 (right) placing a 755 PBX "outside" call via a trunk (left) to a central office.

phones; after selecting the proper one, the operator dialed the last two digits. To provide service to large PBXs quickly and with reasonable economy, the 606B switchboard was developed. With service features similar to the 605A, the 606B was adapted to the reuse of dial equipment that previously had been manufactured for use with the smaller switchboards of the 605A type.[3]

When the war ended, priority was essential for the development of new central office switching systems. As a result, development of PBX facilities was resumed only gradually. However, an interesting switchboard containing several equipment design innovations was introduced in 1948.[4] Coded 555, the new switchboard brought the plug-in concept to the switching field. Trunk circuits, attendant telephone circuits, and the major switching links—the cord circuits—were designed as removable plug-in units, thus facilitating growth and maintenance.

Although the 555 was introduced in 1948, it was being developed before the war and had proceeded to the trial installation stage. However, production was delayed until final design and manufacturing information could be completed. The circuits of the 555 were

Fig. 13-3. Equipment for the 755 PBX, the first PBX to use crossbar switches.

fundamentally the same as those of previous switchboards, but the operating devices were different. For example, the keys were installed in a sloping key shelf; they were rotated for answering and talking (instead of the conventional push/pull operation). Buttons were provided for ringing.

Fig. 13-4 shows the switchboard. Designed for a capacity of 120 lines, 15 cords, and 13 trunks, these switchboards could be operated side by side to provide capacity for 240 lines without multipling. The 555 replaced the 551 for requirements up to these limits. Fig. 13-5 shows a cord circuit being removed and Fig. 13-6 shows a plug-in trunk.[5]

Also added to the manual switchboard family in 1948 were the 607A and B switchboards—multiple switchboards for large installa-

Fig. 13-4. The 555 switchboard. This switchboard was developed to the trial stage before World War II and introduced in 1948.

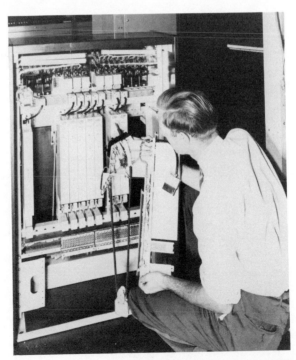

Fig. 13-5. For ease of maintenance and for growth, the 555 made extensive use of plug-in cord circuits. Here a plug-in circuit is being removed.

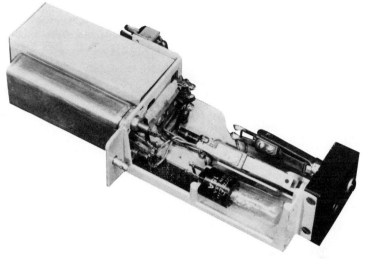

Fig. 13-6. Plug-in trunk circuit of the 555 switchboard.

tions—which consolidated the improvements accumulated after the development of the 606A and B boards. The 607 boards could be used either for manual PBX service up to 3500 lines or as a dial auxiliary switchboard for the 701A system to serve up to 5600 lines. The features of this board included symmetrical cord circuits, automatic flashing recall, machine ringing, and idle-indicating lamps associated with the outgoing trunk circuits.

2.3 The Fifties—Improvement, Change, Innovation

By the beginning of the 1950s the "post-war" environment faded as the nation faced new social and economic challenges. The business scene was characterized by new methods, products, and services, and by accelerating growth. PBX communications, a fundamental part of business operations, kept pace. For example, the quantity of PBX equipment manufactured in the 1950s was more than double that of the 1940s (which in turn was double that of the 1930s). More significantly, manufacture of dial PBX equipment in the 1950s was triple that of the 1940s and drew even with equipment for manual service.

Faced with this imminent increased demand, the most expeditious course of action appeared to be to improve the manufacturing processes of existing manual and step-by-step systems and to increase their engineering capabilities, their flexibility, and their service features. Accordingly, since the larger step-by-step (701/607) systems and the manual systems (607 and 555) had been only recently improved, attention turned to the small and mid-range dial systems of the 740 type.

The 740E PBX[6] was standardized in 1950 to replace the 740AX. It retained the basic step-by-step line finder and selector-connector arrangements but was manufactured in standard "packages" which were equipped, wired, and tested in the factory. The system was engineered to be readily expanded beyond the capacity of the 740AX, up to a nominal maximum of 300 lines. Thus, the 740E could grow with the customer from a small size requiring only two-digit dialing up to an intermediate range requiring three-digit dialing. Very importantly, the system could grow without being taken out of service simply by adding line frames and selectors, and by changing a flexible cross-connection field associated with the switching frame. A modern-appearing attendant's switchboard, the 556A, similar to the 555A in features and equipment flexibility, was developed for use with the dial equipment.

Continuing the practice of improving existing technology, the earlier cordless PBXs of the 506 type were redesigned. The 506 models were used by large numbers of customers requiring service for no more than 12 lines. The redesigned model was introduced in 1951 as the 507.[7] Its styling and operating features permitted it to blend well with the commercial office equipment then being introduced. The 507 is pictured in Fig. 13-7. The 506, which was replaced by the 507, was the last PBX in the Bell System using magnetic "drops"[8] as line and supervisory signals.

In the early 1950s, new customer equipment parameters were being formulated. Moreover, terms like marketing, modernizing,

Fig. 13-7. The 507 cordless PBX, an improvement of existing technology in the 1950s.

packaging, flexibility, office decor, etc., were entering the engineering vocabulary and so enhanced basic technical and economic concepts and placed in perspective new design objectives. It was time now, in 1953, to see what could be done again to meet the objectives through the use of crossbar technology, which had previously been limited commercially to the small (20-line) 755. Crossbar technology by now had been advanced by improved switches, new wire spring relays, solderless wrapped connections and other device improvements—all of which led to lower cost and greater reliability.

The target in 1953 was a small crossbar system to meet the demand in the 20- to 40-line range—a range above the viable 755 but below where the 740E was economically competitive with manual operation. Studies indicated that a common-control marker-register type of system would be technically feasible for small PBXs, but a major problem was to make this type of system economical and reliable in the target range. This was because the cost of the common-control equipment, which was shared by each line, was mostly constant and not much affected by the number of lines served. Thus, systems with a small number of lines had to carry a major burden. However, it was anticipated that a system of this type could be designed for low installation, engineering, and maintenance costs. In addition, compared to previous systems, such a system could be attractive to customers because of a reduction in floor space requirements, better performance, and simple operating procedures for the attendant. It was further anticipated that if these objectives were attained, dial service in the target range would be sufficiently attractive to customers to result in substantial growth in dial PBX service—a desirable objective for both the customer and the Bell System.

These objectives led to the development of the 756 crossbar PBX,[9,10] the initial design for which was completed in 1956. The 756 met its market objectives, performed reliably, and provided desirable customer features. As finally developed, equipment options permitted capacities of 40 or 60 lines. It seemed almost axiomatic in the PBX field that a system originally intended for a maximum upper limit was always extended somewhat in the final design. Such extension came about, of course, as a result of the desire to expand the use of the system as much as possible.

The 756 PBX functioned much like a small central office. Making use of a marker, dial pulse registers, and a crossbar switching network, it had in addition a cordless attendant position for handling inward and special traffic. In retrospect, the success of the 756 system stemmed from its many design and innovative features, among which were as follows.

(a) The use of a simple but efficient switching network helped to meet the cost objective and provided reliable operation. The design permitted lines, trunks, and attendant circuits to have access to and be connected by links, as shown in Fig. 13-8. Sixteen links were derived from the 10 horizontals of the crossbar switches. This technique was the same as used in the No. 1 and No. 5 crossbar trunk link frame (see Chapter 4, section 2.1). Also, the use of a single marker aided in meeting the cost objective without undue sacrifice in reliability by using dual channels for the critical paths of the marker. The 756 was the first to use twin wire spring relays for this purpose, and their use minimized the space required for the dual channel technique.

(b) The high concentration of equipment permitted by the use of sliding racks (see Fig. 13-9) achieved the physical objectives without sacrificing maintainability. This caused the 756 to be the smallest system yet provided for the range above 20 lines. In addition, the design provided low noise levels and modern styling in keeping with the customer's office decor.

(c) A small desk-top cordless position for the attendant, as shown in Fig. 13-10, provided new and pleasing operating features, which were fundamental objectives of the development. The position's pushbutton control, display, and service features, coupled with the changing attitudes of modern attendants, caused it to be the forerunner of a line of compact cordless facilities for future systems (see below, section 3.2).

(d) The 756A included the introduction of new operating features for the first time. These included camp-on service for incoming calls

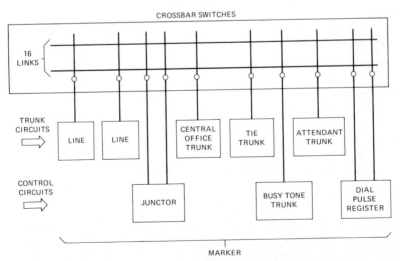

Fig. 13-8. Switching plan for the 756, a PBX featuring common-control switching. Design of this PBX was completed in 1956.

Fig. 13-9. Front view of the 756, a PBX switching cabinet with two slides pulled out.

to a busy line; delayed through supervision, which allowed an extension user to flash the receiver hook to recall the attendant; and restriction of service facilities, including the diverting of toll calls to the attendant on an individual-line basis.

Design improvements and service features were added to the 756 as the years progressed, and it became the prototype of several systems to come. The 756 system remained in production through the 1960s.

2.4 The Sixties—Solid State and Super Services

The 1960s saw the birth of what was perhaps the most significant innovation in the PBX field since its inception—the practical application of solid state technology with all its ramifications: time-division electronic switching networks, ferreed networks, sophisticated program control, and wired logic control. Also flowering in the 1960s was a host of service innovations (see below, sections 3.1 through 3.4). Some, such as TOUCH-TONE® dialing, and PIC-

Fig. 13-10. Cordless attendant position for the 756 PBX. Its simplicity of operation set a pattern for a subsequent line of consoles.

TUREPHONE® visual telephone service, stemmed from contemporary system trends. Others, stimulated by the possibilities of the solid state art itself, resulted in the conception of new ways for the customer's attendant and PBX telephone users to manipulate incoming and outgoing calls.

The 1960s brought added emphasis also to the development of switching systems of a PBX nature for specialized purposes—systems for telephone answering, for distributing calls to order-taking positions (such as for airlines, department stores, etc.), and for special municipal and government services (see below, section V). These years also saw substantial strides in key telephone systems (see below, section IV). It is of interest that key telephone system technology, which had its roots in PBX requirements (see No. 2 PBX in *The Early Years: 1875–1925*, p. 667), took over many of the customer's requirements for small manual and dial PBXs in the 1960s. Manufacture of the 20-line 755 crossbar dial system was discontinued in 1964, and by 1966 Western Electric shipments of the small manual cordless 507A and B positions (7 and 12 lines) fell to zero, largely because service requirements in these sizes were satisfied better by key telephone systems.

The 1960s also saw developments in what might be called the "bread and butter" line of PBXs. Among the notable milestones were the introduction of a new "universal" cord switchboard, the expansion of crossbar techniques in PBXs to serve up to 200 lines, and the refinement of this technology for more economical service to certain customers with 20 to 40 lines. And by no means to be overlooked was the "modernization" of the PBX workhorse—the step-by-step 701—to accommodate some of the new services such as Centrex (see below, section III). Not all of this was done at once, of course. Much that had been conceived and planned in the 1950s came to fruition in the 1960s.

There were many interactions and interrelations between the old technologies and the new. While this at times resulted in puzzling marketing approaches, it can best be viewed as resulting from the need both to meet the urgent requirements of the present and to assure the best technology for the future. An example is the development of the new cord switchboard in the late 1950s and its introduction and improvement in the 1960s. This switchboard was planned and developed while considerable emphasis was being placed on expanding the service and economic value of dial systems—the 756A PBX and subsequent crossbar and electronic systems. The objective of the cord switchboard development was to provide a "universal" board to cover the field of use of most of the cord switchboards that had been previously developed and were then standard for manual and dial auxiliary use—the 552, 555, 556, 605, and 607. At the same time, the objective was to design a board with a modern appearance, one that attendants would find easier to use. It also had to give better service for connected telephones and needed manufacturing and engineering flexibility. If these goals were achieved, the board would expedite manufacturing, simplify engineering and service choices, and update the switchboard line. This was important because there was a large, continuing demand for cord switchboards even though the longer-range trends were toward dial systems with cordless attendant positions.

These objectives were quite substantially achieved by the development of the 608 line of switchboards. By 1969, 95 percent of manual and dial auxiliary shipments were of the 608 type. The 608 switchboard[11] combined new design features with the best features of existing boards. It had the service features of the 607 but occupied less space. Flexibility was obtained through plug-in keys and relay units. By designing the jack field for operation as a single position or a multiple position, the board could serve from as few lines as desired to as many as 2400. Among its unique features was a new cord guide arrangement that permitted the height of the board to be decreased. Also, new illuminated pushbutton keys were provided. Fig. 13-11 shows the 608A switchboard, the last new Bell System cord board to be designed. The 608A was followed

Fig. 13-11. The 608A switchboard, serving from a few telephones to as many as 2400. The 608A was the last new cord switchboard to be designed in the Bell System.

within a few years by improved versions coded 608B and 608D, but the basic appearance and features remained the same.

About the middle of the 1950s, exploratory development was started on a PBX using solid state devices. By 1958 the possibilities of using this technology appeared attractive enough to begin commercial development. However, enough had been learned by then of the nature of electronics as applied to PBXs to indicate that the final development would take longer than originally supposed. In addition, it appeared that for some time there would continue to be a field of use for modern systems with conventional crossbar and step-by-step technology. In parallel with the solid state development, therefore, new crossbar and step-by-step developments were undertaken which resulted in the 757A and SS400 crossbar systems and a modernized step-by-step 701 system. We will defer the narrative of the electronic development in order to review first the objectives and technology of the electromechanical systems.

The 757 system was in concept an expanded 756. The objective was to extend as rapidly as possible what had been shown by now to be a highly successful system from the standpoint of equipment, performance, and service features. It was decided to carry this extension up to a capacity of 200 lines, a point where the traffic capacity of a single marker was still adequate. In terms of field of use, the 200-line limit appeared to be within the range of 90 percent of the systems customers. The register-marker scheme of the 756 was continued, as was a similar but larger and somewhat more complex crossbar network. Cordless operation was to be the predominant attendant mode. The service and equipment features were largely the same as with the 756. Development of the basic 757 system was completed in 1962, with improvements incorporated for several years thereafter, especially in the provision of new service features to which a common-control system of this type was well adapted. After manufacture began in 1963, the demand for the 757 increased each year until, by the end of the 1960s, it had come into considerable use in serving Bell System customers.

The SS400 was also an application of 756 technology. The target of this more or less special system was an economical arrangement for customers who required fewer than 40 lines and who had a particular traffic pattern. Traffic studies had indicated that many customers required central office access for just a small number of their telephones—perhaps 15 percent or less of the total—with all other telephones satisfied by intercom service only. Accordingly, after a brief development period, a version of the 756 made available in 1962 provided the desired service with just one 756-type cabinet. Economy was achieved by simplifying the marker somewhat, and by omitting central office and attendant trunk equipment and all special attendant equipment. The traffic requiring attendant service was handled in a manner similar to that of the 750 and 755. Telephones requiring central office service were served by key telephone sets, with the central office lines terminated directly on the buttons of the sets. These sets also had access to the switching system via a button on the set whereby users as well as all other users on the system could intercommunicate by dialing. One further important feature was included. If in rare cases one of the telephones not having direct central office access was needed on a central office call, the answering telephone could use the intercom and then add the telephone to the central office call. At the start of the development, this system was given the PBX code 759, but because its operation was similar to that of key telephone systems, it was coded the KTS SS400.

In 1959 the equipment and engineering features of the 701A were improved and the system was recoded 701B. Shortly after the 757 development was started, attention was concentrated on adapting the 701 system to the new service concepts then being considered for the crossbar and electronic systems. The 701 had prior use for direct inward dialing to extensions; this simply required the installation of an incoming selector train. What was desired now was to adapt the cordless attendant method of operation to the 701 to make it consistent with the new systems under development. Coordination of the attendant switching with the direct inward dialing function was required because, should a telephone user wish to transfer an inward call that had been directly dialed, it was necessary to recall the attendant to make the transfer. In addition, there was also the problem of providing access between the attendant and a large number of central office trunks, since the 701 generally served large customers. The smaller systems where cordless operation had been used successfully did not have this problem. Finally, the scheme had to be practical for systems in service that might need to be converted to direct inward dialing and cordless operation. The problem was solved and appropriate arrangements made available in 1960 by applying the "switched loop" idea (see below), which had been conceived early in the development of the electronic PBX.

Over many decades, the goal of PBX development remained relatively constant: to reduce prices to Bell operating companies by minimizing the cost of manufacturing, engineering, installing, and maintaining PBX equipment over the entire range of customer sizes, while at the same time maximizing the communication services and the ability to provide them flexibly and reliably. Also, constant efforts were made to minimize the space occupied on the customer's premises, to improve the equipment's appearance, and to provide service and equipment features that would be novel and attractive and that would provide savings to the end users. Over the years the technology of step-by-step and crossbar switching—at one point even panel—was applied to the problem, and the market was fragmented in various ways in order to reach these objectives in an optimum manner.

Solid state technology appeared to be an opportunity to make a massive assault on all of the traditional PBX problems. Economy, better service, and high reliability appeared attainable. Also the new art held out the hope of achieving great improvements in flexibility, physical parameters, and providing new and attractive services.

But there were new problems resulting from the immense job of transforming an art which, for more than 80 years, had been painstakingly developed and which had acquired scores of operational requirements together with all their nuances. The transmutation from electromagnets, contact closures, and electromechanical circuit logic to transistor logic, solid state memory, and call-processing techniques was required not only for all functions within the PBX but also at the interfaces of the system with conventional equipment—telephones, attendant equipment, central offices, other PBXs, and special service terminals. Further, the new technology was aimed at creating additional configurations and new service, traffic, administrative, and maintenance features. Although the PBX engineers were able to profit from much of the central office solid state switching development, many of the problems required unique solutions since they stemmed from requirements and operational plans that were unique to the PBX field.

Implementing the PBX requirements with solid state technology took time, more than was originally anticipated; hence the electromechanical developments previously mentioned. A specific development was started in 1958 to design a system for PBX service using electronic controls and switching networks (see Chapter 9, section 4.5). By 1960 the trial of stored-program control had been successfully started in Morris, Illinois (see Chapter 9, section 4.6) and SPC was chosen for the electronic PBX. This technological revolution required some time to solve new challenges it created in the design of PBXs. But solutions were found and the resulting system, called the No. 101 Electronic Switching System (ESS), successfully demonstrated a new art which, by its plan, organization, methods of implementation, and service capabilities, produced more technological and service innovations than any previous PBX.

The technology of the 101 ESS has been thoroughly documented in the technical literature.[12] A detailed description of its technical features is beyond the scope of this history, but the focus will be on important elements that delineate the technical evolution of the system and help to bring it into perspective with other systems.

The 101 ESS was a stored-program solid-state system somewhat similar to the No. 1 ESS with respect to its control methods. It differed from No. 1 ESS and all other common-control systems, however, in several important aspects. First, it was completely solid state, in the switching network as well as in the control elements. Second, the network was physically separated from and remotely supervised and controlled by a control unit located in the central office. And third, a plurality of switching networks, each serving a different customer, could be simultaneously controlled by the same control system. A design having this remote, multinetwork configuration was decided upon so as to distribute the control system costs over a large number of lines. This provided a uniform cost per line (for the control part), independent of whether a large or small customer was being served. The plan also resulted in less equipment on the customer's premises, so the system would need less floor space, installation effort, and maintenance. Centralization of controls also made practical shared administration, traffic measurement, and maintenance.

As in other PBX systems, the switching networks installed on the customer's premises were the means of connecting customer's telephones to each other or to central office trunks, attendant positions, or other special terminals. To do this, electronic communication was required between the switch unit (which contained the switching network) and the control unit. This function was performed over new paths, called data links and digit trunks, between the customer's switch unit and the control unit in the central office. Acting upon service request bids, dialed information, and supervisory states received over these paths from the switch units, the control unit "processed" the call and determined how and where the switch unit would set up the connection. The control unit could operate up to 32 switch units in this manner. The system plan as it existed at the time of the introduction of the 101 ESS is shown in Fig. 13-12.

The "call processing" function of the control unit depended principally upon its stored information and its programmed logical sequences. The latter coordinated the stored information with the on-line information reflecting the status of demands from switch units and central office interfaces. Similar to the No. 1 ESS, the 101 ESS used memory devices called twistor stores, which contained information for each line, such as class of service, special features assigned, hunt numbers, switch unit numbering plan, abbreviated dialing translations, and the like. For the system as a whole, the twistor store also contained the vital information for guiding the processing of calls. The stored information was contained in banks of magnetically encoded cards, each card individually accessible. The cards were only a little larger than the pages of a textbook. The tremendous flexibility and versatility of the system stemmed from the characteristics of these stores—their high information content, their accessibility in a matter of microseconds, and the ability to change the encoded information easily. These characteristics permitted rapid adjustments to accommodate changes in equipment and traffic requirements, and equally rapid changes to adapt to service requirements. Of particular significance over the longer term was the ability to adapt to service innovations.

An important role in this stored-program system was played by a "call status store," which provided by means of a ferrite sheet a continuously changing record of the status of each call in progress. An interesting illustration of the interplay between developments is that 101 ESS followed the lead of No. 1 ESS in adopting the twistor program store, and No. 1 ESS followed the 101 ESS in adopting the ferrite sheet call store. For each switch unit time slot (described later), the record contained the identities of the calling and called telephones, identification of the attendant and other equipment used in the call, and the status of the call at the time, such as whether there is ringing, holding, conversing, disconnect, etc. The

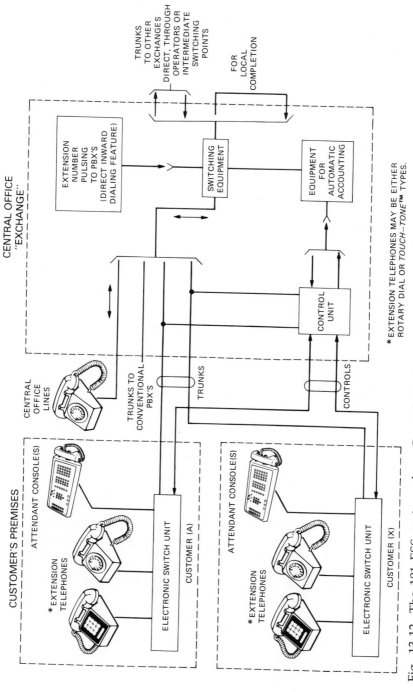

Fig. 13-12. The 101 ESS system plan. Control, in the central office, can serve a number of customers at different locations.

control logic initiated and continuously updated the record, correlating new information with old to determine and initiate new actions. A photograph of the control unit is shown in Fig. 13-13.

The switch units employed time-division switching. In this method of switching, terminals to be switched, such as lines, trunks, attendant loops, etc., were connected, each through a high-speed electronic switch, to a common transmission path called a bus. Any two terminals could be connected for a short interval by simultaneously operating their individual switches, thus exchanging a "sample" of the conversation. The 101 ESS practice was to sample at a repetition rate of about 12.5 kilohertz. (Many years earlier, H. Nyquist of Bell Labs had shown that a band-limited signal, such as voice, can be transmitted with fidelity if the sampling rate is at least twice the highest frequency contained in the signal. The 101 ESS exceeded the Nyquist rate somewhat to accomplish component economies.) During the sampling closure time, energy was transferred from one terminal to another by a phenomenon known as resonant transfer. The complete process was known as pulse-amplitude modulation. Fig. 13-14 shows the time-division transmission path for two terminals.

Fig. 13-13. Control unit of the No. 101 ESS. Left to right: M. A. Townsend and W. J. Means checking memory element, while H. F. Priebe checks line data circuits.

The duration of the sample was 2 microseconds, but additional time was required to dissipate residual energies left on the bus; hence a proper transfer required a little over 3 microseconds. This time duration was termed a time slot. Each terminal was sampled every 80 microseconds, the sampling period. It is obvious that the number of time slots available in a bus is equal to the sampling period divided by the duration of a time slot. The initial 101 ESS provided 25 (80 divided by 3+) time slots per bus, but subsequent developments increased this somewhat by reducing the time slot duration and repetition rate.

The control unit determined which two terminals (lines, trunks, etc.) should be connected and in which time slot and instructed the switch unit to carry out those orders. Switching was accomplished by recording the identity of the two terminals in a time slot position in a switch store, which was then read out sequentially and repetitiously to cause the proper pair of switches to operate. Assigning a pair of lines or other terminals to a time slot can be likened to assigning them to a link in an electromechanical system or to a cord circuit in a manual switchboard.

The initial 101 ESS switch unit contained two buses, each with a capability of 25 time slots for a total of 50. This number of time slots, or links, provided very high traffic-carrying capacity for the 200 lines of the initial switch unit. One might think of this as equivalent to the traffic-carrying capacity of 50 cord circuits, or more

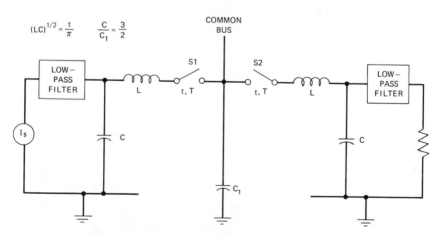

Fig. 13-14. Time-division transmission path. An information signal (left) is bandlimited by the low-pass filter. Switches S1 and S2 operate synchronously. The switches are closed for time t and go through one open-close cycle every T seconds. Thus the signal is sampled once every T seconds, and samples are transferred from the left circuit to the right.

than three switchboards. A photograph of the switch unit is shown in Fig. 13-15.

A field trial of the 101 ESS was begun early in 1963 in New Brunswick, New Jersey (see Chapter 9, section 5.2). Switch units were installed on the premises of two customers with the control unit located in a nearby No. 5 crossbar central office. Performance of the system and customer reaction to the service and the new features were highly favorable. First commercial service was provided by the system November 30 of the same year in Cocoa Beach, Florida. Two customers having about 100 lines each were served by December of that year, and later, two others were added to the control complex. Early in 1964 a system was cut into service at the World's Fair in New York, where it provided service to a number of administrative telephones and also served to demonstrate electronic switching to the public. All of these early commercial installations were highly successful.

At the time of its introduction in 1963, the service capabilities of the 101 ESS included (in addition to conventional PBX service) Centrex, TOUCH-TONE calling, cordless attendant operation, and an imposing list of new service features. Some of these new features were being considered at the time for general PBX use, but many of them could be implemented economically only by a stored-program

Fig. 13-15. Attendant controlling an initial 101 ESS switch unit (left), which serves up to 200 telephone lines.

system. The 101 ESS also uniquely provided automatic routine testing of the control and switch units (with automatic switch-out of defective circuits) and automatic traffic measurements. The system illustrated that solid state technology and "super services" did indeed appear to go hand-in-hand.

The historical significance of the services mentioned above might be made clearer by examining their technologies.

Centrex: Centrex service is based on direct inward dialing and identified outward dialing to and from telephones. The 101 ESS was the first customer switching system to provide *automatic* telephone-number identification of outward dialed Centrex calls. The prior use of the 701 system for Centrex service required an operator at a centralized AMA switching point to ask the user for the calling number. Automatic identification was, of course, inherent in the No. 5 central office Centrex arrangement. This function was a "natural" for the 101 system since the number of the calling telephone was retained in the memory of the call status store, as mentioned previously. By directly coupling the control unit with the central office Local Automatic Message Accounting (LAMA) or Automatic Number Identification (ANI) equipment (see Fig. 13-12), the telephone identity could be transferred to those equipment units on request. A few years later, the inward dialing function was performed through another direct-coupled interface with the No. 5 central office. This innovation, Direct Inward Dialing (DID), speeded the completion of inward dialing. Also, the parallel transfer of telephone number digits through this interface was considerably more economical than serially pulsing the digits from the central office.

TOUCH-TONE calling: The organization of the 101 ESS system was such that dial pulsing or TOUCH-TONE calling could be provided optionally without changing any equipment on the customer's premises except, of course, the telephone sets. The first commercial use of TOUCH-TONE calling by PBX customers was at the Boeing Company installation, Cocoa Beach, Florida, in November 1963. In December 1963, the Chrysler corporation became the second customer served by the Cocoa Beach Control unit. Other customers added subsequently included the Brown Engineering Company, North American Aviation, International Business Machines, and a pool of network television companies including ABC, CBS, and NBC.

Cordless attendant operation: The development program of the 1960s contemplated uniform attendant operating techniques with cordless equipment for the 757, 701, No. 5, and 101 ESS systems. The attendant operating methods for the electromechanical systems were the outgrowth of studies made for the 101 ESS and were a good illustration of behind-the-scenes system coordination. The 101 ESS demonstrated these methods in the form of the then new "universal console" (see Fig. 13-16). In accordance with call-distributing principles, the attendant was "switched-in" to connections when such connections were required. Thus, there was no need for directly terminating trunks at the position, resulting in a simplification of the overall operation. This technique, called switched loop operation, was another "natural" for time-division switching. It required only that the attendant loop number appear in the same time slot and thus be activated simultaneously with the line switches. In the further interest of simplifying operations and improving service, a unique feature was added to the "camp-on" feature. This feature automatically reminded the attendant every 30 seconds to check the status of a camped-on call. Thus, there was less chance of customers being left "high and dry" after the PBX attendant answered.

New service features: Services that came naturally to the 101 ESS by virtue of its switching and control technology were of two principal types: those that involved some form of re-switching after the call had come into the system, and those that simplified or influenced the origination of the call. In the re-switching category were such services as transferring, conferencing, answering a call to another telephone, and automatic rerouting a call to another predetermined telephone. These were achieved fairly easily because the source and

Fig. 13-16. The "universal console," developed for No. 101 ESS and other PBX systems. It featured switched loop operation, by which direct trunk connections are not required. Connections are switched to the operator only when assistance is needed on calls.

destination information associated with the time slots could be readily changed, and because the program technology was highly flexible. Services in the category of simplifying or influencing the origination of a call included abbreviated and compressed dialing ("speed calling") of internal and external calls, respectively, and the ability to restrict calls as a function of the exchange area codes dialed. These relied greatly on the memory stores and, of course, the program flexibility (see below, section 3.3.).

Experience with several commercial installations gave assurance that service objectives were being achieved and that the technology was sound. Developments were therefore undertaken in 1964 to increase the field of use of the 101 ESS system by providing arrangements for larger customers having more than the 200-line limit of the 1A switch unit. This program resulted in the introduction of the 2A switch unit (1965, maximum capacity 340 lines), the 3A switch unit (1966, 820 lines), the 4A (1967, 2000 lines), and the larger 4A unit (1969, 4000 lines). Network and time slot configurations of the 2A, 3A, and the two 4A switch units are shown in Figs. 13-17, 13-18, 13-19, and 13-20, respectively. The 1967 version of the 4A switch unit was first used to provide service to 1300 lines at the Bell Labora-

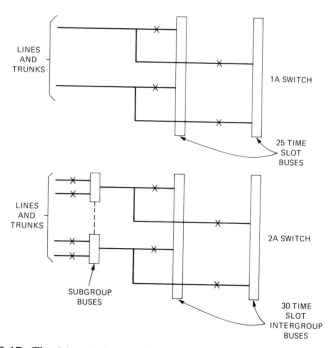

Fig. 13-17. The 1A switch (top) had two buses of 25 time slots each. The 2A switch (bottom) had 30 time slots per bus and served 340 lines.

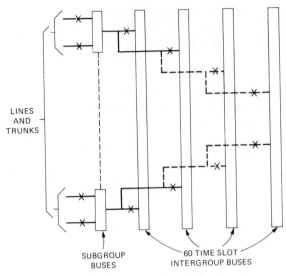

Fig. 13-18. In the 820-line 3A switch, up to four intergroup buses of 60 time slots each serve subgroup buses, which in turn connect with lines and trunks.

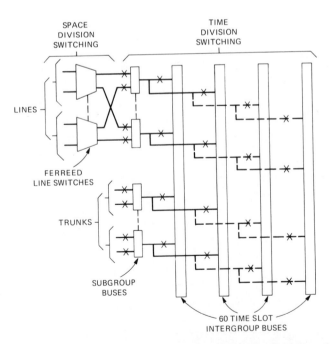

Fig. 13-19. The 4A switch carries the 3A plan one step further, through a stage of ferreed switches (upper left) to serve more than 2000 telephones.

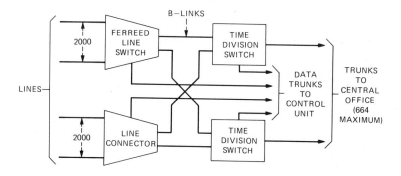

Fig. 13-20. The 4A could grow via an additional time-division switch unit. This configuration can serve up to 4000 customer stations at a single location.

tories building at Naperville, Illinois. The larger 1969 version was first used at the Mayo Clinic in connection with its expanded operations. This installation also furnished to the Clinic doctors a unique switching combination of radio paging and telephone answering.

With the addition in 1969 of main/satellite operation (Fig. 11-7) and designs for PICTUREPHONE visual telephone service employing a wideband switch coordinated with the voice switch, the 101 ESS story was virtually completed. The development had accomplished its technical and service objectives. The system could furnish PBX and Centrex service over the entire range of customer sizes. It had demonstrated reliable operation and a degree of flexibility far beyond the capabilities of electromechanical systems for adjusting to growth, accommodating service variables, and adapting to new developments. It had, for the most part, provided new services with greater economy than electromechanical systems and had gone well beyond in providing features that were economically infeasible with the older technology. Moreover, the system required only 10 to 20 percent of the customer floor space used by other systems, and its potential for substantially lower installation and maintenance costs was indicated.

During the process of development the 101 system achieved a number of "firsts." It was

1. the first completely electronic switching system in production having not only electronic controls but also electronic switching networks

2. the world's first production-version of a stored-program telephone switching system

3. the first production time-division switching system

4. the first system having remote control of a plurality of customer switches while providing PBX and Centrex service

5. the first customer switching system to provide automatic testing and traffic measuring

6. the first to provide automatic identified outward dialing, TOUCH-TONE calling, and the many new service features previously discussed.

Despite the imposing list of capabilities and "firsts" just discussed, the system failed to meet its objective of being widely used for all levels of service over the complete customer range. The cost of the system seemed fully justified when the control unit was loaded at least to two-thirds of its capacity, and when the customers desired most of the system's service capabilities. However, its cost became less attractive when either of these two factors became seriously eroded. In consequence, the challenge still remained, and the pursuit of systems having optimum economic, service, and engineering relationships continued.

Indeed, the pursuit started shortly after the introduction of the 101 ESS. At that time, it was becoming apparent that the system would not compete economically with the available small electromechanical systems of the order of 80 lines or fewer. This was particularly so when the service requirements were relatively simple. For example, in small sizes the cost of Centrex capability was difficult to justify since Centrex service did not provide appreciable, if any, attendant savings. In fact, no tariffs were available for the small sizes at the time. Also, many of the more exotic features of the electronic system appeared to have increasingly less economic value to smaller customers. Moreover, space on the customer's premises was about a stand-off between a 200-line electronic switch unit and a 60-line crossbar system such as the 756A, even though the switch unit was operated at only a 60-line level. Planning thus began to return to the possibility of improving the balance between economics and service by fractionalizing the market, as had been done with earlier systems over the years, while still retaining the electronic approach. The first product of this line of thought was the 800A PBX.

The broad objective of the 800A electronic PBX development[13,14] was to make available a dial PBX system which, through a rigorous application of electronic technology and limited service requirements, could be made sufficiently attractive in services and costs to win favor with customers who might have been served previously by small cord-type switchboards, or who were outgrowing key telephone system equipment. In addition, it was thought that such a system might be used for new installations instead of the 756 crossbar system and the small 740 step-by-step system. Such usage would bring the advantages of electronic switching to this field, especially when adequate concentration of PBXs was not sufficient to justify the 101 ESS. Accordingly, the design was aimed at a system for PBX use only (Centrex was excluded) with the maximum capacity limited to 80 lines. Cordless equipment was planned for the principal attendant operating mode, and service features were limited to those of series 100, 200, and 300 "marketing packages" then coming into vogue (see below, section 3.3), plus a few major options such as TOUCH-TONE calling. All equipment necessary for the operation of the 800A was contained in one or two small equipment enclosures installed on the customer's premises. The height and depth of the enclosures were about the same as file cabinets so that, where desired, the system could be lined up with them, as shown in Fig. 13-21. A system of this type, frequently called "self-contained," was consistent with the traditional method of implementing PBX requirements, from which the 101 ESS, with its separation of functions and remote control principles, had departed.

The 800A system plan employed a switching network of ferreed switches, controlled by decisions resulting from solid state "wired logic" common control. For versatility and economy, a thorough application of the plug-in building-block principle was employed in the physical design, as shown in Fig. 13-22. Services, traffic capaci-

Fig. 13-21. Cabinets of the 800A electronic PBX were sized to blend with office files. (*Communications Présentées au Colloque International de Commutation Electronique,* Paris, March-April 1966.)

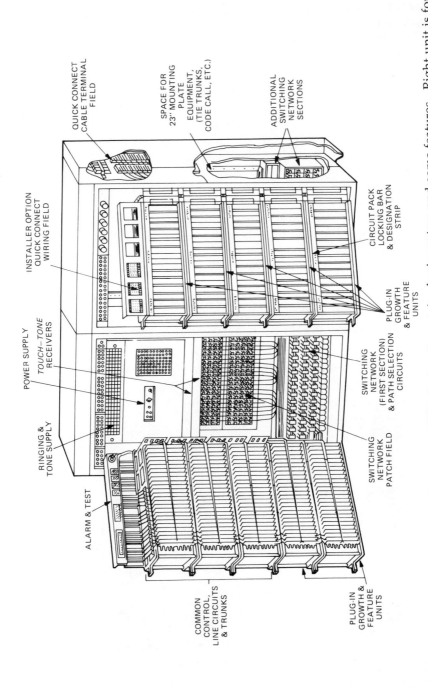

QUICK CONNECT
CABLE TERMINAL
FIELD

SPACE FOR
23" MOUNTING
PLATE
EQUIPMENT,
(TIE TRUNKS,
CODE CALL, ETC.)

ADDITIONAL
SWITCHING
NETWORK
SECTIONS

INSTALLER OPTION
QUICK CONNECT
WIRING FIELD

POWER SUPPLY

TOUCH–TONE
RECEIVERS

RINGING &
TONE SUPPLY

ALARM & TEST

CIRCUIT PACK
LOCKING BAR
& DESIGNATION
STRIP

PLUG-IN
GROWTH
& FEATURE
UNITS

SWITCHING
NETWORK
(FIRST SECTION)
& PATH SELECTION
CIRCUITS

SWITCHING
NETWORK
PATCH FIELD

COMMON
CONTROL,
LINE CIRCUITS
& TRUNKS

PLUG-IN
GROWTH &
FEATURE
UNITS

Fig. 13-22. Equipment cabinets of the 800A PBX. Left unit contains basic system and some features. Right unit is for growth and additional features.

ties, and optional features were arranged in groups and designed as more or less plug-in autonomous units of circuitry. The system organization is shown in Fig. 13-23.

The ferreed switches of the network were like those of the No. 1 ESS but differed in number of contacts per switch. The 800A

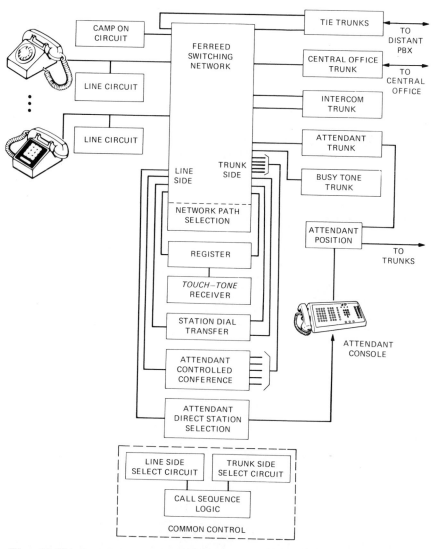

Fig. 13-23. Organization of the 800A system, which represented an attempt to serve smaller PBX customers with modern electronics techniques. (*Communications Présentées au Colloque International de Commutation Electronique*, Paris, March-April 1966.)

ferreeds had three contacts instead of two; these were used to establish a 2-wire transmission path plus a "sleeve" path for control. The switches were wired to form a 3-stage network, as shown in Fig. 13-24. Line circuits were connected to one side of the network and trunks to the other, with registers accessible on either side to trunks and lines. As with other small common-control systems, intercom trunks provided supervision and transmission for station-to-station calls. The principle of end-marking was used to establish a switching path as directed by the common control. With end-marking, source and destination points are "marked" on both sides of the network. Circuits built into the networks then select a path connecting the two points. The latter consisted of three main parts: a line scanner for locating and marking line circuits, an idle circuit scanner for trunks, and call sequence logic for controlling the establishment of connections.

The attendant's console for the 800A system, shown in Fig. 13-25, departed somewhat from the uniform operating features of the "universal" equipment used with the 701, 757, No. 5, and 101 ESS. Designed specifically for the 800A system, a feature unique to this attendant switchboard was a single supervisory lamp per access point, rather than the two conventionally used. By indicating the

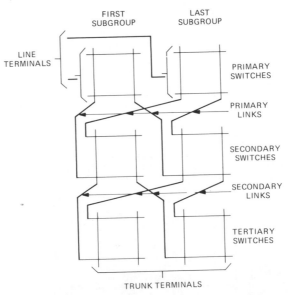

Fig. 13-24. The 3-stage network of the 800A system. Ferreed switches forming this network had two contacts for a transmission path plus a third for control. (*Communications Présentées au Colloque International de Commutation Electronique,* Paris, March-April 1966.)

various supervisory states with different flashing rates, the single lamp simplified console equipment and the related circuitry. An optional feature, shown on the right of the console in the illustration, was a field of illuminated buttons, one per station, for the "direct station selection" and "station busy lamp" function (see below, section 3.2).

The 800A PBX became the Bell System's first self-contained electronic PBX. Production began in 1966 after successful field trials held the previous summer in Philadelphia and New York City. By the end of the decade, more than 4000 systems had been shipped to meet telephone company orders, a statistic attesting to the system's favorable reception. The soundness of the technology was perhaps underscored by the fact that the system became a prototype for several systems to come.

As the decade drew to a close, another larger self-contained electronic system, coded the 810A, was developed. However, commercial production was not undertaken because it appeared that subsequent improvements in the art could be used to make a more economical system. The system is worthy of mention, however, since it too represented another first in the electronic PBX field and, as such, accounted for valuable new technological experience and knowledge.

The 810A system was designed to provide Centrex as well as PBX service for customers having up to 1200 lines. It had most of the service features of the 101 ESS, except for a few of the perhaps more exotic ones. Integrated circuits employing wired logic were used for

Fig. 13-25. Attendant console for the 800A PBX. Operation was simplified by using different flashing rates of a single lamp to indicate various supervisory states. (*Communications Présentées au Colloque International de Commutation Electronique*, Paris, March-April 1966.)

control, plug-in ferreeds were used for the switching network, and miniature wire spring relays were used for switching transmission channels in the line and trunk circuits. Duplicate common-control circuits were provided optionally for increased reliability. Flexibility for growth and for the addition of service features was provided by interconnecting subsystem modules with cables and by inserting appropriate circuit packs.[15] Low-power semiconductor integrated circuits, the principal device components, were designed specifically for this system. These were beam-lead structures and were used with beam-lead transistors and diodes applied to thin-film integrated circuits to form hybrid integrated circuits. Circuit packs were formed by attaching hybrid integrated circuits and discrete components to printed wiring boards.[16]

A block diagram of the 810A system is shown in Fig. 13-26. The system performed successfully during field trials at the Bell Laboratories location in Denver, Colorado.[17]

In the early 1960s, the introduction of a new cord switchboard (the 608 PBX) must be seen as a significant development. Since it

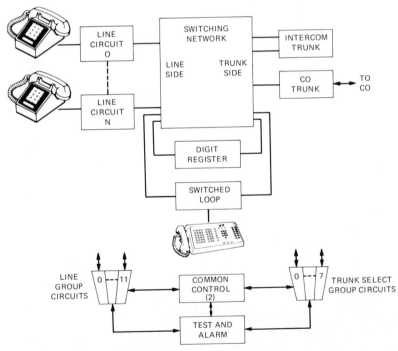

Fig. 13-26. Block diagram of the 810A PBX. While not commercially viable, this system added to experience and knowledge of electronics techniques. (*Conference Record, International Conference on Communications,* Montreal, Canada, June 1971.)

was the most advanced of its kind, its applicability to a wide range of size requirements might cause it to be the last to be needed. Then, during the decade, the refinement, strengthening, and broadening of the field of use of crossbar technology did much to meet customers' urgent service requirements, as did the continued injection of new life into that stubborn old contender, step-by-step. Certainly, the embellishment of dial systems with a wide assortment of new service features was a substantial step forward in customer service, albeit a difficult technological problem to solve at times. Further, the intensive development of electronic switching systems for customer use, as represented by the three solid-state systems evolved during the decade (the 800A and 810A PBXs and the No. 101 ESS), was perhaps far greater than was indicated by the extent of their application. Most important, these developments had demonstrated that the customer switching job could be done by electronic technology for large and small installations, and with a high degree of reliability and versatility.

2.5 The Seventies—Realization of the Electronic Promise

The advance of PBX technology in the 1960s can be viewed as the beginnings of the use of solid-state electronics and stored-program control. So, by 1970 the versatility, flexibility, and potential utility of electronic switching systems installed on the customer's premises was well accepted. What was needed were systems that could meet customers' requirements more economically. Of the two fundamental prior technologies, a hybrid type employing solid state electronics for "wired logic" common control of electromechanical switches was most successfully used with the 800A PBX. This technology appeared highly suitable for specific systems with limited size and service requirements. As a result, two such systems with modest requirements, the 801A and 805A, were introduced early in the 1970s. Later, this type of technology was extended to meet much larger and more complex service requirements, as seen in the PBX coded the 812A. However, the alternative technology of stored-program control of a solid state network, pioneered by the 101 ESS, subsequently resurfaced in the form of the highly sophisticated Customer Switching System (CSS) 201 type systems. The rebirth of this technology, fostered by an explosion in device technology, appeared to fulfill the electronic promise of low cost, small size, versatility, and performance.

Development began at Bell Laboratories in 1969 to respond to the need for a lower-cost PBX to provide basic PBX service in the range from 80 to 200 lines, a field then served by the step-by-step 701, the crossbar 757, and the 101 ESS. The objectives were to provide the series 100, 200, and 300 packages of services from 80 to 180 lines under heavy traffic conditions, and to 275 lines with light traffic. Plug-in circuit packs were to be used to simplify and expedite repair.

It was decided to extend the 800A system concept in the new design. This design approach would achieve a large degree of hardware commonality across the small end of the product line with resulting savings in production inventories and in the training and maintenance of field installation and repair forces. The new system was designated the 801A.[18]

At its introduction in 1971, the 801A provided service and features identical to those of the 800A, but for many more telephones. All the line circuits and trunk circuits, which in a typical installation account for about 80 percent of the plug-in circuitry, are identical to those in the 800A. The 801A retained the unique patch field, which permits adjusting the network traffic balance without changing the extension numbers. A system block diagram is presented in Fig. 13-27.

The features of the 801A were carefully designed to achieve the lowest possible price to the customer consistent with offering the full range of PBX services. Centrex service and sophisticated custom calling features, pioneered in No. 101 ESS, were not planned. A few features of special importance were offered. These included TOUCH-TONE® dialing, conference calling, tie trunks, and toll diversion.

Equipment advantages resulting from the use of electronic circuits and ferreed switches achieved a substantial step forward in packing density. A comparison of the 801A with the 757A shows the new system to require only about one-third the floor space for the average installation.

A significant advantage of the 801A system is its ability to grow in place. Growth is facilitated through the use of connectorized cabling.

New and improved techniques for installing and maintaining electronic PBXs were introduced with the 801A. Task-oriented Bell System Practices (user documents supplied for the equipment), an improved schematic drawing format, sequence charts, and total system preassembly and testing in the factory were all part of this program. Additional maintenance aids consisting of a System Status Indicator, Logic Probe, and Extender Board were introduced in 1974 after their utility was verified in a field trial.[19] The trial showed significant reduction in PBX trouble-clearing times, circuit pack replacement rates, and no-trouble-found rates, thereby lowering PBX annual costs.

The year 1971 was a notable one in the history of Bell System PBX development. The 801A and two additional new customer premises switching systems were introduced in that year alone. A thorough review of the product line in 1969 had indicated the need for a small,

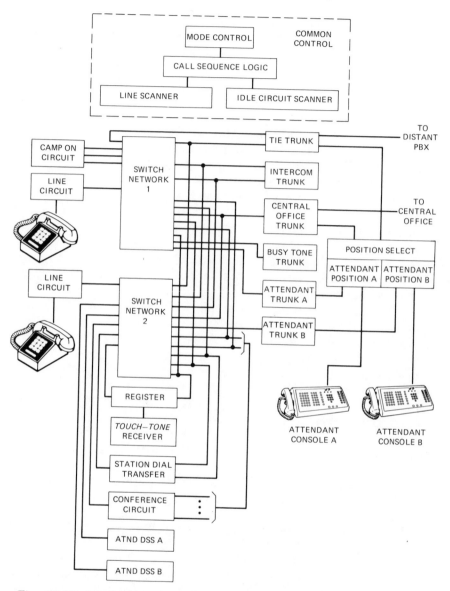

Fig. 13-27. Block diagram of the 801A PBX. Introduced in 1971, it provided the same features and services as the 800A, but for more telephones.

inexpensive dial PBX system. Based on this review, a decision was made to develop a small, dial PBX as soon as possible. This system, coded the 805A,[20] was to be economically attractive to those customers who were currently served by manual switchboards or key telephone systems. In common with the 800A and 801A, the 805A was a hybrid design of electronic common control and metallic contacts in the switching network. In this instance, however, the limited service objectives and the extremely low-cost economic objective resulted in the use of crossbar switching technology.

To achieve the tight economic objectives of the 805A, essentially only series 100 PBX service was provided. Some additional features were offered that were felt to be of special importance to small customers, including TOUCH-TONE calling, attendant transfer of both incoming and outgoing calls, and tie trunk, WATS, and foreign exchange service. The line-size objective was to be roughly competitive with the 756A. An ultimate capacity of 57 lines and 12 trunks was provided. (In-service data indicated that about 60 percent of dial PBX customers required fewer than 60 lines.) System design provided for ease of growth. Line ports could be increased from 19 to 37 or 57 ports, and external trunk ports could be increased from 8 to 12 ports. The system provided capacity for 40 lines at a traffic usage of 5.5 hundred call-seconds (CCS) per line or 57 lines at 3.6 CCS per line. As shown in Fig. 13-28, the design employs a single-stage, full-access network.

The 805A was housed in a single 756A-type cabinet with two frames providing a compact, attractive design that required less than 6 square feet of floor space. As with the earlier electronic systems, the 805A employed plug-in circuit packs for ease of growth, reuse, and simplified installation. Through careful circuit design, innovative multiple-purpose circuits, the use of a single-voltage power source and of readily available components, the 805A achieved its design objective of providing the lowest-cost alternative for basic dial service. The material price per line of the 805A was about two-thirds that of the 756A over the range from 20 to 57 lines.

A built-in test probe, trouble-locating procedures, and other aids were developed for improved maintenance performance. The field trial in September, 1971 was responsible for the increase in capacity from 37 to 57 lines.

The three new systems introduced into the PBX product line in 1971 all possessed different architectures as system designers strove to find new solutions to the perennial problem of the trade-off between cost and features. The two systems already described both employed plug-in electronic circuits while using different switching technologies. The designers of the third system eschewed electronics altogether and returned to the established relay technology for the line and trunk circuits. Switching design was based on established crossbar technology. The new system was to be known as the 770A.

The 770A was designed to have a lower material price than the 801A and to provide for an enhanced line range to 400 lines. As originally planned, series 100, 200, and 300 PBX and hotel/motel ser-

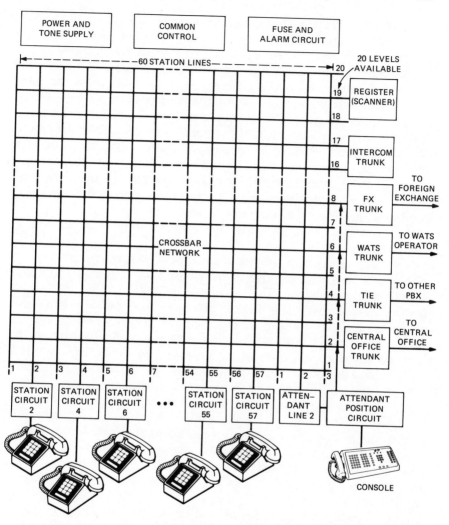

Fig. 13-28. Diagram of the small 805A PBX showing the single-stage, full-access network. An electronic system, the 805A served up to 57 ports.

vices were to be provided. The offering proved to be such a success with the telephone operating companies that additional service and features were developed.[21] These included the Centrex I and II services with their complements of advanced features.

The 770A was developed primarily by the Western Electric Company with assistance from Bell Laboratories. Western Electric recognized that the highly developed electromechanical technology could achieve a cost advantage over its electronic competitors for at least one more design cycle. Even though electronics was clearly the way to the future, the 770A enjoyed a number of years when it was the economic choice on a first-cost basis over comparable designs.

The 770A was designed into cabinets with three hinged gates per cabinet. Good circuit and switching densities were achieved with results that were the equivalent, on the basis of lines per square foot of floor space, to the 801A electronic system. The 770A used three stages of crossbar switching. Line ports were growable from 40 to 400 ports in increments of 40. Trunk ports were growable from 20 to 240 ports in increments of 20. Initially, the trunks were directly terminated on the attendant consoles. Later, switched loops were provided. Up to three attendant consoles were provided for regular service with a fourth available for special services, e.g., WATS. A system block diagram showing the switched loop configuration is shown in Fig. 13-29.

A single marker was provided using wire spring relays. One of the innovations was the use of distributed logic, which allowed a simple marker design. This attribute helped in achieving a low getting-started cost. The marker processed one call at a time and employed a lockout and preference circuit to handle simultaneous call originations. Another design feature that contributed to reduced installation expense and provided ready growth was the use of pluggable elements. All elements of the system were connectorized, and additions could be ordered with the necessary cables for reconfiguring the system with short downtime for installation.

A serious field problem developed in the failure of the system to achieve its objective for call-handling during the busy hour. Measurements showed that the assumed marker holding time was too short and, as a result, busy-hour call processing was reduced. To meet the design objective, the marker was redesigned for faster operation.

Other problems required remedial effort. The resulting changes created administrative problems in the field in coping with various vintages of the 770A design. Contrasted with its wide acceptance, the problems were relatively minor. By 1974 well over 100,000 lines had been shipped.

The low cost of the 770A had repercussions in other areas. A planned addition to the 800A/801A line of PBXs to meet the needs of the hotel/motel market was initiated in 1970. This addition, initially designated the 801H and later the 802A, was designed to provide full feature service to medium-size hotels or motels with 100 to 380 telephones.

In common with its earlier counterparts, the 802A employed ferreed switching and electronic common control. The network of three stages was designed to provide 2 CCS per line with a probabil-

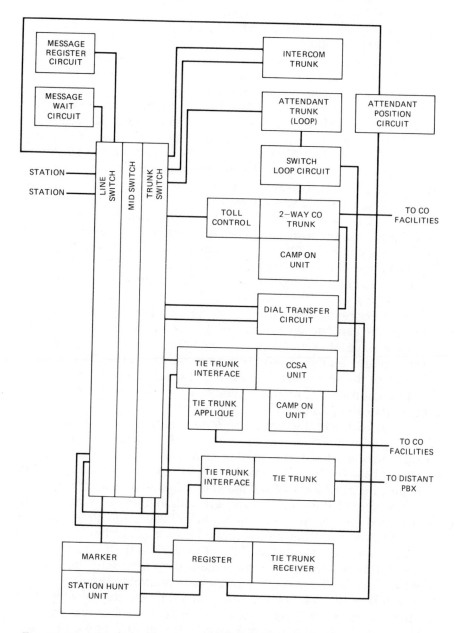

Fig. 13-29. The 770A crossbar PBX, designed by Western Electric for up to 400 lines. Over 13,000 systems were sold by 1970.

ity of blocking of 0.02. A total of 35 central office trunks could be made available, and the system was serviced by one or two attendant consoles. The maximum size configuration was accommodated in three 800A cabinets and thus achieved a compact design that saved customer floor space.

The 802A development design was completed in June 1971, but the decision was made shortly thereafter not to go into production. The 802A took advantage of the design of the 801A PBX, which resulted in a relatively short development time. Although the schedule and other objectives were met, the 770A design had also been completed. The 770A was less expensive than the 802A and was available with the needed hotel/motel features. A decision was reached, therefore, to serve the hotel/motel market with the 770A, and 802A manufacture was not initiated.

The need for a modern PBX using desk-top consoles and remote switching cabinets for the smaller line sizes was met with the 558A PBX, beginning in 1970. It was a manual switchboard serving up to 40 telephones and 10 lines or trunks to the central office. This small manual switchboard was among the last fully electromechanical PBXs introduced by Western Electric.[22]

The emerging design approach of the middle to late 1960s and in some of the early designs of the 1970s was based, as we have seen, on a marriage of electronics in the common-control and line and trunk circuits, and electromechanical switching. (The 770A and the 558A were the sole exceptions, using electromechanical devices for both functions.) This hybrid technology was destined to be pushed yet another step, albeit with modifications.

Having dealt with the small end of the product line, planners now directed their attention, even as the 770A, 801A, and 805A were being introduced, to the market above 400 lines. Data on the installed base in 1971 showed that about 5 percent of the total PBX systems, i.e., those above 400 lines, terminated over 4 million lines, or 33 percent of the total. Of these 4 million lines, 70 percent were terminated on systems with fewer than 10,000 lines. Projections of annual demand for this market ranged from a low of 100,000 lines in 1973 to over 200,000 lines in 1981. Thus, while the number of systems in this market is relatively small, they represent, because of their size, a significant fraction of the total market for lines.

The bulk of this market was being served by the step-by-step 701B system, at this time 20 years old. The 701B in a sense was the system by which all others were judged. The demise of step-by-step switching had been projected for years, yet in 1971 it was still very much alive.

The disadvantages of step-by-step were growing. Installation costs had been rising over the years. The large amount of floor space required represented additional, if hidden, costs compared to the compact cabinetized systems. Furthermore, the provision of modern services such as TOUCH-TONE calling was cumbersome and costly. Such limitations led to the need for a new system for the market above 400 lines. The objectives included provision of PBX series 100, 200, and 300 services and Centrex I and II service over the range from 400 to 2000 lines. TOUCH-TONE calling, CCSA (common control switching arrangements) service, and hotel/motel features were included in the list of optional features. The system was to be known as the 812A.[23] This system was a consequence of studying the 810A to reduce its costs. By drawing from portions of its design and using portions of other designs, the 812A emerged. The traffic objectives were to provide heavy traffic capability (6 CCS/line) at 1600 lines and medium traffic capability (4 CCS/line) at 2000 lines. A maximum call-processing rate of 8000 calls per hour was specified.

Designers chose to use the miniature crossbar switch for the network.[24] Crossbar technology for switching was the result of the economic goal of minimum first cost. The small switch was indicated by the need for a compact design and the advantage of a shorter operate time, which increased call-handling capacity. Although the miniature switch was more expensive, it required fewer frames and reduced cabling. Cost savings associated with these factors essentially offset the higher switch costs.

The requirement to optimize call-handling capacity led to an innovation in network architecture. Analysis showed that the call-processing objective could not be attained even with the faster operating characteristic of the miniature crossbar switch. It was necessary, therefore, to deload the main controller and its associated network and to transfer some functions to a second controller. The alternative selected provided a second network that switched attendant traffic and was controlled by a dedicated controller. These units were designated the Trunk Access Network, a two-stage crossbar network, and the Trunk Access Controller. The system architecture is indicated in the block diagram of Fig. 13-30.

Control functions in the 812A were divided between electronics and electromagnetic relays. The common-control functions, line supervisory circuits, the interface between common control and traffic circuits, and the automatic number identification circuit were all electronic. Relay circuits were used for central office trunks, direct inward dialing (DID) trunks, and common-control switching arrangement circuits. The electronic circuits made use of silicon integrated circuits of the diode-transistor family originally created for the 810A. This technology provided several advantages over the competitive transistor-resistor system of hybrid integrated circuits. The advantages included, most importantly, greater noise immun-

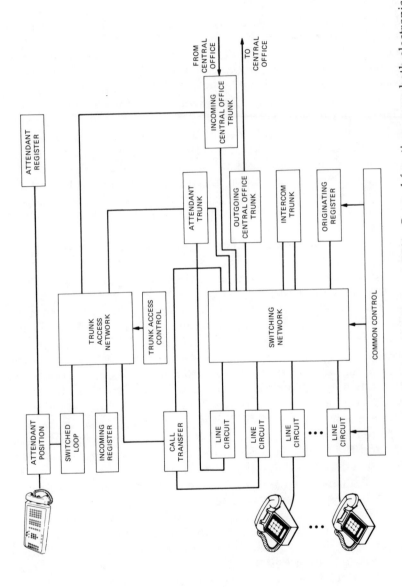

Fig. 13-30. Diagram of the 812A, a large size (up to 2000 lines) PBX. Control functions were both electronic and electromagnetic; the switching network used miniature crossbar switches.

ity, better reliability, and reduced size. The physical design of the 812A made use of the new frame and cabinet designs introduced with the 770A. All equipment modules were connectorized for rapid installation and growth.

The 812A was developed in less than two years by using much of the design of the 810A and "off-the-shelf" components. Even with the overlapping of design and manufacturing processes to meet the needs of operating companies and their customers, there was not a significant increase in field changes over other development projects.

A number of features insured the maintenance and reliability of the system. A maintenance panel provided a means for diagnosing faulty circuits, and a redundant common control could be added for high-reliability applications such as service for hospitals, police, or fire departments.

The goal of providing basic PBX and Centrex services at low cost was, in fact, achieved with the 812A. At the time of its introduction, and for several years thereafter, it was the lowest-priced system within its line range and capability.

The 812A development completed the design cycle initiated with the 800A six years earlier. While modern serving arrangements offering attractive, compact designs were now available or would soon be introduced, there were a number of concerns. Profitability, eroded by inflation, was a problem. After the FCC Carterfone decision of 1968, a number of non-Bell interconnect companies were formed to market PBX systems and other terminal equipment directly to customers. This marketing effort made some inroads into Bell System sales by 1971. Moreover, customers were looking for more capable systems. Large customers, particularly, were becoming increasingly sophisticated in their understanding of their total communication needs. As their costs rose, they looked for every improved means of controlling networks and calling patterns. These concerns led to requirements for data on PBX operations that greatly transcended traditional offerings.

The operating telephone companies also needed improvements in their equipment offerings. Of great interest here were more flexible systems that were easy to install, maintain, and administer. Rapid and inexpensive reconfiguration of systems to meet the requirements for a second installation was a long-sought but as yet unattained goal. Progress to this end would serve to reduce pressing requirements for new capital.

It was apparent that the demands of the market were not to be met by a piecemeal approach that tried to deal with individual problems in a fragmentary way. A more basic plan that dealt with the entire product line was required.

A task force was assembled late in 1971 to examine market requirements and economic and technical opportunities. In the technical area, two systems were studied in great detail, a remreed space-division system and an all-electronic, pulse-amplitude modulated, time-division system. The remreed switch, a refinement of the ferreed switch introduced with the No. 1 ESS into central offices, offered a four-to-one reduction in switching volume and reduced power requirements over its predecessor.[25] Both the space-division and time-division systems studied proposed stored-program electronic control. The task force found that the profitability problem should be addressed through lowered costs rather than increased prices. The maturing of the development of the silicon integrated circuit with its great reduction in per-unit component cost made this approach technologically attainable.

A product line approach was recommended with the initial vehicle serving the range from 40 to 400 lines. Later vehicles would be designed using as much common equipment as possible. Items manufactured in large quantities, such as line and trunk circuits, would be common, as would the equipment cabinets. Commonality has advantages in production economies and in minimizing inventories. It also tends to minimize craft training, improve installation, and lower the costs of maintenance.

For a number of reasons the task force proposed the time-division product line. The time-division system was estimated on the average to require only 80 percent of the total installed price of the remreed system. The price advantage was greatest for small-line-size machines where the economic factor was of greatest importance. For the small system, network traffic engineering is not required, which results in significant savings in telephone company engineering.

The initial system was designated the Customer Switching System 201S (CSS 201S) and was marketed as the DIMENSION* 400 PBX.[26,27] The S in 201S indicates small size, 40- to 400-line range. Development was initiated in mid-1973. The first shipment was scheduled for December 31, 1974, and this schedule was met. Service to the first customer began in January, 1975.

The CSS 201S was at the time the most sophisticated switching system ever placed on a customer's premises by the Bell System. Great care went into the design to ensure the reliability of the stored-program control and the electronic memory system. The main memory uses metal oxide semiconductor (MOS) silicon integrated circuits in a random access memory (RAM) configuration. Large-scale integration achieved a density of 4096 16-bit words of storage on one circuit pack. The volatile electronic memory is protected by a magnetic tape cartridge system. The tape contains the call-processing information as well as the particular customer pro-

---

*Registered trademark of AT&T Co.

cessing and maintenance information. Should a power failure occur, the system automatically reloads the electronic memory from the tape cartridge when power is restored. Short power interruptions do not affect the memory.

The CSS 201S comes in one- or two-cabinet versions. A single cabinet can serve up to 120 lines; two cabinets serve 360 lines with heavy traffic or 420 lines with light traffic. All line, trunk, and special circuits are fabricated on printed wiring boards that plug into carriers. One carrier in the system is always reserved for the common-control and memory circuits.

Traffic capacity of the system is 5 CCS per line at 360 lines and 3.5 CCS at 420 lines. About 2000 busy-hour calls can be processed. Engineering of the network is not required, since the system employs a single time-division network but with full access by all line and trunk circuits.

A technique of time-domain switching that makes use of active energy transfer was used in the design.[28] This innovation enjoys a number of advantages over the passive method used with the No. 101 ESS. Among these are small size, low-cost, and inexpensive 2-wire to 4-wire conversion. A very useful attribute of active energy transfer is the facility it provides for direct 3-way connections without the need for traffic engineered 3-way conference circuits.

Sampling of the analog signals for transmission on the time-division bus is at 16 kHz. This frequency, twice the required rate, was chosen for lower-cost, smaller-size filter circuits. Sixty-four time slots provide the network switching capacity of approximately 1700 call-seconds at 0.01 blocking.

System control is exercised by a special-purpose, 16-bit microprogrammed processor designed specifically for the CSS 201S. A digital distribution system controls the network by applying and removing time slot assignments and effects the scanning and distribution functions of supervision and signaling for the line and trunk circuits. The system block diagram shown in Fig. 13-31 illustrates these functions. Also shown there is the relationship of the processor to the memory, the alarm system, and the other peripherals, including the attendant console.

The initial software for the CSS 201 was developed in the remarkably short time of 18 months,[29] and in doing this, the software team made heavy use of prior Bell Laboratories developments. The program was written in EPL, a powerful high-level language developed for No. 4 ESS and the CSS 201. The availability of this language and its support services was a major factor in meeting the short development schedule.

Many features were made available with the initial offering, and the flexibility of the stored-program control eased the development of additional features. By early 1976, approximately 135 features

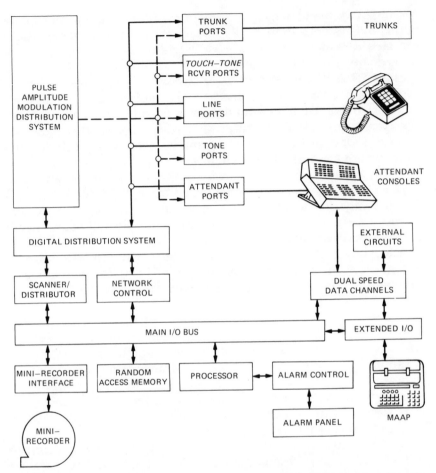

Fig. 13-31. The Customer Switching System (CSS) 201S, marketed as the DIMENSION 400 PBX. First placed in service in 1975, it was at that time the most sophisticated PBX ever offered by the Bell System.

were available, grouped into packages designed to meet the needs of specific industries.

The flexibility of the CSS 201 gives customers a measure of control over their communication systems that was previously not possible. Features such as outgoing trunk queuing and automatic route selection insure optimum use of expensive facilities. Station message detail recording provides call information down to the department or individual level for cost control and allocation. Other features, many available for the first time, increase the utility of the system.

Maintenance requirements received strong emphasis in the design. On-line diagnostics report failures on an alarm panel.

Alarms are divided into major and minor categories, with lamps to give craftspeople initial indications of the problem. Further diagnostics are provided through the Maintenance and Administration Panel (MAAP) to pinpoint troubles. Using MAAP, the craftsperson can enter more comprehensive diagnostic programs from the magnetic tape off-line memory into the electronic memory. With this powerful tool, and by merely following established maintenance procedures, the craftsperson can, in 95 percent of all cases, isolate troubles to a single printed wiring board. With these aids, trouble diagnosis and repair are straightforward and fast, and provide improved service to customers.

Using MAAP, the craftsperson can enter administrative changes in the system. New telephones can be added, and class of service changes can be made.

For efficiently centralizing certain operating functions for a number of CSS (DIMENSION) PBX installations, the Remote Maintenance Administration and Traffic System (RMATS) was introduced in April, 1977, in Minneapolis, Minnesota. A centralized processor, made up of DIMENSION piece-parts, provides dial-up, 300 baud, maintenance access for two operators. It also drives a printer to display traffic or other data.

With RMATS, a cadre of skilled personnel can remotely operate a MAAP and modify services to meet changing customer needs in many DIMENSION PBX installations without time-consuming visits to the customer's premises. RMATS also allows automatic gathering and analysis of traffic measurement data, which anticipates additions and reconfigurations. In this way, efficient operation can be continued while accommodating to the changing demands for service by DIMENSION PBX customers. By January, 1979, 100 RMATS were serving DIMENSION PBX customers. Each RMATS is able to handle up to 150 DIMENSION installations.[30]

Two additional innovations were introduced with the CSS 201. An all-electronic console provides new features not previously available to attendants. An alphanumeric indicator displays much more call information detail than can be shown with indicator lamps. The confusion attending multiple flash rates on lamps was reduced when a total of five lamps were placed on switched loops to indicate call states. The technology used in the console design is all electronic. Communication with the PBX is over a high-speed data link, which greatly minimizes the size of the cable required to interconnect the console and the PBX. A major innovation was the introduction of an electronic key system called the DIMENSION Custom Telephone Service, or DCTS. This system provides a wide range of custom calling and key system features at the touch of a button.

Here again, communication with the sets is over a data link. The cable to the sets requires only three pairs of conductors instead of the usual 25-pair cable used with conventional key sets. The goal of slim cables for key sets was achieved with this development.

The second member of the DIMENSION PBX product line, the CSS 201VS (for Very Small), was coded the DIMENSION PBX 100 and was introduced in mid-1975. This system is limited to 100 lines and has reduced memory; therefore, it has less feature capability than the CSS 201S. It was designed for the smaller customer whose feature needs do not justify the CSS 201S system. Following the CSS 201S and the CSS 201VS, development continued to extend the product line to larger sizes. The CSS 201L (DIMENSION 2000 and DIMENSION CUSTOM) was subsequently introduced in July 1976 for sizes from 650 to 7200 lines.

The development of the all-electronic CSS 201 system has realized the objectives of the designers of the early 1960s. With this system, the advantages of stored-program control have enabled its designers to attain flexible, highly capable service with the small size, improved maintenance, and low acoustical noise of the electronic art. The advance of electronic technology has overcome the cost limitations that hampered the early efforts.

III. TECHNOLOGY OF MAJOR PBX SERVICE INNOVATIONS

In our account of the evolution of PBX systems in section II, we emphasized the technology of the basic switching functions and the shaping of this technology to provide efficient service over the entire range of customer sizes. Reserved for this section is a more comprehensive discussion of the characteristics and evolution of innovations in service features, together with their application and influence on system technology. For the purpose of this section, service features are defined as those variations in the basic service, switching processes, and customer interfaces that tend to improve speed, convenience, usefulness, or general attractiveness.

3.1 Centrex

A striking example of the influence of new service concepts on system technology is illustrated by Centrex. The origin of Centrex (see Chapter 9, sections 6.2 and 7.3, and Chapter 11, section 1.4), whose functions are more or less taken for granted today by those familiar with the art, is of interest. Fostered by the Direct Distance Dialing (DDD) program, undoubtedly one of the most dramatic events of telephone technology, Centrex required solving many problems and it stimulated new technical processes, not only in PBX systems but also in central office systems. Table 13-2 briefly summarizes how Centrex service compares with PBX service.

Centrex service had a profound effect on switching technology. For example, inward traffic routed by Direct Inward Dialing (DID) required new functions and equipment in common-control central offices as well as in common-control PBXs. (Curiously, step-by-step central offices and PBXs that for other reasons were becoming outmoded could be adapted relatively simply to DID.) Identified Outward Dialing (IOD), while easily possible where reliance was placed on verbal self-identification by the user of the calling telephone, required complex automatic identification schemes for PBX equip-

Table 13-2. Centrex and PBX Service–Similarities and Differences.

Type of Traffic	Method of Switching Calls	
	Dial PBX Service	Centrex Service
Inward Local and Toll	Completed to extension by PBX attendant	Dialed directly to extension (can be completed by attendant if desired)
Outward Local	Extension user dials 9 and usually dials remaining digits directly	Same
Outward Toll and Extended Area or Multi-unit Calls	Established by attendant or extension user dials 9 and then remaining digits directly–selected line groups may be diverted on toll calls to an attendant for completion	Extension user dials 9 and dials remaining digits directly–extension number identified for charge purposes at local or tandem offices
Intercom	2-4 digits dialed directly by extension user	2-7 digits dialed directly by extension user

ment and new interfaces with the central office AMA equipment. Again, where central office equipment was used for performing all functions without the use of PBX equipment, extensive modifications were needed to coordinate with the attendant function, even though the DID and automatic IOD (AIOD) functions could be handled in stride.

First, however, why was Centrex needed? In the early 1950s, direct distance dialing was rapidly getting under way (see Chapter 8). DDD opened new possibilities for customers to dial their calls directly and rapidly, not only in the local exchange area but to any telephone in the nation accessed by suitably equipped toll facilities. PBX customers, who accounted for a large percentage of business calls, were quick to realize the potential communication possibilities of this service. At the time, it was estimated that more than 25 percent of all switched calls originated or terminated in PBX systems, and more than 50 percent of long distance calls involved PBX systems at one or both ends. DDD therefore offered fast communication for the customer's PBX telephones; however, there was no way to allocate and bill charges against particular PBX extensions making DDD calls. Many PBX customers wanted this capability for their internal accounting procedures, such as for segregating departmental costs or for determining nonbusiness telephone usage. With DDD, the customer's alternatives were to allow unrestricted access to the DDD network (which was done for some telephones, such as those in executive offices) or to restrict access to the central office trunks reached by dialing "9," and thus cause local and toll calls to be handled by the attendant. The latter alternative obviously defeated the dial 9 procedure and required greater attendant effort and expense. A further alternative was to permit access to the central office trunks upon dialing 9; local calls would be allowed to proceed but extra-charge calls would be diverted back to the attendant. Calls would be diverted by the use of equipment that would recognize the codes dialed after access was gained to the trunk. Diversion at several charge levels was considered possible at the time, and some methods were implemented sporadically. For example, diversion on the basis of toll only was available in step-by-step central offices (on dialed codes such as 0, 110, or 211).

Panel and No. 1 crossbar were modified in 1953 to turn back (divert) to the attendant all multi-unit and toll calls above a fixed charge level; but it was not possible for PBX customers served by these offices to have diverting arrangements that would turn back calls at charge levels according to their own individual requirements. A further alternative was to provide individual equipment arrangements at the PBX associated with the central office trunks.

These arrangements could, through a system of wired code analysis and programmed decisions, divert to the attendant whatever dialed codes the customer wished to restrict. At the time equipment was available from North Electric to accomplish these functions. All of these methods were explored and used to some extent. Systems wherein calls could be dialed directly, identified, and charged precisely are preferred to those that do not take maximum advantage of the universal availability of telecommunications.

While this type of thinking evolved concerning the origination of PBX calls, DDD was also causing a revival of thought on the manner of handling inward calls to PBX telephones. For example, prior to DDD the calling party was content to reach the called telephone by first reaching the attendant at the distant PBX and asking to reach the desired telephone by name or extension number. It will be recalled that, over the years, one of the primary reasons for justifying PBX operations was that inward calls to a business could be efficiently distributed to extensions by an attendant who was knowledgeable regarding personnel and business functions. But with DDD the feeling grew that the originating party would like to dial the terminating PBX extension directly, thereby reducing attendant work load. The call should be just like a non-PBX call. This feeling was supported by the changing character of many business operations, wherein companies with branches in many cities developed large volumes of station-to-station calling requirements among branches. Still other reasons for calling PBX extensions directly came about where a business concern's specific departments were known or advertised to the public, such as in the case of banks, insurance companies, and government agencies.

Putting both of these objectives together—direct outward dialing (with station identification) and direct inward dialing to PBX extensions—seemed to make sense. Accordingly, an intercompany committee of Bell Labs and AT&T engineers was formed to investigate the economics and feasibility of this type of operation and to recommend plans for proceeding if it were found to be feasible. (The PBX at AT&T headquarters, 195 Broadway in New York City, was converted to direct inward dialing in September 1956, thereby providing first-hand experience with this service while this study was under way).

The committee's report, issued in 1957, concluded that the function of direct dialing to and from PBX extensions should indeed be developed, and that such a service would have significant potential benefits to the customer and to the Bell System. The customer would benefit from faster and more accurate service, promotion of lower-cost station-to-station calling, accounting savings through the recording of PBX extension numbers on outgoing calls, and reduction of switchboards and attendants. The Bell System would benefit by efficient use of toll operators, reduction of unproductive circuit-holding times, and increased stimulation of the use of DDD.

Three basic principles were proposed in the 1957 report, principles which shaped the course of the service and the development requirements for the future. First, it was suggested that the telephone extension should be reached on an inward call and identified on an outward call by the same digits, and that these should be within the same numbering plan as applied to non-PBX telephones. That is, it was to be a seven-digit number (preceded, of course, by the area code where necessary), consisting of a three-digit office code prefix and four station digits. This contrasted with the normal PBX seven-digit directory number followed by two to four station digits passed verbally to the attendant. The significance of this was twofold: (a) PBX extension numbers were to be treated by DDD systems like any other telephone numbers that required registration, interpretation, and identification for charge purposes; and (b) the digits had to be compatible with the DDD numbering plan, and the numbering plan had to accommodate not only the numbers of non-PBX telephones but also whatever additional numbers resulted from the new service.

The second principle recommended in the 1957 report was that the direct inward dialing and identified outward dialing functions should be treated as a package. That is, one function should not be provided without the other, since the seven-digit number allocations were somewhat precious and should be used only for the combined service, not dissipated by fractionalizing the service.

The third principle was that verbal identification of outgoing calls by centralized AMA (CAMA) operators would be satisfactory until such time as automatic identified outward dialing (AIOD) could be developed. This was consistent with the DDD system plan, wherein telephones homing on central offices not equipped with automatic message accounting or automatic number identification would be identified by CAMA operators. In the case of this new service it meant, however, that all extra-charge calls from PBXs arranged for identified outward dialing would need to be routed through a CAMA office, until AIOD became available to coordinate with local AMA (LAMA) offices.

One further important concept emerged from the 1957 committee. This was that, since direct dialing to and from PBX extensions resulted in service similar to that obtained by telephones having central office service, PBX extensions might be served directly by central office equipment if certain basic PBX requirements were met. Such requirements included coordinated attendant service, access to tie trunks and to special services, and four-digit intercom dialing. Studies by Bell Laboratories development engineers indicated this was indeed feasible with No. 5 crossbar equipment, and so the groundwork was laid for what was later to become No. 5 Centrex. Over the years a major premise was that the cost of switching PBX extension traffic on the customer's premises was largely justified by the saving of transmission conductors between the customer's location and the central office. It is interesting to note that technological advances now permitted this tradition to be challenged by centralized switching.

With the objectives and principles established, the telephone companies proceeded to implement and inaugurate some forms of the service. At the outset, these efforts were limited by the technology, but not sufficiently to prevent an evaluation of the long-term benefits and requirements. The technological limits faced in getting the service started were as follows.

1. Direct Inward Dialing (DID) was only possible with step-by-step PBXs. This was because an inward train of step-by-step selectors and connectors could fairly easily be established by the use of existing switches. Common-control type PBXs were not designed to accept and register digits received over central office trunks. This was no hardship at the time, since the Bell System's only common-control PBXs, the 755 and 756, served small-size customers who were not considered candidates for DID. It did portend, however, that if the technology was to progress beyond step-by-step, future common-control systems should be able to handle DID.

2. Step-by-step central offices could transmit DID digits to a step-by-step PBX only by trunking from selector levels. In effect, this shifted some of the central office switching functions from the central office to the PBX.

3. Common-control central offices such as panel, No. 1 and No. 5 crossbar could not transmit DID digits to a PBX. This was because all digits were used up in reaching the line terminal occupied by the PBX central office trunk. This was in fact no different from the situation wherein a step-by-step central office connector terminal was dialed, except that in the step-by-step case the dialing train could be intercepted at a selector level as mentioned above.

4. However (and quite importantly), where common-control networks were prevalent, it was possible to pulse DID digits directly to a PBX from a crossbar tandem or a No. 5 crossbar arranged for tandem switching. In effect, this was like trunking from tandem to a terminating local office.

5. As previously mentioned, no methods existed for automatically identifying PBX extensions initiating outward calls, nor for

transmitting and integrating this information with central office charge records.

Many of these limits were removed as the technology advanced, or they were circumvented entirely by using No. 5 crossbar for PBX switching.

One of the first commercial installations of direct inward dialing was by Diamond State Telephone Company in 1958 for the headquarters PBX of the E. I. DuPont Company at Wilmington, Delaware.[31] This consisted of a rearrangement of the switches of the existing 701 PBX (see Fig. 13-32) and of the central office trunking, as shown in Fig. 13-33. Seven-digit numbers were assigned to the PBX extensions, and an entire central office code was reserved for the PBX, which served about 5,000 lines. While the purpose of this system was to provide direct inward dialing to the extensions, cord switchboards were retained for incoming calls dialed to the PBX number listed in the telephone directory. These calls would originate from outside callers who did not know the number of the particular extension to call. Another purpose of the switchboard was to respond to a recall by a user (whether direct inward dialed or originally completed by the attendant) in order to transfer the call to a

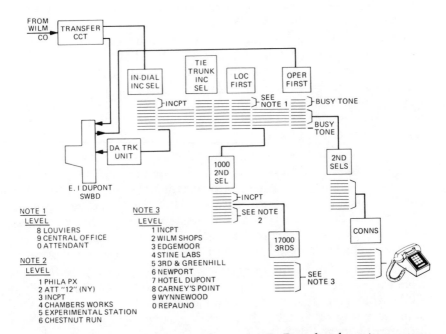

Fig. 13-32. Trunk rearrangements at the DuPont headquarters accommodate a 1958 implementation of 701 PBX Centrex service. (*AIEE Transactions*, Vol. 78, November 1979.)

different telephone. This need to transfer a DID call required development of a function in the incoming trunk which responded to a flash (momentary on-hook) by the user, and caused the trunk to signal and provide access to an attendant. Other uses of the switchboards were to complete special traffic such as outgoing calls from restricted extensions, calls requiring assistance, and tie-trunk or other special service calls.

In the same year, 1958, the Mountain States Telephone Company installed a No. 5 crossbar system to serve both central office main telephones and the extensions of the Air Force Academy in Colorado Springs.[32] All of these telephones were assigned seven-digit numbers. Inward calls to Academy extensions were switched to them directly when their seven-digit numbers were dialed; intercom calls between extensions were made by dialing the last four

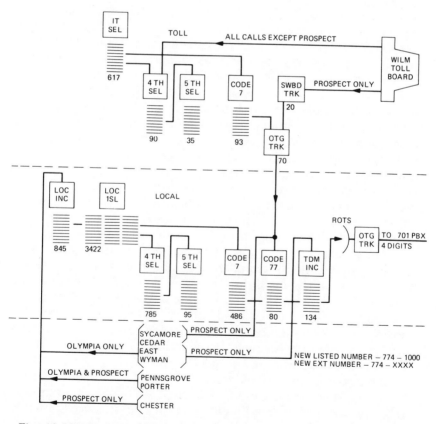

Fig. 13-33. Corresponding central office trunk rearrangements at Wilmington, Delaware accommodate the 1958 Centrex service at DuPont headquarters. (*AIEE Transactions*, Vol. 78, November 1979.)

digits. Outgoing charge calls could be dialed directly by Academy users, and the charges were recorded by the AMA system of the No. 5 crossbar unit (which was also arranged for DDD). Attendant service was provided by cord switchboards, switched into the connections when required. In early 1959, similar offices were installed to serve the Dow Chemical Co. at Midland, Michigan, and the headquarters building of the New York Telephone Co. Service of a similar type was provided later by several other operating companies.

In 1960 the name Centrex came into use for the service previously termed "Direct Dialing to and from PBX extensions." Intended to define a service offering, the term was applicable whether implemented by customer premises systems of the PBX type or by central office No. 5 crossbar equipment. When furnished by PBX type equipment on the customer's premises, the service was called Centrex-CU; when furnished by No. 5 central office equipment it was called Centrex-CO. The term Centrex itself derived from plans to use centralized 701 PBXs to serve a number of customers, and also possibly from the use of centralized No. 5 crossbar equipment. Even though most Centrex-CU installations consisted of individual switching systems installed on the customer's premises, the term Centrex persisted for many years.

The year 1960 saw the completion of design of an early standard implementation of Centrex-CU service using 701B PBX equipment.[33] This design differed from previous step-by-step implementations in that cord switchboards were replaced by pushbutton cordless attendant positions, and dial pulse senders were introduced so that attendants could complete incoming and outgoing calls by operating pushbuttons. The cordless position performed the same major service function as the cord switchboards described previously for the 1958 DuPont installation. The positions were accessed by the trunks through call distributing switches, with the connecting loops switched in when the attendant was needed. An interesting aspect of this switched-loop attendant position was that the service features and interface with the attendant (key operations and lamp signals) were derived from those being developed for the 101 ESS (see above, section 2.4) and used later by the No. 5 crossbar system and 757 PBX. The attendant positions of the first 701 system of this type furnished Centrex service to the Irving Trust Company in New York City and are shown in Fig. 13-34.

The No. 5 crossbar installations of 1958 and 1959 mentioned previously could not serve more than a single PBX. Customer group is perhaps a better term than PBX to use at this point, since the service was now to be called Centrex. This, of course, was economical only when the customer group consisted of several thousand lines.

Fig. 13-34. Centrex attendants at the Irving Trust Company, New York City, using cordless equipment developed for use with the 701 PBX. (*AIEE Transactions*, Vol. 80, November 1961.)

Other limitations of the early installations were that cord switchboards had to be used for the non-DID traffic and that DID calls could not be transferred from the originally called extension to another when desired. Removing these limitations required solving some fundamental switching problems, and development was undertaken for this purpose.[34]

The foremost problem was how to serve more than one customer group. This was perhaps most important because of the economy of using the No. 5 crossbar system over a broad market, for both large and small customers. The basic No. 5 crossbar functions when switching station-to-station, station-to-trunk, and trunk-to-station traffic were about the same for Centrex as for central office operation. But the specific technical question was how to use a common switching vehicle for a plurality of customer groups, each of which had a number of extensions and its own attendant positions, and in each of which traffic was to be freely switched. At the same time, it was necessary to make sure that four-digit intercom calls were confined within the customer group and that attendants served traffic only to and from their own group of extensions. The latter was required whether the traffic was an outgoing assistance call, a non-DID call, or a DID call requiring transfer. The problem was solved by using the No. 5 crossbar class of service feature (associated with the line location on the line link frame) to identify the extension telephones belonging to a particular customer group. As in normal No. 5 crossbar operation, these identifying marks were passed to the marker and registers when needed. The class-of-service capacity was expanded from 60 to 100 classes, and this information was now used to identify and ascertain that intercom and outgoing assistance calls were confined to a group. In the case of incoming calls the class of service (identity of the group) was stored in the incoming central office trunk. This was the key to the solution since the central office trunks were common to all customer groups. Fig. 11-6 illustrates how the identification feature worked to confine a call to the proper attendant and also how the transfer feature operated.

The third principal limitation of the earlier installations—the restriction to cord switchboards—was removed by adapting the cordless attendant position developed for other PBX-type systems to the No. 5 crossbar system. The position was switched through the line link frame and trunk link frame when required, also shown in Fig. 13-34.

The first installation of No. 5 crossbar equipment of this type was the Wabash office in Chicago in June 1961. It served six customers, ranging from 300 to 1700 lines for a total of almost 10,000 lines. About 85 percent of all inward traffic was directly dialed, and cordless attendant positions were used by all customers. The number of cordless positions was far fewer than the number of switchboards that would have been required without direct in and out dialing. The largest customer required only eight positions, and some required only two.

By the end of 1962, nearly 50 No. 5 crossbar systems were in service. Some served large customers such as O'Hare and Idlewild (later named J. F. Kennedy) airports, but most provided Centrex-CO service to multicustomer groups. Also, by year-end about one hundred 701-type systems were providing Centrex-CU service, mostly to individual customers. The service was to continue to grow at a rapid rate, but more technological improvements were needed.

Until 1962, customer requirements for Centrex-CU could be implemented only by the 701 PBX version of Centrex. Moreover, this equipment could be used only in areas where the serving central office was step-by-step, as previously explained, or in panel and crossbar areas where DID could be provided by crossbar tandem or by No. 5 crossbar arranged for tandem operation. Service by tandem equipment was at best economical only where a high volume of DID traffic was to be switched. Also, to this point, Centrex-CU outward charge calls could only be identified verbally via CAMA operators. This placed constraints on the routing of direct outward dialed traffic. During the next five years, most of these constraints were eliminated.

Early in 1963, No. 5 crossbar was modified so that it could function as a terminating central office for calls destined for Centrex-CU service. Thus, the efficiency of exchange networks employing tandem and local offices could be preserved, while at the same time Centrex-CU service could be provided more efficiently. For this innovation, invention was once again required.

To understand what was done, let us review a few of the fundamentals of central office switching. In the simplest case, the first three digits dialed by a customer (the office-code digits) cause the originating office to select, and connect the customer to, a trunk to the desired terminating office. When that office is ready, the remaining four digits dialed by the customer are transmitted to it. These cause the terminating office to connect the trunk to the called line, which could be an individual main-station telephone or a trunk to a PBX. Ordinarily, that is the end of the task of transmitting digits. But with Centrex-CU, these last four digits are needed for an additional purpose: to cause the switching equipment on the customer's premises to respond and connect the incoming trunk to a particular desired telephone. Obviously, a new process was required.

In the new process, called Line Link Pulsing (LLP), trunks on the line link frame to the Centrex-CU system were given access to dial pulse senders. Any of the four-digit numbers assigned to the Centrex-CU telephones would cause the marker to select an idle trunk to the customer's system in the usual manner but, additionally, a dial pulse sender was linked to the trunk and the marker then passed to it the particular four digits involved. The sender then proceeded to transmit the digits to the Centrex system using conventional dial pulse methods. The Centrex system responded according to its mode—by operating selectors and connectors if step-by-step, or by registering the digits if common control (also see Chapter 11, section 1.5).

The No. 5 crossbar system thus opened the door to an increasing application of the Centrex-CU service, not only as implemented by the 701 system but also by subsequently developed systems using new technology. For example, the 101 ESS initial trial installation at New Brunswick in 1963 was coupled to its serving No. 5 central office via LLP, as was the first commercial installation at Cocoa Beach. Later, the 757 crossbar system arranged for Centrex-CU service interfaced with No. 5 offices via LLP. Toward the end of the decade, No. 1 crossbar was similarly arranged for LLP. In 1966 a further improvement was made in the No. 5 crossbar interface with the No. 101 ESS which resulted in the marker directly passing the extension telephone digits to the 101 ESS control unit, thus eliminating the need for the LLP senders.

By the mid-1960s, most of the objectives outlined in the planning program of the late 1950s had been realized: the full development of No. 5 crossbar for Centrex-CO operation, the development in step-by-step PBXs of standard Centrex-CU features, and the embodiment of these features in the new 101 ESS and 757 crossbar system. Inward dialing methods from step-by-step central offices, crossbar tandem, and No. 5 tandem had been refined, and the problems of direct inward dialing to a Centrex-CU from a local crossbar office had been solved. Also, the solution had been applied to No. 5 crossbar and planned for No. 1 crossbar. There remained but one goal to achieve—automatic identification of a Centrex-CU telephone making an outward charge call, and the integration of the telephone number identification with the central office AMA records. The 101 ESS, as previously noted, included Automatic Identified Outward Dialing (AIOD) in its initial design. However, the 101 ESS was being applied on a limited basis, and the large-scale demand for AIOD arose in connection with step-by-step PBXs furnishing Centrex-CU service.

The solution to the AIOD problem had taken longer because of the need for a proper balance between overall system plans, compatibility of switching systems, technology, and cost. It was a problem to coordinate several types of PBX systems with a variety of central office systems having different types of charge-recording systems (see Chapter 11, section 1.5).

As shown in Fig. 13-35, a process was desired wherein telephone number identification information from 701, 757, and 101 ESS systems could be transferred automatically to No. 1 or No. 5 crossbar offices and integrated there with either the AMA process or with the Automatic Number Identification (ANI) process. Furthermore, a compatible interface was required with the ANI systems of panel and step-by-step central offices. These requirements represented perhaps a classic problem in communications systems engineering.

To understand the significance of the problem, let us consider first the problem of interfacing a Centrex-CU system with an AMA-type local crossbar office. Normally, in a crossbar-type central office, a main telephone line is first identified by its location on the line link frame. When AMA is provided, the line location number is delivered to a device called a transverter. The transverter consults a translator to obtain the calling directory number corresponding to the equipment location, after which it proceeds to furnish this, along with other pertinent information, to the AMA recorder. With Centrex-CU AIOD, the trunk between the PBX and the central office has its location on the central office line link frame identified in the

CAMA office. The principal functions of an ANI system are to identify the seven-digit number of the main telephone and to transmit same manner, but subsequent to this an important difference occurs: while the translation from equipment number to directory number is fixed for main telephone lines and always comes out the same on every call (once the directory number is assigned), the translation from the Centrex trunk equipment number to calling telephone number is different on practically every call. Thus, two basic requirements arise for a system of Centrex-CU telephone number identification: first, information must be furnished to the central office from the Centrex switcher to correlate the central office trunk with the number of the telephone to which it is connected at the time, and second, the AMA transverter must be able to obtain a translation from trunk to telephone number on every call when required, just as it did when it required a translation of main telephone line location to directory number. With these requirements in mind, let us now consider the requirements for interfacing with a central office ANI system.

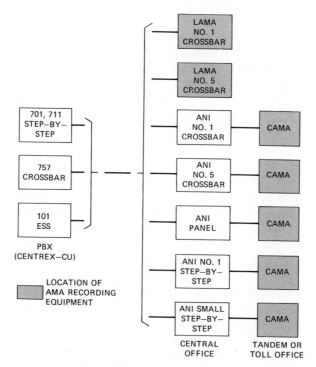

Fig. 13-35. Automatic identification of Centrex-CU telephones represented a classic problem of telecommunications systems compatibility, here the compatibility among Centrex-CU systems (left) and central office and AMA system (right).

As mentioned earlier in this history, ANI is used in a central office when, for network efficiency, charges are recorded at a subsequent this to the CAMA office over the trunk used on the call. Since the details of this process are covered elsewhere, it will be sufficient to note that a central office device known as an out-pulser, which receives the identification of the main telephone and pulses it to the CAMA office, is the key interface for the AIOD process. As in the case of the AMA transverter, two similar requirements for AIOD exist when interfacing with the ANI system. First, information must be furnished to the central office from the PBX to correlate the Centrex telephone number with the line (PBX trunk) number identified in the central office, and second, the out-pulser must be able to obtain this information on demand, so that the seven-digit Centrex telephone number can be transmitted to the CAMA office.

Fig. 13-36 shows how these requirements were met through the use of a plan that was uniformly applicable to local offices equipped with either AMA or ANI. The plan was also applicable not only to 701 step-by-step and 757 crossbar systems furnishing Centrex-CU service, but was compatible with the AIOD plan previously developed for the 101 ESS. Its operation in simplified form was as follows.

Consider first the PBX at the left side of the figure. When a telephone was connected to a trunk through the PBX, a new identifier at the PBX determined the trunk and telephone line numbers, then transmitted them over the data trunk to a new station identification store in the central office. (A plurality of PBXs had access to this store.) Eight digits were transmitted—four to identify the trunk and four to identify the PBX extension. The central office station information store had a separate memory location for each PBX trunk (from all PBXs served), and the extension number was stored in this location. When AMA recording was desired, the PBX trunk location on the line link frame (or the trunk number in ANI-equipped offices) was transmitted via the transverter (or out-pulser) and translator connector to the station information store. This unit returned, from its trunk location memory slot, the number of the PBX telephone. This number was for AMA recording at the local office or for CAMA recording via the out-pulser. As mentioned, the procedure was compatible with the 101 ESS control unit shown at the right of the diagram, which could respond to the trunk number and return the telephone number, both of which were stored in the call status store of the No. 101 ESS.[35]

Details of the solid-state technology developed for these functions are beyond the scope of this history, but some of the highlights may be of interest. Trunks and lines were identified at the PBX by a solid state system wherein trunk and telephone extension numbers were written and stored in a ferrite core matrix memory device, as shown

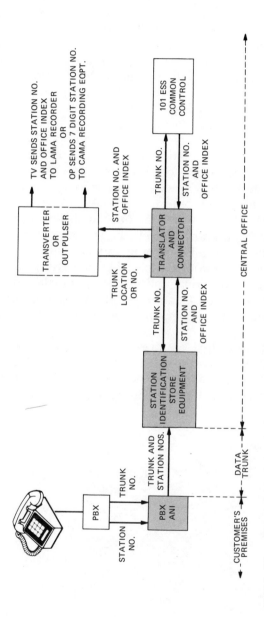

Fig. 13-36. Plan for automatic identified outward dialing, applicable to local offices equipped with AMA or ANI.

in Fig. 13-37. These were then read out and the numbers transmitted to the central office store by frequency-shift carrier at a rate of 737 bits per second. At the station information store, the telephone number was stored in the appropriate trunk location of a solid state memory. Initially designed for a capacity of 1800 trunks to take care of large concentrations of Centrex-CU installations,[36] an alternative store was later designed for more economical service in situations where only a few hundred trunks were to be accommodated.[37]

The first commercial installation of the AIOD system was placed in service in December 1965 for the Prudential Life Insurance Company in Newark, New Jersey (see Fig. 13-38). The system was coordinated with a large 701-type PBX system of 3500 lines and 100 trunks, which was served by a No. 1 crossbar system equipped with ANI for CAMA recording. The completion of this development rounded out the line of facilities described for implementing Centrex-CU service and helped to continue the growth of this service.

Beginning in 1968 the No. 1 ESS was arranged to provide Centrex-CO service. Demonstrating once again the versatility and flexibility of stored-program control, the system provided Centrex service, in addition to local switching service, with a minimum of additional facilities. Additional No. 1 ESS call and program stores provided necessary additional call memory, translation, and new program instructions—the Centrex generic program, and were all that were needed to implement the fundamental Centrex service and features.

The attendant-controlled features and switched loop functions required innovation, even though the cordless attendant positions were virtually the same as those used for the No. 5 crossbar and Centrex-CU systems (so that the operating procedures were uni-

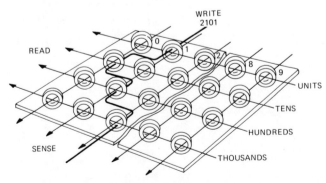

Fig. 13-37. Ferrite core matrix at the PBX, used to identify trunks and lines. The "write" wire shown here as an example could be used to enter the number 2101.

Fig. 13-38. First commercial PBX-ANI installation at Newark, New Jersey being checked by New Jersey Bell craftsman, Jack Walsh.

form from the customer's point of view). These features presented new interface and information requirements; therefore, new hardware and control programs were needed (see Chapter 9, sections 6.2 and 7.3).

As previously indicated, the attendant control processes involve both display and control functions. With cordless attendant equipment, these functions are performed by lamp signals and keys. (For example, lamp signals display the occurrence, identity, assignment and status of calls entering or processed at the position; keys control the selection of calls requiring attention and also control their disposition.) Since the attendant's positions were on the customer's premises, remote from the switching equipment, some means was required to transfer information in both directions—display toward the position and control toward the central office equipment. A two-way data link between the customer equipment and the central office was developed for this purpose. Display information was encoded at the central office and transmitted over the data link to the customer's location, where it was decoded and assigned to operate a specific group of ferreeds at the customer interface. The ferreeds registered and passed the current lamp states to the attendant's position. In the reverse direction, key signals were intercepted at the customer interface, encoded, and transmitted to the central office using a 5-bit binary code. These arrangements are shown in Fig. 13-39, wherein the customer interface is labeled "Console cabinet" and the central office interface "Centrex data link." The

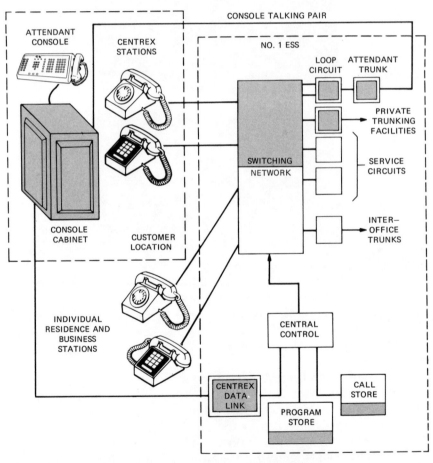

Fig. 13-39. Arrangements developed to interface a Centrex console (upper left) with a No. 1 ESS (right). Stored-program control made this application relatively easy.

figure also shows the direct connection of Centrex telephones to the central equipment, as was done with the No. 5 crossbar Centrex, and the No. 1 ESS elements involved in the provision of Centrex service.[38] The adaptation of the No. 1 ESS to Centrex service was an important step toward making this service more widely available, particularly in view of future use of electronic switching.

By 1970, over two million Centrex telephones were being served, fairly well divided between the Centrex-CO and Centrex-CU modes of operation. The decision made a dozen years earlier to proceed with the concept of Centrex service, and to develop facilities to offer it in two basic forms, were well founded.

The preceding has indicated that Centrex was provided either within a PBX on customer premises (CTX-CU) or from central office switching systems: No. 5 crossbar, No. 1 ESS or No. 2 ESS (CTX-CO). This led to business features being retariffed from a service rather than a hardware point of view.

With the available technology and a new tariff basis, a central office could simulate PBX functions. This possibility of using No. 1 ESS to provide PBX-CO was studied by Bell Labs, AT&T, and Pacific Northwest Bell in the early 1970s. It appeared feasible and attractive for small business customers near the serving central office, and a field trial was conducted in Seattle, Washington in 1972, using No. 1 ESS as the host system.

In the meantime, Bell Labs engineers had developed analytical tools for a more complete and accurate assessment of the total costs of providing vertical services in stored-program control systems. This analysis, when applied to PBX-CO, revealed additional costs, such as the cost of ESS completing two calls for each incoming connection (the first to the customer's PBX attendant and the second to the desired extension within the customer's office). The additional costs returned the economic balance in favor of PBX service using equipment on the customer's premises (PBX-CU), and PBX-CO was dropped.

3.2 PBX Switchboard Innovations

Although the development of the Centrex mode of operation resulted in substantially reducing the number of auxiliary switchboards required for Centrex customer installations, switchboards were still needed to handle the residual assistance calls, which were often complex in character. Furthermore, as mentioned previously, while over two million Centrex lines were in service by the 1970s, there were still many times this number with PBX service requiring dial PBX auxiliary boards or switchboards for manual service only. For a variety of reasons, customers do not always prefer Centrex. Often their switching requirements are not large enough to realize attendant savings, and sometimes their business operations do not fit in with the Centrex mode. Consequently, the demand continued for modern attendant switchboards. Over the years, therefore, Bell Laboratories has developed new technology to keep pace with, and often anticipate, the changing needs of this demand.

In the numerous prior references relating switchboards to specific PBX systems, the reader has seen the trend from manual-only systems, wherein the switchboard was the only switching vehicle, to dial PBX and later Centrex systems, wherein the switchboard was used as an auxiliary to the dial switches. An idea of the distribution of traffic handled at switchboards with these different modes is shown in Fig. 13-40. While this major trend was under way, a supplementary trend was taking place—the use of desk-mounted, cordless, key-operated switching cabinets instead of the familiar cord-type switchboards. We will delve a little into the theory of these arrangements to shed light on their evolution and technology.

The image of the cord switchboard is perhaps as familiar as that of the telephone instrument itself. In a cord switchboard such as the one shown in Fig. 13-11, all telephone lines and trunks are wired to jacks in the face of the board, and the attendant connects the desired two jacks together by plugging in the ends of a pair of cords selected from a group emerging from the cord shelf. Each cord circuit provides ringing, supervision and access to the attendant's telephone via associated relays, lamps, and keys. By contrast, in the cordless board used for manual service, all lines and trunks were wired to keys. By operating the proper key, the attendant connects the required two circuits via a link that functions more or less as the cord circuit. Cordless boards were introduced for small manual PBX

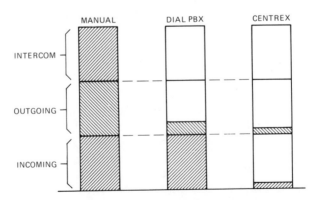

Fig. 13-40. Types of traffic at manual, dial, and Centrex PBXs. Shaded areas represent calls handled by attendants. Unshaded areas represent machine-handling of calls.

service in 1907. (For additional information about these early systems, see the first volume of this History series, subtitled *The Early Years: 1875–1925*, pages 674–677.) Improved in 1928 and later in 1951, cordless boards continued to be manufactured into the mid-1960s. Because of the fixed key matrix of lines, trunks, and links, cordless systems of this type tend to become inefficient and bulky as the number of circuits increases; hence they were confined to a maximum capacity of 12 lines and five trunks. However, customers in the range below 12 lines must have considered these improved boards attractive, since more than 80,000 of them were manufactured. Nevertheless, these systems finally yielded in the mid-sixties to key telephone system technology.

The cordless switchboard was tried as a dial auxiliary position in 1926 in association with the 740A. Here the scope of its control was not limited to the very small size because much of the traffic (all intra and considerable outgoing) was dialed directly by the telephone user, thus removing it from the switchboard. Furthermore, there no longer was a need for a fixed key matrix of lines, trunks, and links at the switchboard—only an appearance of trunks that could be directed by the attendant to connect to the proper line via the switching network (see *The Early Years: 1875–1925*, Fig. 6-110, p. 689). Therefore it was possible to contain such a cordless switchboard in a desk-top cabinet not much different physically from the manual 12-line system, while using it as an auxiliary position for a dial PBX serving nearly 100 lines, such as the 740A. It served with a single attendant position for some years with good success, but the principle was not extended to larger systems, and, in fact, retrogressed somewhat in the 1930s. As previously mentioned, cordless operation was abandoned on subsequent 740-type systems (see above, sections 2.1 and 2.3) because of what might appear to be minor operating deficiencies. For example, the attendant had to handle an incoming call without a prior indication of busy. Also, on an outgoing call the user had to hang up and be called back. These deficiencies, along with perhaps the traditional preference for cord switchboards, caused the pendulum to swing away from cordless operation.

As related above, in section 2.3, it was not until thirty years later that the introduction of the new small crossbar 756A system brought with it a new cordless attendant position, as shown in Fig. 13-10. Tuned more closely to the prevailing business attitudes and office decor, with slanted keyboard and pushbutton operation, this system was reinforced by several new service features. Among these, one of the most important was "camp-on." This feature considerably increased the acceptance of cordless operation since the attendant now had a busy indication before dialing to the called party. In fact, it capitalized on the busy condition: the attendant can now ask the caller whether he or she wishes to wait and, if so, the attendant releases from the connection, leaving the incoming trunk camped-on (continuously monitoring) the busy line. This function was performed via the sleeve circuits so that, of course, there was no violation of privacy. When the telephone became idle, ringing started automatically, and the waiting call was cut through without further action by the attendant.

The camp-on feature was so successful in increasing the attendant's efficiency and improving service that it was included in all subsequent PBX systems. A few years later an improvement was added to it to indicate to the called telephone, by means of a short tone pulse, that it was being camped-on, i.e., that a call was waiting. If, perhaps expecting an important call, the user chose to hang up on the existing call, the user would be rung immediately by the waiting call and cut through to it when he or she answered.

Another improvement in operating efficiency introduced with the 756A PBX permitted an incoming trunk from the central office to distinguish between a switchhook flash (to call the attendant) and a disconnect when the user hangs up. Named "delayed through supervision," it was important because it allowed the user to recall the attendant to transfer a call, yet relieved the attendant of any action if the telephone disconnected.

These improved features were followed a few years later by a Direct Station Selection (DSS) feature which permitted the attendant to call a telephone extension merely by depressing a single button. If the telephone were busy, the button would be lighted. The attendant could report a busy condition to the caller without further action or, if the caller wished to wait, the camp-on feature could be activated merely by depressing the DSS button. A field of such buttons, one per station, was arranged in a coordinate array. The attendant could easily identify the called number, and the digits of the called number were efficiently conveyed to the switching system.[39] This feature was economically applicable to register-type systems, such as the 756A, as shown in Fig. 13-41. Field trials were conducted in conjunction with the 756A system in 1960, and later the DSS feature was standardized for use with this and subsequent systems. The feature further solidified the use of cordless dial auxiliary switchboards.

Before 1960, the technology of cordless positions was generally limited to the smaller systems of 100 lines or fewer, where one attendant could adequately handle the dial auxiliary traffic. This followed from the fact that each of the central office trunks, as well as trunks to the attendant, required a key and lamp appearance on the position. Terminating the additional trunks required by larger systems tended to make the position too large and often could result in more traffic than a single attendant could handle satisfactorily. Multipling positions together was a partial solution (and indeed was done later for some systems) but was inadequate for large systems ranging from several hundred to several thousand lines.

The solution to the large system problem was to employ call distributing switches between the trunks and the cordless positions. This technique opened up the use of the cordless switchboards to the largest systems. The relationship of this method (now called "switched-loop" operation) to the previous method (called "direct-trunk") and to cord switchboard auxiliary positions is shown on Fig. 13-42.

With the switched-looped method, a call from one of a group of trunks enters the distributor and is switched to one of a group of "loops" terminating on the position keys. The call generally remains connected to the loop only so long as the attendant is

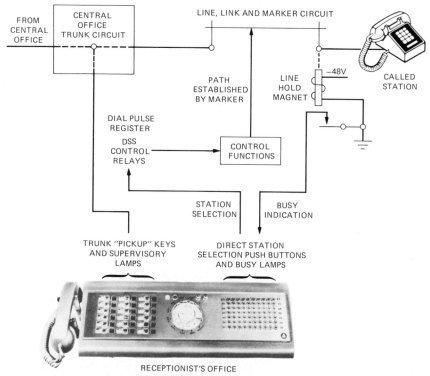

Fig. 13-41. The direct station selection feature (field of buttons on right of console). Attendant pushes unlighted button for connection to a telephone extension. Pushing a lighted button (line busy) causes the incoming call to camp on the line until it is free.

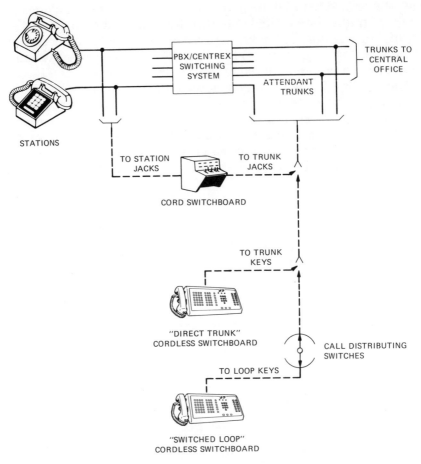

STATIONS

TO STATION JACKS   TO TRUNK JACKS

CORD SWITCHBOARD

TO TRUNK KEYS

"DIRECT TRUNK" CORDLESS SWITCHBOARD

CALL DISTRIBUTING SWITCHES

TO LOOP KEYS

"SWITCHED LOOP" CORDLESS SWITCHBOARD

Fig. 13-42. Principles using call distributing switches to associate cord and cordless switchboards with PBX and Centrex systems. Such methods allowed the use of cordless switchboards with large systems.

needed. For example, incoming calls release from the loop when the called telephone answers. Outgoing calls release when the attendant releases. (The attendant has the option to hold any call to the loop.) Since, under these conditions, the holding time of the loop is only a fraction of the holding time of the trunk, a large number of trunks can be concentrated to a relatively small number of loops. Further, the high efficiency of call distribution permits the use of minimum numbers of positions with effective teamwork.

The switchboard art has, of course, much more complex call-handling subtleties and traffic engineering problems than might be inferred from the previous brief description, so the reader may wish to refer to the technical literature for more detail.[40] Only enough has been indicated here to show the nature and interrelationships of the technology as it evolved. For example, the switched-loop concept grew out of the 101 ESS studies being made in the latter half of the 1950s, for it was an objective of this system from the beginning to serve large as well as small customers with cordless auxiliary switch-boards. The switch unit of the 101 ESS system, in addition to connecting lines and trunks, also served as the switching medium for the trunk-to-loop connections (with time-division switching this was relatively simple). The programmed section of the system handled the call distribution logic. This was really a matter of coupling a prior art to a new technology in a new service environment. For example, the No. 4 toll crossbar system of the early 1940s employed switched-in positions for handling incoming ringdown traffic.

As mentioned above in section 3.1, the call distributing switched-loop method was applied in 1960 to the large step-by-step Centrex systems, and in 1961 to the No. 5 crossbar version of Centrex. The distribution function was implemented by conventional step-by-step switches in the former and by the regular line link/trunk link frames in the latter. The method was subsequently applied to the 757A, No. 1 ESS Centrex, and 810A systems and to later systems requiring a plurality of cordless attendant switchboards.

Throughout this evolution in switching technology—direct-trunk boards for small systems, camp-on, DSS, switched-loop boards for the larger systems—the appearance and human engineering aspects were continuously being improved, as shown in Figs. 13-10, 13-16, and 13-25. Toward the end of the 1960s a more modern-appearing model, shown in Fig. 13-43, was developed to provide an attractive and easily accessible array of control and DSS buttons.

The common application of the cordless switchboard to a number of switching vehicles to provide the same kinds of service focused attention on the need for consistent operating practices. Thus, the customer should see operating features as independent of the serving system. Accordingly, in the late 1950s, uniform standards were defined for a "universal" cordless switchboard. These standards shaped the course of detailed development in the associated systems and did much to stabilize the operating features. As is usually the case, they later yielded, and rightly so, to new technology. But it seemed fairly certain that the cordless idea, which had started as a manual system innovation, had been placed upon firm ground.

3.3 Innovations in Switching Features

Three additional characteristics of PBX and Centrex service form the basis of a distinct group of service features: (1) the use of a unique numbering plan wherein the directing digit 9 completely

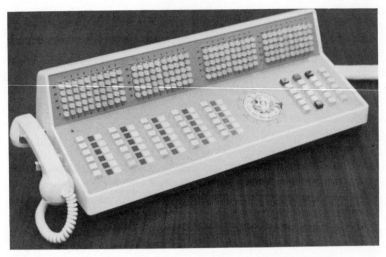

Fig. 13-43. Cordless switchboard designed in the late 1960s to provide many new services in an attractive, human-engineered console.

separates the external from the internal codes, (2) the concentration of telephones having a strong community of interest, and (3) the use of a more or less dedicated switching system to serve these concentrations. While these features are not unique to PBX systems, PBX customers are the predominant users.

Early PBX systems contained few features beyond those needed for the fundamental switching capabilities. However, those few are of interest when related to the features of modern systems. For example, the Western Electric "system for large buildings" in 1887 (see *The Early Years: 1875–1925*, p. 663) provided a somewhat crude capability for adding a third party to a connection. The No. 2 PBX of 1903 (*The Early Years*, p. 670) contained a "hold" feature which permitted retaining a call on one line in order to answer or originate a call on another line. At the turn of the century, "night service" was recognized as a necessary feature and was provided in all of the then standard PBXs. Night service permits selected extensions to receive or originate calls when the switchboard is unattended, by pre-connecting central office trunks to these extensions. It remains as a feature of modern PBXs. It is of interest, too, that the special traffic requirements of hotel PBXs were recognized in the No. 3 PBX of 1903.

No special features beyond night service were included in the No. 4 PBX, a standard that persisted until 1915. However, the use of tie trunks was included in the engineering specifications when the 550-type PBX was introduced in that year. Tie trunks, which are private lines between PBXs reserved for their exclusive use, have over the years been an important communication alternative to the message network. It is possible that tie trunks gradually came into use prior to 1915, evolving from off-premises multistation lines connected to PBXs, such as those shown in the *New York World* PBX of 1897, illustrated on page 665 of *The Early Years*.

With the adoption of dial PBXs by the Bell System around 1917, several new features were introduced. Most of these features were probably made necessary by the automatic mode of operation, since the equivalent services could be given, or were not necessary, with manual operation. The Bell System's first standard dial PBX, the 700C, contained in the early 1920s the features listed and described in Table 13-3. (The features marked with asterisks were carry-overs from the semistandard 700A PBX of 1916.)

Except for the introduction of cordless switchboards in small dial systems in 1926, as previously mentioned, the special features of the 700C, with refinements made in subsequent systems, satisfied customer desires for more than a quarter century, until the 1950s. At that time there was a revival of interest in special features, perhaps as an aspect of the increasing use of and reliance on, telecommunications by American business.

While the less significant advances of the mid-1950s were those accompanying the introduction of the 756A and the cordless attendant innovations, outlined above in section 3.2, there were also features of some interest. For example, in 1954, just prior to the introduction of the 756, a novel service was made available which permitted PBX extension users to dial through a PBX to gain access to a customer-owned recording machine for the purpose of dictating memoranda, letters, etc. After gaining access, the person dictating could start or stop the machine, make corrections, secure playback, etc., by dialing distinctive control digits.[41] Over and above its ability to provide efficient stenographic service for many business organizations, the system probably represented one of the first applications of the use of regular telephones to control business machines via the telephone system.

During the latter 1950s the United States "took to the road" in ever-increasing numbers, and the hotel/motel business expanded enormously. Conventional PBX systems, used in considerable numbers for guest communications in hotels and motels, were usually tailored to the type and size of the hostelry. Among the new features introduced was one that permitted reaching frequently called numbers (such as the registration desk, valet, room service, etc.) by dialing only a single digit. Also introduced in 1958 was a "message-waiting" feature, which is probably familiar to most trav-

Table 13-3. Special Service Features, 700C PBX (1922).

Feature	Technology
Station Hunting*	A "hunting group" consisted of a group of 10 telephone extensions on adjacent connector terminals. A call to the first extension would hunt to the first idle extension in the group. Accomplished with 4-wire connector banks and hunting connector switch logic.
Intercept on Vacant Terminal*	A call to an unassigned number was routed to an attendant. Accomplished by wiring vacant connector bank terminals to trunks to the switchboard.
Dial 9 Restriction*	Access to the central office is denied to designated telephone extensions. A fourth wire, cross-connected at the line switch, encounters a contact at the first selector, which operates at the ninth level, causing denial tone to be sent to the extension.
Through Dialing	Attendant would normally dial outgoing calls. However, a key could be operated to permit the extension user to dial directly.
Through Supervision	The attendant normally controlled the release of the central office trunk. When the through dialing key was operated, the extension user could control release.
Dial Tie Lines	Tie lines were reached through the switches, but attendant at far end was required to complete connection. Dialing could be accomplished over dial-repeating tie lines.

*Features carried over from the 700A PBX (1916).

Table 13-3–*Continued*

Feature	Technology
Code Call	Attendant could dial codes to cause gongs or lamps to alert called individual (such as in department stores). Called individual could dial back to source of call.
Conference Calling	A limited number of extensions could be connected together via a conference bridge at the switchboard.

elers as the lamp on the telephone set, which flashes if there is a message at the desk. The essence of both of these features was extreme simplicity at low cost, an objective met by innovative circuitry.[42]

Later, in 1962, a special PBX designated 761A was developed to provide telephone service integrated with new features, at a cost that would permit economically attractive rates to the small motels that predominated at the time. The control position contained message-waiting keys, and message registers to tally local calls. This position is shown in Fig. 13-44.[43]

The emergence of solid state technology, of course, created possibilities for new service features, and in the development of these features there was considerable cross-fertilization between ESS and PBX work. Some of the resulting innovations stemmed directly from the new technology, and others were more in the nature of by-products:

Call Transfer, Consultation and Add-On. The objective of this group of features was to add another party to a call, be able to consult with this party in private while holding the party to the original call, and then either return to the original call or transfer it to the party consulted. Though such service was not new, details were perfected and implemented by new technology. As mentioned above in section 3.3, the holding feature and the ability to add a third party to a connection were implemented to some extent around the turn of the century. It is believed that European dial systems had also employed a "dial transfer" feature. The action was initiated by the internal party—that is, by the user of the PBX extension. The user flashed the switchhook, obtained dial tone, and dialed the number

Fig. 13-44. Attendant's position for the 761A PBX, developed in 1962 for small motels. It offered direct station selection, message-waiting lamps, and registers to tally local calls.

of another internal party. The switchhook flash placed the external party on "hold" and insured privacy when the second internal party answered. If the first internal party hung up, the call was transferred to the second party. Because of its stored programs and memory capabilities it was possible to implement these features in the 101 ESS on all types of calls: incoming, outgoing, and intra-PBX. Under these conditions, the procedure was subsequently named "call transfer-all calls" and the add-on function "three-way calling." Complete capabilities of this type were not economical in electromechanical systems so that add-on, consultation, and transfer functions were limited to incoming central office calls. The logic for these features was included in the circuits for each incoming trunk. In these applications the features were named "call transfer-individual" with the consultation hold and add-on function being understood to apply to incoming central office calls only.

Call Forwarding Features. The purpose of "call forwarding" would seem to be self-evident, particularly by analogy to the function of forwarding mail. Three types of call forwarding features were developed. The first and more comprehensive type permitted an extension user to instruct the system in advance where to forward (or reroute) incoming calls destined for the user's telephone. The user does this by dialing an access code to identify the feature, followed by the digits of the telephone to which the call should be forwarded. Obviously, the flexibility of this feature required substantial memory capabilities and call processing. Therefore it was economically feasible only in stored-program systems such as the No. 1 and 101 ESS. Two other simpler versions were developed to permit direct inward dialed calls to be transferred to the attendant if the called telephone was busy or did not answer. Named "call forwarding-busy line" and "call forwarding-don't answer," these features were economically applicable to electromechanical and electronic systems since the rerouting was always to the same destination and was independent of the called telephone number. The reswitching could be done in the incoming trunk with only a single logic function for each feature.

Call Hold and Call Pickup. These features were intended for economies when the customer wanted to use them instead of key telephone features. Call hold permitted a user to hold any call by dialing a code and thus free the telephone to originate another call if desired. It could be used in conjunction with "call pickup," which allowed a user to answer a call directed to another telephone in the user's predetermined group by dialing a special code. The memory and processing functions made these features economical only in stored-program systems. A similar but much simpler feature permitted a call on an incoming trunk to be answered by any telephone during periods when the switchboard was not covered. Called "trunk answering from any station," it was an alternative to night service, and its simple logic requirements permitted economical application to any type of system.

Speed Calling. This feature, an abbreviated dialing concept, permitted calling an internal PBX telephone by dialing an access digit followed by a single digit. Ten-digit codes could be compressed into three-digit codes by dialing an access code followed by two identifying digits. A limited list of such numbers could be supplied to each telephone. Obviously requiring memory and call-processing functions, the features were economic only in stored-program systems such as the No. 1 and No. 101 ESS.

Conference Calling. Conference connections heretofore were set up by the attendants in a PBX or by central office operators. Dial conference features became available with stored-program control systems based business services.

As the 1960s began, the service and technological trends launched in the 1950s were becoming clearly defined, and in many instances were well under way. In summary, these included the following.

(1) the improvement of step-by-step PBX systems, development of new crossbar PBX systems (756 and 757), and the development of the 101 solid-state system

(2) the development of Centrex service technology using both PBX equipment and central office systems

(3) the emphasis and improvement of cordless attendant technology and its coordination with Centrex and the new system developments

(4) the development of new service features such as camp-on, DSS, hotel features, and those sophisticated features growing out of the solid-state switching work.

It seemed appropriate, as the 1960s began, to review the interaction of these programs and to effect whatever further integration was required from both technical and service standpoints. Accordingly, a broad program of evaluation and goal-setting was undertaken jointly by AT&T and Bell Laboratories. In this undertaking, the service and technological abilities of the concepts, features, and systems developed up to this point were delineated, together with their economic aspects; and the views of the telephone companies—and through them their customers—were sought with respect to engineering considerations and marketability. Completed in 1961, this survey led to an extensive program to develop and standardize a variety of features in the principal systems of the time.

Subsequently, AT&T decided that these features should be offered to customers via a series of "communication service packages" and options in which the service features were to operate in a consistent manner, independent of the serving system. The "service package" concept was primarily a marketing approach. It did not directly influence the technology except to reduce some inconsistencies between features of different systems. Basically, five service packages were formulated. The first, series 100, contained basic PBX features. Series 200 included these and, in addition, features aiding attendant operation. Series 300 added telephone set capabilities to the previous packages. Two service packages related to Centrex were established. The first of these was similar to the basic PBX package but included also the direct in-and-out dialing capabilities of Centrex. To the second package was added the additional telephone set features of the series 300 package.

Specific features of the communication service packages are shown in Table 13-4. In addition, various options were offered where the capabilities of the serving systems permitted. These included the more or less long-standing conventional features such as tie lines, code calling, access to paging equipment, telephone-

Table 13-4. Features of Communication Service Packages.

Features	PBX Packages			Centrex Packages	
	Series 100	Series 200	Series 300	Centrex I	Centrex II
Attendant's Position (Console)	X	X	X	X	X
Direct Outward Dialing	X	X	X	X	X
Station-to-Station Calling	X	X	X	X	X
Station Hunting	X	X	X	X	X
Call Transfer-Attendant	X	X	X	X	X
Restriction from Outgoing Calls	X	X	X	X	X
Power Failure Transfer	X	X	X	X	X
Night Service	X	X	X	X	X
Direct-in-Dialing				X	X
Identified Outward Toll Dialing				X	X
Attendant DSS with Busy Lamp Field		X	X	O	O
Attendant Camp-on		X	X	O	O
Indication of Camp-on		X	X	O	O
Attendant Conference	O	X	X	O	O
Call Transfer-Individual			X		X
Consultation Hold			X		X
Add On			X		X
Trunk Answer from Any Station			X		X

X-Package Feature
O-Optional

dial-controlled dictation, etc. Also offered were new service features such as the new call-forwarding features of various types, three-way calling, call hold and call pickup, and speed calling.[44] Except for the busy line and don't answer types of call forwarding, the new services mentioned were implemented only in the stored-program electronic switching systems.

Subsequent to the formulation of the service package concepts, other features were developed, such as the previously mentioned main/satellite features of the 101 ESS. Also implemented in this decade were the PBX aspects of the broad system programs of TOUCH-TONE® calling and PICTUREPHONE® service. These developments are discussed in the next section.

3.4 TOUCH-TONE Calling and PICTUREPHONE Visual Telephone Service

Aimed at providing a simple, rapid, and attractive pushbutton dialing method for telephones of all types, TOUCH-TONE calling presented an exercise in signaling technology, the solutions to which were similar for the PBX and the central office. Likewise, PICTUREPHONE visual telephone service, aimed at providing a new communications dimension, needed extraordinary means to switch bandwidths several orders of magnitude greater than previously contemplated for voice. Again, the central office and PBX solutions were similar so far as the basic function was concerned. This similarity of solutions is perhaps not surprising in view of the overall system approach, in which the telephone sets, signal format, and switching principles were standardized.

Despite the similarities, what made the PBX problem different, and increasingly interesting, was the need for a graceful merger of these new services and those enhanced PBX systems and services, developed over the years, which now caused PBX service to differ from main telephone service. These differences led to such questions as: How were the attendant features to be handled? What about tie trunk and foreign exchange traffic, and the control of special terminals such as telephone dictation, etc? Indeed, a formidable question of judgment was the extent to which the new service capabilities should be applied to the proliferation of PBX systems.

After experimental trials of ac pushbutton signaling in 1948 had proved the technical practicability of this technique, the concept was shelved until better technologies could be developed. During this period, the idea of providing a form of pushbutton dialing for PBXs continued to be passed around with the thought that such a service would be particularly attractive to business customers. For example, an early form of the 756 PBX contained pushbutton dialing (using dc pulsing for inward calls handled by the attendant), and plans of the mid-1950s contemplated pushbutton dialing for telephones served by the 101 ESS. As noted above in section 3.1, an installation of a 701B Centrex-CU in 1960 permitted pushbutton dialing by the attendant of incoming and outgoing calls using a dc keyset interfacing with dial pulse senders. But it was not until the broad systems plan formulated in the closing years of the 1950s that ideas began to solidify for developing this service, now called TOUCH-TONE calling, for all PBX customers.

In simplest terms, TOUCH-TONE calling meant that PBX switching systems must respond to digits which were frequency encoded instead of the traditional dc serially encoded digits. The approach was ordered by adopting as axiomatic the principles that the signal format and power standards would be identical for all types of telephones; i.e., the signal generators and key sets would be the same for PBX extensions and attendants' positions as for telephones served directly by the central office. At the outset, other signaling methods, both dc and ac, offered some good possibilities when the PBX alone was considered (and were indeed used in some European approaches). But the overall system benefited by the common station approach. Other "ground rules" adopted were that the implementation of TOUCH-TONE service in PBXs would assume that they would generally be served by central offices equipped for TOUCH-TONE service, and that TOUCH-TONE would be implemented only in the principal PBXs then in production or planned. Planning proceeded on this basis with the major hurdle, low cost, left as a challenge to the ingenuity of the designer.

As discussed, the major PBXs in use or planned in the early 1960s were step-by-step types (701 and 740) and crossbar common-control types (756 and 757). The 755, a common-control system which had extensive prior application, was initially considered for TOUCH-TONE service but the idea was dropped later in anticipation of its manufacturing demise (see above, section 2.4). The common-control solution was fairly simple. As shown on Fig. 13-45(a), a TOUCH-TONE receiver was added to each of the registers in the 756 and 757 systems where it accepted TOUCH-TONE digits, converted them to a one-out-of-ten dc code, and held them in existing storage relays in the register. The same register could also receive dial pulse digits. This was necessary since, in some cases, only a fraction of the total telephones might be equipped for TOUCH-TONE signaling. The register, whether primed by TOUCH-TONE or by dial-equipped telephones, proceeded to interact with the marker in the normal manner to establish calls to other telephones terminated on the PBX, or to central office trunks or to special terminals. With the central office converted to TOUCH-TONE signaling, the PBX extension user needed only to press the "9" button and then, using the

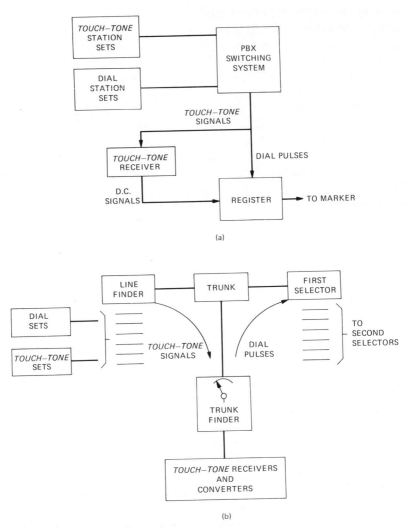

Fig. 13-45. Modifications of PBXs of the 1960s to incorporate TOUCH-TONE calling: (a) crossbar and (b) step-by-step systems.

same key set and after receiving dial tone, pulse the area and/or exchange digits directly to the central office. Similarly, the attendant pulsed directing digits to the register using a keyset.

The solution for step-by-step PBX systems required more equipment. Multifrequency digits had to be received, and these digits had to be converted to serial-pulsed dc digits to operate the succeeding step-by-step switches. As in common-control PBXs, only one digit was required to reach a central office trunk, after which the remaining digits required by the central office were pulsed directly from the TOUCH-TONE telephone. For station-to-station calls, two to four TOUCH-TONE digits required conversion to dc pulses, depending on the size of the PBX. Fig. 13-45(b) shows how the conversion equipment was accessed via special trunks connected between the line finders (only those on which TOUCH-TONE telephones were terminated) and first selectors. Since both dial pulse and TOUCH-TONE telephones might be terminated on the same line finder group, a converter might be called in on a call by a dial-equipped telephone. The converter would recognize this, repeat the first digit to the selector and then release, cutting the trunk through to the selector for ensuing digits. This arrangement was similar to that evolved for the step-by-step central office.[45]

Despite continuous dial system innovation, as noted often in this history, manual cord and cordless switchboards continued to be used by many customers, some for manual PBX service only, others for auxiliary positions with dial systems. In order that such switchboards might be used for TOUCH-TONE signaling to a central office or to an associated TOUCH-TONE-equipped dial PBX, they needed to be arranged for TOUCH-TONE service. This required only the addition of a TOUCH-TONE keyset which, with appropriate modifications, could be associated with the cord circuits. As is often the case, fitting tomorrow's plans into today's plant represents a formidable problem, and the switchboard section of the existing PBX plant was no exception. The Bell System has long recognized the need to solve these problems, so designs were made available to modify a number of types of manual boards then in use to permit TOUCH-TONE calling where desired by the customer. Along the same lines, to make TOUCH-TONE calling fully usable under all conditions, receiver-converter devices were designed for recorded telephone dictation and code-calling trunks.

As mentioned earlier, a major hurdle in the provision of TOUCH-TONE calling in PBXs was the attainment of marketable costs. Conversion costs were technically assessable to the telephones having TOUCH-TONE service. For a given technology, the minimum cost level of common-control equipment of this type is often determined by the minimum number of circuits needed for reliable service, a cost which remains constant even though the number of telephones served becomes very small. Under these conditions, the cost per telephone becomes quite high. This effect is uncomfortable in PBXs, particularly since large numbers of them are small switching systems to begin with (fewer than 200 stations) and TOUCH-TONE service might be desired for only a fraction of the lines served by the system. In consequence, the cost per line for serving just a few of the lines of a step-by-step PBX was many times greater than the cost per line when all telephones were TOUCH-TONE. Similar cost relationships existed in common-control PBXs but were not so drastic because of the lesser amount of conversion equipment needed.

To reduce the impact of these effects, a solid-state converter was designed for the step-by-step systems. This provided, in addition to pulse conversion, memory capacity for 13 digits, which permitted its use for tie-line signaling as well as control of the PBX switches. This solid-state converter was the first application of solid-state technology to step-by-step PBX. It was soon followed by the solid-state AIOD system mentioned above in section 3.1. Another step was to design a lower-cost TOUCH-TONE receiver which was consistent with the less severe signaling requirements of the PBX environment: shorter loops, less exposure to digital interference, and absence of charging penalty in the event of error. The receiver was applied to both step-by-step and common-control PBXs.

The first application of TOUCH-TONE calling in a step-by-step PBX was for the John Deere Company at East Moline, Illinois, in the spring of 1964.

We turn now to the PICTUREPHONE visual telephone development, upon which system emphasis was directed toward the end of the 1960s. It is interesting to note that during the early exploratory period of PICTUREPHONE technology, PBX systems were again impressed into service just as they were during the development of early dial systems. For example, the eight-station switched network exhibited at the New York World's Fair in 1964, and the 1965 trials of video telephones at Bell Laboratories locations as well as at the offices of the Union Carbide Corporation in New York and Chicago, all used a modified version of the SS400 system mentioned above in section 2.4.

While PICTUREPHONE service fundamentally involved the technology of wideband switching, in adding it to PBX switching systems the objective was to make the new service appear to the customer as a natural extension of the telephone service—i.e., the action required by users or attendants to initiate, receive, or extend PICTUREPHONE calls was to be compatible with the operation performed on ordinary telephone calls. PBX PICTUREPHONE service was designed to be consistent with general system principles, which included the ability to use common station equipment and common telephone numbers for both telephone and PICTUREPHONE calls. The operation of the system was based on the provision of TOUCH-TONE calling. The PICTUREPHONE switching function was brought into play through the use of the identifying "#" prefix generated by the twelfth button on a TOUCH-TONE telephone set. Subsequent to the initial application of TOUCH-TONE calling discussed previously, the TOUCH-TONE capability was expanded from 10 to 12 digits for use by PICTUREPHONE service and other services.

A basic precept was that the video features in the different PBX and Centrex systems should be consistent with each other and should coordinate with the "service package" concept underlying the PBX and Centrex marketing philosophy at the time (see above, section 3.3). The latter meant that each of the telephone-type features would have, to the extent possible, a companion video feature, and these features would be optionally available in groups, or individually, to complement the regular telephone service packages or individual options, respectively.

PICTUREPHONE service was adapted to the 701 step-by-step PBX system, which at the time provided PBX and Centrex service to a large number of Bell System customers. It was adapted also to the 757A crossbar system. To minimize modifications of existing systems, an auxiliary switching arrangement, the 850A PBX was developed. As shown in Fig. 13-46(a), the 850A auxiliary system was effectively placed in parallel with the existing 701 or 757 PBX. An ordinary telephone call would be switched through the existing system, but a caller wanting to place a PICTUREPHONE call would press the # button, and the receipt of this signal by the TOUCH-TONE telephone equipment would cause the call to be completed through the 850A auxiliary system.

The 850A was designed as a complete PBX so that it could be modified to operate as a stand-alone PICTUREPHONE PBX, to provide only PICTUREPHONE service to a customer if desired. It was a solid-state machine, using a building-block equipment arrangement that allowed for easy growth from 16 to 89 PICTUREPHONE lines. The system was arranged to switch the voice channel on a 2-wire basis and the PICTUREPHONE channel on a 4-wire basis. Growable switching networks were provided by plug-in ferreed packages. To achieve low manufacturing costs, logic and circuit pack sizes were chosen to be the same as in the high-production 800A PBX.

PICTUREPHONE service capability was also added to the No. 101 electronic switching system. Any of the family of switch units comprising this system could be arranged to provide PICTUREPHONE service. The video component of the service was handled by a wideband switch, controlled (via the audio switch unit) by the stored program in the control unit. A block schematic of this modification is also shown in Fig. 13-46. To complete the picture, the No. 5 crossbar system was arranged so that PICTUREPHONE service capability could be made available to Centrex-CO lines. An optional wideband remote switch controlled from the PICTURE-

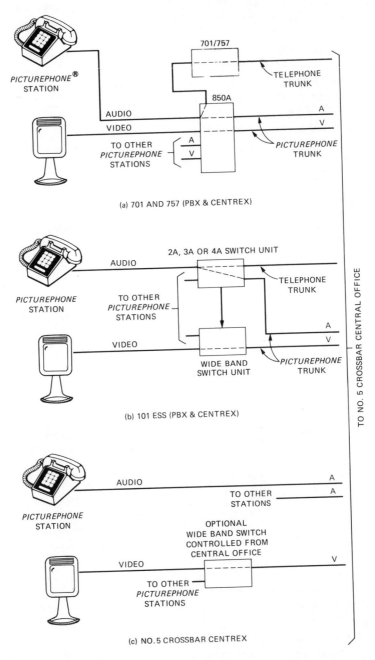

Fig. 13-46. Block schematic of arrangements for adding video switching to various PBX systems.

PHONE central office was used on the customer's premises as shown in part (c) of the illustration.

As mentioned, the ability to have an attendant assist in handling calls is fundamental to PBX and Centrex service. As an employee of the customer, the attendant is often a "telephone receptionist," portraying the company's image. In the development of PICTURE-PHONE service for PBX and Centrex customers, provision was made so that this concept could be enhanced where desired by the customer through the use of video telephony for the attendant. Fig. 13-47 shows a PBX attendant position with a cordless attendant switchboard and PICTUREPHONE set. The design objectives were that the attendant perform the same relative functions on PICTURE-PHONE calls as on telephone calls and that the video operating procedures be identical with, or natural extensions of, the standard telephone operating procedures. This objective provided opportunity for considerable innovation.

During the establishment of connections, the attendant is in the middle of communications between inside and outside parties. This process involves accepting voice instructions from one of the parties and taking action to advance the call, an action which sometimes

Fig. 13-47. Attendant arrangements for PICTUREPHONE service. All procedures were the same as those for telephone PBX service, or natural extensions of these procedures.

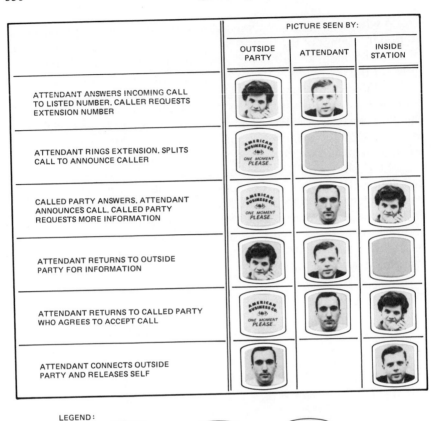

ATTENDANT   OUTSIDE   FIRST INSIDE
                   PARTY   STATION

Fig. 13-48. "Who sees whom" in a typical PICTUREPHONE transaction under control of the attendant.

involves communication with the other party, and, on some calls, communicating at the same time with both parties. The general rule that evolved, after extensive simulation experiments, was that the video connection should accompany the audio connection; that is, the parties that hear each other should also see each other. When the attendant was involved with both calling and called parties at the same time, the video path to the attendant was not completed. Fig. 13-48 shows "who sees whom" sequences during the process of a typical attendant operation.

It will be noted from the illustrations in Fig. 13-48 that another new feature was introduced. The attendant was able to transmit a stationary image to video telephone parties outside the customer group when no live pictures would otherwise be transmitted. These stationary images, representing patterns or concepts which were devised by the customer and which could be changed, were provided at the customer's option.[46,47,48]

The PBX aspects of PICTUREPHONE capped two decades of extensive innovations in customer switching. These decades (1) saw the introduction of compact, efficient, and reliable common-control crossbar systems, (2) saw solutions to fundamental problems of electronic switching and their reduction to practice in diverse functional forms for customer switching, and (3) gave birth to numerous new and useful services and features: Centrex, sophisticated cordless attendant technology for large and small systems, and exotic signaling and transfer features, all of which were widely accepted by the telephone companies and their customers.

IV. KEY TELEPHONE SYSTEMS

4.1 Some Comparisons With PBX Systems

For 50 years, the PBX mode of operation was the predominant method of satisfying requirements for a simple means of communicating between telephones on a customer's premises and for switching these telephones to circuits to the central office. But beginning in the 1930s and accelerating in the 1950s, switching technology began to point the way to a new line of services. Principally among these were key telephone switching services which, used extensively today, are characterized by the familiar six-button key telephone set and multibutton CALL DIRECTOR* telephone shown in Figs. 13-49 and 13-50. Such key telephone systems (KTSs) are usually interposed between telephones and lines to a central office or PBX. They interface also with private (tie) lines to distant telephones or PBX systems, and with local intercommunication arrangements.

Although implemented differently, key telephone systems and PBX systems provide services that in many respects are similar. With both, for example, one or more telephones can originate calls to, or receive calls from, the central office over a common group of circuits. With both systems, various ratios of telephones-to-line (or trunk) concentrations are possible. Both modes allow intercommunicating between the customer's extensions without switching through the central office, a feature generally provided with PBX but optional with KTS.

There are, however, important differences between KTS and PBX operation, differences which have influenced their relative economics, customer preference, and technology. These differences are especially evident when KTSs are compared with dial PBX or Cen-

---

*Registered trademark of AT&T Co.

Fig. 13-49. The familiar six-button key telephone set.

trex systems. For example, selecting and switching a KTS circuit is mostly a matter of operating a particular key at the telephone. By contrast, most PBX and Centrex switching involves interpreting numerical codes initiated at the telephone; thereafter, specific paths are selected automatically. The concept could be stretched to include manual PBXs where the attendant receives verbal instructions, or codes, from users and thereafter selects specific paths.

Additionally, in the PBX or Centrex mode the attendant, when required, is interposed between the telephones and the trunk to the

Fig. 13-50. The multibutton CALL DIRECTOR set.

central office. In the KTS mode, telephones have direct access to lines to the central office; the attendant function, when required, is performed by temporarily bridging onto the connection. These differences have led to new service functions in KTS, permitting direct customer control over the origination and reception of calls. This is done with the aid of status lamps per circuit which show the arrival of new calls or show whether the circuits are busy or are being held while another call is being served.

4.2 Common Ancestry

Today's key switching and PBX systems stem from a common ancestry among the early PBX systems. As described in the first volume of this series, the No. 2 PBX, introduced in 1903, first contained the basic key switching functions. The No. 2 system was made available for customers who did not have sufficient traffic to justify a full-time attendant. The reader is referred to *The Early Years*, p. 667 for a description of the system. The operating features were outlined by AT&T (1903):

"Private branch exchange No. 2 furnishes a system of intercommunication whereby a subscriber at any station may call any other station of the branch exchange without the assistance of an operator. Facilities can be provided for central office connections with either common battery or magneto switchboards. In such cases no private branch exchange operator is needed for outgoing calls from the private branch exchange, but for incoming calls from the central office, services of an attendant or a clerk at one of the private branch exchange stations, arranged as a receiving station, will be required to distribute such calls to the proper stations. There is no delay from slow disconnections at the private branch exchange, the supervisory signal at the central exchange being under control of the private branch exchange subscriber who is talking."

4.3 Divergence From PBX Technology

While the No. 2 key switching PBX served its purpose, it was neither a long-term solution to the small PBX requirements nor to the line switching requirements of the individual telephone user. The No. 2 was followed four years later by the 505 PBX approach, which centralized the central office and intercom switching for small PBXs at an attendant's key cabinet (see *The Early Years*, page 674). This approach continued for PBX service through several generations of the cordless 505, 506, and 507 switchboards up to 1966. But the 505 approach still did not satisfy the switching requirements where just a few extensions and lines were involved and where an attendant was neither required nor desired. Often the small groups required considerable variations in features. For example, customers with one or more telephones desired options to connect to any one of a number of central office, PBX, private or intercommunicating lines; they also required options to hold one line while using another, to cut off extensions or ringers or to signal on intercommunicating circuits. Accordingly, in the intervening years, up to the 1930s a series of "wiring plans" was designed for these customers, each of which grouped the options in different configurations for a particular number of extensions and lines. The wiring plans also specified the equipment to be mounted on the desk, such as the particular push-button or lever-type key, ringers, lamps, etc. The installer mounted and wired these apparatus elements together in whatever manner seemed best for the particular installation.

4.4 Early Key Switching Systems

From the vantage point of the present it might appear that the wiring plan approach lacked the system discipline which we insist upon today. It must be remembered, however, that this was a period where customers' usage of the telephone and their business communication requirements were rapidly growing and changing. The wiring plan approach was undoubtedly good and proper at the time, since it met the customer's needs. Later, however, a better understanding was gained of the requirements for systems embodying the most frequently desired features. Furthermore, the practice of providing and keeping records of a multitude of wiring plans was becoming unwieldy and uneconomical. In the late 1920s, Bell Laboratories was called upon to see what could be done to systematize the solution to the customized installations.

Several approaches were taken to standardize line switching arrangements that would provide convenient and attractive telephone equipment. The arrangements were also to provide switching and signaling that were better than those of the wiring plans. One of the first of these arrangements, introduced in the late 1920s, was the No. 100 key equipment. It consisted of a key box, shown in Fig. 13-51, connected to separately mounted relay units. This equipment could be applied where it was desired to switch one or more telephones to one of a number of lines. The key box contained lamps to indicate incoming calls or busy lines. Each line key could be operated to answer a call or, by moving it further, to place a line on hold. Several methods of connecting and using the key boxes were developed. With the key box shown, two people could access six lines from opposite sides of a desk. Alternatively, single-sided key boxes with minimum capacities of three lines were also available. For larger numbers of lines, key boxes could be placed side-by-side and connected to allow the user's telephone to access all of the line keys. Where several telephones were required, the lines of each key box could be multipled to as many as six desks,

Fig. 13-51. Double-sided six-line keybox of the No. 100 key equipment. Two people seated opposite each other could access any of the six lines, and could place calls on hold.

which could be equipped with single- or double-sided key boxes. With such design flexibility, the No. 100 key equipment could satisfy a variety of requirements ranging from a one-telephone/two- or three-line situation up to multiline telephone groups for use where a number of employees doing work of a similar nature desire to handle calls for each other. At the time it was also pointed out that the equipment could be installed for a clerk to answer calls on a group of employee's lines, a secretarial function which continues today with modern equipment.[49]

The 100-type key equipment was followed in a few years by an improved key arrangement. While similar to the 100-type, it provided considerably greater capacity. Called 101A and 101B, this key equipment had as many as 40 lines that could appear before the user, and the lines could be multipled before as many as 12 telephone positions. As shown in Fig. 13-52(a), a single key box provided for ten line units. Five line keys were used, each connecting to two different lines, depending on whether the key was moved up or down. A common hold key was provided per unit. The faceplate was designed to be box-mounted (101A version) or flush-mounted in the top of a desk or table (101B version). Fig. 13-52(b) shows the circuitry of the 101-type equipment.[50]

The No. 100 and 101-type key equipments supplemented a trend toward the use of this type of technology in special switching services, such as multiline complexes in brokerage houses, department stores, and airlines, and for dispatching and government services (see below, section V).

Another approach to replacing wiring plans were the 15A and 23A key equipment units,[51] which provided access to one or two central office lines, respectively. Devised in the early 1930s, shortly after the No. 100, the system used a special hand telephone with five

(a)

(b)

Fig. 13-52. No. 101 key equipment. (a) Box-mounted version, showing five keys used to access to lines. (b) Schematic showing one line circuit and the operator's circuit.

Fig. 13-53. Pushbutton handset used with 15A and 23A key telephone equipment (early 1930s). Buttons accessed central office and intercom lines, put calls on hold, and signaled other telephones.

pushbuttons in the base, as shown in Fig. 13-53. Three of the buttons accessed two central office lines and an intercom line. The other two button positions provided a hold function and a way to signal other telephones. A typical arrangement is shown in Fig. 13-54. Incoming calls were signaled by bells arranged to give different tones to indicate the particular line. A lamp indicated a busy line. For privacy when a user was on an outside line, all other telephones would normally be cut off, but this feature could be waived if desired. The similarity of the 15A/23A to the 750PBX produced a few years earlier (see *The Early Years*, p. 691) once again illustrates the common ancestry of PBX and KTS. Perhaps more striking is the similarity of this system to modern KTS. (Key systems coded 107 and 108 were essentially the same as the 15A and 23A except that they provided for five extensions and one central office trunk. Since the base of the telephone was of limited volume, the keys were assembled in a small metal box that could be mounted on a desk, thus permitting the use of standard telephones without keys in the base.)

4.5 The Key Telephone Systems Pattern Emerges

In 1938 the third generation of desk telephones—the combined 300-type set containing the bell and associated equipment in the base—was expanded to include models having line switching buttons in the base. Interconnected with these buttons were switching and signaling arrangements which formed a coordinated key-operated system. Called the 1A key telephone system, it was the prototype of today's KTS.

The 1A had a set of interlocking keys: when one key was pushed down it locked in that position, and any previously depressed key popped up. Depressing any key permitted calls to be originated or answered on up to five central office, PBX, intercommunicating, or private lines—six if the hold function was not required. When used, the hold function was performed with a single key common to the central office or PBX lines.

While the system had service features similar to those of the wiring plans and key boxes, the features were provided by a combination of key telephone units (KTUs), each of which was composed of a relay assembly equipped with screw terminals. The aggregate of these was controlled by the keys in the base of the telephone set and returned incoming call or busy signals to lamps associated with these keys. Installers mounted the KTUs in an apparatus box and wired them together via the screw terminals. Thus, a combination of features could be selected and installed without special engineering by the telephone company.

Several new features were provided with this system, such as a common ringer for several lines and an "exclusion" key. As shown

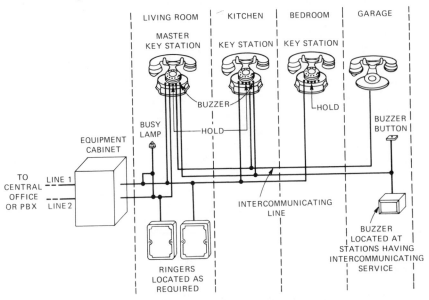

Fig. 13-54. Typical arrangement for the 23A key equipment: two central office lines and intercommunications among four telephones within a household.

in Fig. 13-55, the exclusion key was made part of the switchhook plunger. When pulled up, it cut off extensions to insure privacy.[52] A 300-type telephone forming part of the 1A system is shown in Fig. 13-56.

By the 1950s, telephone sets with four or six pushbuttons along the front edge were a common sight in business offices. Used by small business groups, by departmental groups of large businesses having lines to PBXs, by executives, and by receptionists, key telephones accounted for about one out of every ten sets manufactured.

Reflecting the increased importance of this service, the 1A system was redesigned in 1952 to improve its economy and to incorporate equipment and service improvements. The central office and PBX line circuit was reduced from five to three relays, a substantial saving as shown in simplified form in Fig. 13-57. In this illustration, it can be seen how the telephone was connected through the pick-up keys to the line circuit, and how the latter was multipled to other telephones. Of interest also is the hold function (when the hold key was operated, the operated line key was restored) and the circuitry which changes the lamp signals to identify incoming calls and busy lines.

The redesigned system was called the 1A1 key telephone system. An innovation with this system was a "winking" lamp signal to distinguish between a line on hold and one on which an incoming call

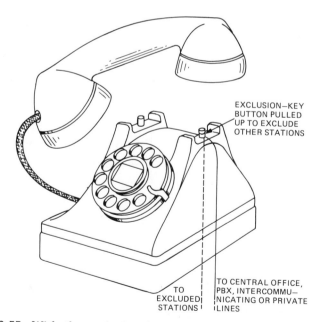

EXCLUSION—KEY BUTTON PULLED UP TO EXCLUDE OTHER STATIONS

TO EXCLUDED STATIONS

TO CENTRAL OFFICE, PBX, INTERCOMMU—NICATING OR PRIVATE LINES

Fig. 13-55. With the exclusion feature, user pulled up the switchhook button to disconnect other telephones on the same line.

Fig. 13-56. A 300-type telephone set forming part of the 1A key telephone unit.

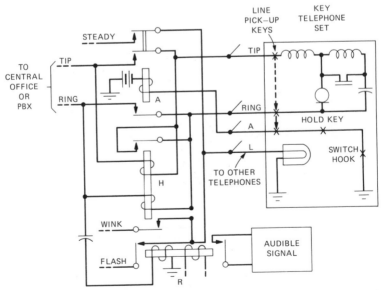

Fig. 13-57. The 1A1 line circuit, with only three relays, was a significant
improvement over earlier key telephone system circuits.

or busy signal was displayed. Another new service feature was an intercommunication line which permitted selectively dialing up to eight telephones having access to the intercom.

A few years later the single-link, dial selective intercom was augmented to permit dialing up to 80 numbers with two switchable links and improved supervisory features. Improved equipment features were also introduced, and the system was referred to as key telephone system No. 6A.[53] Later, the features of this system with additional supervisory improvements were reincorporated in the 1A2 key telephone system.

The 1A1 system incorporated wire spring relays which, as noted elsewhere in this history, were a contemporary development. Commonly used functions were combined in a single KTU, and several groups of multifunctional interconnected KTUs were available in equipment packages (called key service units) to facilitate ordering and installation.[54]

With the introduction of the 1A1 system, key telephone service, already undergoing substantial growth, was beginning to show its great potential for the future. Customers liked the simple and rapid operating features, and were even beginning to prefer them to those of some of the small PBXs. As noted above in section 2.4, this preference led eventually to the discontinuance in the mid-1960s of the 755 small dial PBX, and the small cordless 507 PBXs, systems which had prevailed for many years but now bowed to the KTS technology.

For further improvements, engineers turned in the early 1960s toward electronic solid-state techniques, mixing this technology with miniaturized electromechanical two-state devices (relays). The result was the 1A2 key telephone system in 1964.

The 1A2 system provided several new service features, but the principal difference was physical. As shown in Fig. 13-58, a substantial reduction in size was achieved through the use of solid-state components, plug-in printed wiring boards, and miniature relays. As a result, less space was required on a customer's premises, and the system offered greater flexibility, lower idle plant investment, and easier installation and maintenance.[55,56] The 1A2 development helped to accelerate the growth of key telephone systems, as indicated by Fig. 13-59.

As KTS development proceeded, numerous service features evolved. The principal elements of these have been mentioned—multistation/multiline selection, manual and dial intercom, hold, exclusion, and distinctive supervisory signals. But other, auxiliary features were also important. Among these, introduced with the 6A key telephone system in 1958, were the following features.

Fig. 13-58. Solid-state components and miniature relays meant a significant reduction in size for the 1A2 line circuit (right) compared to the 1A1
unit (left).

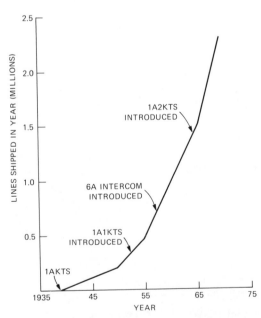

Fig. 13-59. Growth in numbers of lines of key telephone system equipment. The 1A2 system of 1964 was a factor in this growth.

Add-on conference: A telephone reached via the intercom could be added to a central office or PBX call.

Pre-set conference: A predetermined group of telephones accessed via the intercom line could be called in by a single code for a conference.

Camp-on: Similar to the PBX function, this was applied to the intercom telephones.

Direct station selection: Intercom telephone could be called by depressing a particular button per telephone.

An innovation with the 1A2 system in the mid-1960s was an expansion of the exclusion feature, which could permit principal telephones to exclude multipled subordinate telephones from more than one of the central office or PBX lines serving the principal telephone. Also, in view of the effect of mass commercial power failures, which had occurred in the 1960s, a feature was devised which automatically connected bells to the line circuits to announce incoming calls in the absence of line lamps—a seemingly trivial detail but of importance when a city was blacked out.

4.6 Adding TOUCH-TONE Calling and PICTUREPHONE Visual Telephone Service to Key Telephone Systems

As with PBX systems, key telephone systems were arranged for TOUCH-TONE calling and PICTUREPHONE visual telephone service. In key telephone system technology, switching between telephones and lines to the central office is independent of whether the telephone employs TOUCH-TONE calling or dial pulse signaling, since the telephone-to-line switching is accomplished directly by keys (as contrasted with digital control in PBXs). However, control of the dial intercom features of key telephone systems did require making this facility compatible with the signal output of the TOUCH-TONE telephone. The system philosophy was, as before, that the signal format and power standards would be identical for all types of telephones. Accordingly, a method was developed of applying a TOUCH-TONE receiver so that its output could control the signaling of telephones associated with a dial intercom. Because the signaling parameters encompassed only the telephones and local intercom switch, a much simplified and lower-cost TOUCH-TONE receiver was possible. First applied to the 1A1 and 6A key telephone systems, the cost of the receiver was later halved by the printed circuit solid-state techniques of the 1A2 system.

Applying PICTUREPHONE technology to key telephone system service was far more complex. This application required that users should, if desired, be able to see and be seen by their PICTURE-PHONE communicants on calls controlled by their key telephone buttons. This added dimension was desired whether these calls were originated to or received from their connected central office, or PBX, or over their local intercom. Together with other functions aimed at enhancing the service, it was necessary at the same time to avoid video interference between stations which might be multipled to the same call at the key telephone system.

The broad requirements called for introducing video switching to supplement the audio switching functions of key telephone systems, adhering at the same time to the general PICTUREPHONE principles laid down for the system as a whole—the use of common station equipment and common telephone numbers for both telephone and PICTUREPHONE calls, with the PICTUREPHONE distinction being made by a # prefix generated by the twelfth button of a TOUCH-TONE telephone set. The service was to appear to the customer as a natural extension of telephone service; that is, initiating, receiving, or extending PICTUREPHONE calls would be compatible with the actions required for ordinary telephone calls.

As in the case of central office and PBX systems, the video switching requirement meant that key telephone systems had to be adapted to 4-wire broadband switching for both station-to-line switching and for intercom switching. A somewhat subtle but important consideration was that the use of a signaling prefix to distinguish between ordinary telephone and video switching meant that station-to-line switching was no longer independent of coded signaling as it was heretofore. These basic considerations, together with the opportunity to provide some improved service features, dictated that a new key telephone system be developed, rather than modify the efficient building-block structure of the 1A2 system.

Completed at the close of the decade, the 1P2 key telephone system interfaced with standard key telephone and PICTUREPHONE sets. It contained the basic communication features of systems used for audio only service, and it provided technology to furnish practical and compatible wideband video service. The service was made operable for station-to-line switching, for intercom traffic, and for conferencing. Circuits consisted of solid-state elements, miniature relays, and other components assembled on plug-in circuit packs, as shown in Fig. 13-60, with plugged-in packs wired together in one key service unit (KSU) assembly. A typical equipment unit is shown in Fig. 13-61. Some of the service possibilities provided for are conferencing and two-line pickup. Fig. 13-62 shows a frame for the key service units. For additional details the reader is referred to the published technical literature.[57]

V. SPECIAL SYSTEMS

The history of PBX and key telephone system technology involved switching systems with features responsive to the needs of millions

Fig. 13-60. Circuit packs for the 1P2 key telephone system: line circuit, left, and video switch, right.

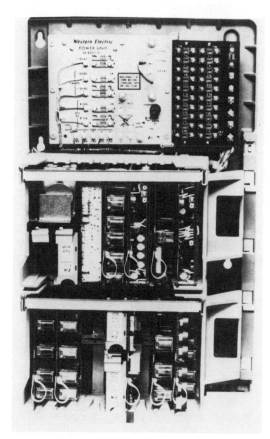

Fig. 13-61. Typical key telephone equipment units serving both telephone and PICTUREPHONE sets.

Fig. 13-62. A frame for mounting PICTUREPHONE key service units.

of business customers. By contrast, there are small groups of customers who have unique and important communication requirements. For these, special systems were developed, even though the
field of use may have numbered only in the hundreds, or fewer.
Such systems are of interest not only for their novel communication
features but also as an illustration of the Bell System's concern for
these specialized needs.

Some special systems stemmed from a PBX base, and some were
of the nature of key telephone systems. Others were a mixture of
both technologies, and still others could be characterized by special
signaling technologies.

This history would be unduly lengthy if we were to attempt to
cover all special systems developed in the past 50 years, or even all
of the nuances of those that are mentioned. However, a few
highlights may be of interest, including special systems for tele-

phone answering service, systems for order-taking and reservation services, and highly specialized systems for emergency-type services required by government agencies. Regarding the latter, the past quarter century has witnessed the development of a number of special switching and signaling systems which were integral parts of special networks leased to the U.S. government to meet the communication requirements of the defense and air traffic control agencies. A comprehensive account of these highly interesting and important systems will be found in Chapter 12 of the volume of this history series subtitled *National Service in War and Peace (1925–1975)*.

5.1 Telephone Answering Service

Most people have made telephone calls which were answered by an answering service. Such calls may have been placed to physicians after office hours, or to other professional people or small business concerns who found it advantageous when their offices were closed to have someone receive calls, take messages, and convey information. To provide such service, telephone answering "bureaus" generally lease switchboard and connecting facilities from the telephone companies. They employ their own attendants to operate the switchboards and work out procedures and charges with their clients. Such bureaus might serve as few as a hundred clients or many hundreds. They use one or many switchboards installed in a convenient location, usually near the central office, but often remote from their clients.

As early as the 1920s, telephone companies furnished switchboards and associated facilities for answering services. These consisted of a variety of jack- or key-ended switchboards, adapted from the then standard PBX and key equipment facilities. However, by the mid-1930s, the need for standard answering service arrangements became apparent.

Although it was first called "secretarial service," it is of interest that one of the applications considered of importance in the mid-1930s was for answering telephones in an apartment building. However, the advantage of centralized answering bureaus for use by professional people such as physicians was also recognized. The objective of the design at the time was to give customers central office service in the normal manner, and to permit them to bring in the secretarial function only when needed. Two ways of securing this were developed. In one of these, the customer could operate a key at a telephone to make the connections to the "secretarial" board, as shown in Fig. 13-63(a). In the other method, a direct connection was made from the customer's line to the secretarial board, as shown in Fig. 13-63(b). The latter was felt to be advantageous since it did not require the customer to be at the telephone to make

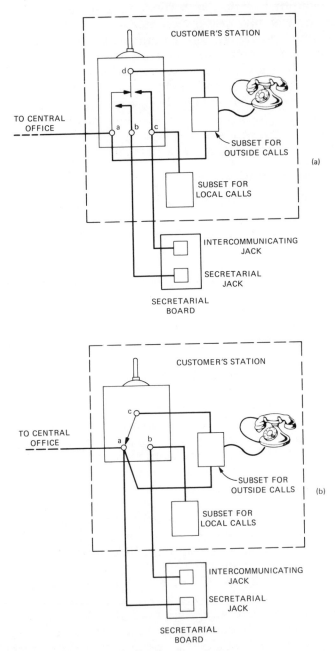

Fig. 13-63. Two arrangements for switching between regular service and answering service: (a) customer operates a key, and (b) attendant removes dummy plug at secretarial jack.

the switchover. With the second arrangement, the attendant inserted a plug into the secretarial jack when service was not required, and this prevented the line lamp from lighting and also prevented answering. To insure privacy, an alternative arrangement automatically opened the line to the secretarial board when the client was talking. In all cases, the circuits prevented the attendant from originating calls over the customer's telephone line. Developed in 1935, these answering arrangements were available in boards coded 554B and 554C, the former employing the equipment framework of the 605A PBX and the latter that of the 551B.[58]

As answering services continued to become more widespread, regulatory bodies established certain additional requirements for particular areas. In some parts of the country, combinations of PBX and answering service were permitted. In other areas, the extension of a call beyond the attendant at the answering bureau was not allowed. In nearly all instances, however, guard features were required to insure privacy and to prevent unauthorized use of a client's telephone service. In consequence, two new answering switchboards, coded 557A and 557B, were developed in 1955, the former for combined PBX and answering service, the latter for answering service only. A line of 557A positions is shown in Fig. 13-64. (The pigeonhole bins above the switchboard were provided by the bureau for filing messages to the clients.) This board used the self-contained cord circuits developed for the 555 switchboard. The 557B was equipped with single-ended cords (for

Fig. 13-64. Telephone answering service, using 557A positions developed in 1955.

answering only) using new retractable cord reels instead of the usual cord weights.

In these boards the design was such that the attendant could not establish a connection to a client's line except during the ringing interval of an incoming call, thus insuring privacy on established calls and preventing unauthorized call origination on the client's line.[59]

Until the early 1950s, telephone answering service required an individual pair of wires between the bureau and the central office terminals for each client's line. This arrangement was generally not economical, because of the costs of interoffice wire plant, for a bureau in one central office area to serve clients in another central office area. Thus, a concern furnishing answering services generally provided separate bureaus in each central office area in which it wished to offer service. This meant duplication of office space, equipment, and personnel, and it restricted the establishment of branch bureaus to those areas serving sufficient clients to warrant the expenditure. Since line concentration techniques had long been used in Bell System switching systems to effect economies in wire plant, it was natural to consider similar techniques for answering services, since it was highly improbable that all lines would need to be served at the same time. Applied to this service, the fundamental objectives were (1) to concentrate a large number of customers' lines so that they could be served by a relatively few pairs of conductors at the answering service bureau, and (2) to identify to the answering bureau the individual line connected at the time to a trunk. Through the application of specially designed concentrator-identifier equipment, it was possible to concentrate and identify as many as one hundred different clients' lines over only four pairs of wires between a remote central office and an answering bureau. By greatly reducing the number of conductors from a distant central office, it was now possible to realize sufficient economies to permit centralization of an answering service and to offer the bureau service to areas where heretofore it was financially unattractive.

Developed in 1953, the concentrator-identifier consisted of two units interconnected by trunks. As shown in Fig. 13-65, the concentrator, located in the central office, automatically switched the clients' lines requiring service to one of two, three, or four (later increased to six) trunks to the identifier at the answering bureau. At the central office, a signaling system encoded the identity of a particular line connected to any trunk at any one time and transmitted this to the bureau equipment, where the line identity was decoded and caused a line lamp to light in the answering bureau switchboard. Each line had its own lamp and associated jack arranged in

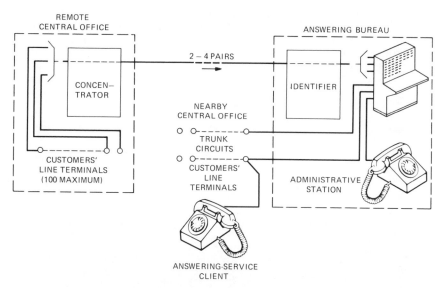

REMOTE
CENTRAL OFFICE

ANSWERING BUREAU

2 – 4 PAIRS

CONCEN-
TRATOR

IDENTIFIER

NEARBY
CENTRAL OFFICE

TRUNK
CIRCUITS

CUSTOMERS'
LINE TERMINALS
(100 MAXIMUM)

CUSTOMERS'
LINE
TERMINALS

ADMINISTRATIVE
STATION

ANSWERING-SERVICE
CLIENT

Fig. 13-65. By concentrating lines from customers to the answering service, the 1953 concentrator-identifier lowered costs and allowed an expansion of answering services.

the same manner as if connected directly to the client's line with an individual pair of wires. With this arrangement, both individual lines and concentrated lines could be terminated in the same answering service switchboard.[60]

It is interesting to note that, during the development of personalized answering service, a movement was under way to use machine-type answering devices located on customers' premises and connected to their lines. Trials of the first machine-type service were held in New York and Cleveland in 1950. The trials were successful, and this type of service continued to grow.

However, the use of personalized answering services also continued to expand, and in the mid-1960s after close collaboration with the telephone answering industry, several new systems were developed to provide new features and to modernize the equipment. The first of the new systems was the 1A telephone answering system, a pushbutton-controlled system, as shown in Fig. 13-66. The line circuits used solid-state components and miniature relays assembled on printed wiring cards, and could terminate direct or concentrator-identifier lines. The attendant's console contained newly designed 20-button key strips. Each key was a nonlocking, illuminated, push-and-turn button associated with a line circuit. A key could be turned to one of three positions so that the key lamp

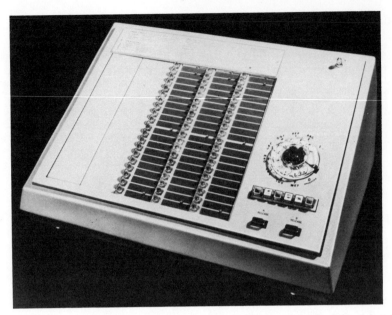

Fig. 13-66. Pushbutton-controlled attendant's console for the 1A telephone answering system.

would light immediately when the line was rung, or the key lamp would light after three rings (most clients preferred this arrangement), or the lamp would not respond to ringing at all. When "on," the lamp flashed until answered by the attendant, who depressed the key associated with the lamp. A call could be put on "hold" by reoperating the pick-up key of an answered call. The steady lamp signal changed immediately to a winking signal, and the attendant was free to answer another call.

A second innovation in telephone answering systems provided occasional service for clients served by answering bureaus. With this equipment, the answering bureau could selectively connect and disconnect clients who desired only part-time answering service. These facilities extended answering services to a wider range of clients. Any one of 100 clients' lines could be optionally selected for connection to any one of ten associated trunks between the equipment in the central office and the answering bureau for as long as necessary. The trunks terminated in the jacks or keys at an attendant's position at the bureau. With direct-line systems, ten trunks terminated in line circuits in the bureau switchboard or console equipment. With concentrator-identifier systems, the occasional service trunks terminated in line circuits on the concentrator equipment at the central office, and were treated as regular customer lines. A special cable pair terminating at the telephone answering bureau was used as a control path to permit the bureau attendant to set up a connection by dialing.

The third innovation in equipment was known as the No. 2A telephone answering system, which featured improvements upon the concentrator-identifier system of the previous decade. The improvements concerned two of the vital elements of this technology. First, instead of displaying the calls on each client's line as an individual lamp associated with a jack, the improved system decoded the line number and gave a four-digit numerical display at the bureau. This permitted the use of small, modern pushbutton positions instead of the large jack and lamp switchboards. The second major improvement permitted the bureau to remotely set the number of rings which would be counted before the call was displayed to the bureau. It was hoped that this would minimize lost or delayed answering of calls by the bureau attendant, by replacing the traditional attendant counting of rings by mechanized counting. In addition to these features, the improved concentrator, patterned after the type 520 emergency reporting system (described below) provided greater capacity and reliability, and permitted sharing equipment among a number of answering bureaus. A trial of this system in Wilmington, Delaware in 1964 showed that unfortunately, while the service requirements had been worked out in close collaboration with the industry, and the system implementation embodied significant technological advances, it was not economical for the customer to use this system in an answering service complex for which it was designed.

5.2 Order-Taking Systems

"Shopping by telephone is widely accepted as a modern convenience. Small business establishments such as grocers and butchers have employed the telephone for soliciting and accepting orders ever since it came into commercial use, obtaining by this means a considerable increase in business at the small expense of telephone service . . . Large department stores have realized that the telephone could be profitably employed for shopping in their line also if the personal contact, which is automatic in the case of a small establishment, could be obtained, and if the switching required to handle telephone orders were of a simple character . . . Ordinarily the PBX in large organizations is a clearing house for incoming calls, but telephone shoppers as a rule do not know which department they want to talk to, and the attention of several departments may be necessary for a single order. This requires special attention on the part of the switchboard attendant in making connection to the proper department and later in transferring the call to other departments. The load from telephone shopping may be considerably greater than that from other business, and the handling of all calls at a single switchboard often necessitates more attendants and a larger PBX than would be required if different types of calls were separated . . . A study of the problem indicated that if the telephone shopping service could be separated from the regular service, economies in handling both would be effected."

These words in the *Bell Laboratories Record* (March, 1929, p. 270) illustrate the clear concept, more than five decades ago, of the needs of customers for special facilities for order-taking communications. During the intervening years, the requirements of these customers have been filled variously by both manual and automatic switching systems. Tailored to the needs of small and large users, as had been done in other branches of the customer switching art, developments over the years continuously improved the features as well as the economic and engineering aspects of this service.

At first used mostly by department stores and telegraph offices, the field of use for order-taking facilities expanded in the 1930s and 1940s to include such operations as taxicab dispatching and stockbrokers' offices. After World War II, accelerated air travel stimulated demand for sophisticated order-taking facilities for ticket reservation systems. The field of use continued to spread, so that today, in addition to those businesses mentioned, special order-taking systems are used by mail order concerns, car rental agencies, motel chains, utility company inquiry services (including the Bell System "dial 611" repair service), and the Internal Revenue Service!

One of the first special order-taking systems, introduced about 1928, was called the No. 2 order turret. Shown in Fig. 13-67, the order turret consisted of a jack field and cord circuits on both sides of the turret so that one or two clerks could handle calls on each side, thus making it usable by from one to four clerks, depending on the traffic load. An order clerk seated before this equipment could answer calls placed by customers through the central office network to the department store or other business. The calls arrived over central office trunks (or lines) and appeared directly in the jack field before the clerk. After answering with one of the two cord circuits, the order clerk could take the customer's order or impart information. If additional information was needed, the order clerk could place the customer on hold and then call and consult an appropriate PBX station via the other cord. By proper cord manipulation, the customer could be transferred to the PBX if necessary. An installation of No. 2A order turrets for the John Wanamaker store in New York is shown in Fig. 13-68.

A degree of call distribution to the order clerks was obtained in the No. 2 system by the method in which the trunks were distributed and multipled among the turrets.[61] An alternative method of

Fig. 13-67. The No. 2 order turret, introduced about 1928 to allow stores and other organizations to take telephone orders or transact different types of telephone business.

manually distributing calls to order clerks consisted of having the PBX attendant switch calls from the central office trunks to order clerks' stations equipped with key equipment. While this was not consistent with the objective of reducing the PBX attendant's load and speeding service by separating the order-taking function from the PBX, it helped assure that a call was routed to an idle attendant and provided a simple way of determining the load. Distributing through the PBX also permitted assigning calls to order clerks han-

Fig. 13-68. Installation of No. 2 order turrets in the John Wanamaker department store.

dling particular kinds of merchandise. Accordingly, a No. 4 order turret consisting of a few keys which could terminate lines from the PBX and which provided some other detail functions helpful to the service was developed for this purpose in 1938.[62] An installation at Macy's department store is shown in Fig. 13-69.

Manual distribution of calls to order clerks was also implemented in the 1930s by the 101-type key equipment (see above, section 4.4 and Fig. 13-52) and by key telephone systems of the 1A and subsequent types (see above, section 4.5). The 101 key equipment was used for smaller groups of clerks than served by the No. 2, and the key telephone systems were usually used for the very smallest groups.

Early in the history of this service, it became apparent that the efficiency of the order clerks and the quality of service to the calling customer could be improved by mechanizing the call distributing and call sequencing techniques. Accordingly, an automatic call distributing system, the No. 3 order turret, was developed in 1932 to provide these features. In addition, the system contained usage indicators which yielded information to the supervisory staff so that

Fig. 13-69. Order-taking office, Macy's department store, New York City. Equipment was the No. 4 order turret, developed in 1938.

they could adjust the force of clerks to meet changing traffic loads. An installation of the No. 3 order turrets, the first automatic call distributor for this type of customer service, is shown in Fig. 13-70 as provided for the Western Union Telegraph Company. In this application, work consisted mostly of receiving and typing messages dictated by Western Union clients. The system, with a capacity of 120 trunks and 100 attendant positions, was particularly adaptable to large installations.

Fig. 13-71 shows in simplified form the major elements of the No. 3 system. The position selector used 22-point rotary selectors of the 206 type. Distribution of calls to positions was determined by the selector control circuit which operated the selectors in order, assigning calls to subgroups of clerks in turn. Calls over incoming trunks were passed on immediately to the selectors if an idle position were available; if not, their sequence of arrival was stored and then passed on in the order received when a position became idle.[63]

In 1941, development was started on an improved call-distributing system to replace the No. 3 order turret. The objectives were lower unit costs and a capacity increased to 198 trunks and 200 attendants' positions. The first installation of an early version, known as the No. 6 order turret, was for Montgomery Ward in Chicago by the end of 1941. With the beginning of World War II, the

Fig. 13-70. Western Union installation of No. 3 order turrets, developed in 1932. The No. 3 was the first turret with automatic call distributing and call sequencing.

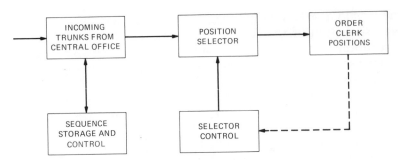

Fig. 13-71. Call-distributing arrangement for the No. 3 order turret. Position selector was a 22-point rotary switch.

basic switching principles of this system were employed in a modernized information desk for the large PBXs being built up for the War Department and national war agencies in Washington.[64] Further development for business purposes was deferred until after the war. At that time, development was resumed and by 1951 an improved version, known as the 6A order turret, was giving service to many large business concerns.

Instead of the rotary selectors of the No. 3 system, the 6A used "trunk finders" (similar to step-by-step system line finders) to switch between the key box attendant positions (see Fig. 13-72) and the incoming trunks. The distribution of calls to the positions and the sequencing of calls under heavy load conditions were controlled

Fig. 13-72. Attendant position for the 6A order turret. New techniques incorporating gate circuits and trunk finders lowered costs and improved telephone service.

by relay lock-out and preference circuits called "gates."[65] These gates sequenced and distributed calls in small groups, and were found to be considerably less expensive than previous techniques used for sequencing and distributing calls. In service, the gate principle was found to be very satisfactory. A view of the 6A switching equipment is shown in Fig. 13-73.

In the early 1960s a two-phased program was initiated to improve automatic call distributing facilities so that customers desiring order-taking communications for merchandise, reservations, or the like, or for inquiry or information services, could be offered still better service and economy. Two systems were developed having modern equipment features similar to contemporary PBX systems of the time—the 3A for the field previously served by the 6A system, and the 2A to provide economical facilities for users with lesser traffic requirements.

Fig. 13-73. Switching equipment for the 6A order turret, a post World War II development for distributing and sequencing telephone calls.

The 3A automatic call distributor retained the step-by-step switching mechanisms of the 6A and provided the same maximum capacity—200 positions and 198 trunks. Plug-in trunks and trunk finders were mounted in frames similar to those of the 701B PBX. The 2A used crossbar technology and was packaged to serve the smaller customer economically. With an upper limit of 56 trunks and 60 positions, plug-in trunks and crossbar switches were contained in cabinets similar to those of the 757A PBX.

Both the 3A and 2A systems employed modern pushbutton-type positions for the order-taking and information clerks and also modern positions and usage indicators for supervisory personnel. Designed for compatible operating features, the systems transferred incoming calls to the PBX and to other positions. They also provided several innovations, such as the identification of the area of origin of a call (when foreign exchange circuits were involved) and recorded voice announcements to inform the caller if a delay in answering was anticipated. Fig. 13-74 shows the switching equipment and operating positions of the 2A and 3A automatic call distributors.

The 1970s saw continued improvement. The 2B automatic call distributor, replacing the 2A, used small crossbar switches recently developed for central office switching. It provided in a single cabinet the equipment for a system of 20 incoming trunks and 10 attendant positions. The system was growable to a somewhat larger capacity than the 2A (68 trunks and 70 positions) by adding supplementary cabinets. The 2B provided features similar to those of the 2A; additionally, however, a customer with two or three automatic call distributor systems at the same location could have calls from one of the systems flow to one of the other systems when its attendants were busy, thus expanding the total capability of the system. Since its introduction in 1973, over 100 systems have been installed; soon thereafter the No. 2B automatic call distributor could be found in almost every state. A photograph of the supervisor's console at the Internal Revenue Service installation in Camden, New Jersey is shown in Fig. 13-75.[66]

5.3 Systems for Dispatch and Emergency-Type Services

In the 1950s, organizations engaged in transmitting and distributing electric power, pumping oil or natural gas through pipelines, and operating railroads or other transportation facilities, used vast communication networks spreading over large areas and long distances. Over these networks, a dispatcher at a headquarters location was informed of the status of operations and coordinated many activities, including emergency repairs and routing. To do this efficiently, the dispatcher needed finger-tip access to all of the communication channels. In the early 1950s, a new PBX switchboard, the No. 508, was developed to meet the special requirements of such customers. An installation for the General Electric Co. in Portland, Oregon is shown in Fig. 13-76.

The dispatcher placed or received most calls served by the 508 switchboard. For rapid access for these calls, lines and trunks were connected to keys. The arrangement was similar to that of such cordless switchboards as the 507-type or 101 key equipment (see

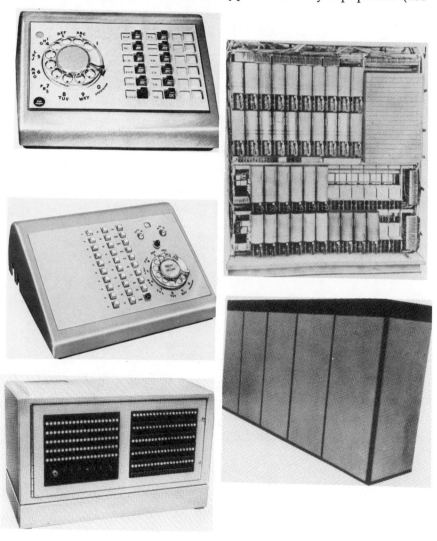

Fig. 13-74. Switching (right), attendant (upper and middle left), and supervisory (lower left) equipment for the 2A and 3A automatic call distributors.

Fig. 13-75. Supervisor's console for the 2B automatic call distributor, introduced in 1973.

Fig. 13-76. Typical 508 PBX installation, developed in the early 1950s to meet the special requirements of utilities, railroads, pipeline operations, and similar markets needing dispatching services.

above, sections 2.3 and 4.4). Occasionally, however, the dispatcher needed through switching between lines and trunks. To meet this requirement with the simplest form of linkage, all circuits were also connected to jacks which could be interconnected with cords and plugs. Spring-loaded cord reels were introduced in this PBX instead of conventional cords and cord weights. The usual PBX supervisory and control signals were available, plus some special features which aided holding, call transfer, monitoring, and preferential use where lines and trunks were used in common with a regular PBX. The first installation of the 508 PBX was in 1953 for the Bonneville Power Administration, whose operations were spread over the states of Washington, Oregon, Idaho, and Montana.[67]

Another special system innovation developed in the 1950s—the Civil Emergency Reporting System—was made available for use by municipal governments. Its purpose was to aid citizens to report, from the streets, emergency situations such as fires, accidents, rescue needs, and incidents needing police assistance. Originally developed for reporting fires from outdoor telephone sets over direct lines to a headquarters location, the 520 PBX was subsequently expanded during the 1950s for dual use to provide communication with both fire and police headquarters. The system was also arranged for various size switchboards for the headquarters location, and for optional concentration of reporting lines. Several new service features were developed, and the entire system was designed so that it could be engineered in building block form to meet economically the varied requirements of small and large cities. An outdoor reporting telephone used with this system is shown in Fig. 13-77.

Municipalities using the Emergency Reporting System felt that telephone-type emergency reporting systems had many advantages over the older telegraph-type fire alarm systems. For example, the operator at a municipal headquarters received not only a visual indication of the location of the reporting telephone, but also a verbal description of the exact location and details of the emergency. This assured immediate dispatch of the proper kind of equipment. The improvement in accuracy and completeness of report, together with the demonstrated fact that voice contact reduced the possibility of false alarms, increased the over-all efficiency of the emergency effort. The high reliability of the system, derived from the use of individual loops under continuous electrical test, as compared to the older common multistation loop technology, became apparent. Finally, the system was maintained by skilled telephone company personnel backed by large reserves of special manpower and material in the event of catastrophic situations.

Fig. 13-77. An outdoor reporting telephone, first used in the 1950s for reporting fires, then expanded to include calls to police.

Fig. 13-78 shows a system concept of the civil emergency reporting facilities, and Fig. 13-79 shows the concepts of direct line and concentrated line applications. For any of these applications, a person desiring to originate an emergency call needed only to open the door of the outdoor telephone set and remove the handset from the switchhook: the call was automatically indicated at the headquarters switchboard by an audible signal and flashing lamp until the operator answered. (Operation of an optional pushbutton at the outdoor set would have automatically routed the call to police headquarters.) The switchboard, shown in Fig. 13-80, followed the previously described 508 PBX philosophy—that is, circuits were terminated in keys (pushbuttons in the 520 PBX) for rapid answering and were terminated also in jacks for cord switching to other points when required. Features of the system included a recorder which printed a ticket showing the station number, date, and time of day of each call. Commercial voice recording equipment could also be connected where desired.[68]

Yet another system designed for emergency use in the mid-1950s permitted a dispatcher at a central location to broadcast an alert to volunteer firemen in suburban communities over their regular telephone lines, and to inform them of the nature and location of fires. In addition to fire alerting, this system, called the Group Alerting

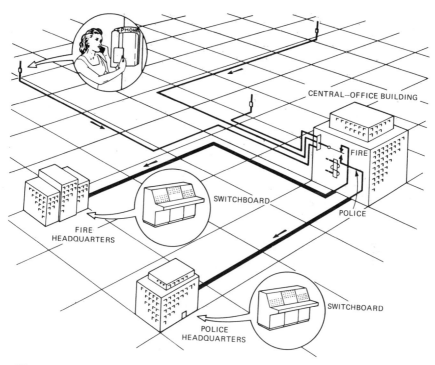

Fig. 13-78. System concept of the civil emergency reporting system. Loops under continuous electrical test helped insure dependability.

System, was adaptable to alerting civil defense personnel and plant personnel in large industrial concerns. Appliquéd to the regular telephone lines, initiation of an alert by the dispatcher caused the system to test each line for busy, seize idle lines (while "camping-on" the busy lines), and ring the telephones with a distinctive ring. The dispatcher's message was received directly by those who answered immediately, or received from an announcement machine by those who answered at a later time. Fig. 13-81 shows the plan for this system first installed in Garden City, Long Island in 1958.[69]

The 1950s and 1960s saw the introduction of other special customer switching systems—systems that automatically controlled and supervised power and pipeline facilities, systems that provided selective signaling over long multistation private lines for trucking companies and the like,[70] and systems for special communications in hospitals. An innovation with this system was a new self-checking code that could be transmitted over line facilities by a two-state signal. The code—similar in structure to the parallel 2-out-of-5 code used in No. 5 crossbar for signaling between common-control units—used five serial pulses, any two of which were short and the other three long.

Among the most interesting of the special systems were those developed for the defense agencies of the U.S. government. In 1941, with the country on the brink of war, the nation's defense agencies organized an air raid warning service to help protect against surprise attack from hostile aircraft. Developed in coopera-

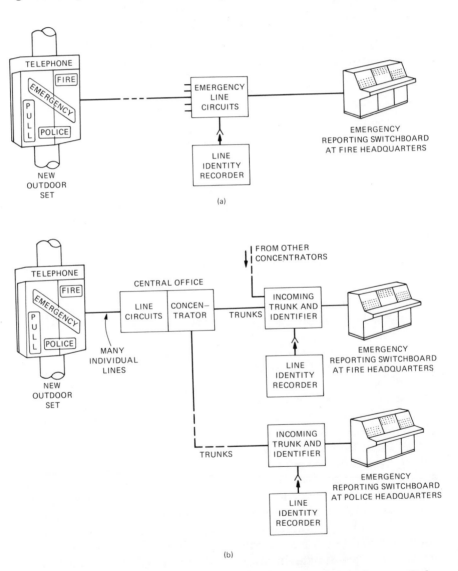

Fig. 13-79. Emergency lines could be connected (a) directly to switchboards or (b) through concentrators.

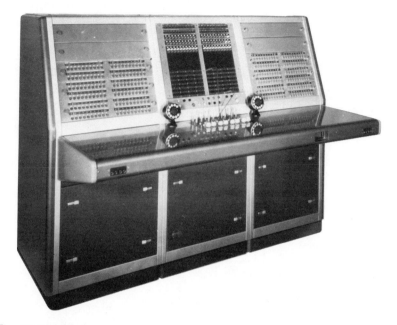

Fig. 13-80. Emergency reporting switchboard. A lamp lit and an audible alarm sounded when user lifted handset from the switchhook of an emergency telephone.

tion with the Bell System, the warning service was based upon visual observations by thousands of civilians. Radar, just then coming into use, was at the time highly secret, and was used only by the military. At observation posts, observers reported their findings by telephone to operational centers along the north Atlantic coast. Air raid information centers were installed in cities such as Boston, New York, Philadelphia, Baltimore, Harrisburg, and Norfolk. A typical center is shown in Fig. 13-82. Observers' reports describing an aircraft's type, heading, and estimated altitude were received at a filter position by civilian plotters seated around a large map of the area (as indicated by notations 1 and 2 of the figure) who in turn placed markers on the map corresponding to the observer's location. Cumulative reports of aircraft positions helped to filter out erroneous judgments and to establish potential courses and strengths of numbers. The information developed at the filter board was communicated to other operational rooms at the center, where military personnel made firm evaluations and decided upon courses of action.

As might be apparent from this brief description, rapid and reliable communications were required between a multitude of outlying points and the center, with instantaneous communication between

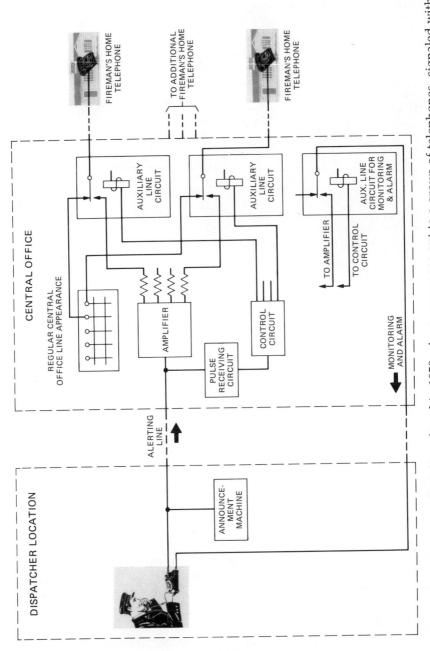

Fig. 13-81. Group alerting system, introduced in 1958. A message goes out to a group of telephones, signaled with a distinctive ring. System camps on busy lines until the message can be delivered.

the center's operations posts, and from there to the air raid warning wardens, the defending fighter squadrons, the searchlights, and the anti-aircraft batteries. It was obvious that the communications were a firm responsibility of the Bell System, a responsibility further emphasized by the added requirement that a minimum of costly circuits should be set up. This was necessary since reports from any

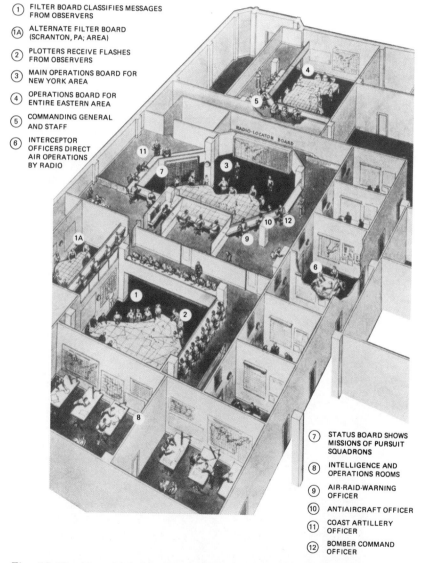

① FILTER BOARD CLASSIFIES MESSAGES FROM OBSERVERS

(1A) ALTERNATE FILTER BOARD (SCRANTON, PA; AREA)

② PLOTTERS RECEIVE FLASHES FROM OBSERVERS

③ MAIN OPERATIONS BOARD FOR NEW YORK AREA

④ OPERATIONS BOARD FOR ENTIRE EASTERN AREA

⑤ COMMANDING GENERAL AND STAFF

⑥ INTERCEPTOR OFFICERS DIRECT AIR OPERATIONS BY RADIO

⑦ STATUS BOARD SHOWS MISSIONS OF PURSUIT SQUADRONS

⑧ INTELLIGENCE AND OPERATIONS ROOMS

⑨ AIR-RAID-WARNING OFFICER

⑩ ANTIAIRCRAFT OFFICER

⑪ COAST ARTILLERY OFFICER

⑫ BOMBER COMMAND OFFICER

Fig. 13-82. Air raid information center, 1941. Civilian spotters over a wide area reported aircraft sightings to center, where information was plotted and evaluated.

particular observation post would be infrequent. Moreover, standard telephone equipment and circuits had to be used as much as possible to expedite installation and to make maximum use of the engineering, installation, and maintenance know-how such standardization would bring. Accordingly, calls from the observers were routed over regular exchange facilities to a nearby central office operator. A cryptic phrase such as "Army-Flash-Hickory" was used, which meant to the local operator and subsequent toll operators (the nation's toll system was still operator-handled) that the call should be completed to a set of jacks labeled the "Hickory" sector of the filter board. At this board, the circuits terminated before the plotters in a key arrangement. The talking, signaling, and control functions were performed by key telephone units designed for the 1A key telephone system (see above, section 4.5). As shown in Fig. 13-83, supervisory and operational personnel monitored and

Fig. 13-83. Wartime personnel using 101-type key equipment to communicate information derived from air raid observers.

intercommunicated using 101-type Key equipment (see above, section 4.4).

This system, seemingly primitive by today's standards, nevertheless was not inconsistent with the state of the aviation art at the time. Moreover, the system was rapidly implemented and made maximum use, at a reasonable cost, of the Bell System's technological and operational capabilities. An idea of the value placed upon it can be gained from a quotation by a military spokesman who said at the time: ". . . We have the finest telephone service and equipment in the world, all concentrated under one company; a company that has been so enthusiastically helpful in cooperating with the Army that it can be said with assurance that it couldn't have been done without the telephone company. They have developed special equipment; their engineers have worked with the Army over long periods; they have designed and built information centers and lent their experts to teach people how to run them; they have done a magnificent job." Sentiments such as these have since been expressed more than once by federal agencies involved in assuring adequate communications for the nation's defense.[71]

Further development of systems for government communications is described in Chapters 5 and 12 of the volume of this history series subtitled *National Service in War and Peace (1925–1975)*. Many of these systems leaned heavily on the PBX, key telephone system, and special systems technology described in this volume. For example, the SAGE system, developed in the 1950s for air defense communications, employed key telephone technology for the controller's consoles and the self-checking "pulse link" signaling technique originally developed for power and pipeline control systems. The air route traffic control systems Nos. 300 and 301 also stemmed from key telephone system technology. And the 758-type switching systems, developed in the 1960s as a 4-wire switching system to meet both specific and general-purpose requirements and applied to the Tennessee Valley Authority, NASA, the Army, and the Pentagon, were derived from the 756 PBX design.

5.4 Teletypewriter and Data Switching

The interest by the Bell System in telegraphy and its descendants in data communication systems dates back to (1) Alexander Graham Bell's work on the harmonic telegraph leading to his fundamental patent on the telephone (1875), (2) the beginnings of the Bell System providing private lines for the telegraph business (1879), and (3) the work on composite circuits beginning in the 1890s to serve voice and low-speed telegraphy on common wires. Western Electric began building early page printers (teletypewriters) in 1912. During this time, the Bell System studied the products of various manufacturers and subsequently standardized a design of a teletypewriter made by the Morkrum Co. of Chicago. Morkrum later consolidated with Kleinschmidt Electric Co. to become the Teletype Corporation in 1923, and the Bell System acquired this company on October 1, 1930. By 1927 the Bell System had 280,000 miles of lines serving printing telegraphs and 785,000 miles serving manual telegraph systems. The latter was just beginning its decline in favor of the page printing systems using teletypewriters. (See Chapter 7 on non-voice communications in another volume of this series, *The Early Years: 1875–1925*, for more details of these beginnings.)

Since teletypewriters were much more expensive than the telegraph keys they replaced, there was an incentive to let one or a small number of teletypewriters service a larger number of lines. This required a switching mechanism to connect the machines to the lines—a function performed by a small key-type manual switch, developed to serve as many as 24 lines, primarily for broadcasting messages to a selected number of stations.[72] This was known as the 65-B-1 PBX.

From its beginning the Bell System provided private-line telegraph service. Leased circuits were also used with teletypewriters. With the purchase of the Teletype Corporation, the Bell System took its first step toward making switched teletypewriter service a public offering. This two-way service became a reality on November 21, 1931.[73] Initially there were about 900 stations served. A No. 1 manual telephone switchboard was modified to include a teletypewriter in the keyshelf for the operator (see Fig. 13-84). Instead of a transmitter and headset, the operator used this teletypewriter to communicate with users.

By 1938 TWX service, as the teletypewriter service came to be known, had grown to serve 11,000 stations in 160 cities, and it had a hierarchical network much like that of the telephone network. Regenerative repeaters were developed so that the asynchronous digital pulses representing the characters could be sent over long distances.[74]

To provide central switching for this service, a number of switchboards were developed, most of them adapted from the correspondingly numbered manual telephone switchboards.[75] The first to be deployed was the No. 1 and 1A TWX multiple switchboard for use in large switching centers.[76] The 1A switchboard could serve as many as 3720 lines and 1200 trunks. The No. 3 and 3A multiple switchboards, shown in Fig. 13-85, can be arranged to serve the mid-range of needs up to 1400 lines and 240 trunks. The cordboard and teletypewriters were arranged in an over-under configuration rather than side-by-side for each operation to conserve space and minimize the length of wiring for the board-to-board multipling.[77]

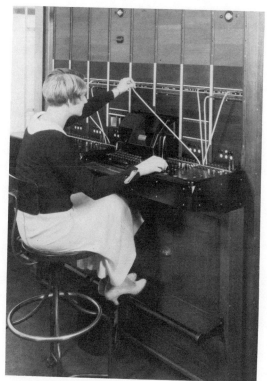

Fig. 13-84. Manual switchboard adapted to teletypewriter service, 1931. Instead of a telephone headset and microphone, the operator used the teletypewriter keyboard.

For the smallest installations, a nonmultipled switchboard, the No. 5, was developed to serve a maximum of 60 lines.[78] Later, to serve lines that were not near the established switching centers, a remote line concentrator using crossbar switches, known as the 101A concentrator, was developed.[79]

Manual TWX service developed well despite the depression of the 1930s. Prior to World War II, it became evident that the expansion of certain large national corporations created a need for faster service more readily adapted to their specific needs. As a result, an automatic system, the 81-B-1 private-line teletypewriter switching system, was developed and first placed in service at Republic Steel in Cleveland, Ohio in October 1941.[80] This system employed crossbar switches and paper tape reperforators.[81] Incoming messages were transmitted to reperforators that represented the outgoing destinations. These reperforators stored the messages in the order of reception for retransmission when the facilities became

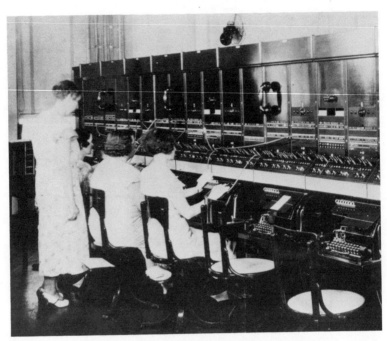

Fig. 13-85. 3A teletypewriter exchange (TWX) switchboard, developed for centers smaller than the 3720-line 1A switchboard.

idle, after all previously received messages were transmitted. A similar operation took place on incoming facilities before routing traffic across the office through the crossbar switches. These and many teletypewriter switching innovations described herein were the result of work at Bell Laboratories led by W. M. Bacon, G. A. Locke, R. D. Parker, F. J. Singer, and W. F. Watson.

After World War II, the need for private teletypewriter networks increased, particularly for airline companies. Pan Am was the first to install a large network, with three switching centers in October 1948, followed rapidly by General Motors and Eastern Airlines. This system was called the 81-C-1 and included an improved typing reperforator and a few additional features over the 81-B-1 system.[82] A block diagram of the system is shown in Fig. 13-86. Provision was made for selective calling to stations. At the station, a motor-driven selecting unit known as SOTUS (Sequentially Operated Tele-typewriter Universal Selector) responded to characters representing the station.

The 81-D-1 system followed in 1953 with the capability of temporarily storing undelivered messages in the switching system. The first customer was American Airlines. As shown in Fig. 13-87, this

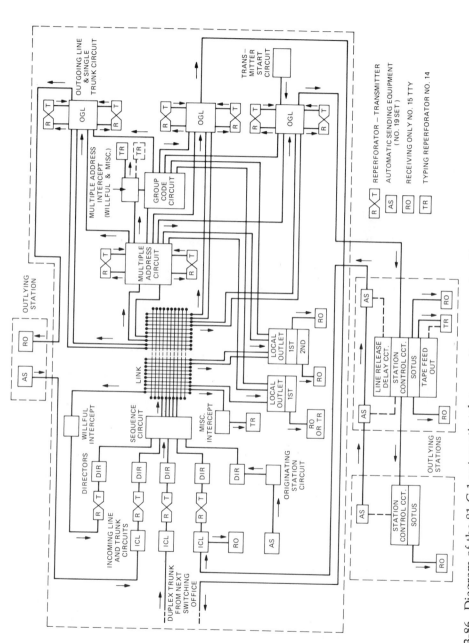

Fig. 13-86. Diagram of the 81-C-1 automatic teletypewriter system, developed after World War II and first used by Pan American Airlines, General Motors, and Eastern Airlines.

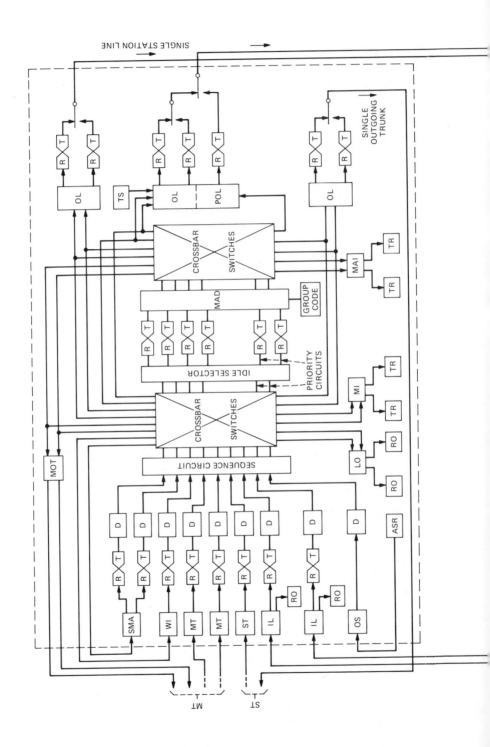

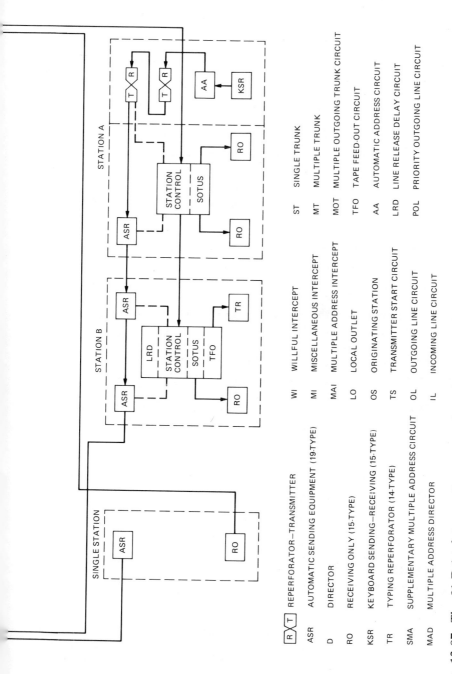

Fig. 13-87. The 81-D-1 teletypewriter system, introduced in 1953. It could temporarily store undelivered messages in the switching system.

R⨯T REPERFORATOR–TRANSMITTER

ASR AUTOMATIC SENDING EQUIPMENT (19-TYPE)

D DIRECTOR

RO RECEIVING ONLY (15-TYPE)

KSR KEYBOARD SENDING–RECEIVING (15-TYPE)

TR TYPING REPERFORATOR (14-TYPE)

SMA SUPPLEMENTARY MULTIPLE ADDRESS CIRCUIT

MAD MULTIPLE ADDRESS DIRECTOR

WI WILLFUL INTERCEPT

MI MISCELLANEOUS INTERCEPT

MAI MULTIPLE ADDRESS INTERCEPT

LO LOCAL OUTLET

OS ORIGINATING STATION

TS TRANSMITTER START CIRCUIT

OL OUTGOING LINE CIRCUIT

IL INCOMING LINE CIRCUIT

ST SINGLE TRUNK

MT MULTIPLE TRUNK

MOT MULTIPLE OUTGOING TRUNK CIRCUIT

TFO TAPE FEED-OUT CIRCUIT

AA AUTOMATIC ADDRESS CIRCUIT

LRD LINE RELEASE DELAY CIRCUIT

POL PRIORITY OUTGOING LINE CIRCUIT

involved the addition of another stage of crossbar switching and reperforators.[83] The Civil Aeronautics Administration used one of these systems, with magnetic drum storage, for the experimental distribution of flight plans. The growth of nationwide public and private TWX service prompted improvements in maintenance facilities. The No. 2 Telegraph Serviceboard was placed in service in the early 1950s.[84]

The 82-B-1 switching system was placed in service in 1960, with the U.S. Navy as the initial customer.[85,86] This system provided for regular and priority service, variable speed operation (60, 75, or 100 words per minute), and greater redundancy to insure against component and common machine failures. The cross-office reperforating speed was increased to 200 words per minute.

Since teletypewriter operation frequently involved the broadcasting of messages and a number of stations on one line, it was natural that a distributed rather than central type of switching be applied to this service. The 83-A-1 and 83-B-1 systems were developed in the mid-1950s to fill service needs more economically. These and later systems of this type were known as selective-calling teletypewriter systems.[87] The 83-A-1 system was relatively simple and required no special equipment at the stations other than teletypewriters that could perform circuit functions for specific characters (called "stunt boxes") and reperforators.

The 83-B-1 system included a polling function to eliminate contention for stations that desired to originate messages simultaneously (see Fig. 13-88). A single line served a maximum of 38 stations. Regular and priority messages were polled separately. Traffic could be interchanged among several lines, with a reperforator in each direction between them.

These systems were half duplex. Later, the 83-C-1 was developed wherein messages could be sent and received simultaneously (full duplex).

By 1962 the nationwide TWX service had grown to 60,000 stations with manual switchboards at 100 locations. The average call required two and one-half minutes to be interpreted and repeated by the operators using teletypewriter machines. As a result, it was decided to improve the service by automating the switching for public teletypewriter service.[88] As described earlier (see Chapter 11, section 1.6), the No. 5 crossbar system was modified to provide for the automatic switching of TWX calls. The stations were modified by providing dials, telephones, and data (digital-to-analog) modems. The 2A remote concentrator was developed to provide access to the nationwide network where a modified No. 5 crossbar office was not located within range. A new telegraph carrier system was developed so that more trunks could be derived for this service.[89]

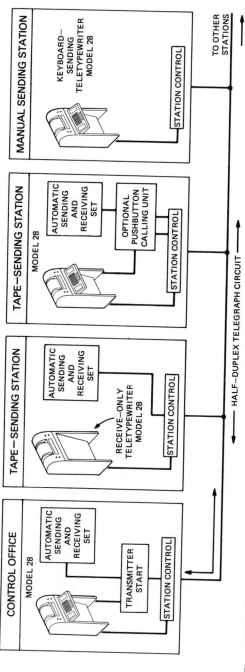

Fig. 13-88. Control office of an 83-B-1 system (left) and various types of stations. A polling operation eliminated contention for the circuit.

All 60,000 stations, switchboards, switching systems, and concentrators were converted to this service on the Labor Day weekend on August 31, 1962. For those calls still requiring the assistance of an operator, a new (6A) switchboard was developed.[90] These were placed around the country at 16 locations, including directory assistance in St. Louis.

As data transmission and solid state electronics grew, an improved selective-calling system became desirable. Higher-speed teletypewriters appeared (150 words per minute) and new expanded 7-bit ASCII codes (in place of the original 5-bit codes) became popular for data transmission. The 85 and 86 selective-calling systems were developed to meet the new service needs, and were first placed in service in 1971.[91] The systems are completely electronic with improved maintenance and reliability features, including parity checks and loop-around testing. The 85 system is half duplex, and the 86 system is for both half and full duplex service.

Several central office switching systems for private networks of teletypewriters and higher-speed data communications were developed and deployed using No. 5 crossbar (see Chapter 11, section 1.6) and No. 1 ESS (Chapter 9, section 6.3). The turnover of the responsibility of the public TWX network from the Bell System to Western Union in April, 1971, terminated the further deployment and development of these systems.

As data transmission increased in popularity, the need to query central data bases became evident. One of the first message switches developed for non-teletypewriter application was the Transaction Network (see Fig. 13-89). It also involved station polling as well as high-speed data transmission at 1200 bits per second.[92]

Originally (1973), a special station for reporting transactions was developed using the public telephone network and data modems. However, with the very short holding time of each "transaction," the regular dial network was too slow. The transaction network was able to gather information from a data station selector (the polling switch) that served a maximum of 30 stations and transmit transaction information at higher speed (up to 9.6 kilobits per second) to a message switch. The message switch consisted of a 3A central control (see Chapter 9, section 7.2) that could serve many hundreds of these networks, each capable of serving several different customer data bases. Transaction systems began service in 1976, the first being in Seattle, Washington.

5.5 Switching of Network Facilities

5.5.1 Broadcast

With the advent of radio networks in the early 1930s the need arose for arrangements to switch links between the sources of net-

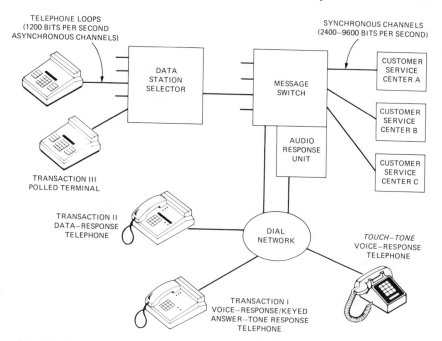

TELEPHONE LOOPS
(1200 BITS PER SECOND
ASYNCHRONOUS CHANNELS)

SYNCHRONOUS CHANNELS
(2400–9600 BITS PER SECOND)

DATA STATION SELECTOR

MESSAGE SWITCH

AUDIO RESPONSE UNIT

CUSTOMER SERVICE CENTER A

CUSTOMER SERVICE CENTER B

CUSTOMER SERVICE CENTER C

TRANSACTION III POLLED TERMINAL

TRANSACTION II DATA–RESPONSE TELEPHONE

DIAL NETWORK

TOUCH–TONE VOICE–RESPONSE TELEPHONE

TRANSACTION I VOICE–RESPONSE/KEYED ANSWER–TONE RESPONSE TELEPHONE

Fig. 13-89. Structure of the Transaction Network, developed to handle short data messages of the types used in banking, credit-card, and airline reservation transactions.

work programs and the radio stations.[93] The radio stations, because of time-zone differences and nonpermanent affiliations with networks, required access to different networks at the same time. Also, it was more economical to use the same facilities for different networks when such facilities were not needed full time. Operating centers using coordinate arrays of pushbuttons were developed to perform the switching function more efficiently. Complex switching could take place on queue with this arrangement, switching on a preprogrammed basis.[94] The development included special lighted buttons. The initial installations with operating centers in major cities took care of seven permanent networks designated by color (red, blue, etc.) and five other sources. These color codings subsequently became known to the public as the designations of certain public broadcasting networks by their use in identification announcements and promotional advertising. By 1932 there were 175 stations using over 35,000 miles of facilities.

When television came along, similar facilities were developed.[95] The pushbuttons and program logic in this case controlled transmission pads and wire spring relays that switched the higher-frequency television signals. Fig. 13-90 shows the manual switch used at one of the technical operating centers. They handled preselection of not

Fig. 13-90. Manual system for switching television signals. When TV programs change on the hour and half-hour, many circuits must be switched simultaneously.

only studio but remote sources. Many simultaneous changes, called salvos, would be required at the same time, usually on the hour or half-hour.

In addition to the switching equipment, technical operating centers (TOCs) were developed. These centers included positions for monitoring the programs and for maintaining the transmission facilities. TOCs came into operation in the early 1950s, and some 26 were in service in the mid-1970s. Remote switching and further automation of TOCs were introduced by the use of SCOTS (surveillance and control of transmission systems) in 1978 (see Fig. 13-91). As a result, the number of TOCs was reduced to six, and they were used for controlling the entire 20,000 mile Bell System nationwide television facilities network.[96]

5.5.2 *Protection*

As described in Chapter 7, people at testboards, using manual switching (patching) techniques, could substitute individual channels for bad ones when trouble was encountered in equipment or transmission facilities. Then, as broadband transmission facilities carrying hundreds and later thousands of channels were introduced into the nationwide network, it became prudent to provide spare facilities so as to insure service quality and to avoid undue conges-

Fig. 13-91. Automatic switching and surveillance of television network transmission in 1978.

tion in central offices. Initially, these spare broadband facilities were also switched manually by patching techniques.

In 1955, arrangements were developed for automatically switching the spare facilities of the TD2 radio system. One spare channel was provided for six service channels. This arrangement took care of equipment failures and additionally proved helpful under conditions of selective radio fading. It was found that deep fading of radio signals did not affect all channels equally, and that the switching-in of good channels improved service.[97] A special arrangement of mercury contacts was developed to switch the 70-MHz signals within the required crosstalk level.[98]

Later, these techniques were applied to the TH radio system[99] and to the L3[100] and L4[101] coaxial cable systems. A separate protection system, coded 400A, was developed for mastergroup terminals for the L4 system[102] and the T2 digital transmission system.[103] The 400A employed high-speed solid state switches[104] with improved crosstalk attenuation. In the Bell System, spare facilities with automatic switching has become a general requirement to insure service quality for multiplex transmission systems employing large numbers of channels.

Readers may have noted the interplay of technology between PBX and key telephone systems and the application of these disciplines to special systems. Highly significant in this transition—particularly from the commercial to the defense environment—is the fact that this technological carryover could not have been achieved as efficiently, nor could systems have been produced meeting the same high standards of quality and performance, except for the fact that it was done by a unified organization. In some time frames the two results were achieved by virtually the same people; and where it was necessary to draw upon fresh talent, either because of expanded scope, new device technology, or the passage of time, the torch of integrity, fueled by knowledge, was passed along with facility and enthusiasm.

As one looks back over the Bell System's accomplishments in switching, one is impressed with the sure, deliberate and steady way developments have been carried out, independent of the particular generation of technology involved. Switching has also grown in complexity and, as a result, the development process has also grown in complexity. No longer can individual engineers be fully cognizant of all details of a switching system. Thus, such new and complex developments as No. 4 ESS, the SPC network, and the sophisticated DIMENSION PBXs are as much a tribute to management skills as to the engineers who develop the hardware and, now, software systems and subsystems and their components and design tools. It is because of the dedication and abilities of past and present designers and managers that new services and improved methods of operation have been compatibly introduced into the nationwide network as it grew many times in size and complexity.

REFERENCES, CHAPTER 13

1. Gray, C. R. "The 755 PBX." *Bell Laboratories Record* 16, June 1938, p. 336.
2. Abbott, H. H. "Sixty Years of PBX Development." *Bell Laboratories Record* 46, January 1968, p. 9.
3. Per conversation with H. H. Abbott.
4. Sohnle, G. F. "The 555 PBX." *Bell Laboratories Record* 27, April 1949, p. 125.
5. See ref. 2.
6. Williams, R. D. "The 740-E PBX." *Bell Laboratories Record* 29, October 1951, p. 460.
7. Treptow, F. W. "The 507A and 507B PBX." *Bell Laboratories Record* 30, May 1952, p. 205.
8. Fagen, M. D., ed. *A History of Engineering and Science in the Bell System: The Early Years, 1875–1925.* Murray Hill, New Jersey, 1975, p. 516.
9. Williford, O. H. "A Modern Crossbar PBX." *Bell Laboratories Record* 35, December 1957, p. 485.
10. Williams, R. D. "Crossbar Circuitry for a Small PBX." *Bell Laboratories Record* 37, January 1959, p. 23.
11. Olsen, O. C. and Walsh, J. G. "A Pushbutton PBX Switchboard." *Bell Laboratories Record* 39, May 1961, p. 161.
12. Depp, W. A. "The 101 Electronic Switching System." *Bell Telephone Magazine* 41, Winter 1962/63, p. 11.
    Williford, O. H. "The No. 101 Electronic Switching System." *Bell Laboratories Record* 41, November 1963, p. 374.
    Averill, R. M. and Stone, R. C. "No. 101 ESS: The Time-Division Switch Unit." *Bell Laboratories Record* 41, December 1963, p. 425.

Hughes, E. G. and Taylor, R. G. "No. 101 ESS Control Unit." *Bell Laboratories Record* **42**, February 1964, p. 61.

Seley, E. L. and Vigliante, F. S. "Common Control for an Electronic Private Branch Exchange." *IEEE Trans. on Communication and Electronics* **83**, July 1964, p. 321.

Depp, W. A. and Townsend, M. A. "An Electronic Private-Branch-Exchange Telephone Switching System." *IEEE Trans. on Communication and Electronics* **83**, July 1964, p. 329.

Irland, E. A. and Vogelsong, J. H. "Memory and Logic System for an Electronic Private Branch Exchange." *IEEE Trans. on Communication and Electronics* **83**, July 1964, p. 332.

Herndon, J. A. and Tendick, F. M., Jr. "A Time Division Switch for an Electronic Private Branch Exchange." *IEEE Trans. on Communication and Electronics* **83**, July 1964, p. 338.

Depp, W. A. "No. 101 Electronic Switching System." Paper delivered at Colloque International de Commutation Electronique, Paris, France, April 1966.

Breen, C. "Expanding the No. 101 ESS." *Bell Laboratories Record* **44**, May 1966, p. 150.

Browne, T. E., Wadsworth, D. J. and York, R. K. "New Time Division Switch Units for No. 1 ESS." *Bell System Technical Journal* **48**, February 1969, p. 443.

Priebe, H. F., Jr. and Seley, E. L. "No. 101 ESS 4A Switch Unit." *Bell System Technical Journal* **48**, February 1969, p. 477.

Carlson, R. G., Weber, N. D. and Wolf, R. B. "New Switching Concept for Multilocation Customers." *Bell Laboratories Record* **49**, September 1971, p. 230.

13. Abbott, H. H. "The 800A Electronic PBX for 20 to 80 Lines." Paper delivered at Colloque International de Commutation Electronique, Paris, France, April 1966.

14. Baker, D., Botsford, N., Jr., Gagne, D. J. and Singer, F. L. "Electronic Switching for Small PBXs." *Bell Laboratories Record* **45**, February 1967, p. 49.

15. Meise, H. A., Jr. and Singer, F. L. "810A PBX System Description." *International Conference on Communications*, Montreal, Canada, June 1971, p. 16–1.

16. Burtness, R. D. "810A PBX Semiconductor Integrated Circuits and Hybrid Technology." *International Conference on Communications*, Montreal, Canada, June 1971, p. 16.

17. "Field Trial Under Way for 810A PBX." *Bell Labs News*, Vol. 14, April 23, 1971, p. 1.

18. Lane, M. S. "The 801A: Midi-PBX." *Bell Laboratories Record* **50**, May 1972, p. 134.

19. Wiidakas, J. D. "PBX Maintenance Comes Wrapped in a New Package." *Bell Laboratories Record* **53**, July/August 1975, p. 300.

20. Lemp, J., Jr. "The 805A PBX—A Switching Bargain for Small Businesses." *Bell Laboratories Record* **51**, May 1973, p. 136.

21. Hoffman, M. A. and Ryan, A. P. "New Features for the 770A PBX." *Bell Laboratories Record* **53**, May 1975, p. 242.

22. Marek, J. J. "A Small PBX for the Small Business." *Bell Laboratories Record* **49**, January 1971, p. 23.

23. Singer, F. L. "812A PBX: Answering the Market's Call." *Bell Laboratories Record* **52**, November 1974, p. 302.

24. Holtfreter, R. P. "A Switch to Smaller Switches." *Bell Laboratories Record* **48**, February 1970, p. 46.

25. Gashler, R. J., Liss, W. A. and Renaut, P. W. "The Remreed Network: A Smaller, More Reliable Switch." *Bell Laboratories Record* **51**, July/August 1973, p. 202.

26. Gerrish, A. M., Lohmiller, R. V. and Saltus, G. E. "The DIMENSION PBX: A New All-Electronic Customer Switching System." *Bell Laboratories Record* **53**, September 1975, p. 316.

27. Lewis, T. G. "DIMENSION PBX—Many Features in a Compact System." *Proceedings of the National Electronics Conference* **30**, Chicago, Illinois, October 1975, p. 97.

28. Bauman, L. M., Braun, E. J., Hill, D. G., Moran, J. C. and Trimble, D. C. "The DIMENSION PBX: System and Hardware." *National Telecommunications Conference*, New Orleans, La., December 1975, p. 11–1.

29. Chao, C., Cicon, J. P., Fong, K. T. and Parker, W. W. "The DIMENSION PBX: Software." *National Telecommunications Conference*, New Orleans, La., December 1975, p. 11–8.

30. Smathers, J. E. and Tsao-Wu, N. T. "RMATS—Remote Maintenance System for DIMENSION PBXs." International Communications Conference, Boston, Massachusetts, June 1979, p. 55.3.1.

31. Schleinkofer, G. N. "Indialing to PBX Extensions: Application in a Step-by-Step Central Office Area." *Trans. AIEE* **78**, November 1959, p. 549.

32. Spiro, George. "CENTREX Service with No. 5 Crossbar." *Bell Laboratories Record* **40**, October 1962, p. 328.

33. Shea, P. D. "Centrex Service: A New Design for Customer Group Telephone Service in the Modern Business Community." *Trans. of the American Institute of Engineers* **80**, November 1961, p. 474.

34. See ref. 32 above.

35. Fuller, R. A. "Identifying CENTREX-CU Station Numbers Automatically for AMA Recording." *Bell Laboratories Record* **45**, September 1967, p. 256.
    Anderson, H. P. and Baker, D. "PBX Automatic Number Identification System." *Bell Laboratories Record* **45**, November 1967, p. 332.

36. Backman, G. A. and Pina, R. F. "Automatic Identified Outward Dialing for PBXs: Central Office Facilities." *Bell Laboratories Record* **46**, April 1968, p. 112.

37. "A New Central Office Facility for Automatic Identified Outward Dialing." *Bell Laboratories Record* **48**, September 1970, p. 251.

38. Liss, W. A., McGowan, J. K. and Wickham, T. F. "Centrex Service in No. 1 ESS." *Bell Laboratories Record* **46**, November 1968, p. 332.

39. Gagne, D. J. "Speeding Calls Through a PBX." *Bell Laboratories Record* **39**, June 1961, p. 220.

40. Coyne, J. H. "PBX Consoles." *Bell Laboratories Record* **41**, June 1963, p. 236.

41. Coyne, J. H. "Recorded Dictation Using PBX Extension Telephones." *Bell Laboratories Record* **34**, January 1956, p. 5.

42. Benson, M. L. "Message-Waiting Service." *Bell Laboratories Record* **37**, September 1959, p. 342.

43. Braund, R. J. "761A PBX." *Bell Laboratories Record* **42**, July-August 1964, p. 247.

44. Witkus, V. W. "New Services in PBX and CENTREX Systems." *IEEE Trans.* **81**, June 1962, p. 492.

45. Gagne, D. J. and Schulz, C. J. "Central Office and PBX Arrangements for TOUCH-TONE Calling." *IEEE Trans. on Communication and Electronics* **82**, March 1963, p. 5.

46. Breen, C. "The PICTUREPHONE® System: Customer Switching Systems." *Bell System Technical Journal* **50**, February 1971, p. 553.

47. Anderson, H. P. "The PICTUREPHONE® System: The 850A PBX." *Bell System Technical Journal* **50**, February 1971, p. 585.

48. Brown, D. W., Horvath, J. R. and Paxton, T. S. "The PICTUREPHONE® System: No. 101 ESS." *Bell System Technical Journal* **50**, February 1971, p. 605.

49. Cruser, V. I. "Multiplying the Subscriber's Line." *Bell Laboratories Record* **8**, July 1930, p. 527.

50. Malone, W. F. and Beaumont, W. M. "101-Type Key Equipments." *Bell Laboratories Record* **15**, August 1937, p. 370.

51. Beaumont, W. M. "A New Service for Residences." *Bell Laboratories Record* **11**, April 1933, p. 244.

52. Allen, L. H. "The 1A Key Telephone System." *Bell Laboratories Record* **18**, June 1940, p. 315.

53. Carter, H. T. "A Versatile New Intercom System." *Bell Laboratories Record* **36**, March 1958, p. 81.

54. Allen, L. H. "The 1A1 Key Telephone System." *Bell Laboratories Record* **34**, April 1956, p. 140.

55. Wood, W. F. B. "Key Telephone Systems: The Latest Chapter." *Bell Laboratories Record* **44**, March 1966, p. 85.

56. Bush, S. E. "Advances in the 1A2 Key Telephone System." *Bell Laboratories Record* **48**, October 1970, p. 259.

57. See ref. 44 above. Also see Daskalakis, A. "The PICTUREPHONE® System: Key Telephone Systems." *Bell System Technical Journal* **50**, February 1971, p. 567.

58. Hagland, H. M. "Secretarial Service." *Bell Laboratories Record* **14**, February 1936, p. 190.

59. Braund, R. J. "Secretarial Answering Services." *Bell Laboratories Record* **34**, October 1956, p. 370.

60. Watson, R. E., Jr. and Weinberg, S. B. "Telephone Answering Services." *Bell Laboratories Record* **43**, December 1965, p. 447.

61. Bowne, L. J. "A New Telephone Door for the Retail Shop." *Bell Laboratories Record* **7**, March 1929, p. 270.

62. Beaumont, W. M. "The No. 4 Order Turret." *Bell Laboratories Record* **17**, November 1938, p. 100.

63. Hagland, H. M. "Order Turret No. 3." *Bell Laboratories Record* **11**, September 1932, p. 2.

64. Abbott, H. H. "Modernized 'Information' for Large PBXs." *Bell Laboratories Record* **22**, January 1944, p. 218.

65. Abbott, H. H. "The 6A Order Turret." *Bell Laboratories Record* **29**, August 1951, p. 371.

66. Morse, C. E. "Meeting Business Needs with the No. 2B ACD." *Bell Laboratories Record* **53**, April 1975, p. 180.

67. Schulz, C. J. "Dispatcher's PBX Switchboard." *Bell Laboratories Record* **34**, July 1956, p. 259.

68. Michael, H. J. "Civil Emergency Reporting System." *Bell Laboratories Record* **34**, August 1956, p. 285.

69. Orost, J. and Seckler, W. H. "A New Group-Alerting System." *Bell Laboratories Record* **38**, December 1960, p. 446.

70. Gayet, P. J. "Automatic Control of a Pipeline." *Bell Laboratories Record* **37**, November 1959, p. 425. See also Bachelet, A. E. and Michael, H. J. "SS1 Selective Signaling System." *Bell Laboratories Record* **41**, February 1963, p. 51.

71. Tradup, A. "Telephone Network Aids Air Raid Interceptors." *Bell Laboratories Record* **20**, December 1941, p. 87.

72. Locke, G. A. "Telephone-Typewriter PBX Systems." *Bell Laboratories Record* **9**, January 1931, p. 214.

73. Locke, G. A. "Nation-Wide Teletypewriter Service." *Bell Laboratories Record* **10**, January 1932, p. 145.

74. Bell, J. H. "Reforming Telegraph Signals." *Bell Laboratories Record* **14**, July 1936, p. 355.

75. Locke, G. A. "Teletypewriter Exchange Systems." *Bell Laboratories Record* **15**, September 1936, p. 7.

76. Burgess, A. A. "The 1A Teletypewriter Switchboard." *Bell Laboratories Record* **16**, October 1937, p. 34.

77. Knowlton, A. D. "Novel Design Adapts 3A TWX to Wide Range of Conditions." *Bell Laboratories Record* **14**, January 1936, p. 146. See also Singer, F. J. "The Teletypewriter Exchange Network." *Bell Laboratories Record* **16**, January 1938, p. 167.

78. Koos, P. V. "The No. 5 Teletypewriter Switchboard." *Bell Laboratories Record* **16**, January 1938, p. 171.

79. Knandel, G. J. "An Automatic Teletypewriter Switching Office." *Bell Laboratories Record* **21**, October 1942, p. 49.

80. Bacon, W. M. "Automatic Switching for Private-Line Teletypewriter Service." *Bell Laboratories Record* **26**, January 1948, p. 20.

81. Lake, R. A. "Teletype Reperforator Transmitter for Automatic Switching Systems." *Bell Laboratories Record* **26**, March 1948, p. 106.

82. Bacon, W. M. "The 81-C-1 Teletypewriter Switching System." *Bell Laboratories Record* **27**, April 1950, p. 145.

83. Locke, G. A. and Robinson, E. R. "Automatic Private-Line Teletypewriter Switching System." *Bell Laboratories Record* **33**, September 1955, p. 321.

84. Purvis, M. R. "Service Features of the No. 2 Telegraph Serviceboard." *Bell Laboratories Record* **33**, March 1955, p. 100.

85. Robinson, E. R. "Automation in Teletypewriter Switching." *Bell Laboratories Record* **38**, May 1960, p. 182.

86. Crowson, F. B. and MacLaughlin, R. R. "Circuit Design of an Improved Teletypewriter Switching System." *Bell Laboratories Record* **38**, August 1960, p. 304.

87. Votaw, C. J. "Selective-Calling Teletypewriter Systems." *Bell Laboratories Record* **37**, February 1959, p. 64.

88. Tyberghein, E. J. "TWX Goes Dial." *Bell Laboratories Record* **40**, July-August 1962, p. 232.

89. Bowyer, L. R. "The B1 Data Trunking System." *Bell Laboratories Record* **43**, April 1965, p. 120.

90. Smith, T. A. "DTWX Assistance Operator Switchboard." *Bell Laboratories Record* **42**, January 1964, p. 8.

91. Carlson, D. E. and Votaw, C. J. "New Selective-Calling Stations for Low-Speed Private Line Data Service." *Bell Laboratories Record* **49**, August 1971, p. 203.

92. Pamm, L. R. "Transaction Network: Data Communications for Metropolitan Areas." *Bell Laboratories Record* **55**, January 1977, p. 8.

93. Entz, F. S. "A New Switching Unit for Program Circuits." *Bell Laboratories Record* **10**, August 1932, p. 430.

94. Murphy, P. B. "Program Switching and Pre-Selection." *Bell Laboratories Record* **20**, February 1942, p. 142.

95. Collins, C. A. and Hoffman, L. H. "Switching Control at Television Operating Centers." *Bell Laboratories Record* **35**, January 1957, p. 10.

96. Curnal, J. R. and Lorenz, J. A. "Automating Television Operating Centers." *Bell Laboratories Record* **51**, March 1978, p. 64.

97. Bellows, B. C. "Automatic Protection Switching for TD-2 Radio." *Bell Laboratories Record* **34**, March 1956, p. 98.

98. Volz, A. H. "High-Speed Magnetically-Operated Coaxial Switch." *Bell Laboratories Record* **34**, August 1956, p. 305.

99. Higgins, R. H., Klenk, L. M., and McClelland, W. R. "Automatic Protection Switching For the TH System." *Bell Laboratories Record* **40**, May 1962, p. 173.

100. Marki, G. P. "Protection Switching For the L3 Carrier System." *Bell Laboratories Record* **41**, November 1963, p. 381.

101. Albert, W. G., Haley, T. J., and Merrick, T. B. "L-4 Terminal Equipment: The MMX-2." *Bell Laboratories Record* **45**, July-August 1967, p. 218.

102. "New Protection Switching System." *Bell Laboratories Record* **52**, February 1974, p. 30.

103. Bobsin, H. H., and Forman, L. E. "The T2 Digital Line—Extending the Digital Network." *Bell Laboratories Record* **51**, September 1973, p. 239.

104. Purvis, M. B., and Kordos, R. W. "Reed-Contact Switch Series for the I.F. Band." *Bell System Technical Journal* **49**, February 1970, p. 229.

Abbreviations and Acronyms

ACD	automatic call distributor
ACTS	automatic coin telephone service
ADCI	automatic display call indicator
ADF	arranged for data features
AFADS	automatic force adjustment data system
AIC	automatic intercept center
AIOD	automatic identified outward dialing
AIS	automatic intercept system
ALIT	automatic line insulation test
AMA	automatic message accounting
AMARC	automatic message accounting recording center
ANC	all number calling
ANF	automatic number forwarding
ANI	automatic number identification
ARU	audio response unit
ATA	automatic trouble analysis
AUTOVON	AUTOmatic VOice Network
AV-3	third AUTOVON generic program
BDT	billing data transmitter
BIS	business information system
BLF	busy line field
CAMA	centralized AMA
CC1	central control-1
CCIS	common channel interoffice signaling
CCITT	Comité Consultatif International Télégraphique et Téléphonique
CCS	hundred call-seconds
CCSA	common-control switching arrangement
CDA	call data accumulator
CDO	community dial office
Centrex-CO	Centrex using central office
Centrex-CU	Centrex using customer unit
CLR	combined line and recording

CMD	centralized message distribution
CMS	circuit maintenance system
COER	central office equipment report
COMAS	central office maintenance and administration system
CONUS AUTOVON	CONtinental U.S. AUTOmatic VOice Network
COSMIC*	COmmon System Main InterConnecting frame
COSMOS	COmputer System for Main frame Operations System
CREG	concentrated range extension with gain
CRT	cathode ray tube
CSACS	centralized status, alarm and control system
CSP	control switching point
CSS	customer switching system
CX	composite (circuit)
DA	directory assistance
DA/C	computerized directory assistance
DA/M	directory assistance using microfiche and microfilm
DCTS	DIMENSION† custom telephone service
DDD	direct distance dialing
DIAD	(magnetic) drum information assembler-dispatcher
DAIS	defense automatic integrated switch
DID	direct inward dialing
DOC	dynamic overload control
DP	dial pulse
DRE	directional reservation equipment
DSA	dial system assistance (switchboard)
DSB	dial system "B" (switchboard)
DSS	direct station selection
DX	duplex (circuit)
EADAS	engineering and administrative data acquisition system
EAS	extended area service
ECASS	electronically controlled automatic switching system
ECDO	electronic community dial office
ECO	electronic central office
ENIAC	electronic number integrator and calculator
EPBX	electronic private branch exchange

*Trademark of Western Electric Company
†Trademark of AT&T Company

ESS	electronic switching system
ESSEX	Experimental Solid State EXchange
ETS	electronic translator system
FACD	foreign area customer dialing
FAT	foreign area translation
FTS	Federal Telephone System
FX	foreign exchange
HACD	home area customer dialing
HOBIS	HOtel Billing Information System
IDDD	international direct distance dialing
IGFET	isolated gate field effect transistor
INWATS	inward wide area telephone service
IOD	identified outward dialing
KDCI	key display call indicator
KRF	traffic simulator by Keister, Ritchie, and Frost
KSU	key service unit
KTS	key telephone system
KTU	key telephone unit
LAMA	local AMA
LLL	low level logic
LLN	line link network
LLP	line link pulsing
LSI	large scale integration
LSS	loop switching system
MAAP	maintenance and administration panel
MCC	master control console
MDAS	magnetic drum auxiliary sender
MDF	main distributing frame
MF	multifrequency
MOS	metal oxide semiconductor
MTR	magnetic tape recording
MTSO	mobile telephone switching office
NEASIM	NEtwork Analytical SIMulator
NORAD/ADS	NOrth American Air Defense command/ Automatic Dial Switching system
NOTIS	network operator trouble information system
NPA	numbering plan area
OCAP	operating company associate program
OETP	operating engineers training program
ONI	operator number identification
OSS	operation support system
PAM	pulse-amplitude modulation
PATROL	program for administrative traffic reports on-line

PBC	peripheral bus computer
PBT	piggy-back twistor
PBX	private branch exchange
PCI	panel call indicator
PECC	product engineering control center
PECS	programmable electronic call simulator
PETS	programmable electronic traffic simulator
PMT	permanent magnet twistor
POTS	plain old telephone service
PPCS	person-to-person, collect, special
RAM	random access memory
RCC	radio common carrier
RMATS	remote maintenance administration and traffic system
ROTS	rotary out-trunk selectors
RTA	remote trunk arrangement
SAMA	step-by-step AMA
SARTS	switched access remote test system
SCAN	switched circuit automatic network
SCC	switching control center
SCOTS	surveillance and control of transmission systems
SDDS	switched digital data service
SF	single-frequency
SLIM	stored logic in memory
SLN	service link network
SO	signal transfer point only
SOTUS	sequentially operated teletypewriter universal selector
SPC	stored-program control
SSI	small scale integration
STP	signal transfer point
SX	simplex (circuit)
TAC	technical assistance center
TASC	telecommunications alarm surveillance and control system
TASI	time assignment speech interpolation
TDRS	traffic data recording system
TG	trunk guard
TGUE	trunk group usage equipment
TLN	trunk link network
TMS	time multiplexed switch
TNDS	total network data system
TNOP	total network operations plan

TOC	technical operating center (also trunk operating center)
TORC	traffic overload reroute control
TSI	time slot interchange
TSP	traffic service position
TSPS	traffic service position system
TUR	traffic usage recorder
TWX	teletypewriter network
UNICOM	UNiversal Integrated COMmunications system
USP	usage sensitive pricing
UT	universal trunk
WATS	wide area telephone service

Credits

Acknowledgment is made for permission to reprint the following copyrighted material:

Figures 3-2, 3-3, 3-4, 3-5, and 3-37 from E. H. Goldsmith, *The Panel Type Dial Telephone System.* New York Telephone Company, October 1930, Third Edition.

Figures 3-7, 3-8 and 3-10 from K. B. Miller, *Telephone Theory and Practice*, 1st ed. Copyright 1933 by McGraw-Hill Book Company, Inc. Used with permission.

Figure 4-12 from R. E. Collis, "Crossbar Tandem System." *Transactions of the American Institute of Electrical Engineers*, Vol. 69 (1950). Copyright 1950 by the American Institute of Electrical Engineers. Reprinted with permission.

Figure 4-13 from J. Meszar, "The Full Stature of the Crossbar Tandem Switching System." *Transactions AIEE*, Vol. 75 (1956). Copyright 1956 by the American Institute of Electrical Engineers. Reprinted with permission.

Figure 5-16 from Charles W. Hadlock, "Reweaving the Long Lines Circuit Fabric." *Bell Telephone Magazine*, Vol. 30 (1951). Reprinted with permission.

Figure 5-18 from W. E. Ogren, "Network Management." *Bell Telephone Magazine*, Vol. 41 (1962). Reprinted with permission.

Figure 9-12 from C. E. Brooks, J. L. Henry, G. E. Markthaler and W. C. Sand, "Distributed Line Concentrator with Unique Intraconcentrator Completion Circuits." *Transactions AIEE*, Vol. 82 (1963). Copyright 1960 by the American Institute of Electrical Engineers. Reprinted with permission.

Figures 9-14, 9-15 and 9-16 from H. F. May, "Magnetic Drum Storage System Considered for Use as Common Sender in Nationwide Dialing." *Transactions AIEE*, Vol. 77 (1958). Copyright 1958 by the American Institute of Electrical Engineers. Reprinted with permission.

Figures 9-27 and 9-28 from T. S. Greenwood, "A 2.2-Megabit Photographic Store for an Electronic Switching System." Institute of

Bell System Switching Technology

A Chronology 1887-1979

Bold face numbers refer to
page numbers in this book

mid-1920s Introduction of No. 100 key equipment **540**

1926   First production of step-by-step equipment **22**

1926   Step-by-step tandem: first operator distance dialing (AB toll) (Los Angeles, California) **29**

1926   Trial of 350A step-by-step CDO (Sinking Springs, Pennsylvania) **33**

1926   Step-by-step: first line finder developed **27**

1926   Coordinate system development canceled **9**

1926   Manual alternate routing **174**

1926   First automatic alternate routing proposed **174**

1926   Cordless switchboard trial with 740A step-by-step PBX **515**

1926   March: First power rotary sender links **17**

1927   Toll: first combined line recording operation **54**

1927   Panel: cost reduced by 60 percent **11**

1927   Panel: first panel sender links **17**

1927   No. 3 toll switchboard: first cutover (over 50,000 positions installed in 35 years) (Reading, Pennsylvania) **36**

1927   January: Step-by-step system cutover: (Springfield, Massachusetts) **23**

1927   July: First 350A step-by-step CDO cutover (San Clemente, California) **32**

1928   Cordless switchboard: wire toll switching first proposed **78**

1928   T. C. Fry's book on probability and traffic published **116**

1928   First No. 2 order turret introduced **560**

1928   Improvements in cordless manual switchboards **515**

1929   First 360A step-by-step CDO cutover **33**

1929   Panel: ground cutoff type, 600,000 lines shipped and installed **20**

1929   Step-by-step: first trial of tandem switching (Connecticut) **32**

1929   Panel: first battery cutoff office **20**

1929   Network of fourteen 350A step-by-step cutover offices (southern California) **33**

1929   Panel: completion of cost reduction and improvement phase **63**

1929   No. 2 step-by-step call distributor developed **373**

1930   First manual mass announcement and distribution system, introduced with time-of-day announcements **42**

1930   First manual switchboard senders introduced (Detroit, Michigan) **50**

1930   Prepayment coin operation introduced **356**

1930   October 1: Bell System acquired Teletype Corporation **578**

1930   October: Panel: crossbar sender link development started **64**

1930   December: Crossbar switch design of new unit switch started **63**

1930s Broadcast network switching service provided to 175 radio stations **587**

1930s First key telephone equipment on customer premises **540**

1930s Wiring plans used for customers with a number of extensions and lines **540**

1931   December: 14-type local test desk: first cutover **40**

1931   No. 12 manual switchboard developed **39**

1931   Step-by-step tandem standardized (Los Angeles, California) **32**

1931   January: First panel sender tandem office cutover **11**

1931   November 21: First public offering of two-way teletypewriter service **578**

1932   370A & B step-by-step CDO: first cutover **33**

1932   740AX step-by-step PBX introduced **445**

1932   No. 3 order turret introduced **562**

1932   July: Crossbar: first satisfactory design tested **64**

1933   Introduction of 15A and 23A key equipment units **542**

1933   Third quarter: Crossbar switch: study application to PBX tandem and toll switching **67**

1934   Crossbar system: study completed; proceeding with final development **64**

1934   Crossbar tandem first proposed **74**

1934   No. 1 crossbar development funding provided **68**

1934   Systems engineering: founded with move of D&R Department from AT&T **92**

1934   First patents on AMA **92, 135**

1935   Crossbar inward toll call distribution: first Bell System application of crossbar switches (New York City) **39**

1935   Step-by-step intertoll system: first cutover; at peak maximum 800 in service **54**

1935   380 crossbar CDOs, development started **78**

1935   4-wire crossbar switching first proposed **81**

1935   554B and 554C secretarial switchboards for telephone answering service introduced **555**

1935   745A crossbar PBX development started **78, 446**

1935 November: Crossbar toll concentrator and call distributor: first commercial application of crossbar switches (New York City) **39**

mid-1930s Standardized telephone answering arrangements, called secretarial service, introduced **553**

1936 Operator and long distance dialing **11**

1936 U- and Y-type relays first developed **66**

1937 3B switchboard: improved toll tandem operation **39**

1937 September: No. 1 crossbar: precut testing started, 350,000 calls (Brooklyn, New York) **68**

1938 No. 2 crossbar development started **76**

1938 Electron beam switching tube invented **88**

1938 Combined 300-type telephone set included multiple buttons for 1A key telephone system **543**

1938 First crossbar PBX: 755 introduced **445**

1938 February: No. 1 crossbar: first cutover (Brooklyn, New York) **20, 68**

1938 July: No. 1 crossbar: first large installation cutover with added features **72**

1939 355A step-by-step CDO: first of 3500 installations totaling 4 million lines (Batavia, Ohio) **34**

1939 Magnetic tape recorder first used with weather announcements **42**

1939 745A crossbar PBX cutover (Philadelphia, Pennsylvania) **78**

1939 Step-by-step automatic ticketing: development started **92**

1939 Crossbar traffic studies by C. A. Lovell

1939 Traffic: Kittredge and Molina formula for crossbar networks proposed **102**

1940 3C switchboard: first introduced including 3CF package **38**

1940 Panel maintenance improvements **22**

1940 No. 2 crossbar lab model in operation **76**

1940 Step-by-step senderization development started **76**

1940 380 crossbar CDO cutover (Jonesville, New York) **78**

1940 Motorelay exploratory development **93**

1940 Traffic: dial tone delay measurement **106**

1940s Renewed study of call wire signaling **432**

1941 Crossbar tandem: first service **74**

1941 Electronic frequency-division switching proposed **88**

1941 Traffic: analysis of holding time measurements **104**

1941 No. 3 step-by-step call distributor developed **373**

1941 No. 6 order turret, first installation (Chicago, Illinois) **563**

1941 First 81-B-1 automatic teletypewriter switching system cutover (Cleveland, Ohio) **579**

1941 Air raid warning system developed (North Atlantic coast) **572**

1941 April: Crossbar tandem: first interzone tandem with remote control zone registration (New York City) **76**

1942 Traffic control: network management established (New York City) **108**

1942 First studies of electronic time-division switching **201**

1943 No. 5 toll switchboard: first cutover in association with No. 4 crossbar (Philadelphia, Pennsylvania) **83**

1943 Multi-zone coin service introduced using panel sender tandem **356**

1943 October: No. 4 toll crossbar: first cutover (Philadelphia, Pennsylvania) **83**

1944 January: First cutover of step-by-step automatic ticketing system (Los Angeles, California) **92, 133**

1945 Crossbar switch and relay contact studies and improved protection development **113**

1945 No. 5 crossbar simulator developed **108**

1945 First area code map **124**

1945 Ring translator invented by T. L. Dimond **161**

1945 Establishment of 10-digit nationwide numbering plan with area codes **370**

1945 October: Start of No. 5 crossbar development **157**

1946 Robot operator: exploratory development **94**

1946 First switching school organized **112**

1946 Design of 385 crossbar CDO **201**

1946 Studies of gas tube and semiconductor crosspoints **201**

1946 First standard 3-channel mobile radio system in service (St. Louis, Missouri) **295**

1946 April: 380 crossbar CDO removed from service (Jonesville, New York) **78**

1947 First 356 step-by-step CDO cutover **34**

1947 Trial of AMA central office recording (Washington, D.C.) **139**

1947 First Bell Labs branch laboratory (Allentown, Pennsylvania) **170**

1947 First crossbar tandem with toll features **190**

1947 Proposal for zero for dialing **308**

development started with time-division network **324**

1967 Nonconvertible TOUCH-TONE in step-by-step to use crossbar link **342**

1967 DATAPHONE 50 service started (No. 5 crossbar) **350**

1967 Interstate INWATS introduced **342**

1967 Standard dial-tone-first coin service available in No. 5 crossbar **358**

1967 2000-line 4A switch unit for No. 101 ESS introduced **469**

1967 4000-line 4A switch unit for No. 101 ESS introduced **469**

1967 January 8: First No. 1 ESS with generic CC1 program cutover (Los Angeles, California) **261**

1967 February: First No. 101 ESS 4A switch unit cutover (Naperville, Illinois) **256, 469**

1967 March: First new subscriber senders (No. 1 crossbar) **191**

1967 December: No. 1 ESS in service in 11 Bell Operating Companies and Bell of Canada **269**

1968 First No. 5 crossbar using smaller crossbar switches (Blue Island, Illinois) **168**

1968 Crossbar tandem peak: 34 local and 213 toll **190**

1968 Fourth issue of Notes on Distance Dialing **180**

1968 2-wire No. 2 ESS in operation (Indian Hill) **297**

1968 Adopted CCITT signaling system No. 6 **321**

1968 Standard dial-tone-first coin service available in No. 1 crossbar **358**

1968 Computerized directory assistance simulation trial (East Orange, New Jersey) **375**

1968 First field installation of traffic data recording system cutover (Washington, D.C.) **403**

1968 10 PTT administrations agree to participate in CCITT signaling system No. 6 trial **432**

1968 Proposals to FCC for high-capacity mobile radio telephone system **368**

1968 January 14: First cutover of No. 1 ESS Centrex-CO (Philadelphia, Pennsylvania) **346, 510**

1968 January 15: Announcement of 911 emergency calling **354**

1968 March 2: First service of No. 1 ESS office with signal processor **272**

1968 November: First No. 1 ESS with local tandem feature (Nashville, Tennessee) **328, 371**

1969 No. 1 crossbar: last new terminating marker group installed (Philadelphia, Pennsylvania) **73**

1969 First cutover of F-type signaling **130**

1969 No. 101 ESS arranged for main-satellite operation **256**

1969 First studies of electronic community dial office (ECDO) using integrated circuit technology **330**

1969 Call-waiting feature added to No. 1 ESS **411**

1969 No. 23 crossbar call distributor modified to improve reliability and for use as AIS concentrator **373**

1969 Developed wideband switching on No. 5 crossbar system for PICTURE-PHONE service **362**

1969 First No. 5 crossbar automatic call distributor cutover **373**

1969 First commercial use of larger No. 4A ESS switch unit at Mayo Clinic (Rochester, Minnesota) **471**

1969 Field trial of 810A ferreed PBX (Denver, Colorado) **487**

1969 January 19: Cutover of first TSPS (Morristown, New Jersey) **315**

1969 February: First and only No. 1 ESS ADF cutover (New York City) **278**

1969 April 20: First cutover of No. 4A crossbar ETS: new office (Grand Rapids, Michigan) **319**

1969 June: First standard Unigauge No. 5 crossbar office cutover (Dubuque, Iowa) **369**

1969 June 1: First cutover of No. 4A crossbar ETS (Los Angeles, California) **319**

1969 December: No. 1 ESS Centrex placed in service, 17,000 lines **277**

1960s Late 1960s: Local integrated circuit switching proposal by H. S. McDonald **202**

1970 16-type local cordless test desk introduced **40**

1970 Traffic: Feiner and Kappel extend network analysis to include control as well as switch cost **102**

1970 First No. 5 crossbar trunk link frame with smaller crossbar switch (Port Huron, Michigan) **168**

1970 13,600 directory assistance positions in service **373**

1970 Application of multiparty service in No. 1 ESS **382**

1970 Study of possible SPC modification of electromechanical switching systems **365**

1970 Beginning of New York City service crisis **385**

1970 558A manual PBX introduced **486**

1970 Over two million Centrex telephones in service **573**

1970 January: Decision (by W. H. C. Higgins) that digital time-division network will be developed for No. 4 ESS **422**

1970 March: Extension of IDDD (additional No. 5 crossbar offices) **192**

1970 March: No. 4 ESS digital time-division network expanded from 65,000 to 107,000 terminations **425**

1970 April: No. 1 crossbar peak deployment: 7.25 million lines, 325 terminating entities **73**

1970 April: No. 1 crossbar: last originating marker group installed (Chicago, Illinois) **73**

1970 April: First service link network No. 1 ESS (Chicago) **274**

1970 June: AIOD-A2 cutover (Wilmington, Delaware **346**

1970 June 11: Development of 1A processor authorized **292**

1970 September 13: First cutover of No. 1A AIS (Hempstead, New York) **324**

1970 October: Standard dial-tone-first coin service available for step-by-step (Cheyenne, Wyoming) **358**

1970 November 28: First cutover of No. 2 ESS (Oswego, Illinois) **297**

1971 No. 5 crossbar call waiting trial (Upper Arlington, Ohio) **168**

1971 Customer switching lab established (Denver, Colorado) **170**

1971 Start of No. 5A crossbar development **169**

1971 First IDDD on No. 1 ESS (New York City World Trade Center) **193**

1971 Growth procedures standardized for adding signal processor to No. 1 ESS offices **274**

1971 Peak of 45 4-wire No. 1 ESS in service (including 3 in Canada) **269**

1971 Bell System proposes cellular mobile radio telephone system **296**

1971 First use of integrated circuits in No. 1A SPC on TSPS **316**

1971 Computerized directory assistance live traffic trial (Oakland, California) **375**

1971 770A crossbar PBX introduced **482**

1971 April: First application of minicomputers to assist in central office maintenance and administration (COMAS) (New York City) **398**

1971 April 4: No. 1 ESS: first 32,000 core stores in service (Alton, Illinois) **282**

1971 August 29: First cutover of No. 2 ESS Unigauge office (North Madison, Connecticut) **346**

1971 September: Field trial of 805A crossbar PBX introduced **482**

1971 October: First cutover of double size No. 1A-AIS (Cleveland, Ohio) **327**

1971 November: Technical trial of improved call waiting on No. 5 crossbar (Upper Arlington, Ohio) **365**

1972 2B automatic call distributor smaller crossbar switches **168**

1972 Subscriber loop multiplexer with smaller crossbar switches **168**

1972 Trial of switching control center for ESS (Chicago, Illinois) **289**

1972 First trial of mini COMAS (Manchester, New Hampshire) **398**

1972 USITA informed of plans for employing CCIS **438**

1972 Field trial of PBX-CO using No. 1 ESS (Seattle, Washington) **513**

1972 January: First standard COMAS cutover (Boston, Massachusetts) **398**

1972 July: Development of Quick tests for No. 5 crossbar **399**

1972 August 30: First cutover of No. 5A crossbar (Portville, New York) **169**

1972 August 31: Start of No. 3 ESS development **330**

1972 November 5: First cutover of No. 2A ESS (Sun Valley, Nevada) **298**

1972 December: 812A PBX with smaller crossbar switches, first cutover **168, 487**

1973 No. 5 crossbar lines exceed number of lines of step-by-step **34**

1973 Step-by-step over 24 million lines **11**

1973 No. 4A crossbar: smaller crossbar switches **168**

1973 SMAS No. 3 with smaller crossbar switches **168**

1973 Type 300 special switching system with smaller crossbar switches **168**

1973 First service with Centrex console 50A **277**

1973 No. 1 ESS original call capacity objectives met **276**

1973 Computer system main interconnecting frame (COSMIC) developed **388**

1973 Introduction of more precise supervisor timing **380**

1973 First standard installation of mini COMAS cutover (New York City) **398**

1973 About 100 offices of ELMMSs installed (New York Telephone Company) **382**

1973 Studies started on other uses for the CCIS network **438**

1973 2B automatic call distributor introduced **566**

1973 March: First cutover of ANI-D (Van Dyne, Wisconsin) **153**

1973 April: Local step-by-step peak deployment 20 million lines **11**

1973 April: Step-by-step peak deployment, 24.4 million lines **34**

1973 June: First cutover, remreed trunk link network for No. 1 ESS (Detroit, Michigan) **288**

1976 April: Last of 182 No. 4A crossbar offices (Bell System) plus 20 (Independents) cutover (Madison, Wisconsin) **180, 321**

1976 April: Toll CCIS becomes operational **322**

1976 May: First cutover of TSPS: RTA and 2A position subsystem uses smaller crossbar switches (Utica and Syracuse, New York) **168, 319**

1976 June: First No. 2B ESS in service (Elgin, Illinois) **299**

1976 Second quarter: First automatic trunk analysis (ATA) for No. 1 crossbar (New York City) **399**

1976 July: First cutover of No. 1A service evaluation system (Dallas, Texas) **362**

1976 July 31: First No. 3 ESS placed in service (Springfield, Nebraska) **331**

1976 August: First concentrated range extension in service on No. 2 ESS (North Madison, Connecticut) **300**

1976 October: Remreed network serving 6 million lines and 3 million trunks **288**

1976 October: First cutover of No. 1A ESS (Chicago) **294**

1976 At year end: 180,000 (OUT)WATS lines in service **342**

1976 At year end: 108,000 INWATS lines in service **344**

1976 At year end: 22 AMARCs in service **380**

1976 At year end: 6.5 million Centrex telephones (70 percent Centrex-CO) **346**

1976 At year end: 74 percent of numbers are ANC **370**

1976 At year end: 911 in use in 600 areas serving 50 million people **354**

1976 At year end: TOUCH-TONE available to 70 percent of lines and subscribed to by 30 percent of their customers **342**

1976 At year end: Three of 10 signaling regions established; 700 CCIS trunks in service **436**

1977 Manufacture discontinued of No. 2 ESS processor **330**

1977 Application of 3A CC to 2B ESS **330**

1977 Application of 3A CC to No. 5 crossbar ETS **331**

1977 Application of 3A CC to transaction network **330**

1977 First application of HiLo transmission **329**

1977 Development started on HiLo transmission through No. 1 ESS **329**

1977 13A announcement system using magnetic bubble memory introduced **361**

1977 AIS No. 1A served 40 percent of the lines (3.3 million calls per day) **361**

1977 Field test of loop switching system **384**

1977 First switching control center for electromechanical switching cutover (Clinton, Michigan) **400**

1977 H. E. Vaughan receives IEEE medal of honor **422**

1977 April: First retrofit of 2B processor in service (Northbrook, Illinois) **300**

1977 April: First No. 1 ESS 4-wire HiLo (Sioux Falls, South Dakota) **291**

1977 April: Remote maintenance and traffic system (RMATS) for PBXs introduced (Minneapolis, Minnesota) **493**

1977 July: First 1A ESS semiconductor memory in service (Wilmington, Delaware) **295**

1977 July: National control center cutover (Bedminster, New Jersey) **406**

1977 August: Network operator trouble information system No. 2 in service **388**

1977 August 6: Third generic program (EF-2) in service on No. 2 ESS (Seattle, Washington) **300**

1977 September 9: First cutover hotel billing information system (Boston, Massachusetts) **316**

1977 October: First cutover of No. 5 crossbar ETS (Tarrytown, New York) **366**

1977 November: First no. 2 ESS DCT in service (Lake Villa, Illinois) **300**

1977 November: First TSPS ACTS (Phoenix, Arizona) **319**

1977 At year end: All 10 signaling regions in service with CCIS **436**

1978 January 20: First 1A processor retrofit (San Francisco, California) **294**

1978 Second quarter: Remote switching of television facilities introduced using SCOTS **588**

1978 July: First cellular mobile radio service with No. 1 ESS in service (Oakbrook, Illinois) **296**

1978 July: Trial of expanded 911 service starts (Alameda County, California) **355**

1978 August: Peak deployment of community dial offices, 4.8 million lines **34**

1978 October: No. 5 crossbar peak deployment, 28.5 million lines **170**

1978 December: Start marketing trial of high-capacity cellular mobile radiotelephone (Chicago, Illinois) **367**

1979 Conversion to all number dialing completed **125**

Index

This book was set in Palatino type by
Information Sciences Corporation,
Washington, D.C., using a typesetter
driven by a UNIX^{TM} operating system
from copy on UNIX word processing tapes
supplied by Bell Laboratories.